PEARSON CUSTOM

ENGINEERING GRAPHICS

ENGR& 114
Engineering Graphics
Bellevue College

PEARSON

Please visit our website at *www.pearsonlearningsolutions.com*.

Attention bookstores: For permission to return any unsold stock, contact us at *pe-uscustomreturns@pearson.com*.

Pearson Learning Solutions, 501 Boylston Street, Suite 900, Boston, MA 02116
A Pearson Education Company
www.pearsoned.com

 ISBN 10: 1-256-57925-4
ISBN 13: 978-1-256-57925-0

Table of Contents

LAYOUTS AND LETTERING

From Chapter 2 of *Modern Graphics Communication*, Fourth Edition, Frederick E. Giesecke, Alva Mitchell, Henry Cecil Spencer, Ivan Leroy Hill, John Thomas Dygdon, James E. Novak, Shawna Lockhart. Copyright © 2010 by Pearson Education, Inc. Published by Pearson Prentice Hall. All rights reserved.

LAYOUTS AND LETTERING

OBJECTIVES

After studying the material in this chapter, you should be able to:

1. Identify six types of technical drawings based on the projection system they use.

2. Identify the line patterns used in technical drawings and describe how they are used.

3. Read and measure with the architects' scale, engineers' scale, and metric scale.

4. Identify standard drawing media and sheet sizes.

5. Add lettering to a sketch.

6. Fill in a standard title block with the appropriate information.

7. Lay out a drawing sheet.

Refer to the following standards:
- Y14.100—2004 Engineering Drawing Practices
- Y14.2M—1992 Line Conventions and Lettering
- Y14.1—2005 Decimal Inch Drawing Sheet Size and Format
- Y14.1M—2005 Metric Drawing Sheet Size and Format

The companion website for this text is www.prenhall.com/chet_giesecke_modgraphic_4.

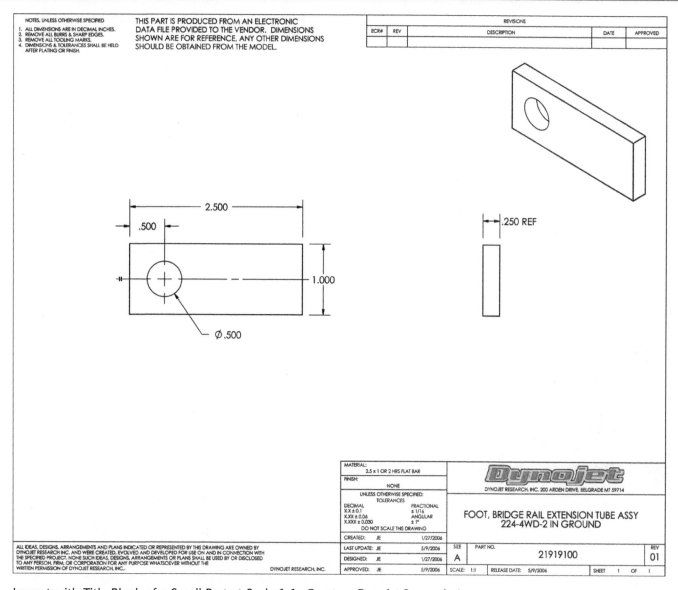

NOTES, UNLESS OTHERWISE SPECIFIED
1. ALL DIMENSIONS ARE IN DECIMAL INCHES.
2. REMOVE ALL BURRS & SHARP EDGES.
3. REMOVE ALL TOOLING MARKS.
4. DIMENSIONS & TOLERANCES SHALL BE HELD
   AFTER PLATING OR FINISH.

THIS PART IS PRODUCED FROM AN ELECTRONIC
DATA FILE PROVIDED TO THE VENDOR. DIMENSIONS
SHOWN ARE FOR REFERENCE, ANY OTHER DIMENSIONS
SHOULD BE OBTAINED FROM THE MODEL.

Layout with Title Block of a Small Part at Scale 1:1. *Courtesy Dynojet Research, Inc.*

OVERVIEW

Two dimensional technical drawings, whether they are sketched by hand, drawn using instruments, drawn using a CAD program, or generated from 3D solid models, follow certain rules so that they can be correctly interpreted. Unlike artistic drawings, which communicate self expression and emotional content, technical drawings communicate how to manufacture or construct a product, system, or device. In order to clearly describe this information, technical drawings adhere closely to formal standards.

These formal standards include systems of projection for developing and understanding drawing views.

They also include an "alphabet of lines," where each line of the drawing represents certain information. Lettering is also standardized, to make drawings quick to create and easy to read and reproduce. Standard sheet sizes for drawings include a title block that provides important information such as the drawing name, company information, scale, revision numbers, and approvals for release of the drawing.

Check the sites below for engineering graphics supplies and equipment
- http://www.reprint-draphix.com/
- http://www.eclipse.net/~essco/draft/draft.htm
- http://www.graphic-design.com/Type/index.html

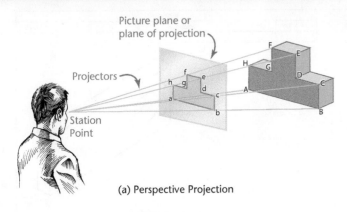

Picture plane or plane of projection

Projectors

Station Point

(a) Perspective Projection

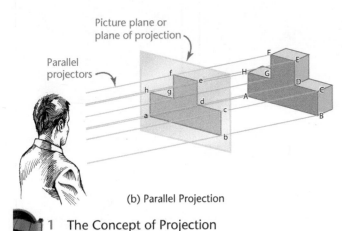

Picture plane or plane of projection

Parallel projectors

(b) Parallel Projection

1   The Concept of Projection

2   A View of a 3D Object "Projected" onto a Computer Monitor

UNDERSTANDING PROJECTIONS

Behind every 2D drawing of an object is a space relationship involving the object and three "imagined" things:

1. The observer's eye, or **station point**
2. The **plane of projection**
3. The **projectors** (also called *visual rays* or *lines of sight*).

Figure 1 shows two drawings of a shape projected onto a plane as viewed by an observer, whose eye represents the station point. The lines projecting from the corners (or vertices) of the object are the imagined lines, called projectors.

To understand projection, imagine that the drawing is produced by points, called **piercing points,** where the projectors would pierce the projection plane. The drawing may be a two-dimensional representation on a sheet of paper, or it may be a two-dimensional representation shown on your computer screen, as shown in Figure 2, but the basic principles are the same. One reason 2D projection skills remain relevant, even with the advent of 3D modeling, is that computer monitors still display a 2D view on their flat screens.

Types of Projections

There are two main types of projection: perspective and parallel. These are broken down into subtypes as shown in Figure 3.

In **perspective projections,** the projectors come together at the station point to form a cone, as in Figure 1a. Perspective drawings represent objects as we see them or as they would appear in a photograph.

In **parallel projections,** the projectors are parallel, as shown in Figure 1b.

Orthographic projections are one type of parallel projection. In orthographic (meaning right-angle) projections, the parallel projectors are perpendicular to the plane of projection. Because orthographic projections show objects in a way that their features can be represented at true size or scaled at a proportion of true size, they are especially useful in specifying the dimensions needed in technical applications.

If the projectors are parallel to each other, but are at an angle *other than 90°* to the plane of projection, the result is called an **oblique projection.**

Technical drawings of 3D objects usually use one of four standard types of projection, shown in Figure 3:

- Multiview
- Axonometric (isometric)
- Oblique
- Perspective

Multiview projection shows one or more necessary views. Either of two systems are used to arrange the views in a multiview drawing: Third Angle or First Angle.

Axonometric, oblique, and perspective sketches are methods of showing the object pictorially in a single view.

The main types of projection are listed in Table 1.

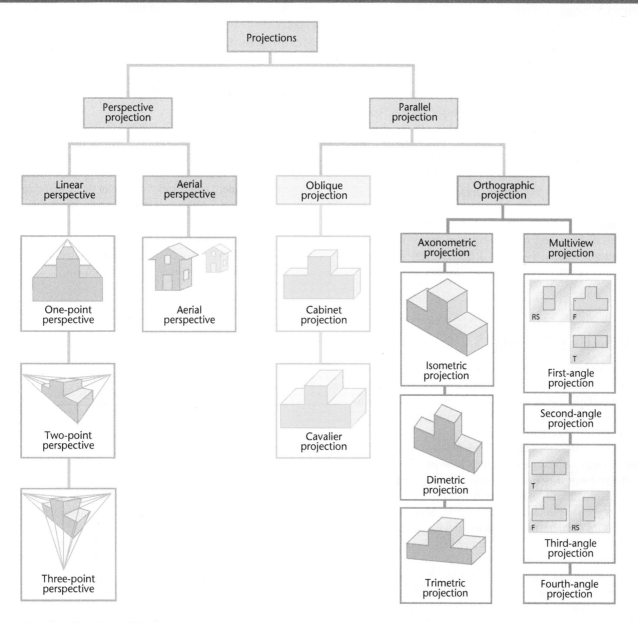

3   Classification of Projections

Table 1 Classification by Projectors.

Class of Projection	Distance from Observer to Plane of Projection	Direction of Projectors
Perspective	Finite	Radiating from station point
Parallel	Infinite	Parallel to each other
Oblique	Infinite	Parallel to each other and oblique to plane of projection
Orthographic	Infinite	Perpendicular to plane of projection
Axonometric	Infinite	Perpendicular to plane of projection
Multiview	Infinite	Perpendicular to plane of projection

Drawing Vocabulary

Drawing lines, lettering, measurement systems, scale, sheet sizes and title blocks are presented in this chapter.

Drawing Lines Projected drawing views use specific line patterns to represent object features. For example, when showing a three dimensional object, some lines represent the edges of surfaces that are hidden from that viewing direction. These hidden lines have a dashed line pattern to help the reader understand the drawing. Another type of line indicates the location of the center of a symmetric feature, such as a hole. Familiarity with the types of lines used in technical drawings helps you read drawings and create drawings that others can easily understand.

Lettering The shapes of letters that are easy to read and write are described as part of drawing standards. Often freehand sketching is used early in the design process to present ideas and showing notes and information legibly helps present your ideas to others clearly. Good lettering often makes or breaks a sketch.

Measurement Systems Two measurements systems are used for technical drawings: the metric system and U.S. customary units. It is important to be familiar with both measurement systems to create and read drawings that are used worldwide.

Scale Obviously a large item, a house or bridge for example, cannot be shown full size on a paper sheet. To clearly convey important information about particularly large or small objects, you need to select an appropriate sheet size and show drawings to scale (proportionately smaller or larger than the actual size). Standard lettering sizes for drawings depend on the sheet size.

Title Blocks Company information, the drawing scale, sheet size, and other information is included in a standard title block located in the lower right corner of the drawing to make it easy to locate these important details on every drawing layout.

1 ALPHABET OF LINES

The meaning of each line on a technical drawing is indicated by its width (thick or thin) and its particular line style. The person who reads the drawing will depend on these line styles to know if a line is visible or hidden, if it represents a center axis, or if it conveys dimension information.

To make your drawings easy to read, make the contrast between thick and thin lines distinct. **Thick lines** (0.6 mm) should be twice the width of **thin lines** (0.3 mm) as shown in Figure 4. The line gage in Figure 5 shows various widths.

Figure 6 shows freehand line technique. You may find it helpful to use 1/8" graph paper at first to get a feel for the length of dashes used in hidden lines and centerlines. Soon you will be able to estimate the lengths by eye.

Figure 7 illustrates line styles for technical drawings. All lines (except construction lines) must be sharp and dark. For visible, cutting-plane, and short-break lines use thick lines. Thin drawing lines should be just as sharp and black, but only half the thickness of thick lines. Construction lines and lettering guidelines should be thin and light so that they can barely be seen at arm's length and need not be erased. All lines should be uniform in width and darkness. Ideal lengths of the dashes used to form the line patterns are also shown in Figure 7.

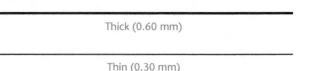

Thick (0.60 mm)

Thin (0.30 mm)

4   Thick and Thin Drawing Lines

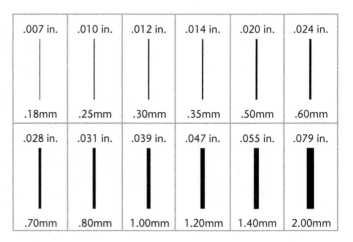

.007 in.	.010 in.	.012 in.	.014 in.	.020 in.	.024 in.
.18mm	.25mm	.30mm	.35mm	.50mm	.60mm
.028 in.	.031 in.	.039 in.	.047 in.	.055 in.	.079 in.
.70mm	.80mm	1.00mm	1.20mm	1.40mm	2.00mm

5   Line Gage

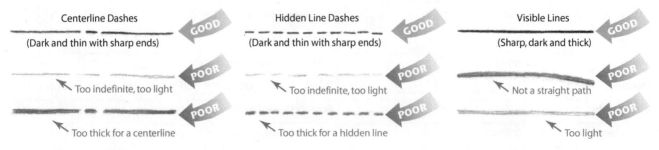

Centerline Dashes	Hidden Line Dashes	Visible Lines
(Dark and thin with sharp ends) GOOD	(Dark and thin with sharp ends) GOOD	(Sharp, dark and thick) GOOD
Too indefinite, too light POOR	Too indefinite, too light POOR	Not a straight path POOR
Too thick for a centerline POOR	Too thick for a hidden line POOR	Too light POOR

6   Good and Poor Freehand Line Technique

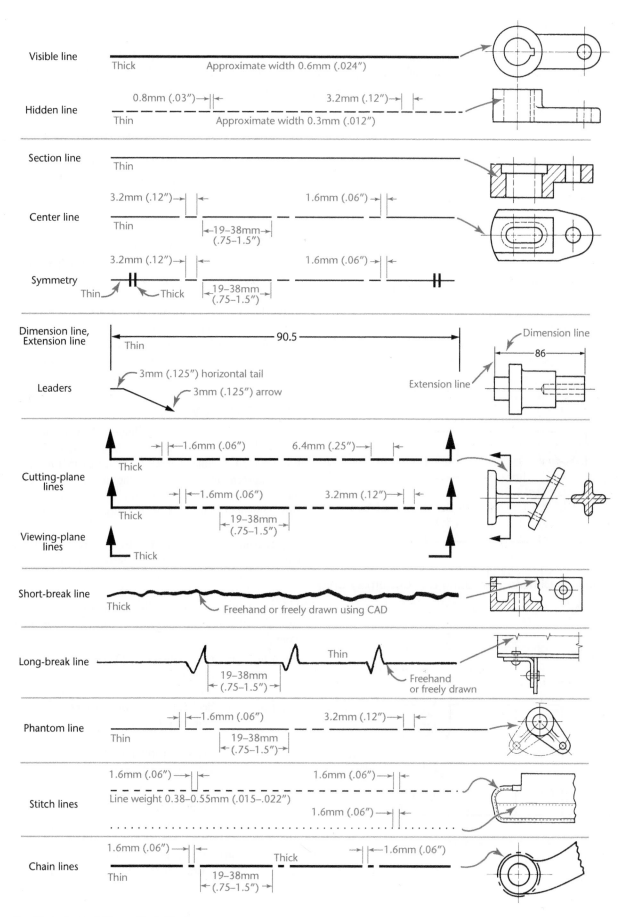

Visible line — Thick — Approximate width 0.6mm (.024″)

Hidden line — 0.8mm (.03″) — 3.2mm (.12″) — Thin — Approximate width 0.3mm (.012″)

Section line — Thin

Center line — 3.2mm (.12″) — 1.6mm (.06″) — Thin — 19–38mm (.75–1.5″)

Symmetry — 3.2mm (.12″) — 1.6mm (.06″) — Thin — Thick — 19–38mm (.75–1.5″)

Dimension line, Extension line — 90.5 — Thin — Dimension line — 86 — Extension line

Leaders — 3mm (.125″) horizontal tail — 3mm (.125″) arrow

Cutting-plane lines — 1.6mm (.06″) — 6.4mm (.25″) — Thick — 1.6mm (.06″) — 3.2mm (.12″) — Thick — 19–38mm (.75–1.5″)

Viewing-plane lines — Thick

Short-break line — Thick — Freehand or freely drawn using CAD

Long-break line — Thin — 19–38mm (.75–1.5″) — Freehand or freely drawn

Phantom line — 1.6mm (.06″) — 3.2mm (.12″) — Thin — 19–38mm (.75–1.5″)

Stitch lines — 1.6mm (.06″) — 1.6mm (.06″) — Line weight 0.38–0.55mm (.015–.022″) — 1.6mm (.06″)

Chain lines — 1.6mm (.06″) — 1.6mm (.06″) — Thick — Thin — 19–38mm (.75–1.5″)

7 Alphabet of Lines (Full Size)

2 FREEHAND LINES

The main difference between an instrument or CAD drawing and a freehand sketch is in the appearance of the lines. A good **freehand line** is not expected to be precisely straight or exactly uniform, as is a CAD or instrument-drawn line. Freehand lines show freedom and variety. Freehand **construction lines** are very light, rough lines. All other lines should be dark and clean.

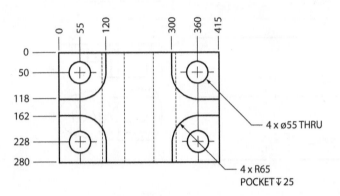

8   A Drawing Dimensioned Using Metric Units

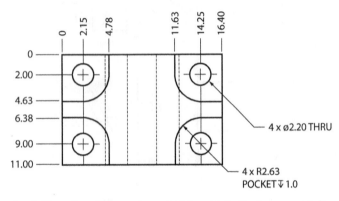

9   A Drawing Dimensioned Using U.S. Customary Units

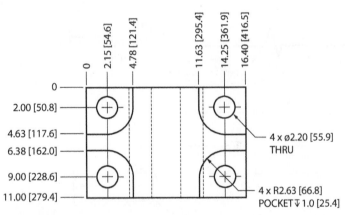

10   A Dual Dimensioned Drawing Using U.S. Customary Units as the Primary Units

3 MEASUREMENT SYSTEMS

When you create a technical drawing, the item you show will be manufactured or constructed using a particular system of measurement, which you indicate on the drawing. The metric system is the world standard used for measuring lengths.

U.S. Customary Units

U.S. customary units based on inch-foot and yard measurements (where a yard equals exactly 0.9144 meter, there are 3 feet to the yard, and 12 inches to the foot) continue to be used in the United States. Drawings may use either measurement system and still follow ANSI/ASME drawing standards as long as the system of measurement is stated clearly on the drawing. Figure 8 and Figure 9 show the same part dimensioned with the two different measurement systems.

The Metric System

Today's metric system is the International System of Units, commonly referred to as SI (from the French name, le Système International d'Unités). It was established in 1960 by international agreement and is now the international standard of measurement, with all countries in the world adopting it, although some continue using traditional U.S. units to a greater or lesser degree.

The meter was established by the French in 1791 with a length of one ten-millionth of the distance from the Earth's equator to the pole. A meter equals 39.37 inches or approximately 1.1 yards.

The metric system for linear measurement is a decimal system similar to the U.S. system of counting money. For example,

1 mm	= 1 millimeter (1/1000 of a meter)	
1 cm	= 1 centimeter (1/100 of a meter)	
	= 10 mm	
1 dm	= 1 decimeter (1/10 of a meter)	
	= 10 cm = 100 mm	
1 m	= 1 meter	
	= 100 cm = 1000 mm	
1 km	= 1 kilometer = 1000 m	
	= 100,000 cm = 1,000,000 mm	

The primary unit of measurement for engineering drawings and design in the mechanical industries is the millimeter (mm). Secondary units of measure are the meter (m) and the kilometer (km). The centimeter (cm) and the decimeter (dm) are rarely used on drawings.

Some industries have used a dual dimensioning system of millimeters and inches on drawings. However, this practice can be confusing because the sizes displayed in the two systems may contain rounding errors. If two systems are shown, the primary units are used for all manufacturing measurements and the secondary system units (shown in parentheses) are for general information purposes only. Figure 10 shows a drawing using dual dimensioning. Most large manufacturers use all metric dimensions on the drawing for ease and consistency.

Many of the dimensions in the illustrations and the problems in this text are given in metric units. Dimensions that are given in U.S. customary units (inches and feet, either decimal or fractional) can be converted easily to metric values. In standard practice, the ratio 1 in. = 25.4 mm is used. Many handy unit conversion sites are available on the Web, at sites such as www.onlineconversion.com.

4 DRAWING SCALE

Unlike drawing using a computer (where an object is drawn at its actual size so that the information stored in the computer file is accurate) a printed or paper drawing may represent the object at its actual size (full size), or may be larger or smaller than the object, depending on the size of sheet used. **Drawing scale** is the reduction or enlargement of the drawn object relative to the real object (Figure 11).

Scale is stated as a ratio of the number of drawing units to the number of actual units. For example, a machine part may be shown on a sheet at half its actual size, a scale of 1:2; a building may be drawn 1/48 of its size, a scale of 1:48 (or in U.S. customary units, 1/4" = 1'); a map may be drawn 1/1200 actual size, a scale of 1" = 100' or 1:1200; or a printed circuit board may be drawn four times its size, a scale of 4:1.

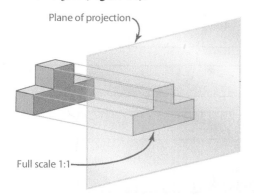
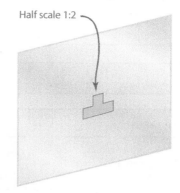
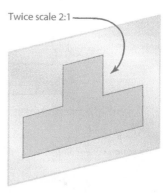

Plane of projection

Half scale 1:2

Twice scale 2:1

Full scale 1:1

11 Reduced and Enlarged Scale. Many drawings must be shown at reduced scale for the object to fit on the paper.

5 SPECIFYING THE SCALE ON A DRAWING

There are several acceptable methods to note scale on the drawing, but all of them show the relationship of the size of the object as drawn to the size of the actual object. For a part that is shown on the paper at half its actual size, list the scale one of these three ways:

SCALE: 1:2
SCALE: 1/2
SCALE: .5

For machine drawings, the scale indicates the ratio of the size of the drawn object to its actual size, regardless of the unit of measurement used. Expansion or enlargement scales are given as 2:1, 4:1, 5:1, 10:1, and so on. Figure 11 illustrates how the actual object relates to a drawing at half size and how that might be noted in the title block of the drawing. Figure 12 shows the scale for a 1 to 24 reduction noted in a title block.

Architectural drawings in the U.S. typically list the scale based on the number of fractions of an inch on the drawing that represent one foot on the actual object. For example, SCALE: 1/8" = 1'.

The various scale calibrations available on the metric scale and the engineers' scale provide almost unlimited scale ratios.

Preferred metric scale ratios are 1:1; 1:2; 1:5, 1:10, 1:20, 1:50, 1:100, and 1:200.

Map scales are indicated in terms of proportions such as Scale 1:62500, fractions such as Scale 1/62500, or graphically, such as

12 List the predominant drawing scale in the title block. *Courtesy of Dynojet Research, Inc.*

6 SCALES

Scales are measuring tools used to quickly enlarge or reduce drawing measurements. Figure 13 shows a number of scales, including (a) metric, (b) engineers', (c) decimal (d) mechanical engineers', and (e) architects' scales. On a full-divided scale, the basic units are subdivided throughout the length of the scale. On open-divided scales, such as the architects' scale, only the end unit is subdivided.

Scales are usually made of plastic or boxwood. The better wood scales have white plastic edges. Scales can be either triangular or flat. The triangular scales combine several scales on one stick by using each of the triangle's three sides. A scale guard shown in Figure 13f can save time and prevent errors by marking the side of the scale currently in use.

Several scales that are based on the inch-foot system of measurement continue in domestic use today, along with the metric system of measurement, which is accepted worldwide for science, technology, and international trade.

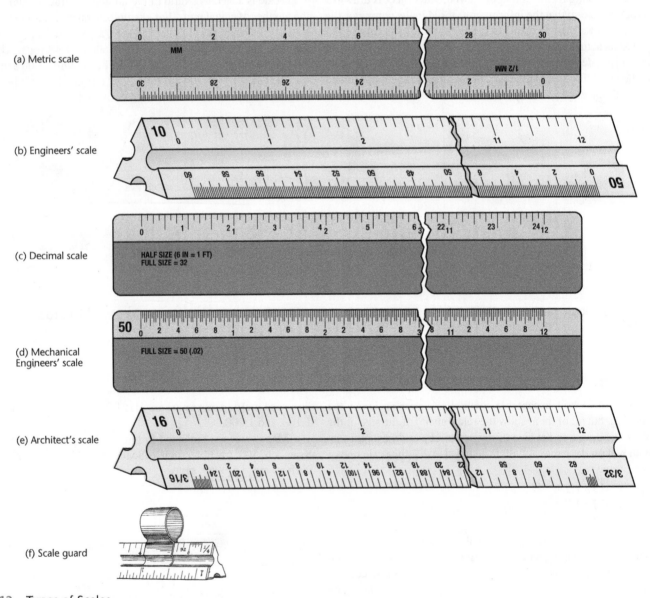

(a) Metric scale

(b) Engineers' scale

(c) Decimal scale

(d) Mechanical Engineers' scale

(e) Architect's scale

(f) Scale guard

13   Types of Scales

7 METRIC SCALES

Metric scales are available in flat and triangular styles with a variety of scale graduations. The triangular scale illustrated (Figure 14) has one full-size scale and five reduced-size scales, all fully divided. Using these scales, a drawing can be made full size, enlarged sized, or reduced sized.

Full Size The 1:1 scale (Figure 14a top) is full size, and each division is actually 1 mm in width with the numbering of the calibrations at 10 mm intervals. The same scale is also convenient for ratios of 1:10, 1:100, 1:1000, and so on.

Half Size The 1:2 scale (Figure 14a bottom) is one-half size, and each division equals 2 mm with the calibration num-

bering at 20-unit intervals. This scale is also convenient for ratios of 1:20, 1:200, 1:2000, and so on.

The remaining four scales on this triangular metric scale include the typical scale ratios of 1:5, 1:25, and 1:75 (Figures 14b and c). These ratios may also be enlarged or reduced by multiplying or dividing by a factor of 10. Metric scales are also available with other scale ratios for specific drawing purposes.

Metric scales are also used in map drawing and in drawing force diagrams or other graphical constructions that involve such scales as 1 mm = 1 kg and 1 mm = 500 kg.

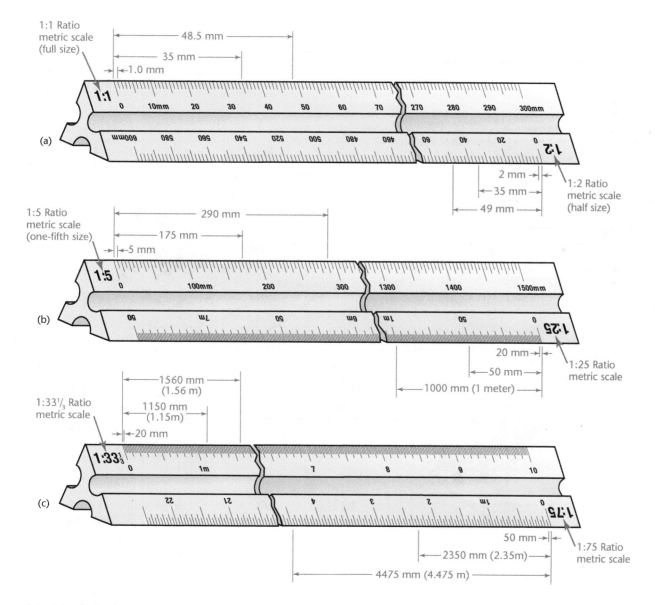

MAKING MEASUREMENTS TO LAY OUT A ONE-FIFTH SIZE METRIC DRAWING

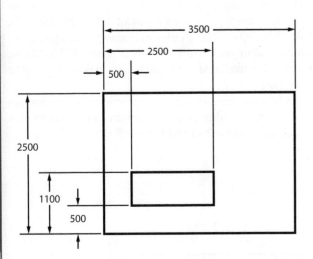

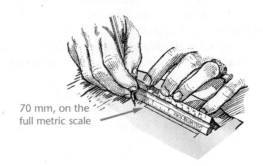

70 mm, on the full metric scale

1 Determine the full size measurements of the object you will draw. This example will lay out a 3500 × 2500 mm flat plate with a rectangular slot in it. A picture of the part to be drawn with dimensions representing its actual size is shown above.

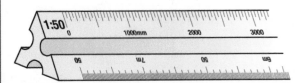

2 Find your 1:50 ratio metric scale, like this one.

4 Check length of your scaled line by calculating how many millimeters the length should be, then measuring the line you have drawn with a full-scale metric scale. In this case the 3500 mm length should be 70 mm when shown at 1:50 scale.

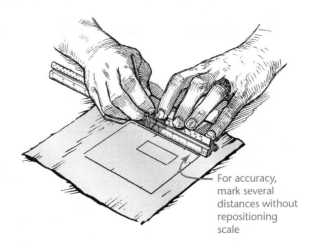

For accuracy, mark several distances without repositioning scale

5 Continue to lay out the remaining lengths. Even slight errors in measurements when using a scale may accumulate to produce a significant error, so work carefully.

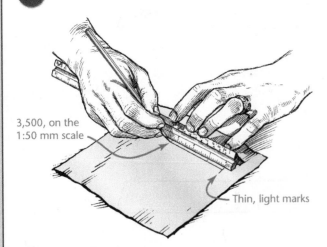

3,500, on the 1:50 mm scale

Thin, light marks

3 Starting from the 0 end of the 1:50 scale, use a sharp pencil to make a thin, light, short line to mark off the length of the 3500 mm line. To make accurate measurements, be sure to place the scale edge parallel to the line you are measuring on the drawing, and make your dashes at right angles to the scale, at the correct graduation mark, as shown.

To avoid cumulative errors, instead of setting off distances individually by moving the scale to a new position each time, position the scale once and mark all of the distances by adding each successive measurement to the preceding one.

This is useful in dimensioning drawings, too. Keep in mind that providing dimensions from one end to each successive location (say, in the case of building a wall) makes it easier for the worker to lay it out quickly and accurately.

8 ENGINEERS' SCALES

An *engineers' scale* is a decimal scale graduated in units of 1 inch divided into 10, 20, 30, 40, 50, and 60 parts. These scales are also frequently called the civil engineers' scales because they were originally used in civil engineering to draw large scale structures or maps. Sometimes the engineers' scale is referred to as a chain scale, because it derived from a chain of 100 links that surveyors used for land measurements.

Because the engineers' scale divides inches into decimal units, it is convenient in machine drawing to set off inch dimensions expressed in decimals. For example, to set off 1.650" full size, use the 10 scale and simply set off one main division plus 6-1/2 subdivisions (Figure 15). To set off the same dimension half size, use the 20 scale, since the 20 scale is exactly half the size of the 10 scale. Similarly, to set off the dimension quarter size, use the 40 scale.

An engineers' scale is also used in drawing stress diagrams or other graphical constructions to such scales as 1" = 20 lb. and 1" = 4000 lb.

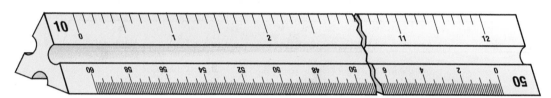

15   Engineers' Scale

9 DECIMAL INCH SCALES

The widespread use of *decimal inch* dimensions brought about a scale specifically for that use. On its full-size scale, each inch is divided into fiftieths of an inch, or .02". On half- and quarter-size decimal scales, the inches are compressed to half size or quarter size and then are divided into 10 parts, so that each subdivision stands for .1" (Figure 16).

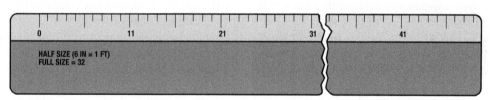

16   Decimal Inch Scale

10 MECHANICAL ENGINEERS' SCALES

The objects represented in machine drawing vary in size from small parts that measure only fractions of an inch to parts of large dimensions. For this reason, mechanical engineers' scales are divided into units representing inches to full size, half size, quarter size, or eighth size (Figure 17). To draw an object to a scale of one-half size, for example, use the mechanical engineers' scale marked half size, which is graduated so that every 1/2" represents 1". In other words, the half-size scale is simply a full-size scale compressed to half size.

These scales are useful in dividing dimensions. For example, to draw a 3.6" diameter circle full size, we need half of 3.6" to use as radius. Instead of using math to find half of 3.6", it is easier to set off 3.6" on the half-size scale.

TIP

Triangular combination scales are available that include full- and half-size mechanical engineers' scales, several architects' scales, and an engineers' scale all on one stick.

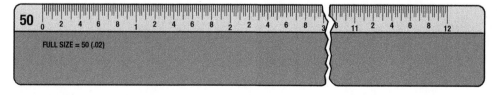

17   Mechanical Engineers' Scale

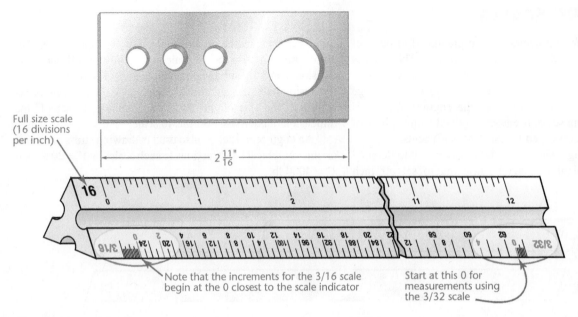

Full size scale
(16 divisions
per inch)

$2\frac{11}{16}$"

Note that the increments for the 3/16 scale
begin at the 0 closest to the scale indicator

Start at this 0 for
measurements using
the 3/32 scale

18 Architects' Scale

11 ARCHITECTS' SCALES

The **architects' scale** is intended primarily for drawings of buildings, piping systems, and other large structures that must be drawn to a reduced scale to fit on a sheet of paper. The full-size scale is also useful in drawing relatively small objects, and for that reason this scale has rather general usage.

Architects' scales have one full-size scale and ten reduced-sized scales. To fit them all on a three-sided scale, there are two scales on the same edge of the scale, but each starts from the opposite end. Simply find the scale you want, and read the units from the zero closest to that end.

Architects' scales can be used to draw various sizes from full size to 1/128 size. In all of the reduced scales, the major divisions represent feet and their subdivisions represent inches and fractions of inches.

Note that on an architects' scale, the scale marked 3/4 means 3/4 inch = 1 foot, *not 3/4 inch = 1 inch* (that is, it means one-sixteenth size, *not* three-fourths size). Similarly, on an architects' scale, 1/2 means 1/2 inch = 1 foot, *not 1/2 inch = 1 inch.* In other words, on an architects' scale, 1/2 means twenty-fourth-size, *not* half size.

- Full Size: Each division in the full-size scale is 1/16" (Figure 18). Each inch is divided into halves, then quarters, eighths, and finally sixteenths. You'll notice that the dividing lines are shorter with each subdivision.
  Measurements smaller than 1/16" must be made by estimating. For example, 1/32" is half of one 1/16", so you would visually estimate halfway between 1/16" division lines. To measure 1/64", you would estimate one fourth of 1/16", and so on.

- Half Size: Use the full-size scale, and divide every dimension by two. (Remember, do not use the 1/2" scale, which is intended for drawing to a scale of 1/2" = 1', not half-size.) To create a half scale drawing using an architects' scale, divide your measurements in half and then lay out the drawing.

- Double Size: Use the full-size scale, and multiply every dimension by 2.

TIP

AutoCAD software users sometimes become confused using architectural units. When selecting architectural units in which to enter lengths, keep in mind that a value of 1 is one inch, not one foot.

MEASURING WITH AN ARCHITECTS' SCALE

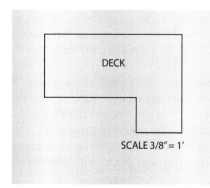

DECK

SCALE 3/8" = 1'

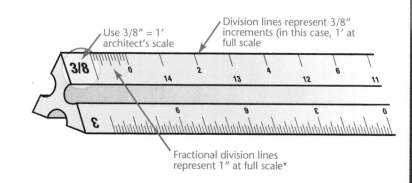

Use 3/8" = 1' architect's scale

Division lines represent 3/8" increments (in this case, 1' at full scale

Fractional division lines represent 1" at full scale*

1 To make measurements with an architects' scale, first determine which scale to use by reading the scale noted in the title block or noted below the view. In the example above, 3/8 inch = 1 foot.

2 Position the scale so that the 0 value is aligned with the left end of the line being measured and note the division mark nearest to the line's right end (in this case, 2).

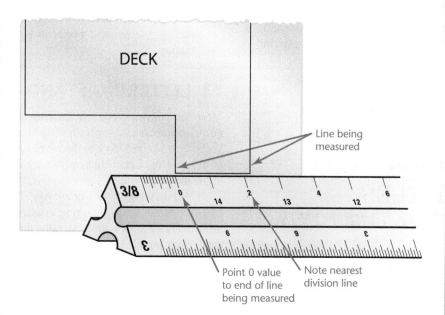

DECK

Line being measured

Point 0 value to end of line being measured

Note nearest division line

3 Slide the scale to the right so that the closest whole division you noted in Step 2 lines up with the right end of the line you are measuring. A fractional portion of the line you are measuring now extends on the left, past the scale's 0 mark.

Counting toward the left, note how many fractional division marks are between zero and the left end of the line. (In this example, there are two.)

Add the fractional value to the whole value that you noted in Step 2. In this example, you noted 2 whole division lines, plus two fractional division lines, so the length of the line is 2'–2" at actual size.

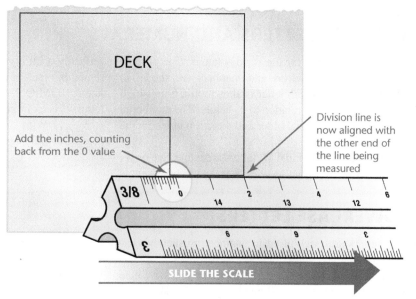

DECK

Add the inches, counting back from the 0 value

Division line is now aligned with the other end of the line being measured

SLIDE THE SCALE

On architects' scales, there are 12 fractional divisions, because there are 12 inches per foot.

S T E P by S T E P

ABCDEFGH
abcdefgh

Sans-serif lettering has no serifs,
or spurs, at the ends of the strokes

ABCDEFGH
abcdefgh

Roman letters are accented by
thick and thin line weights

ABCDEFGH
abcdefgh

Italic letters are slanted,
whether serif or sans serif

19 Distinctions Between Roman,
Italic, Serif, and Sans Serif Lettering

12 LETTERING

Lettered text is often necessary to completely describe an object or to provide detailed specifications. Lettering should be legible, be easy to create, and use styles acceptable for traditional drawing and CAD drawing.

Engineering drawings use single-stroke sans-serif letters because they are highly legible and quick to draw. (Sans-serif means without serifs, or spurs.) A **font** is the name for a particular shape of letters. The particular font for engineering drawings is called Gothic. Figure 19 shows the distinctions between **Roman, italic, serif** and **sans serif** fonts.

Lettering is a standard feature available in computer graphics programs. With CAD software, you can add titles, notes, and dimensioning information to a drawing. Several fonts and a variety of sizes may be selected. When modifications are required, it is easy to make lettering changes on the drawing by editing existing text.

Freehand lettering ability has little relationship to writing ability. You can learn to letter neatly even if you have terrible handwriting. There are three necessary aspects of learning to letter:

- knowing the proportions and forms of the letters (to make good letters, you need to have a clear mental image of their correct shape)
- spacing of letters and words for legibility
- practice

13 LETTERING STANDARDS

AUTOCAD TXT FONT
ROMAN SIMPLEX
ROMAN DUPLEX
TITLES
TRUE TYPE FONTS

20 An Example of Lettering and
Titles Using CAD

Most hand-drawn notes use lettering about 3 mm (1/8") in height. Light horizontal **guidelines** are useful to produce consistent letter heights. CAD notes are set using the keyboard and sized to be in the range of 3 mm (1/8") tall according to the plotted size of the drawing. Lettering heights vary with the size of the sheet and the intended use of the drawing.

CAD drawings typically use a Gothic lettering style, but often use a Roman style for titles. When adding lettering to a CAD drawing, a good rule of thumb is not to use more than two fonts within the same drawing. See Figure 20 for a sample of the fonts available using CAD. You may want to use one font for the titles and a different font for notes and other text. It may be tempting to use many different fonts in a drawing because of the wide variety available, but this tends to look distracting on the drawing. Drawings that use too many lettering styles and sizes have been jokingly referred to as having a "ransom note" lettering style.

14 VERTICAL LETTERS AND NUMERALS

There are standard widths for the various letters. The proportions of **vertical** capital letters and numbers are shown in Figure 21. In the figure, each letter is shown on a 6-unit-high grid that shows its width in relation to its height. The numbered arrows indicate the traditional order and direction in which the lettering strokes are made.

Aside from the letters I and W, letters are either five or six grid divisions wide, or about as wide as they are tall. This is probably a little wider than your usual writing. It is easier to remember the six-unit letters if you think of them as spelling a name: TOM Q. VAXY. The letter I is a pencil width, and the letter W is eight grid-units wide (1-1/3 times its height).

 With the exception of the numeral 1, which uses only a pencil width, all numerals are five units wide.

Use Worksheet 1 to practice lettering.

15 LOWERCASE LETTERS

Lowercase letters are rarely used in engineering sketches except for lettering large volumes of notes. Vertical lowercase letters are used on map drawings, but very seldom on machine drawings. Lowercase letters are shown in Figure 22. The lower part of the letter (or descender) is usually two-thirds the height of the capital letter.

When large and small capitals are combined, the small capitals should be three-fifths to two-thirds the height of the large capitals. The inclined letters and numbers shown in Figures 23 and 24 will be discussed in the next section.

Straight-line letters

Letter "i" has short bars

"W" is only letter over 6 units wide. Letters in "TOM Q. VAXY" are 6 units wide—all others are 5, except "I" and "W"

Curved-line letters

The letters O, Q, C, G and D are based on a true circle. The lower portion of of the J and U is elliptical

Curved-line letters and numerals

The 8 is composed of two ellipses. The 3, S, and 2 are based on the 8

Curved-line letters and numerals

Number "1" is a straight line. The 0, 6, and 9 are elliptical

21   Vertical Capital Letters and Numerals

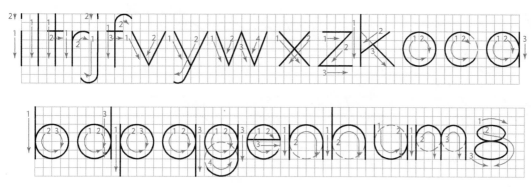

22   Vertical Lowercase Letters

Straight-line letters

Letter "i" has short bars

"W" is only letter over 6 grid units wide. Letters in "TOM Q. VAXY" are 6 grid units wide—all others are 5, except "I" and "W"

Curved-line letters

The letters O, Q, C, G and D are based on a true ellipse. The lower portion of of the J and U is elliptical

Curved-line letters and numerals

The 8 is composed of two ellipses. The 3, S, and 2 are based on the 8

Curved-line letters and numerals

Number "1" is a straight line. The 0, 6, and 9 are elliptical

23 Inclined Capital Letters and Numerals

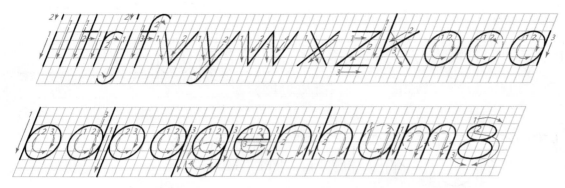

24 Inclined Lowercase Letters

16 INCLINED LETTERS AND NUMBERS

Inclined (italic) capital letters and numerals, shown in Figure 23, are similar to vertical characters, except for the slope. The slope of the letters is about 68° from the horizontal.

While you may practice drawing slanted hand lettering at approximately this angle, it is important in CAD drawings to always set the amount of incline for the letters at the same value within a drawing so that the lettering is consistent. Inclined lowercase letters, shown in Figure 24, are similar to vertical lowercase letters.

Keep in mind that only one style of lettering, either vertical or inclined, should be used throughout a drawing.

17 FRACTIONS

Fractions are shown twice the height of the corresponding whole numbers. Make the numerator and the denominator each about three-fourths as high as the whole number to allow enough space between them and the fraction bar. For dimensioning, the most commonly used height for whole numbers is 3 mm (1/8"), and for fractions 6 mm (1/4"), as shown in Figure 25.

- Never let numerals touch the fraction bar.
- Center the denominator under the numerator.
- Avoid using an inclined fraction bar, except when lettering in a narrow space, as in a parts list.
- Make the fraction bar slightly longer than the widest part of the fraction.

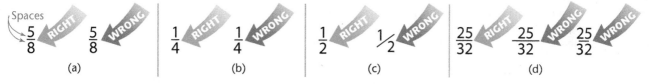

(a) (b) (c) (d)

25 Common Errors in Lettering Fractions

18 USING GUIDELINES

Use extremely light horizontal **guidelines** to keep letter height uniform, as shown in Figure 26. Capital letters are commonly made 3 mm (1/8") high, with the space between rows of lettering being from three-fifths to full height of the letters. Do not use vertical guidelines to space the distance from one letter to the next within a word or sentence. This should be done by eye while lettering. If necessary, use a vertical guideline at the beginning of a column of hand lettered text to help you line up the left edges of the following rows. Beginners can also use randomly spaced vertical guidelines to practice maintaining the correct slant.

Vertical guide lines drawn at random

LETTERING IS EASIER
IF YOU REMEMBER TO
USE GUIDE LINES

Space between lines usually from $\frac{3}{5}$ to total height of letters

26 Using Guidelines

TIP
For even freehand letters

- Use 1/8" gridded paper for drawing to make lettering easy.
- Use a scale and set off a series of spaces, making both the letters and the spaces between lines of letters 1/8" high.
- Use a guideline template like the Berol Rapidesign 925 shown in Figure 27.
- For whole numbers and fractions, draw five equally spaced guidelines.

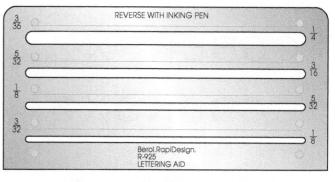

27 The Berol Rapidesign 925 template is used to quickly create guidelines for lettering.

19 SPACING OF LETTERS AND WORDS

Spacing between Letters

Uniform spacing between letters is done by eye. Contrary to what might seem logical, putting equal distances from letter to letter causes them to appear unequally spaced. The background areas between letters, not the distances between them, should be approximately equal to get results that appear balanced. Figure 28 illustrates how using equal spacing from one letter to the next does not actually appear equal. Space your lettering so that background areas appear equal, like the example shown in the bottom half of the figure.

Some combinations, such as LT and VA, may have to be slightly closer than other letters to look correctly spaced. In some cases, the width of a letter may be decreased slightly. For example, the lower stroke of the L may be shortened when followed by A. In typesetting, pairs of letters that need to be spaced more closely to appear correctly are called **kerned pairs.**

Spacing between Words

Space letters closely within words to make each word a compact unit, but space words well enough apart to be clearly separate from adjacent words. For both uppercase and lowercase lettering, make spaces between words approximately equal to a capital O.

Spacing between Rows

Be sure to leave space between rows of lettering, usually equal to the letter height. Rows spaced too closely are hard to read. Rows spaced too far apart do not appear to be related.

Use Worksheet 2 for practice.

LATHING

literate

If equal spacing is used from one letter to another, spacing does not actually appear equal, as in this example

LATHING

literate

Space your lettering so that background areas appear equal, like the example shown above

28 Visually Balancing Letter Spacing

── TIP ──

Creating letters that appear stable

Certain letters and numerals appear top-heavy when they are drawn with equal upper and lower portions like the example below.

To correct this, reduce the size of the upper portion to give a balanced appearance, as in this example.

If you put the central horizontal strokes of the letters B, E, F, and H at midheight, they will appear to be below center.

To overcome this optical illusion, draw the strokes for B, E, F, and H slightly above the center as you letter, keeping letters uniform, as in the second example below.

CGBEKSXZ

CGBEKSXZ

The same practice applies to numerals. In the illustrations below, the example at left looks top-heavy. Note how the example at right looks more balanced.

3852   3852

A good example of uniform lettering

RELATIVELY

These examples show what not to do

Nonuniform style

Relatively

Nonuniform letter height

RELATIVELY
RELATIVELY

Nonuniform angle

RELATIVELY
RELATIVELY

Nonuniform stroke thickness

RELATIVELY
RELATIVELY

Nonuniform letter spacing

RELATIVELY

Nonuniform word spacing

NOW IS THE TIME FOR EVERY GOOD PERSON TO COME TO THE AID OF HIS OR HER COUNTRY

20 LETTERING FOR TITLES

In most cases, the title and related information are lettered in title boxes or title strips as shown in Figure 29. The main drawing title is usually centered in a rectangular space, which is easy to do, using CAD.

When lettering by hand, arrange the title symmetrically about an imaginary centerline, as shown in Figure 30. In any kind of title, give the most important words prominence by making the lettering larger, heavier, or both. Other data, such as scale and date, can be smaller.

Figure 31 shows examples of freehand lettering at actual size.

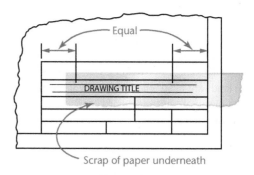

TOOL GRINDING MACHINE
TOOL REST SLIDE
SCALE : FULL SIZE
AMERICAN MACHINE COMPANY
NEW YORK CITY

DRAWN BY ____ CHECKED BY ____

29 Balanced Machine-Drawing Title

30 Centering Title in Title Box

THE IMPORTANCE OF GOOD LETTERING CANNOT BE
OVER-EMPHASIZED. THE LETTERING CAN MAKE OR
BREAK AN OTHERWISE GOOD DRAWING.

PENCIL LETTERING SHOULD BE DONE WITH A FAIRLY
SOFT SHARP PENCIL AND SHOULD BE CLEAN-CUT
AND DARK. ACCENT THE ENDS OF THE STROKES.

31 Pencil Lettering (Full Size)

— TIP —
Lettering with a Pencil

- Since practically all pencil lettering will be reproduced, the letters should be dense black, not gray or blurred. Use a sharp, soft pencil, such as an F, H, or HB to make lettering dark and sharp.
- If you like using wooden pencils, sharpen them to a needle point, then dull the point very slightly.
- Don't worry about making the exact letter strokes unless you find it difficult to make the letters look right, but do use them as a reference if you are having trouble drawing uniform, symmetrical letters.
- Use extremely light, 1/8" (3 mm) horizontal guidelines to regulate the height of letters. A few light, vertical or inclined lines randomly placed help you visually keep the letters uniformly vertical or inclined.

- Draw vertical strokes downward with a finger movement.
- Draw horizontal strokes from left to right with a wrist movement and without turning the paper.
- Draw curved strokes and inclined strokes with a downward motion.

Left-handers: Traditional lettering strokes were designed for right-handed people. Experiment with each letter to find out which strokes are best and develop a system of strokes that works best for you.

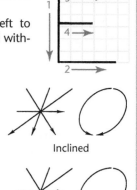

Inclined

Inclined

21 DRAWING PENCILS

High-quality drawing pencils help produce good quality technical sketches and drawings. Use light lines for construction lines, lettering guidelines, and precise layout work. Use dark, dense black lines for the final lines, lettering, and arrowheads. Drawings are often reproduced and the lines need to be dark for the copies to turn out well.

Drawing pencils are made of graphite with a polymer binder or clay binder. They are divided into 18 grades from 9H (the hardest) to 7B (the softest) as shown in Figure 32. Specially formulated leads of carbon black particles in a polymer binder are also available in several grades for use on polyester film (mylar).

Hard leads are used where accuracy is required, such as on graphical computations and charts and diagrams. For other uses, their lines are apt to be too light.

Medium leads are used for general purpose technical drawing, such as sketching, lettering, arrowheads, and other freehand work on mechanical drawings.

Soft leads are not useful in technical drawing. They make smudged, rough lines that are hard to erase, and the lead dulls quickly. These grades are generally used for artistic drawing.

Which grade of pencil works best for you depends on your hand pressure, the humidity, and the type of paper you are using, among other things. For light lines, use a hard lead in the range of 4H to 6H. For dark lines, use a softer lead in the range of 2H to B.

Mechanical pencils are available with 0.3-, 0.5-, 0.7-, or 0.9-mm-diameter drafting leads in several grades (Figure 33). Their thin leads produce uniform-width lines without sharpening. The .5-mm lead is a good general size, or you can use a .7-mm lead for thick lines and .3 mm for thin lines.

9H 8H 7H 6H 5H 4H   3H 2H H F HB B   2B 3B 4B 5B 6B 7B

Hard
The hard leads in this group (left) are used where extreme accuracy is required, as on graphical computations and charts and diagrams. The softer leads in this group (right) are sometimes used for line work on engineering drawings, but their use is limited because the lines are apt to be too light.

Medium
These grades are for general purpose work in technical drawing. The softer grades (right) are used for technical sketching, lettering, arrowheads, and other freehand work on mechanical drawings. The harder leads (left) are used for line work on machine drawings and architectural drawings. The H and 2H leads are widely used on pencil tracings for reproduction.

Soft
These leads are too soft to be useful in mechanical drafting. They tend to produce smudged, rough lines that are hard to erase, and the lead must be sharpened continually. These grades are used for artwork of various kinds, and for full-size details in architectural drawing.

32 Lead Grade Chart

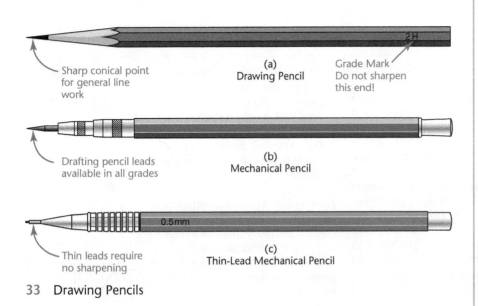

Sharp conical point for general line work

(a)
Drawing Pencil

Grade Mark
Do not sharpen this end!

2H

Drafting pencil leads available in all grades

(b)
Mechanical Pencil

Thin leads require no sharpening

0.5mm

(c)
Thin-Lead Mechanical Pencil

33 Drawing Pencils

TIP

You might be surprised how much your drawings benefit from finding a style of pencil that suits your use. Soft pencils, such as HB or F, are mainly used in freehand sketching. Choose a pencil that:

- Is soft enough to produce clear black lines, but hard enough not to smudge too easily.
- Is not so soft that the point breaks easily.
- Feels comfortable in your hand.
- Grips the lead without slipping.

Be aware that some lead holders require special sharpeners.

You can sometimes tell the difference in hardness of a mechanical pencil lead just by looking at it. Smaller diameter leads are used for the harder grades and larger diameter leads are used to give more strength to the softer grades.

Plain wooden pencils work great. They are inexpensive, and it is easy to produce thick or thin lines by varying the amount that you sharpen them. An old trick to keep the lead sharp longer is to turn the pencil frequently as you work to wear it down evenly.

Gum erasers and nylon erasers work well to pick up smudges without leaving much eraser dust.

Nylon eraser strips that come in refillable holders like mechanical pencils can be convenient for areas that require some precision. A trick for erasing fine details is to sharpen the end of the eraser strip in a small hand-held pencil sharpener.

22 TEMPLATES

Templates are available for a great variety of specialized needs (Figure 34). Templates may be found for drawing almost any ordinary drafting symbols or repetitive features.

23 THE COMPUTER AS A DRAFTING TOOL

Most people who create technical drawings use CAD. Advantages include accuracy, speed, and the ability to present spatial and visual information in a variety of ways.

However, these advantages don't eliminate the need for drawings to be easily and accurately interpreted. CAD drawings use the same general concepts and follow the same drafting standards as drawings created by hand.

Most CAD drawings are plotted on standard sheet sizes and to similar scales as hand drawings. Both CAD and hand drawings should contrast thick lines for objects with thin lines for hidden, center, and dimensions to make the printed drawing easy to read. CAD drawings

34 Drawing Templates. *Courtesy of Chartpak.*

should use correct line patterns. Likewise, lettering on CAD drawings should follow these same general guidelines as for hand drawings.

One benefit of CAD is the ability to draw perfectly straight uniform lines and other geometric elements. Another is the ability to quickly represent the various styles of lines (Figure 35). Making changes to a CAD drawing takes about a tenth the time that it takes

to edit a drawing by hand. Using CAD, you can quickly plot drawings to different scales.

Keeping CAD drawing files organized, backing up data regularly, and following conventions for naming files so that you can find them again are important considerations. Even the most skilled CAD users need to also be skilled in freehand sketching, in order to quickly get ideas down on paper.

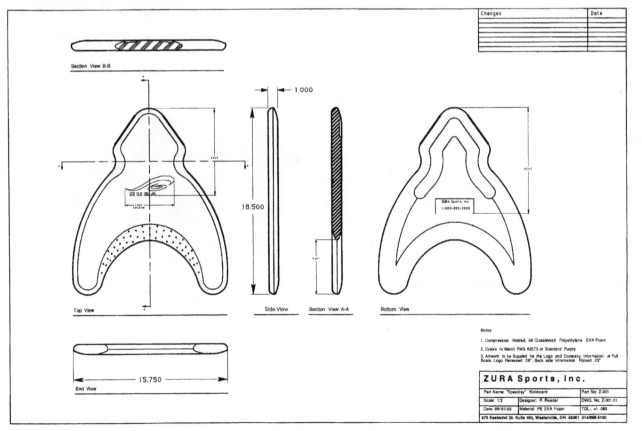

35 A Drawing Created Using CAD. *Courtesy of Zura Sports, Inc.*

MODEL SPACE AND PAPER SPACE IN AUTOCAD 2008

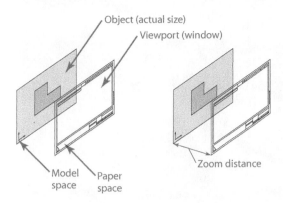

(A) In AutoCAD 2008, paper space allows you to see how various views of the full size model can be shown on a sheet of paper.

Using CAD, you can make an accurate model of the device or structure. To do this, you create the object at the actual size that it exists in the real world, using whatever system of measurement that you would use when constructing it.

On paper it is a different matter. You would have to have some really large sheets to print your building full size. Auto-CAD 2008 software uses the concept of two "spaces," model space and paper space, to describe how to transform the full size CAD model to proportionate views that fit your sheet of paper.

Understanding scale as it relates to paper drawings or as it relates to creating layouts from a CAD drawing is an important concept for technical drawing because the ultimate goal is for drawings to be interpreted and used in the real world. Therefore, they must be easy to print and read.

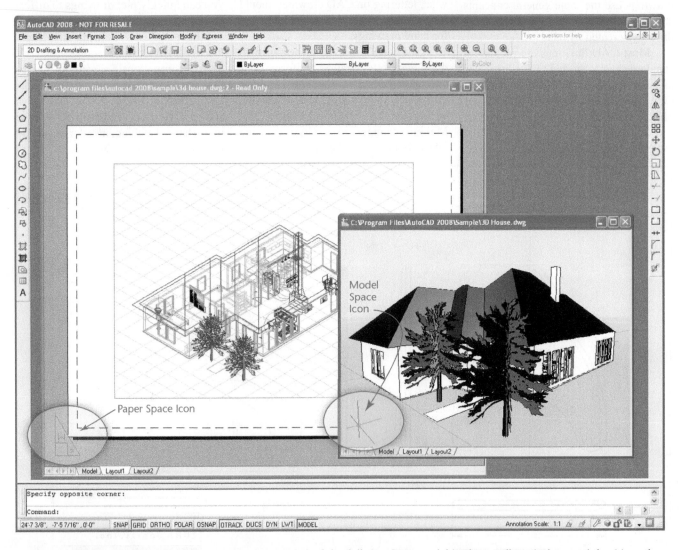

(B) The window at left shows a paper space representation of the full size CAD model in the smaller window at right. Note that AutoCAD uses icons to help users differentiate the two "spaces." *Courtesy of Autodesk, Inc. © 2006-2007. All rights reserved.*

24 SKETCHING AND DRAWING MEDIA

Many choices of **media** (paper and other) are available for particular sketching or drawing purposes. Whether you are sketching or are plotting a drawing from a CAD workstation, choose the type of sheet and size that suits your needs.

Small notebooks or sketch pads are useful when working at a site or when it is necessary to quickly record information. Many companies use bound notebooks of graph paper for recording engineering design notes for patent and documentation purposes. Graph paper can be helpful in making neat sketches like the one in Figure 36. Paper with 4, 5, 8, or 10 squares per inch is convenient for maintaining proportions.

A sketch pad of plain paper with a master grid sheet showing through underneath works well as a substitute for grid paper. You can create your own master grid sheets using CAD. Specially ruled isometric paper is available for isometric sketching, or you can use CAD to create masters.

The best drawing papers have up to 100% pure rag stock. Their strong fibers hold up well for erasing and folding, and they will not discolor or grow brittle with age. Good drafting paper should have a fine grain (or tooth) to pick up the graphite

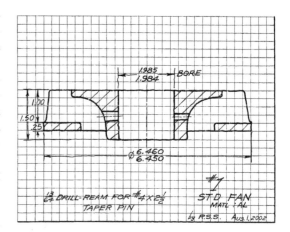

36   Sketch on Graph Paper

and produce clean, dense black lines. Paper that is too rough produces ragged, grainy lines, is harder to erase, and wears down pencils quickly. Look for paper that has a hard surface that will not groove too easily under pencil pressure.

25 POLYESTER FILMS AND COATED SHEETS

Polyester film is a high quality drafting material available in rolls and standard sized sheets. It is made by bonding a matte surface to one or both sides of a clear polyester sheet. Its transparency and printing qualities are good and it provides an excellent matte drawing surface for pencil or ink, it is easy to erase without leaving ghost marks, and it has high dimensional stability. Its resistance to cracking, bending, and

tearing makes it very durable. Many companies still plot their drawings in ink on polyester film for long-term storage and reproduction.

Even large coated sheets of aluminum (which provides a good dimensional stability) have been used in the aircraft and auto industry for full-scale layouts that were scribed into the coating with a steel point rather than a pencil.

26 STANDARD SHEETS

There are ANSI/ASME standards for international and U.S. **sheet sizes.** Table 2 describes the height and width of these standard sheets, the letters used to refer to them, and their margins and zones. Note that drawing sheet size is given as height × width. Most standard sheets use what is called a "landscape" orientation.

The use of the basic sheet size, 8.5" × 11.0" or 210 mm × 297 mm, and its multiples permit filing folded prints in standard files with or without correspondence. These sizes can be cut from standard rolls of media.

Table 2 Sheet Sizes.

Nearest International Size (mm)	International Number of Zones	International Margin	Standard U.S. Size (in.)	U.S. Number of Zones (width)	U.S. Margin (in.)
A4 210 × 297	6	10	A* 8.5 × 11.0	2 (optional)	.50
A3 297 × 420	6	10	B 11.0 × 17.0	2 (optional)	.50
A2 420 × 594	8	10	C 17.0 × 22.0	4	.50
A1 594 × 841	12	20	D 22.0 × 34.0	4	.50
A0 841 × 1189	16	20	E 34.0 × 44.0	8	.50

May also be used as a vertical sheet size at 11" tall by 8.5" wide.

27 STANDARD LAYOUT ELEMENTS

Margins and Borders

Each layout begins with a border drawn inside the sheet margin. Drawings in the U.S. use a .50" margin. Refer to Table 2 for international sheet sizes and margins. Some companies use slightly larger sheets to provide for binding drawings into a set. This extra allowance should be added on to the standard sheet size so that the drawing border meets the size standards (see Figure 37). Figure 38 shows the alternate orientation of an A size drawing.

Zones

You have probably seen **zone numbers** on maps, where the margin is subdivided by letters along one side and by numbers along the other. These are also used along the outer edges of technical drawings so that you can refer to items by the area on the sheet where they are located. This is particularly useful when a client calls with a question. You can use zone numbers to make sure you are talking about the same item. Zone numbers are also useful for locating revisions. You should provide zone numbers on all sheets larger than size B.

Typical Letter Sizes

Most lettering on drawings should be at least 3 mm or .12" (about 1/8") tall. Lettering is typically sized as follows:

Drawing Title, Drawing Size
6 mm (.24")
CAGE Code
6 mm (.24")
Drawing Number, Revision Letter
6 mm (.24")
Section and View Letters
6 mm (.24")
Zone Letters and Numbers
6 mm (.24")
Drawing Block Headings
2.5 mm (.10")
All Others
3 mm (.12")

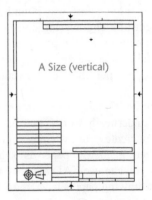

38 Vertical Orientation of A Size

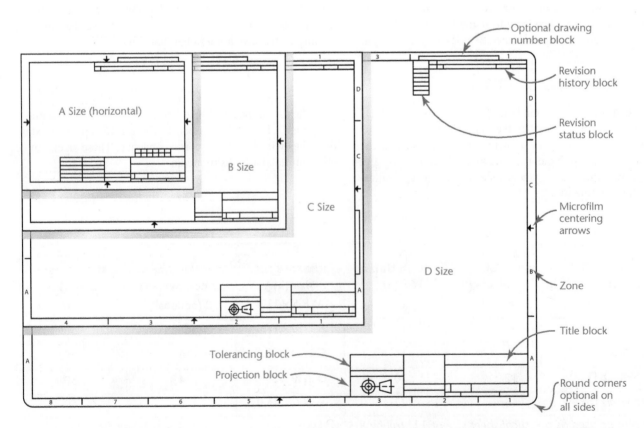

37 Typical Sheet Sizes and Borders. *(See the inside front cover for E size and international standard sizes.)*

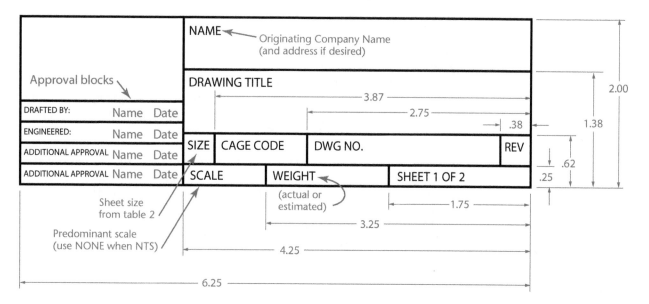

39   Title Block for A, B, and C Sized Sheets

Title Block

The title block is located in the lower right corner of the format. Standard areas in the title block provide the following information. Refer to Figure 39 for dimensions for a typical title block for A, B, and C sized sheets.*

Name Show the originating company or business (and address if desired). Refer to Figure 40.

Drawing Title Briefly describe the item using a singular noun or noun phrase and modifiers if necessary to distinguish it from similar items. Do not use the terms "for" or "or" in the title. For example, "Dust Cap" would be preferred over "Cap or Cover for Dust Protection," which is too wordy.

Drawing Number Give each drawing a unique number, using the company's numbering system.

Sheet Revision Block Track the drawing version using the number of the revision. The original release of the drawing typically shows revision 0.

Approval Block List the name(s) of the person(s) approving the drawing and the date it was approved. Additional areas of this block can be used for various design activities, if separate approval is required. For example, a company may use separate areas for structural design or manufacturing engineering approvals (Figure 41).

Scale List the predominant scale for the drawing. Drawings may include details at other scales, which should be noted below the detail. If the drawing is not made to a particular scale, note NONE in the scale area. Refer to Section 6.

Drawing Size List the sheet size used for the drawing. This helps track the original size when the drawing is reproduced at a smaller size.

Sheet Number List the number of the sheet in the set, using whole numbers starting at 1. A format that lists this sheet out of the total number helps keep track of the entire set. For example, 1 OF 2.

CAGE Code List the Commercial and Government Entity (CAGE) code if applicable. This is a number assigned to

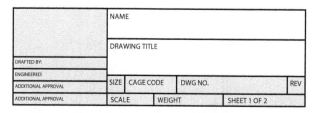

40   Company Name and Drawing Title

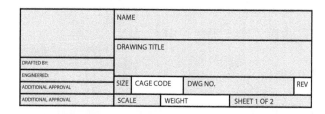

41   Approval Block, Scale, Revision, and Drawing Size

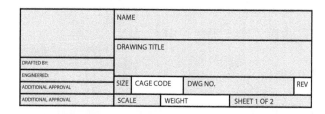

42   CAGE Code and Weight May Be Listed

entities that manufacture items for the government. The code is assigned based on the original design activity.

Weight List the actual or estimated weight of the part if required (Figure 42).

*For more formats, title blocks, revision blocks, and a list of materials blocks, see inside the front cover of this text.

28 LAYOUTS

A particular size sheet with a drawing border is called a **layout.** Using a CAD system, you may often be able to select from standard layouts or templates that set the sheet size limits, the border, and even the title block as the starting point for your drawing. Regardless of whether you draw by hand or use CAD or 3D modeling methods, you need to plan your sheet so that the information will fit and show clearly.

When sketching, your layout may be a simple border and title strip along the bottom of the sheet (or you may be using preprinted tablets that have space to record the sketch title, date, and other pertinent data).

When creating a 2D CAD drawing, you may use a drawing template showing the sheet and border and title block, perhaps using different templates or even software interface settings for different types of drawings, such as mechanical/manufacturing, architectural, or civil.

When creating a 2D drawing to plot from a 3D solid model, you may use a layout space that contains different viewports that allow you to show different views of the same 3D model with a border and title block.

29 PLANNING YOUR DRAWING OR SKETCH

When laying out a drawing sheet, you will need to consider:

- the size and scale of the object you will show.
- the sheet size.
- the measurement system (units) for the drawing.
- the space necessary for standard notes and title block.

The object you are drawing is the "star" of the sketch. Keep the object near the center of the sheet. It should be boldly drawn, using thick visible lines. Make it large enough to fill most of the sheet and so that details show clearly (Figure 43).

Show Details Clearly

Show small objects larger than their actual size to represent the details clearly. If the details are too small, switch to a larger sheet size and use a larger scale. You can also add details at a larger scale if necessary to show features that are smaller than the typical features of the drawing. If you add details at a different scale, label the view, for example, DETAIL A, and note the scale for the detail below it.

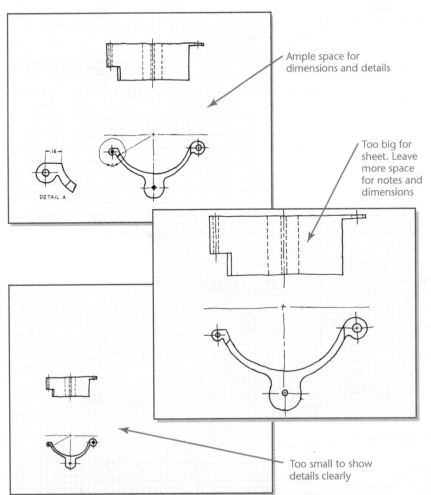

Ample space for dimensions and details

Too big for sheet. Leave more space for notes and dimensions

Too small to show details clearly

DETAIL A

43 Show details clearly by selecting the appropriate scale and sheet size.

SHEET LAYOUT

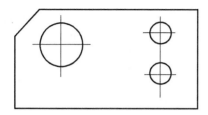

Given drawing

1 To draw the part shown in the given figure, select the sheet size, keeping in mind the size of the objects. Show the part large enough to represent features clearly. Use larger sheets for larger or more detailed

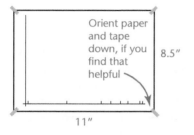

objects. (8.5 × 11" will be large enough for the part shown.) Add the border and title block to the sheet using the margin sizes specified in the standards. Refer to Table 2.

2 Determine the units for the drawing. Will it be metric or U.S. Customary (inches, feet and inches)? What system will be used to construct, manufacture, and inspect the actual object? Use that system of measurement for the drawing. This part is in inches.

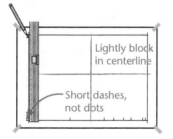

Before you begin drawing, determine the scale at which the object will best fit on the sheet.

First, figure the available space within the drawing border. For example the horizontal 8.5 × 11" sheet with a .5" margin leaves 7.5 × 10". If you subtract space for a .375" title strip across the bottom, it leaves 7.125 × 10" for the drawing.

Now, consider the size of the object. Will it fit on the sheet at full-size? Half-size? Do you need to enlarge it to show small features larger than actual size? The 12" gasket shown in the example will fit well at half-size on the 8.5 × 11" sheet selected and still show the details clearly. Use typical scales when possible. Refer to Section 5.

Approximately center the object on the sheet. To do this, subtract the size of the scaled drawing from the available sheet space and use half of the difference on each side of the object.

3 One quick technique is to find the center of the available space and lay out the drawing on each side of that centerline. Using CAD, you can easily move the drawing to the center of the sheet visually.

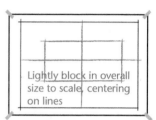

Sketches do not have to be perfectly centered, but plan ahead so the drawing isn't crammed in one corner of the sheet. Let your drawing be the "star" of the page. Remember to leave enough space around your drawing for notes and dimensions. If you don't, you will run out of room and your layout will look crowded.

4 Lightly add details of the drawing.

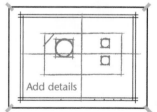

5 Darken final drawing lines.

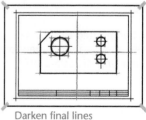

Darken final lines
and add title block

─ TIP ─
Scale When Using CAD

Keep in mind that when using CAD you will create the object the size that it actually exists in real life. On the plotted sheet, when showing the drawing to scale, it is easy to try a few different scales and see which fits. You can always change the scale later if needed.

STEP by STEP

SCALING ANNOTATIONS AUTOMATICALLY USING AUTOCAD 2008

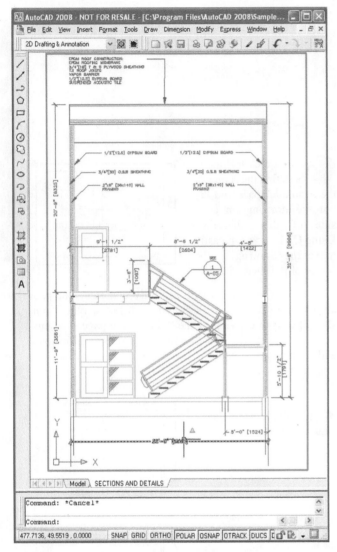

You might think that displaying text in a CAD drawing is one of the easiest things to do. You can quickly type in the text you want to display and select the font, height, slant, and rotation angle. That part *is* easy, but annotations are useless if nobody can read them.

When you create drawings that will be plotted on different sized sheets or at different scales, sizing the text can require a lot of planning. Take the plot architectural plan drawing shown in Figure A for example. When plotted to scale 3" = 1'-0", the text showing dimensions is clearly visible. But when shown at one-twelfth of that size, scale 1/4" = 1'-0", that same text becomes illegible.

The ability to reuse the same CAD data at different scales without having to recreate the drawing is one of its big advantages over pen and paper drawings. Yet, cumbersome workarounds were once necessary to make legible text at different scales. One workaround was to have several different sizes of the same text, which the user would turn on or off depending on what drawing scale was used.

Now, AutoCAD 2008 software provides a feature called annotation scaling. Here is how it works: Drawing objects that are commonly used to annotate drawings (provide text information) can have their annotation property turned on. This allows you to create one annotative object that displays at different sizes, based on scale properties.

In the AutoCAD software, object types that can have annotative object properties include Text, Mtext, Dimensions, Hatches, Tolerances, Multileaders, Leaders, Blocks, and Attributes.

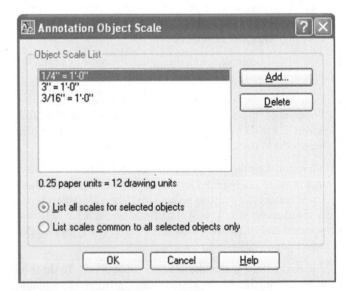

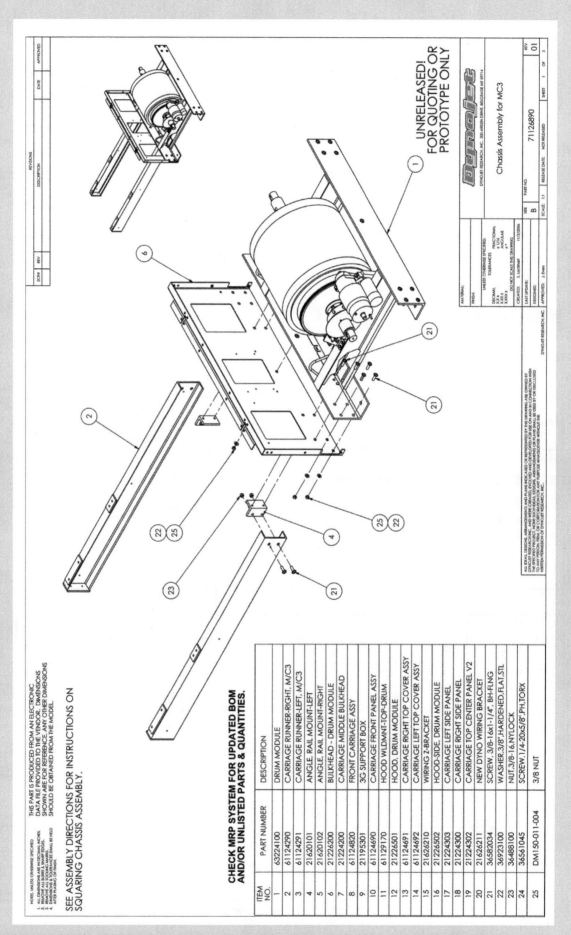

An assembly drawing showing a revision block and a standard title block. *Courtesy of Dynojet Research, Inc.*

PORTFOLIO

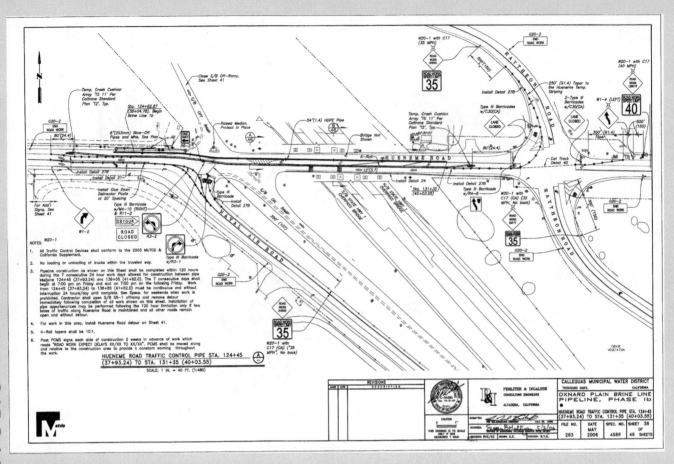

A civil drawing showing approval blocks and engineers' stamp. *Courtesy of Perliter and Ingalsbee Consulting Engineers and Calleguas Municipal Water District.*

WINDOW SCHEDULE

MK	MANUFACTURER/ LINE	TYPE	UNIT SIZE/ MODEL #	R.O.	NOTES
A	PITTSBURG CORNING "LIGHTWISE"	GLASS BLOCK	32X80	33 3/16" X 79 7/8"	8X8 GLASS BLOCK PANEL W/ WHITE VINYL FRAME PATTERN TO BE DETERMINED
B1	SUMMIT VINYL	AWNING	24X24	24" X 24"	PROVIDE AUTOMATIC OPENERS FOR CLERESTORY WINDOWS
B2	SUMMIT VINYL	PICTURE	24X24	24" X 24"	
C	PITTSBURG CORNING "LIGHTWISE"	GLASS BLOCK	24X24	25 3/8" X 25 3/8"	8X8 GLASS BLOCK PANEL W/ WHITE VINYL FRAME PATTERN TO BE DETERMINED
D	KOLBE & KOLBE "TLT N TU..."	SPECIALTY	AB54	48 1/2" X 54 1/2"	WOOD/ CLAD EXTERIOR
E	SUMMIT VINYL				
F	PITTSBURG "LIGHTWIS..."				

DOOR SCHEDULE

MK	SIZE	DOOR TYPE	MANUFACTURER/ LINE	STYLE	MATERIAL	SPECIAL HARDWARE	NOTE
1	10070	OVERHEAD DOOR		FLUSH PANEL		AUTOMATIC OPENER	(4) WINDOWS IN UPPER PANEL
2	3068	EXTERIOR DOOR	SOUTHWEST DOOR/ CLASSIC	18 LITE	ALDER		FINISH & TEXTURE TO BE DETERM...
3	6080	EXTERIOR DOUBLE FRENCH DOORS	WEATHERSHIELD/ PROSHIELD	SINGLE PANE	VINYL		WHITE FRAME, TEMPERED GLAS...
4	5068	EXTERIOR DOUBLE FRENCH DOORS	WEATHERSHIELD/ PROSHIELD	SINGLE PANE	VINYL		WHITE FRAME, TEMPERED GLAS...
5	2668	INTERIOR DOOR		SINGLE PANE			TEMPERED GLASS
6	2468	POCKET DOOR		FLUSH HOLLOW CORE	WOOD		FINISH TO BE DETERMINED
7	2468	POCKET DOOR		FLUSH HOLLOW CORE	WOOD		FINISH TO BE DETERMINED

Window and door schedules are used in architectural drawings to specify the type of window or door, rough opening size, manufacturer and other information. *Courtesy of Frog Rock Design, LLP.*

KEY WORDS

Station Point

Plane of Projection

Projectors

Piercing Points

Perspective Projections

Parallel Projections

Orthographic Projections

Oblique Projection

Multiview Projection

Drawing Lines

Lettering

Measurement Systems

Scale

Title Blocks

Thick Lines

Thin Lines

Freehand Line

Construction Lines

Drawing Scale

Scales

Engineers' Scale

Decimal Inch

Architects' Scale

Font

Serif

Italic

Roman

Sans Serif

Guidelines

Vertical

Inclined

Kerned Pairs

Media

Sheet Sizes

Zone Numbers

Name

Drawing Title

Drawing Number

Sheet Revision Block

Approval Block

Scale

Drawing Size

Sheet Number

CAGE Code

Weight

Layout

CHAPTER SUMMARY

Now that you have completed this chapter you should be able to:

- Understand the basic principles of projection used in drawings.
- Demonstrate the line weights (thickness) and types (dashed or solid) of lines used in the alphabet of lines that specify meaning in technical drawings.
- List the two main systems of measurement used on drawings.
- Use different types of scales to make measurements.
- Note the scale for a drawing in the title block. Paper drawings are scaled before they are drawn. CAD drawings are scaled when they are to be printed.
- List the advantages of several different drawing media and the qualities that distinguish them.
- Add legible and quick to produce notes and dimensions to sketches using uppercase letters drawn by hand.
- Lay out a sheet and fill in the information in the title block using standard letter shapes.

REVIEW QUESTIONS

1. Draw the alphabet of lines and label each line.
2. Which architects' scale represents a size ratio of 1:24? Which metric scale represents a half size? Which engineers' scale would be used for full size?
3. Which scale type is the only one to use fractions of an inch?
4. What are the main advantages of polyester film as a drawing media?
5. What are the four standard types of projections?
6. Which drawing lines are thick? Which are thin? Which are very light and should not reproduce when copied?
7. What font provides the shape of standard engineering lettering?
8. Describe the characteristics of good freehand lettering.
9. Why should guidelines be used for lettering?
10. List the standard items found in a title block.

EXERCISES

Drawing Exercises

Practice your skills for making measurements, laying out drawing sheets, and forming neat standard lettering with these drawing exercises.

These problems are designed to fit easily on a sheet. Draw all construction lines lightly, using a hard lead (4H to 6H), and all required lines dense black with a softer lead (F to H). Draw your construction lines lightly so that they do not need to be erased.

In Exercises 1–3 you will practice measuring, and in Exercises 4–6 you will practice drawing layouts.

Exercise 1 Measure the lines shown above and list their lengths using millimeters. List the inch measurements for each in square brackets [ ] to the right of the millimeter measurement.

Exercise 2 Measure the lines shown above and draw them at Scale 1:2, Scale 2:1, and list their scales below them using the form Scale: X:X.

Exercise 3 Measure the overall interior dimensions of your room. Letter the measured length neatly in the first column as shown in the example. In the second column list how long you would draw that line at a scale of 1/4" = 1', third column at 3/8" = 1', fourth column at 1"= 1', fifth column at 1:100 metric scale (10 mm = 1 meter).

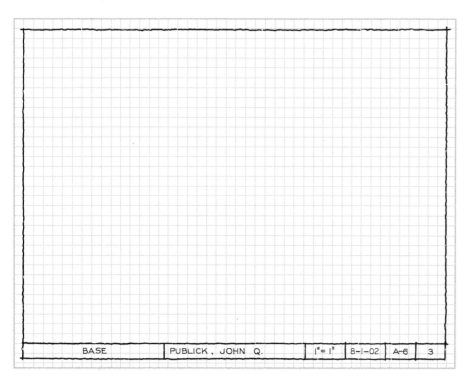

| BASE | PUBLICK , JOHN Q. | 1"= 1" | 8-1-02 | A-6 | 3 |

Exercise 4 Create the layout for an 8.5 × 11" sheet as shown at left.

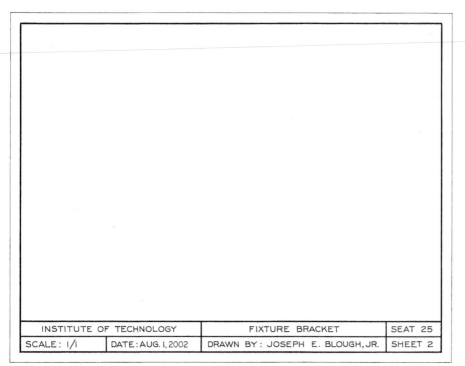

| INSTITUTE OF TECHNOLOGY | | FIXTURE BRACKET | SEAT 25 |
| SCALE: 1/1 | DATE: AUG. 1, 2002 | DRAWN BY : JOSEPH E. BLOUGH, JR. | SHEET 2 |

Exercise 5 Create the layout for the 210 mm × 297 mm sheet shown at left.

Exercise 6 Design a title block and layout for a C-sized sheet. Create a name and logo for your company. Use an attractive but legible font for the titles on your layout. If assigned, design a special north arrow to be used on your drawings.

Lettering Exercises

Layouts for lettering problems are given in Exercises 7–11. Draw complete horizontal and vertical or inclined guide lines very lightly. Draw the vertical or inclined guide lines through the full height of the lettered area of the sheet. For practice in ink lettering, the last two lines and the title strip on each sheet may be lettered in ink, if assigned by the instructor. Omit all dimensions.

Exercise 7 Letter the words to your favorite song, joke, or inspirational quote of 50 words or more. Use 1/8" tall UPPERCASE engineering lettering. Center the words near the middle of the sheet. Make sure to leave a row of space between each row of lettering. Make sure that the subject you choose is professional and appropriate.

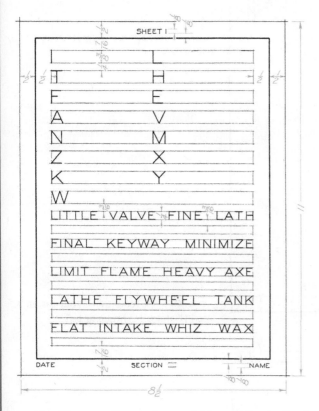

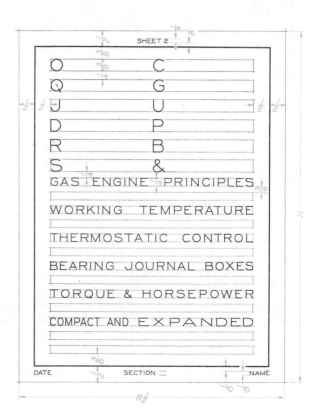

Exercise 8 Lay out sheet as shown. Add vertical or inclined guidelines and fill in vertical or inclined capital letters as assigned.

Exercise 9 See instructions for Exercise 8.

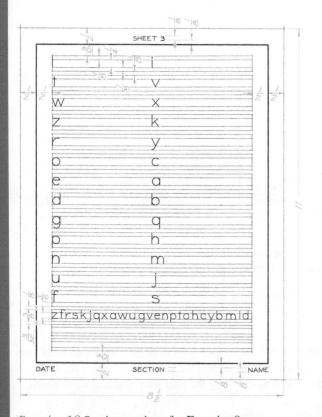

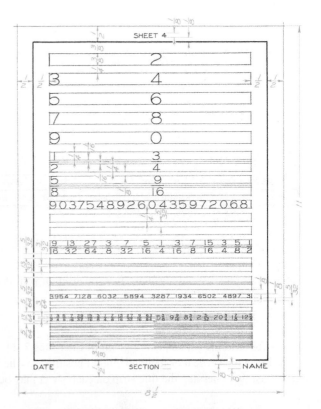

Exercise 10 See instructions for Exercise 8.

Exercise 11 See instructions for Exercise 8.

MEASUREMENTS AND SCALE

A. Measure the lines shown using the scale and units listed. Write your answer in the space provided at the left.

_____   1. _____
                  metric (mm)

_____   2. _____
                  metric (mm)

_____   3. _____
                  U.S. customary units (inch)

_____   4. _____
                  U.S. customary units (inch)

_____   5. _____
                  U.S. customary units (inch)

_____   6. _____
                  U.S. customary units (inch)

B. Redraw the line you measured in part A to the scale listed.
   1. SI metric; Scale 2:1

   2. SI metric; Scale 1:2

   3. Architectural; Scale $\frac{1}{4}$" = 1'

   4. Architectural; Scale $\frac{3}{32}$" = 1'

   5. Inch; Scale 1:30

   6. Inch; Scale 1:5

C. Redraw the shelf at $\frac{3}{8}$" = 1".

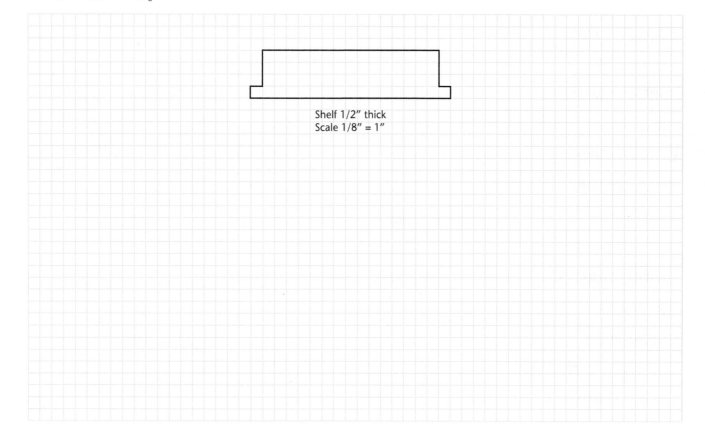

Shelf 1/2" thick
Scale 1/8" = 1"

PRACTICE KERNING PAIRS

Using equal spacing from one letter to the next does not actually appear equal, as in this example.

LATHING
literate

LATHING
literate

ELLIPSES	ELLIPSES
ANCHOR BRACKET	ANCHOR BRACKET
INVOLUTE	
UTILITY	
EQUILATERAL	
VERIGRAPH	
SURFACE WAVINESS	
DRILL	
COUNTERSINK	
COUNTERBORE	
SPOTFACE	
SURFACE FINISH	
UNIFIED THREAD	
DRAWINGS	
ENGINEERING	
LOCATIONAL FIT	
VISUALIZATION	

PRACTICE FREEHAND LETTERING

Use the space provided to repeat each letter or word shown.

A B C D E F G H I J K L M N O P Q R S T U V W X Y Z

A B C D E F G H I J K L M N O P Q R S T U V W X Y Z

PRACTICE LETTERING BY HAND

USING A VARIETY OF SIZES.

ONE-EIGHTH INCH LETTERING IS COMMONLY USED

ON FREEHAND SKETCHES. MAKE LETTERS BLACK

AND CLEAN-CUT — NEVER FUZZY OR INDEFINITE.

$1\frac{1}{2}$ 1.500   45'-6   32°   15.489   1" = 20'   3.75

ONCE YOU HAVE MASTERED VERTICAL LETTERING

ADDING A SLANT FOR INCLINED LETTERS IS EASY.

DOODLE ON THIS PAGE

WORSHEET 1   VERTICAL LETTERING PRACTICE

Repeat each letter on the blue grid provided, paying careful attention to the proportions and stroke direction shown in the example. Then repeat the letter once more in the white space.

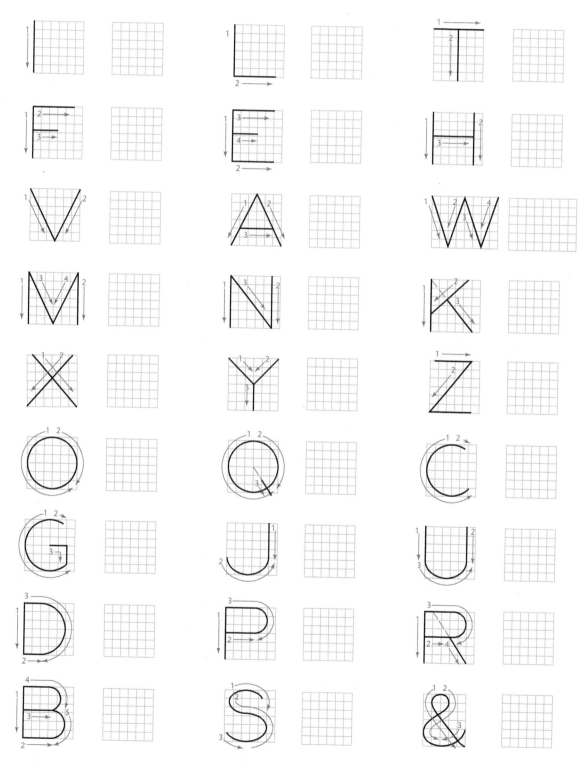

Make copies of these pages to use for additional practice.

WORKSHEET 2   1/8 INCH LETTERING PRACTICE

Use the guidelines provided to letter the drawing notes and dimensions in the appropriate spaces. Use 1/8″ upper-case standard engineering lettering.

SEE DETAIL A

                              SAE 1115 - 4 REQUIRED

2 X .50 - 12 UNC - 2B ↧.688

                      ALL FILLETS AND ROUNDS R.125

.062 X .062 SLOT

                      3 HOLES EQUALLY SPACED

2 X [19.0 - 19.5

                    $\frac{1}{8}$ AMER. STD. PIPE TAP

BOTTOM TAP   FOR BOWEN GREASE CUP

Ø.62 ⊔Ø1.062

                  2 X #10 - 32 UNF - 2B ↧.438

MEDIUM KNURL

                         M14 X 2

F&R R3 UNLESS OTHERWISE SPECIFIED

ALL MEASUREMENTS IN MILLIMETERS

                  JAW PLATE SCREW

Make copies of these pages to use for additional practice.

APPENDIX: GEOMETRIC CONSTRUCTIONS

A.1 ■ Triangles

A triangle is a plane figure bounded by three straight sides, and the sum of the interior angles is always 180° (Figure A.1). A right triangle (Figure A.1d) has one 90° angle, and the square of the hypotenuse is equal to the sum of the squares of the two sides (Figure A.1c). As shown in Figure 1f, any triangle inscribed in a semicircle is a right triangle if the hypotenuse coincides with the diameter.

A.2 ■ Quadrilaterals

A *quadrilateral* is a plane figure bounded by four straight sides (Figure A.2). If the opposite sides are parallel, the quadrilateral is also a *parallelogram.*

A.3 ■ Polygons

A *polygon* is any plane figure bounded by straight lines (Figure A.3). If the polygon has equal angles and equal sides, it can be inscribed in or circumscribed around a circle and is called a *regular polygon.*

A.4 ■ Circles and Arcs

A *circle* is a closed curve, all points of which are the same distance from a point called the center (Figure A.4a).

Circumference refers to the circle or to the distance around the circle. This distance equals the diameter multiplied by π or 3.1416. Other definitions are illustrated in Figure A.4b–e.

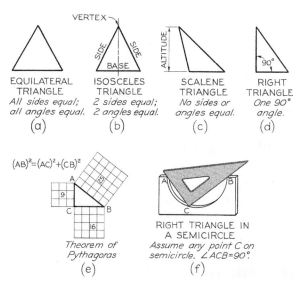

$(AB)^2 = (AC)^2 + (CB)^2$

Theorem of Pythagoras
(e)

RIGHT TRIANGLE IN A SEMICIRCLE
Assume any point C on semicircle. $\angle ACB = 90°$.
(f)

A.1   Triangles

A.2   Quadrilaterals

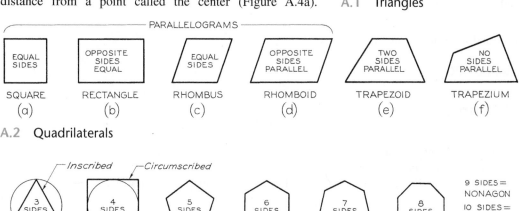

A.3   Regular Polygons

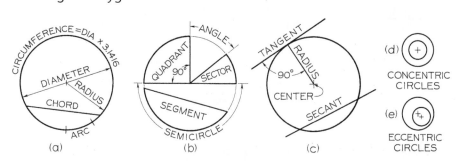

A.4   The Circle

From Appendix 6 of *Modern Graphics Communication*, Fourth Edition, Frederick E. Giesecke, Alva Mitchell, Henry Cecil Spencer, Ivan Leroy Hill, John Thomas Dygdon, James E. Novak, Shawna Lockhart. Copyright © 2010 by Pearson Education, Inc. Published by Pearson Prentice Hall. All rights reserved.

A.5 ■ Bisecting a Line or Circular Arc

Figure A.5a shows the given line or arc AB to be bisected.

I. From A and B draw equal arcs with radius greater than half AB.
II. and III. Join intersections D and E with a straight line to locate center C.

A.6 ■ Bisecting a Line with Triangle and T-Square

As shown in Figure A.6, from endpoints A and B, draw construction lines at 30°, 45°, or 60° with the given line; then through their intersection, C, draw a line perpendicular to the given line to locate the center D, as shown.

A.7 ■ Bisecting an Angle

Figure A.7 shows the given angle BAC to be bisected.

I. Strike large arc R.
II. Strike equal arcs r with radius slightly larger than half BC, to intersect at D.
III. Draw line AD, which bisects the angle.

A.8 ■ Transferring an Angle

Figure A.8 shows the given angle BAC to be transferred to the new position at A′B′.

I. Use any convenient radius R, and strike arcs from centers A and A′.
II. Strike equal arcs r, and draw side A′C′.

A.9 ■ Drawing a Line Through a Point and Parallel to a Line

With given point P as center, and any convenient radius R, strike arc CD to intersect the given line AB at E (Figure A.9a). With E as center and the same radius, strike arc R′ to intersect

the given line at G. With PG as radius and E as center, strike arc r to locate point H. The line PH is the required line.

Preferred Method As shown in Figure A.9b, move the triangle and T-square as a unit until the triangle lines up with given line AB; then slide the triangle until its edge passes through the given point P. Draw CD, the required parallel line.

A.10 ■ Drawing a Line Parallel to a Line and at a Given Distance

Let AB be the line and CD the given distance. As shown in Figure A.10a, draw two arcs with points E and F near A and B, re-

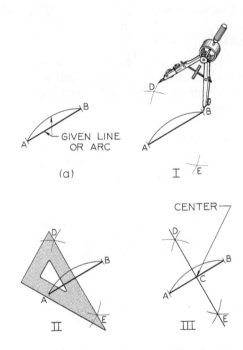

A.5   Bisecting a Line or a Circular Arc

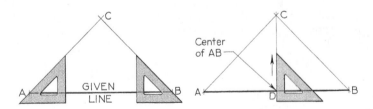

A.6   Bisecting a Line with Triangle and T-Square

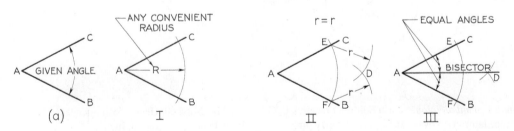

A.7   Bisecting an Angle

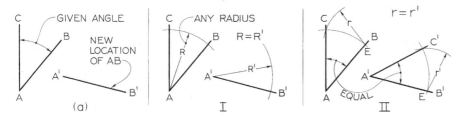

A.8   Transferring an Angle

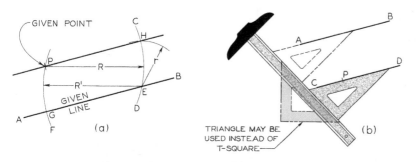

A.9   Drawing a Line Through a Point Parallel to a Line

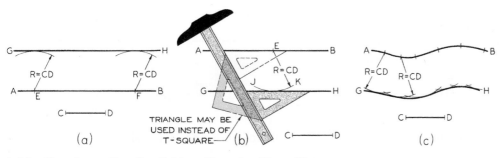

A.10   Drawing a Line Parallel to a Line at a Given Distance

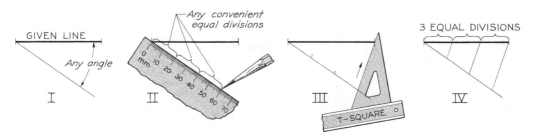

A.11   Dividing a Line into Equal Parts

spectively, as centers, and CD as radius. The line GH, tangent to the arcs, is the required line.

Preferred Method   With any point E of the line as center and CD as radius, strike an arc JK (Figure A.10b). Move the triangle and T-square as a unit until the triangle lines up with the given line AB; then slide the triangle until its edge is tangent to the arc JK, and draw the required line GH.

As shown in Figure A.10c, with centers selected at random on the curved line AB and with CD as radius, draw a series of arcs; then draw the required line tangent to these arcs.

A.11 ■ Dividing a Line into Equal Parts

There are two methods for dividing a line into equal parts. The first method is shown in Figure A.11:

I.   Draw a light construction line at any convenient angle from one end of line.
II. With dividers or scale, set off from intersection of lines as many equal divisions as needed (in this case, three).
III. Connect last division point to the other end of line, using triangle and T-square, as shown.
IV. Slide triangle along T-square and draw parallel lines through other division points, as shown.

The second method for dividing a line into equal parts is shown in Figure A.12:

I. Draw vertical construction line at one end of given line.
II. Set zero of scale at other end of line.
III. Swing scale up until third unit falls on vertical line, and make tiny dots at each point, or prick points with dividers.
IV. Draw vertical construction lines through each point.

Some practical applications of this method are shown in Figure A.13.

A.12 ■ Dividing a Line into Proportional Parts

Let it be required to divide the line AB into three parts proportional to 2, 3, and 4.

Preferred Method Draw a vertical line from point B (Figure A.14a). Select a scale of convenient size for a total of nine units and set the zero of the scale at A. Swing the scale up until the ninth unit falls on the vertical line. Along the scale, set off points for 2, 3, and 4 units, as shown. Draw vertical lines through these points.

Draw a line CD parallel to AB and at any convenient distance (Figure A.14b). On this line, set off 2, 3, and 4 units, as shown. Draw lines through the ends of the two lines to intersect at the point O. Draw lines through O and the points 2 and 5 to divide AB into the required proportional parts.

Given AB, divide into proportional parts, in this case proportional to the square of x, where $x = 1, 2, 3, \ldots$ (Figure A.14c). Set zero of scale at end of line and set off

divisions 4, 9, 16, ... Join the last division to the other end of the line, and draw parallel lines as shown. This method may be used for any power of x.

A.13 ■ Drawing a Line Through a Point and Perpendicular to a Line

The line AB and a point P (Figure A.15) are given.

When the Point Is Not on the Line From P, draw any convenient inclined line, as PD (Figure A.15a). Find center C of line PD, and draw arc with radius CP. The line EP is the required perpendicular.

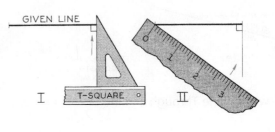
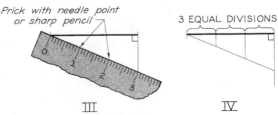

A.12 Dividing a Line into Equal Parts

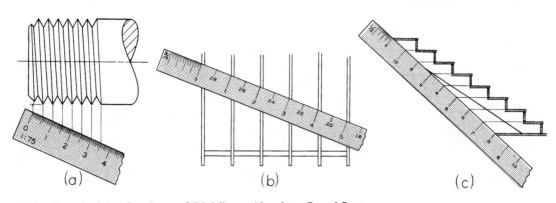

A.13 Practical Applications of Dividing a Line into Equal Parts

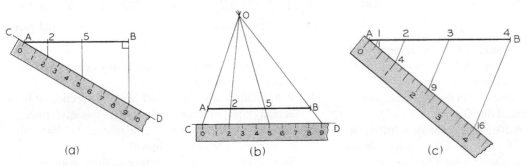

A.14 Dividing a Line into Proportional Parts

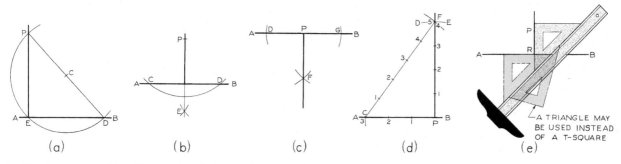

A.15 Drawing a Line Through a Point and Perpendicular to a Line

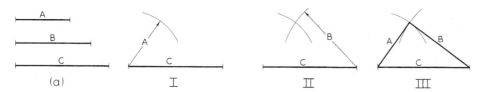

A.16 Drawing a Triangle with Sides Given

With P as center, strike an arc to intersect AB at C and D (Figure A.15b). With C and D as centers and radius slightly greater than half CD, strike arcs to intersect at E. The line PE is the required perpendicular.

When the Point Is on the Line With P as center and any radius, strike arcs to intersect AB at D and G (Figure A.15c). With D and G as centers and radius slightly greater than half DG, strike equal arcs to intersect at F. The line PF is the required perpendicular.

As shown in Figure A.15d, select any convenient unit of length (for example, 6 mm or ¼″). With P as center and 3 units as radius, strike an arc to intersect the given line at C. With P as center and 4 units as radius, strike arc DE. With C as center and 5 units as radius, strike an arc to intersect DE at F. The line PF is the required perpendicular.

This method makes use of the 3–4–5 right triangle and is frequently used in laying off rectangular foundations of large machines, buildings, or other structures. For this purpose a steel tape may be used and distances of 30′, 40′, and 50′ measured as the three sides of the right triangle.

Preferred Method Move the triangle and T-square as a unit until the triangle lines up with AB (Figure A.15e); then slide the triangle until its edge passes through the point P (whether P is on or off the line), and draw the required perpendicular.

A.14 ■ Drawing a Triangle with Sides Given

Given the sides A, B, and C, as shown in Figure A.16a:

  I. Draw one side, as C, in desired position, and strike arc with radius equal to side A.
 II. Strike arc with radius equal to side B.
III. Draw sides A and B from intersection of arcs, as shown.

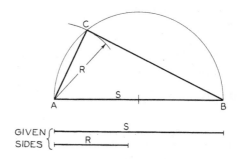

GIVEN SIDES { S
            { R

A.17 Drawing a Right Triangle

A.15 ■ Drawing a Right Triangle with Hypotenuse and One Side Given

Given sides S and R (Figure A.17), with AB as a diameter equal to S, draw a semicircle. With A as center and R as radius, draw an arc intersecting the semicircle at C. Draw AC and CB to complete the right triangle.

A.16 ■ Laying Out an Angle

Many angles can be laid out directly with the triangle, or they may be laid out with the protractor. Other methods, for which considerable accuracy is required, are discussed next (Figure A.18).

Tangent Method The tangent of angle θ is y/x and $y = x \tan \theta$. To construct the angle, assume a convenient value for x, preferably 10 units of convenient length (Figure A.18a). (The larger the unit, the more accurate will be the construction.) Find the tangent of angle θ in a table of natural tangents, multiply by 10, and set off $y = 10 \tan \theta$.

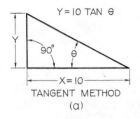
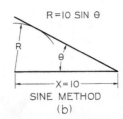
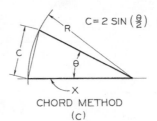

TANGENT METHOD
(a)

SINE METHOD
(b)

CHORD METHOD
(c)

A.18 Laying Out Angles

EXAMPLE To set off $31\frac{1}{2}°$, find the natural tangent of $31\frac{1}{2}°$, which is 0.6128. Then

$$y = 10 \text{ units} \times 0.6128 = 6.128 \text{ units.}$$

Sine Method Draw line x to any convenient length, preferably 10 units (Figure A.18b). Find the sine of angle θ in a table of natural sines, multiply by 10, and strike arc R = 10 sin θ. Draw the other side of the angle tangent to the arc, as shown.

EXAMPLE To set off $25\frac{1}{2}°$, find the natural sine of $25\frac{1}{2}°$, which is 0.4304. Then

$$R = 10 \text{ units} \times 0.4305 = 4.305 \text{ units.}$$

Chord Method Draw line x to any convenient length, and draw arc with any convenient radius R—say 10 units (Figure A.18c). Find the chordal length C in a table of chords (see a machinists' handbook), and multiply the value by 10 since the table is made for a radius of 1 unit.

EXAMPLE To set off 43° 20', the chordal length C for 1 unit radius, as given in a table of chords equals 0.7384; and if R = 10 units, then C = 7.384 units.

If a table is not available, the chord C may be calculated by the formula C = 2 sin θ/2.

EXAMPLE Half of 43°20' = 21°40'. The sine of 21°40' = 0.3692. C = 2 × 0.3692 = 0.7384 for a 1 unit radius. For a 10 unit radius, C = 7.384 units.

A.17 ■ Drawing an Equilateral Triangle

Side AB is given. With A and B as centers and AB as radius, strike arcs to intersect at C (Figure A.19a). Draw lines AC and BC to complete the triangle.

Preferred Method Draw lines through points A and B, making angles of 60° with the given line and intersecting C (Figure A.19b).

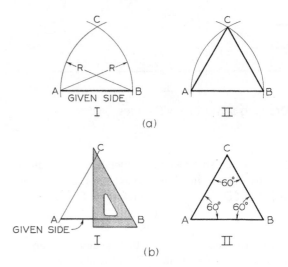

A.19 Drawing an Equilateral Triangle

A.18 ■ Drawing a Square

One side AB (Figure A.20a) is given. Through point A, draw a perpendicular (see Figure A.15c). With A as center and AB as radius, draw the arc to intersect the perpendicular at C. With B and C as centers and AB as radius, strike arcs to intersect at D. Draw lines CD and BD.

Preferred Method One side AB (Figure A.20b) is given. Using the T-square or parallel straightedge and 45° triangle, draw lines AC and BD perpendicular to AB and the lines AD and BC at 45° with AB. Draw line CD.

Preferred Method Given the circumscribed circle (distance "across corners"), draw two diameters at right angles to each other (Figure A.20c). The intersections of these diameters with the circle are vertexes of an inscribed square.

Preferred Method Given the inscribed circle (Figure A.20d) (distance "across flats," as in drawing bolt heads), use the T-square (or parallel straightedge) and 45° triangle and draw the four sides tangent to the circle.

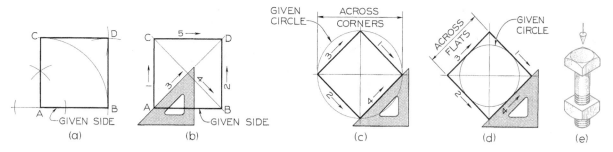

A.20 Drawing a Square

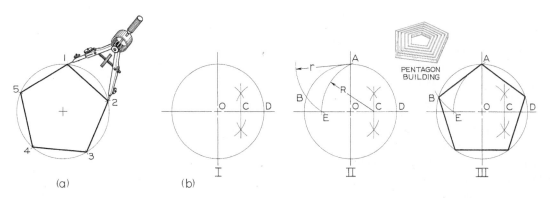

A.21 Drawing a Pentagon

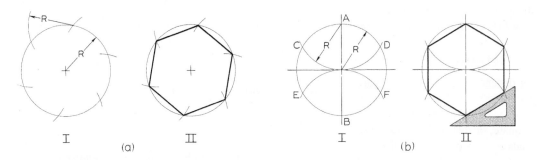

A.22 Drawing a Hexagon

A.19 ■ Drawing a Regular Pentagon

Given the circumscribed circle, do the following:

Preferred Method Divide the circumference of the circle into five equal parts with the dividers, and join the points with straight lines (Figure A.21a).

Geometrical Method As shown in Figure A.21b:

I. Bisect radius OD at C.
II. With C as center and CA as radius, strike arc AE. With A as center and AE as radius, strike arc EB.
III. Draw line AB; then set off distances AB around the circumference of the circle, and draw the sides through these points.

A.20 ■ Drawing a Hexagon

The circumscribed circle (Figure A.22) as given. Each side of a hexagon is equal to the radius of the circumscribed circle (Figure A.22a). Therefore, using the compass or dividers and the radius of the circle, set off the six sides of the hexagon around the circle, and connect the points with straight lines. As a check on the accuracy of the construction, make sure that opposite sides of the hexagon are parallel.

Preferred Method This construction (Figure A.22) is a variation of the one shown in Figure A.22a. Draw vertical and horizontal centerlines. With A and B as centers and radius equal to that of the circle, draw arcs to intersect the circle at C, D, E, and F, and complete the hexagon as shown.

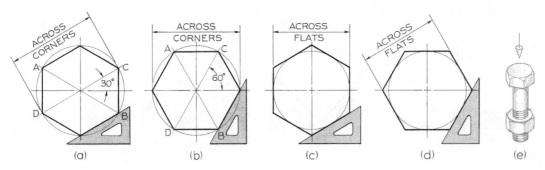

A.23   Drawing a Hexagon

Given the circumscribed circle (distance "across corners") (Figure A.23a and b), draw vertical and horizontal centerlines, and then diagonals AB and CD at 30° or 60° with horizontal; finally, with the 30° × 60° triangle and the T-square, draw the six sides as shown.

Given the inscribed circle (distance "across flats") (Figure A.23c and d), draw vertical and horizontal center lines; then with the 30° × 60° triangle and the T-square or straightedge, draw the six sides tangent to the circle. This method is used in drawing bolt heads and nuts. For maximum accuracy, diagonals may be added, as in Figure A.23a and b.

As shown in Figure A.24, use the 30° × 60° triangle and the T-square or straightedge; draw lines in the order shown in Figure A.24a, where the distance AB ("across corners") is given or, as shown in Figure A.24b, where a side CD is given.

A.21 ■ Drawing an Octagon

Given an inscribed circle, or distance "across flats" (Figure A.25a), use a T-square or straightedge and a 45° triangle to draw the eight sides tangent to the circle, as shown.

Given a circumscribed square, or distance "across flats" (Figure A.25b), draw diagonals of square; then with the corners of the given square as centers and with half the diagonal as radius, draw arcs cutting the sides as shown in I. Using a T-square and 45° triangle, draw the eight sides, as shown in II.

A.22 ■ Drawing a Circle Through Three Points

I. Let A, B, and C be the three given points not in a straight line (Figure A.26). Draw lines AB and BC, which will be chords of the circle. Draw perpendicular bisectors EO and DO intersecting at O (see Figure A.26).

II. With center at O, draw required circle through the points.

A.23 ■ Finding the Center of a Circle

Draw any chord AB, preferably horizontal as shown (Figure A.26b). Draw perpendiculars from A and B, cutting the circle at D and E. Draw diagonals DB and EA whose intersection C will be the center of the circle. This method uses the principle that any right triangle inscribed in a circle cuts off a semi-circle.

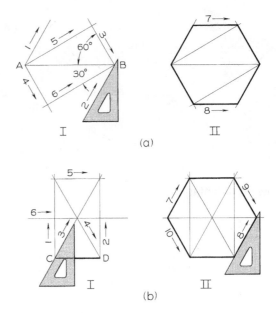

A.24   Drawing a Hexagon

Another method, slightly longer, is to reverse the procedure of Figure A.26a. Draw any two nonparallel chords and draw perpendicular bisectors. The intersection of the bisectors will be the center of the circle.

A.24 ■ Drawing a Circle Tangent to a Line at a Given Point

Given a line AB and a point P on the line (Figure A.27a):

I. At P, erect a perpendicular to the line.

II. Set off the radius of the required circle on the perpendicular.

III. Draw a circle with radius CP.

A.25 ■ Drawing a Tangent to a Circle Through a Point

Preferred Method   Given point P on the circle (Figure A.28a), move the T-square and triangle as a unit until one side of the triangle passes through the point P and the center of the circle; then slide the triangle until the other side passes through point P, and draw the required tangent.

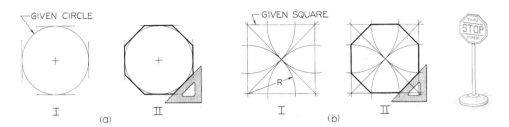

A.25 Drawing an Octagon

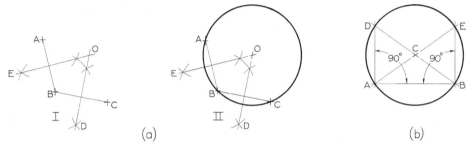

A.26 Finding the Center of a Circle

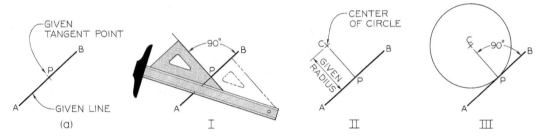

A.27 Drawing a Circle Tangent to a Line

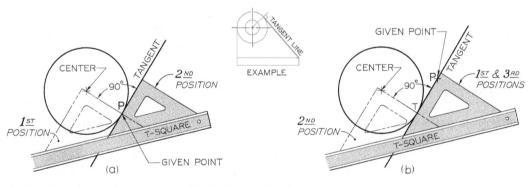

A.28 Drawing a Tangent to a Circle Through a Point

Given point P outside the circle (Figure A.28b), move the T-square and triangle as a unit until one side of the triangle passes through point P and, by inspection, is tangent to the circle; then slide the triangle until the other side passes through the center of the circle, and lightly mark the point of tangency T. Finally, move the triangle back to its starting position, and draw the required tangent.

In both constructions either triangle may be used. Also, a second triangle may be used in place of the T-square.

A.26 ■ Drawing Tangents to Two Circles

Move the triangle and T-square as a unit until one side of the triangle is tangent, by inspection, to the two circles (Figure A.29a and b); then slide the triangle until the other side passes through the center of one circle, and lightly mark the point of tangency. Then slide the triangle until the slide passes through the center of the other circle, and mark the point of tangency. Finally, slide

53

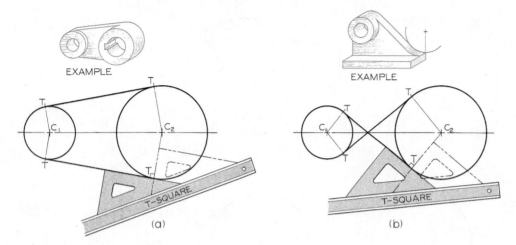

A.29   Drawing Tangents to Two Circles

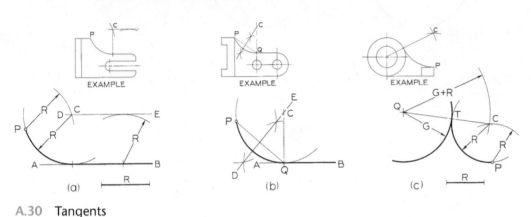

A.30   Tangents

A.31   Drawing a Tangent Arc in a Right Angle

the triangle back to the tangent position, and draw the tangent lines between the two points of tangency. Draw the second tangent line in a similar manner.

A.27 ■ Drawing an Arc Tangent to a Line or Arc and Through a Point

Given line AB, point P, and radius R (Figure A.30a), draw line DE parallel to the given line and distance R from it. From P draw arc with radius R, cutting line DE at C, the center of the required tangent arc.

   Given line AB, with tangent point Q on the line and point P (Figure A.30b), draw PQ, which will be a chord of the required arc. Draw perpendicular bisector DE, and at Q erect a perpendicular to the line to intersect DE at C, the center of the required tangent arc.

Given arc with center Q, point P, and radius R (Figure 30c), from P, strike arc with radius R. From Q, strike arc with radius equal to that of the given arc plus R. The intersection C of the arcs is the center of the required tangent arc.

A.28 ■ Drawing an Arc Tangent to Two Lines at Right Angles

I.   Two lines are given at right angles to each other (Figure A.31a).
II. With given radius R, strike arc intersecting given lines at tangent points T.
III. With given radius R again, and with points T as centers, strike arcs intersecting at C.
IV. With C as center and given radius R, draw the required tangent arc.

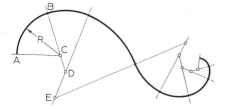

A.36 Drawing a Series of Tangent Arcs Conforming to a Curve

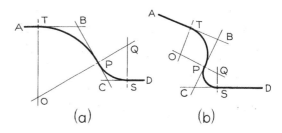

(a)   (b)

A.38 Drawing Two Curves Tangent to Three Intersecting Lines

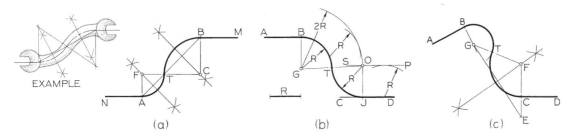

EXAMPLE   (a)   (b)   (c)

A.37 Drawing an Ogee Curve

ters D, E, and so on will be on lines joining the centers with the points of tangency, as shown.

A.34 ■ Drawing an Ogee Curve

Connecting Two Parallel Lines   Let NA and BM be the two parallel lines. Draw AB, and assume inflection point T (at midpoint if two equal arcs are desired) (Figure A.37a). At A and B, erect perpendiculars AF and BC. Draw perpendicular bisectors of AT and BT. The intersections F and C of these bisectors and the perpendiculars, respectively, are the centers of the required tangent arcs.

Let AB and CD be the two parallel lines, with point B as one end of the curve and R the given radii (Figure A.37b). At B, erect perpendicular to AB, make BG = R, and draw the arc as shown. Draw line SP parallel to CD at distance R from CD. With center G, draw the arc of radius 2R, intersecting line SP at O. Draw perpendicular OJ to locate tangent point J, and join centers G and O to locate point of tangency T. Using centers G and O and radius R, draws the two tangent arcs as shown.

Connecting Two Nonparallel Lines   Let AB and CD be the two nonparallel lines (Figure A.37c). Erect perpendicular to AB at B. Select point G on the perpendicular so that BG equals any desired radius, and draw the arc as shown. Erect perpendicular to CD at C and make CE = BG. Join G to E and bisect it. The intersection F of the bisector and the perpendicular CE, extended, is the center of the second arc. Join centers of the two arcs to locate tangent point T, the inflection point of the curve.

A.35 ■ Drawing a Curve Tangent to Three Intersecting Lines

Let AB, BC, and CD be the given lines (Figure A.38a and b). Select point of tangency P at any point on line BC. Make BT equal to BP, and CS equal to CP, and erect perpendiculars at the

points P, T, and S. Their intersections O and Q are the centers of the required tangent arcs.

A.36 ■ Rectifying a Circular Arc

To *rectify* an arc is to lay out its true length along a straight line. The constructions are approximate, but well within the range of accuracy of drawing instruments.

To Rectify a Quadrant of a Circle, AB   Draw AC tangent to the circle BC at 60° to AC, as shown (Figure A.39a). The line AC is almost equal to the arc AB; the difference in length is about 1 in 240.

To Rectify Arc, AB   Draw tangent at B (Figure A.39b). Draw chord AB and extend it to C, making BC equal to half AB. With C as center and radius CA, strike the arc AD. The tangent BD is slightly shorter than the given arc AB. For an angle of 45° the difference in length is about 1 in 2,866.

Use the bow dividers and, beginning at A, set off equal distances until the division point nearest B is reached (Figure A.39c). At this point, reverse the direction and set off an equal number of distances along the tangent to determine point C. The tangent BC is slightly shorter than the given arc AB. If the angle subtended by each division is 10°, the error is approximately 1 in 830.*

A.37 ■ Setting Off a Given Length Along a Given Arc

To transfer distances from the tangent line to the arc, reverse the preceding method (Figure A.39c).

*If the angle θ subtending an arc of radius R is known, the length of the arc is $2\pi R \dfrac{\theta}{360°} = 0.01745R\theta$.

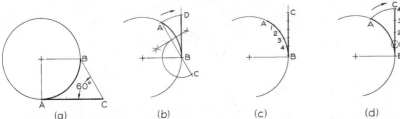

A.39 Rectifying Circular Arcs

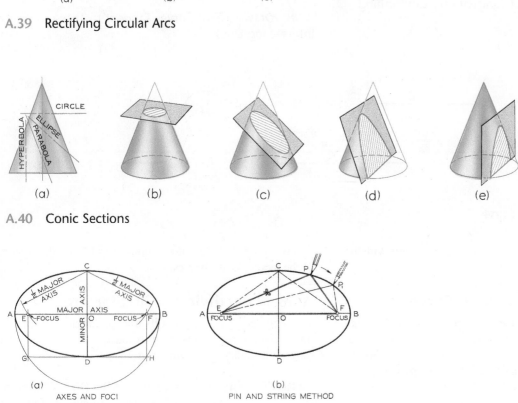

A.40 Conic Sections

A.41 Ellipse Constructions

To set off the length BC along the arc BA, draw BC tangent to the arc at B (Figure A.39d). Divide BC into four equal parts. With center at 1, the first division point, and radius 1–C, draw the arc CA. The arc BA is practically equal to BC for angles less than 30°. For 45° the difference is approximately 1 in 3,232, and for 60° it is about 1 in 835.

A.38 ■ The Conic Sections

The conic sections are curves produced by planes intersecting a right circular cone (Figure A.40). Four types of curves are produced: the *circle, ellipse, parabola,* and *hyperbola,* according to the position of the planes, as shown. These curves were studied in detail by the ancient Greeks and are of great interest in mathematics, as well as in technical drawing. For equations, see any text on analytic geometry.

A.39 ■ Ellipse Construction

The long axis of an ellipse is the major axis and the short axis is the minor axis (Figure A.41). The foci E and F are found by striking arcs with radius equal to half the major axis and with center at the end of the minor axis. Another method is to draw

a semicircle with the major axis as diameter, and then to draw GH parallel to the major axis and GE and HF parallel to the minor axis as shown.

An *ellipse* is generated by a point moving so that the sum of its distances from two points (the foci) is constant and equal to the major axis. As shown in Figure A.41b, an ellipse may be constructed by placing a looped string around the foci E and F and around C, one end of the minor axis, and moving the pencil point P along its maximum orbit while the string is kept taut.

A.40 ■ Drawing a Foci Ellipse

Let AB be the major axis and CD the minor axis (Figure A.42). This method is the geometrical counterpart of the pin-and-string method. Keep the construction very light, as follows:

I.   To find foci E and F, strike arcs R with radius equal to half the major axis and with centers at the ends of the minor axis.

II. Between E and O on the major axis, mark at random a number of points (spacing those on the left more closely), equal to the number of points desired in each quadrant of the ellipse. In this figure, five points were deemed sufficient. For large ellipses, more points should be used—enough to

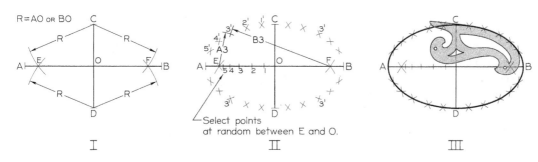

A.42   Drawing a Foci Ellipse

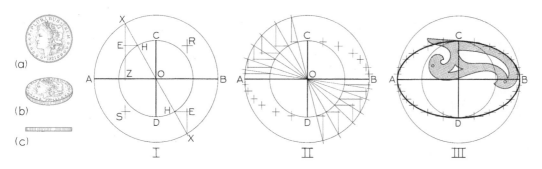

A.43   Drawing a Concentric Circle Ellipse

ensure a smooth, accurate curve. Begin construction with
any one of these points, such as 3. With E and F as centers
and radii A–3 and B–3, respectively (from the ends of the
major axis to point 3), strike arcs to intersect at four
points 3', as shown. Using the remaining points 1, 2, 4,
and 5, for each find four additional points on the ellipse
in the same manner.

III.   Sketch the ellipse lightly through the points; then heavy
in the final ellipse with the aid of an irregular curve.

A.41 ■ Drawing a Concentric Circle Ellipse

If a circle is viewed so that the line of sight is perpendicular
to the plane of the circle, as shown for the silver dollar in
Figure A.43a, the circle will appear as a circle, in true size and
shape. If the circle is viewed at an angle, as shown in Figure
A.43b, it will appear as an ellipse. If the circle is viewed edgewise, it appears as a straight line, as shown in Figure A.43c.
The case shown in Figure A.43b is the basis for the construction of an ellipse by the concentric circle method, which follows. (Keep the construction very light.)

I.   Draw circles on the major and minor axes, using them as
diameters; draw any diagonal XX through center O. From
the points X, where the diagonal intersects the large circle, draw lines XE parallel to the minor axis, and from the
points H, where the diagonal intersects the small circle,
draw lines HE parallel to the major axis. The intersections
E are points on the ellipse. Two additional points, S and R,
can be found by extending lines XE and HE, giving a total
of four points from the one diagonal XX.

II.   Draw as many additional diagonals as needed to provide a
sufficient number of points for a smooth and symmetrical

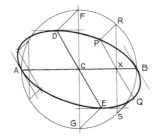

A.44   Oblique Circle Ellipse

ellipse, each diagonal accounting for four points on the ellipse. Notice that where the curve is sharpest (near the ends
of the ellipse), the points are constructed closer together to
determine the curve better.

III.   Sketch the ellipse lightly through the points, and then heavy
in the final ellipse with the aid of an irregular curve.*

*In Figure 43, part I, the ordinate EZ of the ellipse is to the
corresponding ordinate XZ of the circle as b is to a, where b
represents the semiminor axis and a the semimajor axis. Thus, the
area of the ellipse is equal to the area of the circumscribed circle
multiplied by b/a; hence, it is equal to πab.

A.42 ■ Drawing an Ellipse on Conjugate Diameters: The Oblique Circle Method

Let AB and DE be the given conjugate diameters (Figure
A.44). Two diameters are conjugate when each is parallel to
the tangents at the extremities of the other. With center at C
and radius CA, draw a circle; draw the diameter GF perpendicular to AB, and draw lines joining points D and F and
points G and E.

Assume that the required ellipse is an oblique projection of the circle just drawn; the points D and E of the ellipse are the oblique projections of the points F and G of the circle, respectively; similarly, the points P and Q are the oblique projections of the points R and S, respectively. The points P and Q are determined by assuming point X at any point on AB and drawing the lines RS and PQ, and RP and SQ, parallel, respectively, to GF and DE and FD and GE.

Determine at least five points in each quadrant (more for larger ellipses) by assuming additional points on the major axis and proceeding as explained for point X. Sketch the ellipse lightly through the points; then heavy in the final ellipse with the aid of an irregular curve.

A.43 ■ Drawing a Parallelogram Ellipse

Given the major and minor axes, or the conjugate diameters AB and CD, draw a rectangle or parallelogram with sides parallel to the axes, respectively (Figure A.45a and b). Divide AO and AJ into the same number of equal parts, and draw *light* lines through these points from the ends of the minor axis, as shown. The intersection of like-numbered lines will be points on the

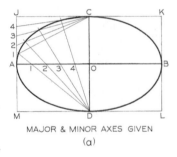

MAJOR & MINOR AXES GIVEN
(a)

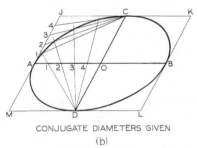

CONJUGATE DIAMETERS GIVEN
(b)

A.45   Parallelogram Ellipse

ellipse. Locate points in the remaining three quadrants in a similar manner. Sketch the ellipse lightly through the points; then heavy in the final ellipse with the aid of an irregular curve.

A.44 ■ Finding the Axes of an Ellipse with Conjugate Diameters Given

Conjugate diameters AB and CD and the ellipse are given (Figure A.46a). With intersection O of the conjugate diameters (center of ellipse) as center, and any convenient radius, draw a circle to intersect the ellipse in four points. Join these points with straight lines, as shown; the resulting quadrilateral will be a rectangle whose sides are parallel, respectively, to the required major and minor axes. Draw the axes EF and GH parallel to the sides of the rectangle.

An ellipse only is given (Figure A.46c). To find the center of the ellipse, draw a circumscribing rectangle or parallelogram about the ellipse; then draw diagonals to intersect at center O as shown. The axes are then found as shown in Figure A.46a.

Conjugate diameters AB and CD only are given (Figure A.46c). With O as center and CD as diameter, draw a circle. Through center O and perpendicular to CD, draw line EF. From points E and F, where this perpendicular intersects the circle, draw lines FA and EA to form angle FAE. Draw the bisector AG of this angle. The major axis JK will be parallel to this bisector, and the minor axis LM will be perpendicular to it. The length AH will be one half the major axis, and HF one half the minor axis. The resulting major and minor axes are JK and LM, respectively.

A.45 ■ Drawing a Tangent to an Ellipse

Concentric Circle Construction   To draw a tangent at any point on an ellipse, such as E, draw the ordinate at E to intersect the circle at V (Figure A.47a). Draw a tangent to the circumscribed circle at V, and extend it to intersect the major axis extended at G. The line GE is the required tangent.

To draw a tangent from a point outside the ellipse, such as P, draw the ordinate PY and extend it. Draw DP, intersecting the major axis at X. Draw FX and extend it to intersect the ordinate through P at Q. Then, from similar triangles QY:PY = OF:OD. Draw a tangent to the circle from Q, find the point of tangency R, and draw the ordinate at R to intersect the ellipse at Z. The line ZP

A.46   Finding the Axes of an Ellipse

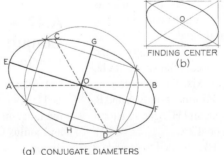

FINDING CENTER
(b)

(a) CONJUGATE DIAMETERS
AND ELLIPSE ARE GIVEN

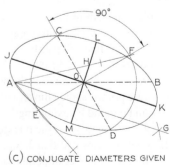

(c) CONJUGATE DIAMETERS GIVEN

is the required tangent. As a check on the drawing, the tangents RQ and ZP should intersect at a point on the major axis extended. Two tangents to the ellipse can be drawn from point P.

Foci Construction To draw a tangent at any point on the ellipse, such as point 3, draw the focal radii E–3 and F–3, extend one, and bisect the exterior angle, as shown in Figure A.47b. The bisector is the required tangent.

To draw a tangent from any point outside the ellipse, such as point P, with center at P and radius PF, strike an arc as shown. With center at E and radius AB, strike an arc to intersect the first arc at points U. Draw the lines EU to intersect the ellipse at the points Z. The lines PZ are the required tangents.

A.46 ■ Ellipse Templates

To save time in drawing ellipses and to ensure uniform results, ellipse templates are often used (Figure A.48a). These are plastic sheets with elliptical openings in a wide variety of sizes, and they usually come in sets of six or more sheets.

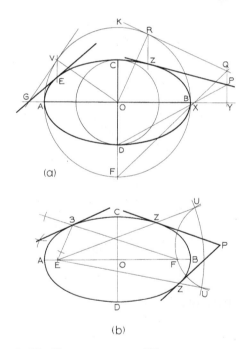

(a)

(b)

A.47 Tangents to an Ellipse

Ellipse guides are usually designated by the ellipse angle, the angle at which a circle is viewed to appear as an ellipse. In Figure A.48b, the angle between the line of sight and the edge view of the plane of the circle is found to be about 49°; hence the 50° ellipse template is indicated. Ellipse templates are generally available in ellipse angles at 5° intervals, such as 15°, 20°, and 25°. The 50° template provides a variety of sizes of 50° ellipses, and it is only necessary to select the one that fits. If the ellipse angle is not easily determined, you can always look for the ellipse that is approximately as long and as "fat" as the ellipse to be drawn.

A simple construction for finding the ellipse angle when the views are not available is shown in Figure A.48c. Using center O, strike arc BF; then draw CE parallel to the major axis. Draw diagonal OE, and measure angle EOB with a protractor. Use the ellipse template nearest to this angle; in this case a 35° template is selected.

Since it is not feasible to have ellipse openings for every exact size that may be required, it is often necessary to use the template somewhat in the manner of an irregular curve. For example, if the opening is too long and too "fat" for the required ellipse, one end may be drawn and then the template may be shifted slightly to draw the other end. Similarly, one long side may be drawn and then the template may be shifted slightly to draw the opposite side. In such cases, leave gaps between the four segments, to be filled in freehand or with the aid of an irregular curve. When the differences between the ellipse openings and the required ellipse are small, it is only necessary to lean the pencil slightly outward or inward from the guiding edge to offset the differences.

For inking the ellipses, a technical drawing pen with a "0" or "00" size designation is recommended (Figure A.48d).

A.47 ■ Drawing an Approximate Ellipse

For many purposes, particularly where a small ellipse is required, the approximate circular arc method is perfectly satisfactory (Figure A.49). Such an ellipse is sure to be symmetrical and may be quickly drawn.

Given axes AB and CD,

I. Draw line AC. With O as center and OA as radius, strike the arc AE. With C as center and CE as radius, strike the arc EF.

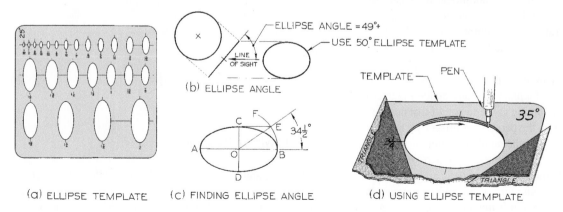

(a) ELLIPSE TEMPLATE (c) FINDING ELLIPSE ANGLE (d) USING ELLIPSE TEMPLATE

A.48 Using the Ellipse Template

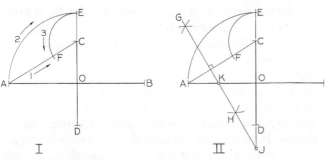

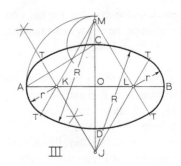

A.49 Drawing an Approximate Ellipse

II. Draw perpendicular bisector GH of the line AF; the points K and J, where it intersects the axes, are centers of the required arcs.
III. Find centers M and L by setting off OL = OK and OM = OJ. Using centers K, L, M, and J, draw circular arcs as shown. The points of tangency T are at the junctures of the arcs on the lines joining the centers.

A.48 ■ Drawing a Parabola

The curve of intersection between a right circular cone and a plane parallel to one of its elements is a parabola (see Figure A.50d). The parabola is used to reflect surfaces for light and sound, for vertical curves in highways, for forms of arches, and approximately for forms of the curves of cables for suspension bridges. It is also used to show the bending moment at any point on a uniformly loaded beam or girder.

A *parabola* is generated by a point moving so that its distances from a fixed point, the focus, and from a fixed line, the directrix, remain equal.

Focus F and directrix AB are given. A parabola may be generated by a pencil guided by a string (Figure A.50a). Fasten the string at F and C; its length is GC. The point C is selected at random; its distance from G depends on the desired extent of the curve. Keep the string taut and the pencil against the T-square, as shown.

Given focus F and directrix AB, draw a line DE parallel to the directrix and at any distance CZ from it (Figure A.50b). With center at F and radius CZ, strike arcs to intersect the line DE in the points Q and R, which are points on the parabola. Determine as many additional points as are necessary to draw the parabola accurately, by drawing additional lines parallel to line AB and proceeding in the same manner.

A tangent to the parabola at any point G bisects the angle formed by the focal line FG and the line SG perpendicular to the directrix.

Given the rise and span of the parabola (Figure A.50), divide AO into any number of equal parts, and divide AD into a number of equal parts amounting to the square of that number. From line AB, each point on the parabola is offset by a number of units equal to the square of the number of units from point O. For example, point 3 projects 9 units (the square of 3). This method is generally used for drawing parabolic arches.

To find the focus, F, given points P, R, and V of a parabola (Figure A.50), draw a tangent at P, making a = b. Draw perpendicular bisector of AP, which intersects the axis at F, the focus of the parabola.

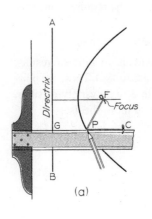

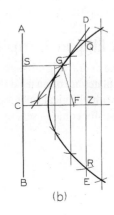

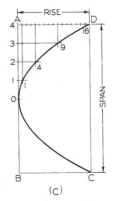

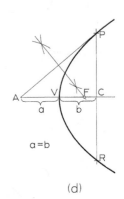

A.50 Drawing a Parabola

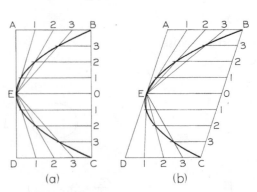

A.51 Drawing a Parabola

Draw a parabola given rectangle or parallelogram ABCD (Figure A.51a and b). Divide BC into any even number of equal parts, divide the sides AB and DC each into half as many parts, and draw lines as shown. The intersections of like-numbered lines are points on the parabola.

A.49 ■ Joining Two Points by a Parabolic Curve

Let X and Y be the given points (Figure A.52). Assume any point O, and draw tangents XO and YO. Divide XO and YO into the same number of equal parts, number the division points as shown, and connect corresponding points. These lines are tangents of the required parabola and form its envelope. Sketch a light smooth curve, and then heavy in the curve with the aid of an irregular curve.

These parabolic curves are more pleasing in appearance than circular arcs and are useful in machine design. If the tangents OX and OY are equal, the axis of the parabola will bisect the angle between them.

A.50 ■ Drawing a Hyperbola

The curve of intersection between a right circular cone and a plane making an angle with the axis smaller than that made by the elements is a hyperbola (see Figure A.53e). A *hyperbola* is generated by a point moving so that the difference of its distances from two fixed points, the foci is constant and equal to the transverse axis of the hyperbola.

Let F and F′ be the foci and AB the transverse axis (Figure A.53a). The curve may be generated by a pencil guided by a string, as shown. Fasten a string at F′ and C; its length is FC minus AB. The point C is chosen at random; its distance from F depends on the desired extent of the curve.

Fasten the straightedge at F. If it is revolved about F, with the pencil point moving against it and with the string taut, the hyperbola may be drawn as shown.

To construct the curve geometrically, select any point X on the transverse axis produced (Figure A.53b). With centers at F and F′ and BX as radius, strike the arcs DF. With the same centers, F and F′, and AX as radius, strike arcs to intersect the arcs first drawn in the points Q, R, S, and T, which are points of the required hyperbola. Find as many additional points as are necessary to draw the curves accurately by selecting other points similar to point X along the transverse axis and proceeding as described for point X.

To draw the tangent to a hyperbola at a given point P, bisect the angle between the focal radii FP and F′P. The bisector is the required tangent.

To draw the asymptotes HCH of the hyperbola, draw a circle with the diameter FF′ and erect perpendiculars to the transverse axis at the points A and B to intersect the circle in the points H. The lines HCH are the required asymptotes.

A.51 ■ Drawing an Equilateral Hyperbola

Let the asymptotes OB and OA, at right angles to each other, and the point P on the curve be given (Figure A.54).

In an equilateral hyperbola, the asymptotes, which are at right angles to each other, may be used as the axes to which

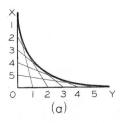
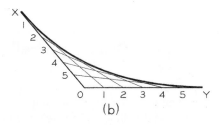
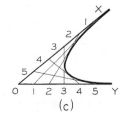

A.52   Parabolic Curves

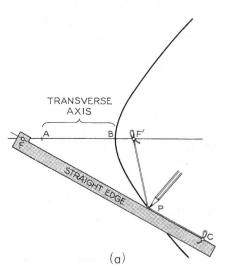
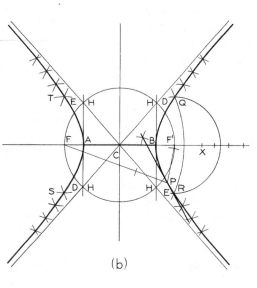

A.53   Drawing a Hyperbola

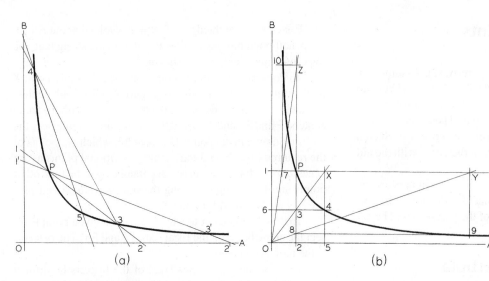

A.54   Equilateral Hyperbola

the curve is referred. If a chord of the hyperbola is extended to intersect the axes, the intercepts between the curve and the axes are equal (Figure A.54a). For example, a chord through given point P intersects the axes at points 1 and 2, intercepts P–1 and 2–3 are equal, and point 3 is a point on the hyperbola. Likewise, another chord through P provides equal intercepts P–1′ and 3′–2′, and point 3′ is a point on the curve. Not all chords need be drawn through given point P, but as new points are established on the curve, chords may be drawn through them to obtain more points. After enough points are found to ensure an accurate curve, the hyperbola is drawn with the aid of an irregular curve.

In an equilateral hyperbola, the coordinates are related so their products remain constant. Through given point P, draw lines 1–P–Y and 2–P–Z parallel, respectively, to the axes (Figure A.54b). From the origin of coordinates O, draw any diagonal intersecting these two lines at points 3 and X. At these points draw lines parallel to the axes, intersecting at point 4, a point on the curve. Likewise, another diagonal from O intersects the two lines through P at points 8 and Y, and lines through these points parallel to the axes intersect at point 9, another point on the curve. A third diagonal similarly produces point 10 on the curve, and so on. Find as many points as necessary for a smooth curve, and draw the parabola with the aid of an irregular curve. It is evident from the similar triangles O–X–5 and O–3–2 that lines P–1 × P–2 = 4–5 × 4–6.

The equilateral hyperbola can be used to represent varying pressure of a gas as the volume varies, since the pressure varies inversely with the volume; that is, pressure × volume is constant.

A.52 ■ Drawing a Spiral of Archimedes

To find points on the curve, draw lines through the pole C, making equal angles with each other, such as 30° angles (Figure A.55). Beginning with any one line, set off any distance, such as 2 mm or $\frac{1}{16}$″ set off twice that distance on the next line, three times on the third, and so on. Through the points thus determined, draw a smooth curve, using irregular curve.

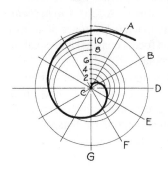

A.55   Spiral of Archimedes

A.53 ■ Drawing a Helix

A **helix** is generated by a point moving around and along the surface of a cylinder or cone with a uniform angular velocity about the axis, and with a uniform linear velocity about the axis, and with a uniform velocity in the direction of the axis (Figure A.56). A cylindrical helix is generally known simply as a helix. The distance measure parallel to the axis traversed by the point in one revolution is called the lead.

If the cylindrical surface on which a helix is generated is rolled out onto a plane, the helix becomes a straight line (Figure A.56a). The portion below the helix becomes a right triangle, the altitude of which is equal to the lead of the helix; the length of the base is equal to the circumference of the cylinder. Such a helix, therefore, can be defined as the shortest line that can be drawn on the surface of a cylinder connecting two points not on the same element.

To draw the helix, draw two views of the cylinder on which the helix is generated (Figure A.56b). Divide the circle of the base into any number of equal parts. On the rectangular view of the cylinder, set off the lead and divide it into the same number of equal parts as the base. Number the divisions as shown (in this case 16). When the generating point has moved one sixteenth of the distance around the cylinder, it will have risen one sixteenth of the lead; when it has moved halfway around the cylinder, it will have risen half the lead;

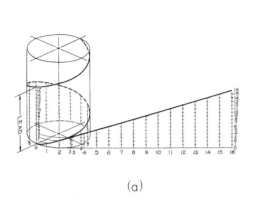
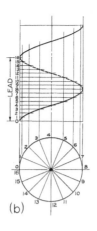

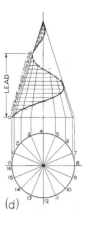

(a) (b) (c) A LEFT-HAND HELIX (d)

A.56 Helix

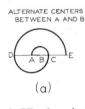
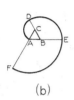
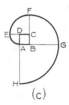

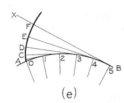

(a) (b) (c) (d) (e)

A.57 Involutes

and so on. Points on the helix are found by projecting up from point 1 in the circular view to line 1 in the rectangular view, from point 2 in the circular view to line 2 in the rectangular view, and so on.

Figure A.56b is a right-hand helix. In a left-hand helix (Figure A.56c), the visible portions of the curve are inclined in the opposite direction—that is, downward to the right. The helix shown in Figure A.56b can be converted into a left-hand helix by interchanging the visible and hidden lines.

The helix finds many applications in industry, as in screw threads, worm gears, conveyors, spiral stairways, and so on. The stripes of a barber pole are helical in form.

The construction for a right-hand conical helix is shown in Figure A.56d.

A.54 ■ Drawing an Involute

An *involute* is the path of a point on a string as the string unwinds from a line, polygon, or circle.

To Draw an Involute of a Line   Let AB be the given line. With AB as radius and B as center, draw the semicircle AC (Figure A.57a). With AC as radius and A as center, draw the semicircle CD. With BD as radius and B as center, draw the semicircle DE. Continue similarly, alternating centers between A and B, until a figure of the required size is completed.

To Draw an Involute of a Triangle   Let ABC be the given triangle. With CA as radius and C as center, strike the arc AD (Figure A.57b). With BD as radius and B as center, strike the arc DE. With AE as radius and A as center, strike the arc EF. Continue similarly until a figure of the required size is completed.

To Draw an Involute of a Square   Let ABCD be the given square. With DA as radius and D as center, draw the 90° arc AE (Figure A.57c). Proceed as for the involute of a triangle until a figure of the required size is completed.

To Draw an Involute of a Circle   A circle may be regarded as a polygon with an infinite number of sides (Figure A.57d). The involute is constructed by dividing the circumference into a number of equal parts, drawing a tangent at each division point, setting off along each tangent the length of the corresponding circular arc (Figure A.39c), and drawing the required curve through the points set off on the several tangents.

An involute can be generated by a point on a straight line that is rolled on a fixed circle (Figure A.57e). Points on the required curve may be determined by setting off equal distances 0–1, 1–2, 2–3, and so on, along the circumference, drawing a tangent at each division point, and proceeding as explained for Figure A.57d.

The involute of a circle is used in the construction of involute gear teeth. In this system, the involute forms the face and a part of the flank of the teeth of gear wheels; the outlines of the teeth of racks are straight lines.

A.55 ■ Drawing a Cycloid

A *cycloid* generated by a point P in the circumference of a circle that rolls along a straight line (Figure A.58).

Given the generating circle and the straight line AB tangent to it, make the distances CA and CB each equal to the semicircumference of the circle (see Figure A.58). Divide these distances and the semicircumference into the same number of equal parts (six, for instance) and number them consecutively, as shown. Suppose the circle rolls to the left;

when point 1 of the circle reaches point 1′ of the line, the center of the circle will be at D, point 7 will be the highest point of the circle, and the generating point 6 will be at the same distance from the line AB as point 5 is when the circle is in its central position. Hence, to find the point P′, draw a line through point 5 parallel to AB and intersect it with an arc drawn from the center D with a radius equal to that of the circle. To find point P″, draw a line through point 4 parallel to AB, and intersect it with an arc drawn from the center E, with a radius equal to that of the circle. Points J, K, and L are found in a similar manner.

Another method that may be employed is shown in the right half of Figure A.57. With center at 11′ and the chord 11–6 as radius, strike an arc. With 10′ as center and the chord 10–6 as radius, strike an arc. Continue similarly with centers 9′, 8′, and 7′. Draw the required cycloid tangent to these arcs.

Either method may be used; however, the second is the shorter one and is preferred. It is evident, from the tangent arcs drawn in the manner just described, that the line joining the generating point and the point of contact for the generating circle is a normal of the cycloid. The lines 1′–P″ and 2′–P′, for instance, are normals; this property makes the cycloid suitable for the outlines of gear teeth.

A.56 ■ Drawing an Epicycloid or a Hypocycloid

If the generating point P is on the circumference of a circle that rolls along the convex side of a larger circle, the curve generated is an epicycloid (Figure A.59a). If the circle rolls along the concave side of a larger circle, the curve generated is a hypocycloid (Figure A.59b). These curves are drawn in a manner similar to the cycloid (Figure A.58). Like the cycloid, these curves are used to form the outlines of certain gear teeth and are, therefore, of practical importance in machine design.

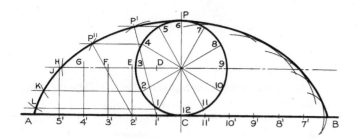

A.58   Cycloid

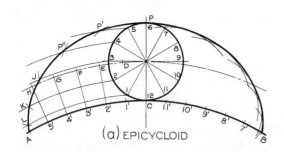

(a) EPICYCLOID

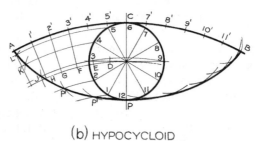

(b) HYPOCYCLOID

A.59   Epicycloid and Hypocycloid

TECHNICAL SKETCHING

From Chapter 3 of *Modern Graphics Communication*, Fourth Edition, Frederick E. Giesecke, Alva Mitchell, Henry Cecil Spencer, Ivan Leroy Hill, John Thomas Dygdon, James E. Novak, Shawna Lockhart. Copyright © 2010 by Pearson Education, Inc. Published by Pearson Prentice Hall. All rights reserved.

TECHNICAL SKETCHING

OBJECTIVES

After studying the material in this chapter, you should be able to:

1. Define vertex, edge, plane, surface, and solid.

2. Identify four types of surfaces.

3. Identify five regular solids.

4. Draw points, lines, angled lines, arcs, circles, and ellipses.

5. Apply techniques that aid in creating legible well-proportioned freehand sketches.

6. Apply techniques to draw irregular curves.

7. Create a single view sketch.

8. Create an oblique sketch.

9. Create perspective sketches.

10. Create an isometric sketch of an object.

The companion website for this text is www.prenhall.com/chet_giesecke_modgraphic_4.

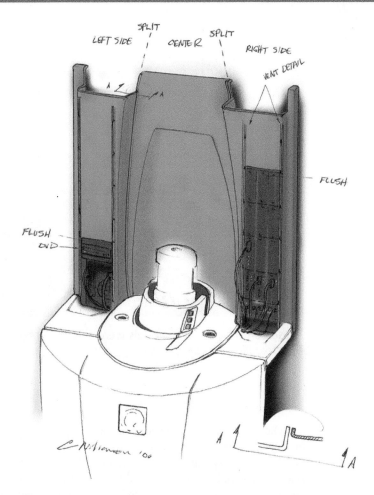

Shaded Sketch Showing Details of Wire Placement. *Courtesy of Quantum Design.*

OVERVIEW

The ability to envision objects in three dimensions is one of the most important skills for scientists, designers, engineers, and technicians. Learning to visualize objects in space, to use the constructive imagination, is something you can learn by studying technical drawing. People who are extraordinarily creative often possess outstanding ability to visualize, but with practice anyone can improve their ability.

In addition to developing spatial thinking skills, sketching is a valuable tool that allows you to quickly and accurately communicate your ideas. During the development stage of an idea, a picture is often worth a thousand words.

Sketching is also an efficient way to plan your drawing and record notes needed to create a complex object. When you sketch basic ideas ahead of time, you can often complete a final CAD drawing sooner and with fewer errors. Using good technique makes sketching faster, easier, and more legible.

Search the following Web sites for platonic solids (wikipedia, korthalsaltes), convex shapes (ibiblio), and octahedrons (korthalsaltes):

- http://en.wikipedia.org/wiki/Platonic_solid
- http://ibiblio.org/e-notes/3Dapp/Convex.htm
- http://www.korthalsaltes.com/platonic_solids_pictures.html
- http://www.korthalsaltes.com/octahedron.html

These complex surface models were created using 3D CAD. *Courtesy of Professor Richard Palais, University of California, Irvine, and Luc Benard.*

UNDERSTANDING SOLID OBJECTS

Sketches and drawings are used to communicate or record ideas about the shape of three-dimensional objects. Before starting to sketch, it helps to develop a vocabulary for understanding and discussing three-dimensional shapes.

Three-dimensional figures are referred to as **solids.** Solids are bounded by the **surfaces** that contain them. These surfaces can be one of the following four types:

- **Planar**
- **Single-curved**
- **Double-curved**
- **Warped**

Regardless of how complex a solid may be, it is composed of combinations of these basic types of surfaces. Figure 1 shows examples of the four basic types of surfaces.

Types of Solids

Polyhedra

Solids that are bounded by plane surfaces are called **polyhedra** (Figures 2–4). These planar surfaces are also referred to as *faces* of the object. A *polygon* is a planar area that is enclosed by straight lines.

Regular Polyhedra

If the faces of a solid are equal regular polygons it is called a **regular polyhedron.** There are five regular polyhedra: the tetrahedron, hexahedron, octahedron, dodecahedron, and icosahedron (Figure 2).

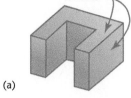

Planar surfaces

(a)

Single curved surface

(b)

Double curved surface

(c)

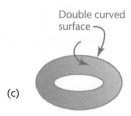

Warped surface

(d)

1 Types of Surfaces

Tetrahedron
(4 triangles)

Hexahedron
(cube)

Octahedron
(8 triangles)

Dodecahedron
(12 pentagons)

Icosahedron
(20 triangles)

2 Regular Polyhedra

Prisms

A **prism** has two bases, which are parallel equal polygons, and three or more additional faces, which are parallelograms (Figure 3). A triangular prism has a triangular base; a rectangular prism has rectangular bases; and so on. (If a prism's bases happen to be parallelograms, the prism is a called a parallelepiped, a word rarely heard in everyday conversation.)

A right prism has faces and lateral (side) edges that are perpendicular to the bases; an oblique prism has faces and lateral edges that are angled to the bases. If one end is cut off to form an end that is not parallel to the bases, the prism is said to be *truncated* (a word that simply means "shortened by having a part cut off ").

Pyramids

A **pyramid** has a polygon for a base and triangular lateral faces that intersect at a common point called the *vertex* (Figure 4). The line from the center of the base to the vertex is called the *axis*. If the axis is perpendicular to the base, the pyramid is called a *right* pyramid; otherwise it is an *oblique* pyramid. A triangular pyramid has a triangular base; a square pyramid has a square base; and so on. If a portion near the vertex has been cut off, the pyramid is truncated, or it is referred to as a *frustum*.

Cylinders

A **cylinder** has a single-curved exterior surface (Figure 5). You can think of a cylinder as being formed by taking a straight line and moving it in a circular path to enclose a volume. Each position of this imaginary straight line in its path around the axis is called an *element* of the cylinder.

Cones

A **cone** has a single-curved exterior surface (Figure 6). You can think of it as being formed by moving one end of a straight line around a circle while keeping the other end fixed at a point, the vertex of the cone. An element of the cone is any position of this imaginary straight line.

Spheres

A **sphere** has a double-curved exterior surface (Figure 7). You can think of it as being formed by revolving a circle about one of its diameters, somewhat like spinning a coin. The poles of the sphere are the points at the top and bottom of the sphere that would not move while it was spinning. The *axis* of the sphere is the term for the line between its poles.

Tori

A **torus** is shaped like a doughnut (Figure 8). Its boundary surface is double-curved. You can think of it as being formed by revolving a circle (or other curve) around an axis that positioned away from (outside) the curve.

Ellipsoids

An oblate or prolate **ellipsoid** is shaped like an egg (Figure 9). You can think of it as formed by revolving an ellipse about its minor or major axis, respectively.

Right square | Right rectangular | Oblique rectangular

Right triangular | Right pentagonal | Oblique hexagonal

3 Right Prisms and Oblique Prisms

Right rectangular | Right square (truncated) | Oblique pentagonal

4 Pyramids

Right circular | Oblique circular

5 Cylinder and Oblique Cylinder

Right circular | Right circular (frustum) | Oblique circular (truncated)

6 Cones

Sphere | Torus

7 Sphere   **8 Torus**

Oblate Ellipsoid | Prolate Ellipsoid

9 Ellipsoids

71

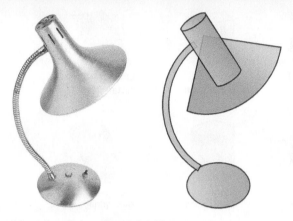

10   Identifying Essential Shapes

11   Using Construction Lines

UNDERSTANDING SKETCHING TECHNIQUES

Analyzing Complex Objects

The ability to break down complex shapes into simpler geometric primitives is an essential skill for sketching and modeling objects.

Before you begin to draw the outline of an object, consider its overall shape and the relationships between its parts. Construction lines can help you preserve the overall dimensions of the object as you sketch.

Bear in mind that you should be thinking in terms of basic shapes whether you are sketching by hand or using a CAD program. Since basic curves and straight lines are the basis of many of the objects that people create, practice in creating the basic elements of a drawing will help you sketch with ease.

Essential Shapes

Look for the essential shapes of objects. If you were to make a clay model of an object, what basic shape would you start with? A ball? A box?

Try squinting your eyes and looking at familiar objects. Do you see their shape as a rectangle? A circle? What other basic shapes do you notice when you look at objects this way?

Think about breaking down more complex objects into their simpler geometric shapes as shown in Figure 10. You can block in these shapes using construction lines to show their relationships to one another. Then add details, continuing to pay attention to the spatial relationships between them.

Construction Lines

Artists often begin a sketch by mocking in light guidelines to help them preserve basic shapes and proportions. In technical drawing these are called **construction lines** (Figure 11).

It is often helpful to begin a sketch by describing the object's main shapes with construction lines, taking some care to accurately represent the relative size and placement of features.

Use the basic shapes as a guide to place key features. Then use those main features as a "reference map" to place smaller details. For example, the sixth fret line is about halfway up the rectangular guitar neck.

Throughout this chapter you will use light construction lines to draw circles, arcs, and ellipses. Section 4 discusses the process of estimating and maintaining the proportions of an object in further detail.

Contours and Negative Space

The **contours** of an object are the main outlines that separate it from the surrounding space. One way to think about the contours of objects is to look at the contrast between the positive and negative space. Positive space is the space occupied by the object. **Negative space** is the unoccupied space around it.

In Figure 12 the space occupied by the contour of a pair of scissors is shown. Note how you can identify specific shapes by looking at the negative space. The individual shapes that make up the negative space are shown in different colors to make them easier for you to see. Some people sketch more accurately when they try to draw the negative space that surrounds the object.

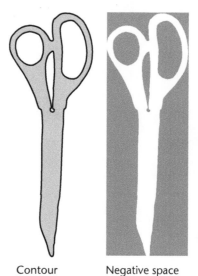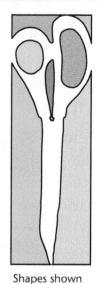

Contour   Negative space   Shapes shown

12   Negative Space

TIP

Practice drawing contours

Try sketching the negative spaces that define the shape of a chair. Look at each space as an individual shape. What is the shape of the space between the legs? What is the shape of the space between the rungs and the seat?

Make a sketch of a chair, paying careful attention to sketching the negative spaces of the chair as they really appear. The positive and negative spaces should add up to define the chair.

If you have difficulty, make corrections to your sketch by defining the positive shapes and then check to see if the negative shapes match.

An 8.5 × 11" sheet of Plexiglas (available at most glass stores) is an excellent tool for developing sketching ability. Using a dry erase marker, hold the Plexiglas up in front of an object and trace its contours on the Plexiglas. If you don't move, the outline should match the object's outline exactly. Lower the Plexiglas and look at the orientation of the lines. Are they what you expected?

Try looking at the object and drawing the sketch with the Plexiglas lying on your desktop or knees. Then raise it up and see if your drawing matches the object.

To develop sketching ability, try drawing everyday objects like your toaster, printer, or lamp, as well as exterior and interior views of buildings and equipment.

First try   Examine negative shapes   Note differences   More accurate proportions

13   Rubber Stamp

14   Hatching

15   Stippling

Viewpoint

As you sketch objects, keep in mind that you want to maintain a consistent **viewpoint** like a camera does. This is easier when you are sketching a picture from a book, because you can't move around the object. When you move, you see a different view of the object, depending on where you stand.

Sometimes people have difficulty sketching because they want to show parts of the object that cannot really be seen from a single viewpoint. For example, knowing that the handle of the rubber stamp in Figure 13 appears circular from the top, you may be tempted to show it as round, even though it may appear elliptical from your viewpoint.

When you are sketching an object pictorially, temporarily set aside your knowledge of the shapes the object is actually made of and carefully examine the shapes you see from a single, static viewpoint. In this type of sketching, instead of trying to envision the object as it *is*, try only to see it as it *looks*.

Shading

Adding **shading** to your sketch can give it a more realistic appearance because it represents the way the actual object would reflect light. Shading doesn't mean "coloring in." You may want to shade only the most prominently shadowed areas. First, identify the darkest and lightest areas on an object. If you want, you can shade various middle tones, placed exactly as they look on the object.

In some ways, shading is like doing a drawing within a drawing, because it is a matter of identifying shapes. When you are shading, instead of identifying the shapes of the object's contours, you are identifying the shape and relative darkness of the shadows.

Hatching lines, shown in Figure 14, and stippling, shown in Figure 15, are commonly used methods to add shading because they are easier to reproduce with a photocopier than continuous tone pencil shading. In the illustration you can see that shadowed areas are simply darkened by adding more hatching lines or stippling dots.

It is not uncommon for people to draw outlines by hand and add digital shaded fills to a scan of the outline. Marker shading is another popular shading method (Figure 16).

Regardless of how you apply shading, darken the outline to define the shape clearly and boldly. Remember that when you are communicating by using a sketch, its subject should be clear. To make the subject—in this case, a rubber stamp—clear, make it stand out with thick bold contour lines.

16   Marker Shading in a Concept Sketch. *Courtesy of Douglas Wintin.*

Edges and Vertices

Edges

An **edge** of the solid is formed where two surfaces intersect. Edges are represented in drawings by visible or hidden lines (Figure 17).

Vertices

A **vertex** (plural, vertices) of a solid is formed where three or more surfaces intersect. The end of an edge is a vertex. These vertices or "points" are very useful in defining the solid object feature locations that you will sketch (Figure 17).

Points and Lines

A **point** is used to represent a location in space, but has no width, height, or depth (Figure 12). A point in a drawing is represented by the intersection of two lines (Figure 18a), by a short crossbar on a line (Figure 18b), or by a small cross (Figure 18c). Do not represent points by simple dots on the paper. This makes the drawing look "blobby" and is not as accurate.

A **line** is used in drawings to represent the edge of a solid object. A straight line is the shortest distance between two points and is commonly referred to simply as a "line." If the line is indefinite in extent, in a drawing the length is a matter of convenience, and the endpoints are not marked (Figure 19a). If the endpoints of the line are significant, they are marked by small drawn crossbars (Figure 19b). Other common terms are illustrated in Figures 19c to 19i. Either straight lines or curved lines

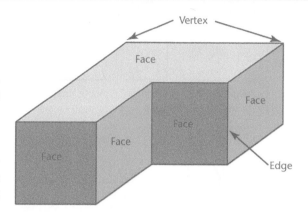

17   Edges and Vertices of a Solid

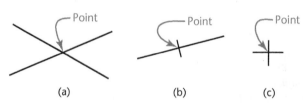

18   Showing Points

are parallel if the shortest distance between them remains constant. The common symbol for parallel lines is ‖, and for perpendicular lines it is ⊥. Two perpendicular lines may be marked with a "box" as shown in Figure 19g. Such symbols may be used on sketches, but not on production drawings.

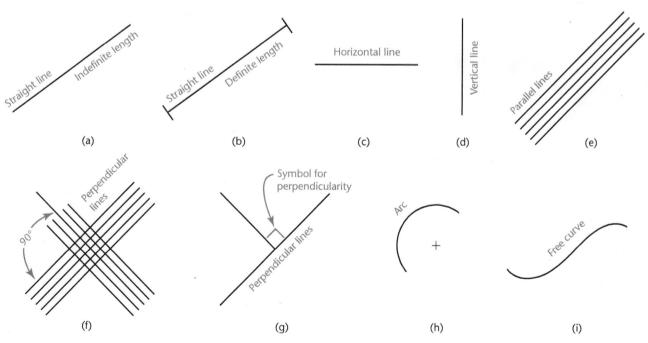

19   Showing Lines

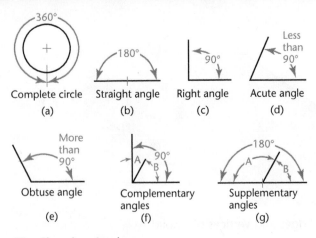

20 Showing Angles

Angles

An **angle** is formed by two intersecting lines. A common symbol for angle is ∠.

There are 360 degrees (360°) in a full circle, as shown in Figure 20a. A degree is divided into 60 minutes (60'), and a minute is divided into 60 seconds (60"). The angle value 37° 26' 10" is read 37 degrees, 26 minutes, and 10 seconds. When minutes alone are indicated, the number of minutes should be preceded by 0°, as in 0° 20'.

The different kinds of angles are illustrated in Figure 20. Two angles are complementary if they total 90° (Figure 20f), and are supplementary if they total 180° (Figure 20g).

In sketching, most angles can be estimated. Use a protractor if necessary when drawing odd angles.

Drawings and Sketches

The following are important skills to keep in mind for sketches and drawings:

1. *Accuracy.* No drawing is useful unless it shows the information correctly.
2. *Speed.* Time is money in industry. Work smarter and learn to use techniques to speed up your sketching and CAD drawings while still producing neat accurate results.
3. *Legibility.* A drawing is a means of communication to others, and it must be clear and legible. Give attention to details. Things that may seem picky and small as you are drawing may be significant and save money or even lives when the product is built.
4. *Neatness.* If a drawing is to be accurate and legible, it must also be clean.

Freehand Sketching

Freehand sketches are a helpful way to organize your thoughts and record ideas. They provide a quick, low-cost way to explore various solutions to design problems so that the best choices can be made. Investing too much time in creating a detailed layout before exploring your options through sketches can be costly.

The degree of precision needed in a given sketch depends on its use. Quick sketches to supplement verbal descriptions may be rough and incomplete. Sketches can be used to convey important and precise information when they are clearly drawn and annotated.

Freehand sketching requires only pencil, paper, and eraser. Master the techniques in this chapter for showing quick single-view, oblique, perspective, and isometric drawings using good freehand line technique and you will possess a valuable tool for communicating your ideas.

The term **freehand sketch** does not mean a sloppy drawing. As shown in Figure 21, a freehand sketch shows attention to proportion, clarity, and correct line widths. Figure 22 shows an as-built drawing with corrected items sketched on the printed CAD drawing.

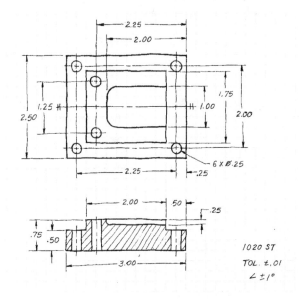

21 Sketch on Graph Paper. Sketches are also used to clarify information about changes in design or to provide information on repairing existing equipment.

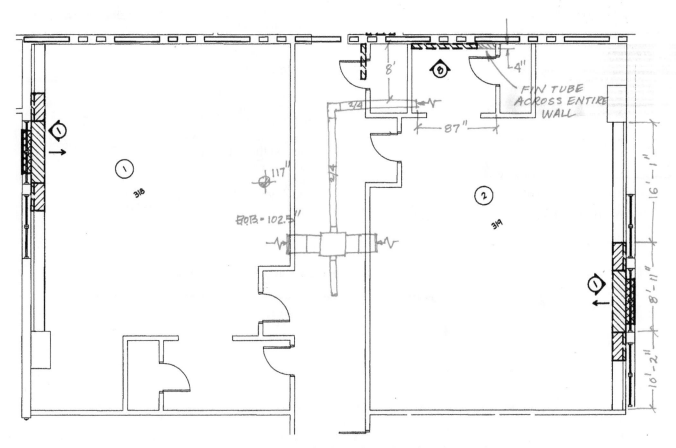

22 An As-Built Drawing with Corrected Items Sketched on the Printed CAD Drawing

1 TECHNIQUE OF LINES

The chief difference between a drawing and a freehand sketch lies in the character or technique of the lines. A good freehand line is not expected to be as rigidly straight or exactly uniform. A good freehand line shows freedom and variety, whereas a line drawn using CAD or instruments should be very exact. Still, it is important to distinguish between line patterns to make your drawing legible.

The **line patterns** in Figure 23 are examples of good freehand quality. Figure 24 shows examples of good and poor technique.

Line Weights

- Make dimension, extension, and centerlines thin, sharp, and black.
- Make hidden lines medium and black.
- Make visible and cutting plane lines thick and black.
- Make construction lines thick and light.

 Use Worksheet 1 for additional practice sketching line patterns.

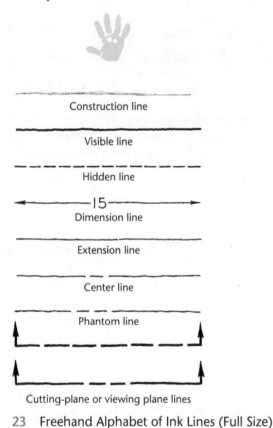

23   Freehand Alphabet of Ink Lines (Full Size)

TIP

Even in freehand drawings, thick lines should be twice the width of thin lines.

Thicknesses do not have to be exact, but there should be an obvious difference between thick and thin lines.

Since visible lines and cutting plane lines are the two thick line patterns, other lines should be distinctly thinner in comparison.

To draw thick and thin lines freehand, you might like to keep two pencils handy, one that is razor sharp for thin lines, and another that is dulled, to create thicker lines.

As the sharp point becomes dulled, switch it with the dull pencil, and sharpen the other, so that there is always one sharp and one dulled point ready to use.

Sharp and black (dimension, extension, and center lines)

Medium and black (hidden lines)

Slightly dull and black (visible and cutting plane lines)

Very dull and light (construction lines)

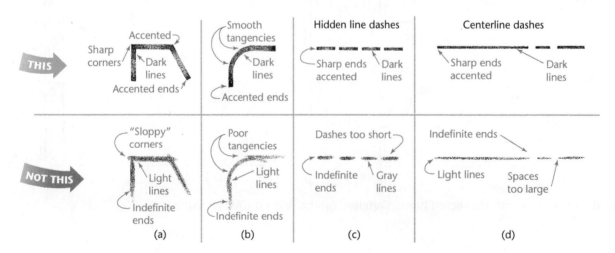

24   Technique of Lines (Enlarged)

2 SKETCHING STRAIGHT LINES

Most of the lines in an average sketch are straight lines. With practice, your straight lines will naturally improve, but these basics may help you improve quickly.

- Hold your pencil naturally, about 1" back from the point, and approximately at right angles to the line to be drawn.
- Draw horizontal lines from left to right with a free and easy wrist and arm movement.
- Draw vertical lines downward with finger and wrist movements.

Blocking in a Freehand Drawing

Over the years, freehand sketchers have developed all sorts of tricks to improve speed and accuracy. Methods for finding midpoints or quickly blocking in straight vertical and horizontal lines are just a few secrets of the technical sketching craft that can come in handy, even today. When a great idea hits, or you need to sketch quickly at a meeting or on a job site, you might have access to a CAD system, or even a ruler.

TIPS

Drawing Long Freehand Lines

For long freehand lines, make light end marks and lightly sweep your pencil between them, keeping your eye on the mark toward which you are moving. When you are satisfied with the accuracy of your strokes, apply more pressure to make a dark line.

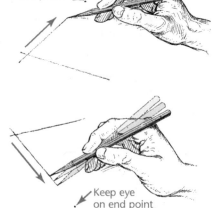

Keep eye on end point →

↙ Keep eye on end point

If you line looks like this you may be gripping your pencil too tightly or trying too hard to imitate mechanical lines.

Slight wiggles are OK as long as the line continues on a straight path.

Occasional very slight gaps are fine and make it easier to draw straight.

Blocking in a Border Freehand

Hold your hand and pencil rigidly and glide your fingertips along the edge of the paper to maintain a uniform border.

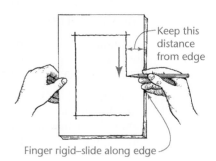

Keep this distance from edge

Finger rigid–slide along edge

Finding a Midpoint Freehand

Use your thumb on your pencil to guess half the distance. Try this distance on the other half. Continue adjusting until you locate the center, then mark it.

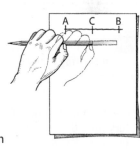

Blocking in a Border Using a Strip of Paper

Mark the distance on the edge of a card or a strip of paper and use it like a ruler to mark at intervals, then draw a final line through the points.

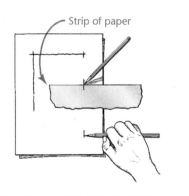

Strip of paper

Folding a Paper to Find a Midpoint

Mark the total distance on the edge of a strip of paper. Then fold the paper to locate its center at the crease. You can fold one half to find quarter points, and so on.

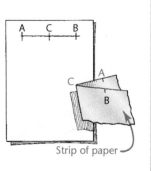

Strip of paper

DIVIDING LINES INTO EQUAL OR PROPORTIONAL PARTS

Proportional Parts

To divide the given line shown into proportions of (for example) 2, 3, and 4 units:

Proportions of 2, 3, and 4 units

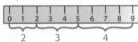

1 Draw a vertical construction line at one end of the line you are dividing.

Sketch vertical line from end

2 Set the zero point of your scale at the other end of the line.

3 Swing the scale so the desired unit falls on vertical line. In this case it will be the 9th unit, since 2 + 3 + 4 = 9.

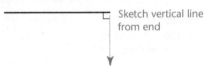

Swing scale so last desired division lines up with vertical line

4 Draw vertical lines upward from the corresponding scale divisions and mark tiny crossbars on the line as shown.

Equal Parts

If you use uniform divisions for the steps above (every third division, for instance) you will get equal parts. Examples of practical applications for dividing lines equally are shown below.

Calculated Proportions

To divide a line into proportions equal to the square of 1, 2, 3, and 4 (1, 4, 9, and 16) find 16 divisions on your scale.

Find desired divisions

(1^2) (2^2) (2^2) (2^2)

1 Set the zero point of your scale at the end of the line and draw a light construction line at any convenient angle from one end of the line you are dividing to the appropriate division on the scale. In this case the 4 mark is 16 equal divisions from the 0.

2 Draw construction lines parallel to the end line through each proportionate scale division.

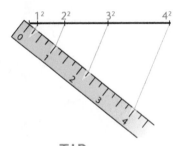

TIP

Exaggerating Closely Spaced Parallel Lines

Sometimes it is helpful to exaggerate the distance between closely spaced parallel lines so there is no fill-in when the drawing is reproduced.

Usually this is done to a maximum of 3 mm or .120". When using CAD it is better to draw the features the actual size and include a detail showing the actual spacing.

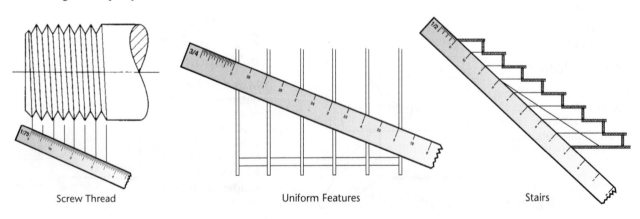

Screw Thread   Uniform Features   Stairs

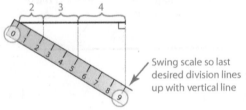

25 Many objects have rounded features that accurate circles, arcs, and ellipses are needed to represent. *Tim Ridley© Dorling Kindersley.*

3 SKETCHING CIRCLES, ARCS, AND ELLIPSES

Circles

Small circles and arcs can be sketched in one or two strokes without any preliminary blocking in.

Circle templates make it easy to sketch accurate circles of various sizes. It may be helpful to experiment with the variety of methods that drafters have devised for sketching accurately sized circles, as the drawing tools available to you may vary under different circumstances. Figure 25 shows an object with rounded features to sketch using circles, arcs, and ellipses.

TIP

The Freehand Compass

Using your hand like a compass, you can create circles and arcs with surprising accuracy after a few minutes of practice.

1. Place the tip of your little finger or the knuckle joint of your little finger at the center.

2. "Feed" the pencil out to the radius you want as you would do with a compass.

3. Hold this position rigidly and rotate the paper with your free hand.

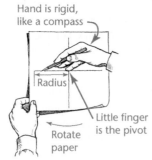

Hand is rigid, like a compass

Radius

Little finger is the pivot

Rotate paper

METHODS FOR SKETCHING CIRCLES

Enclosing Square Method

1 Lightly sketch an enclosing square and mark the midpoint of each side.

2 Lightly draw in arcs to connect the midpoints.

3 Darken the final circle.

Centerline Method

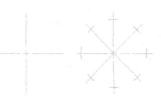

1 Sketch the two centerlines of the circle.

2 Add light 45° radial lines and sketch light arcs across them at an estimated radius distance from the center.

3 Darken the final circle.

Paper Method

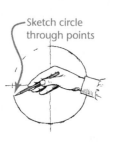

Sketch circle through points

Radius

Scrap of paper

1 Mark the estimated radius on the edge of a card or scrap of paper and set off from the center as many points as desired.

2 Sketch the final circle through these points.

STEP by STEP

METHODS FOR SKETCHING ARCS

Radius Method

1 Locate the center of the arc and lightly block in perpendicular lines. Mark off the radius distance along the lines.

2 Draw a 45° line through the center point and mark off the radius distance along it.

3 Lightly sketch in the arc as shown. Darken the final arc.

Trammel Method

1 Locate the center of the arc and lightly block in perpendicular lines. Mark off the radius distance along the lines.

2 Mark the radius distance on a strip of paper and use it as a trammel.

3 Lightly sketch in the arc, then darken the final arc.

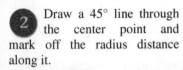

Trammel

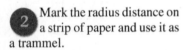

Tangent Method

Use these steps to draw arcs sketched to points of tangency.

1 Locate the center of the arc and sketch in the lines to which the arc is tangent.

2 Draw perpendiculars from the center to the tangent lines.

3 Draw in the arc tangent to the lines ending at the perpendicular lines.

4 Darken in the arc and then darken the lines from the points of tangency.

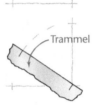

METHODS FOR SKETCHING ELLIPSES

Freehand Method

1 Rest your weight on your upper forearm and move the pencil rapidly above the paper in an elliptical path.

2 Lower the pencil to draw very light ellipses.

3 Darken the final ellipse.

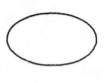

Rectangle Method

1 Lightly sketch an enclosing rectangle.

2 Mark the midpoint of each side and sketch light tangent arcs, as shown.

3 Darken in the final ellipse.

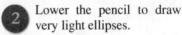

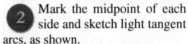

Axes Method

1 Lightly sketch in the major and minor axes of the ellipse.

2 Mark the distance along the axes and lightly block in the ellipse.

3 Darken the final ellipse.

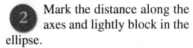

Trammel Method

To sketch accurate ellipses, you can make a trammel.

1 Mark *half* the desired length of the minor axis on the edge of a strip of paper (*A-B*). Using the same starting point, mark *half* the length of the major axis (*A-C*). (The measurements will overlap.)

2 Line up the last two trammel points (*B* and *C*) on the axes and mark a small dot at the location of the first point (*A*).

3 Move the trammel to different positions, keeping *B* and *C* on the axes, and mark more points at *A*. Sketch the final ellipse through the points.

Major axis

Minor axis

1/2 Major axis

1/2 Minor axis

A   B   C

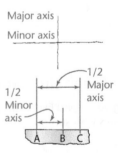

Line up with axes

Mark

A   B   C

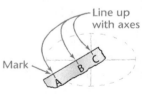

26 A Circle Seen as an Ellipse

27 Estimating Dimensions

Sketching Arcs

Sketching arcs is similar to sketching circles. In general, it is easier to hold your pencil on the inside of the curve. Look closely at the actual geometric constructions and carefully approximate points of tangency so that the arc touches a line or other entity at the right point.

Sketching Ellipses

If a circle is tipped away from your view, it appears as an ellipse. Figure 26 shows a coin viewed so that it appears as an ellipse. You can learn to sketch small ellipses with a free arm movement similar to the way you sketch circles, or you can use ellipse templates to help you easily sketch ellipses. These templates are usually grouped according to the amount a circular shape would be rotated to form the ellipse. They provide a number of sizes of ellipses on each template, but usually include only one or two typical rotations.

 Tear out Worksheet 2 to practice sketching ellipses.

4 MAINTAINING PROPORTIONS

Sketches are not usually made to a specific scale, although it can be handy at times. The size of the sketch depends on its complexity and the size of the paper available. The most important rule in freehand sketching is to keep the sketch in **proportion,** which means to accurately represent the size and position of each part in relation to the whole. No matter how brilliant the technique or how well drawn the details, if the proportions are off, the sketch will not look right.

To maintain proportions, first determine the relative proportions of height to width and lightly block them in. You can mark a unit on the edge of a strip of paper or use your pencil (as in Figure 27) to gage how many units wide and high the object is. Grid paper can help you maintain proportions by providing a ready-made scale (by counting squares). As you block in the medium-sized areas and finally small details, compare each new distance with those already established.

MAINTAINING PROPORTIONS IN A SKETCH

① If you are working from a given picture, such as this utility cabinet, first establish the relative width compared to the height. One way is to use the pencil as a measuring stick. In this case, the height is about 1-3/4 times the width.

② Sketch the enclosing rectangle in the correct proportion. This sketch is to be slightly larger than the given picture.

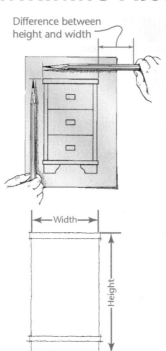
Difference between height and width

←Width→

Height

③ Divide the available drawer space into three parts with the pencil by trial. Hold your pencil about where you think one third will be and then try that measurement. If it is too short or long, adjust the measurement and try again. Sketch light diagonals to locate centers of the drawers and block in drawer handles. Sketch all remaining details.

④ Darken all final lines, making them clean, thick, and black.

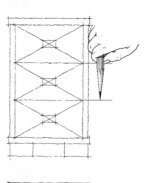
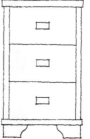

STEP by STEP

HOW TO BLOCK IN AN IRREGULAR OBJECT

STEP by STEP

1 Capture the main proportions with simple lines.

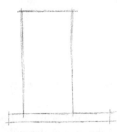

2 Block in the general sizes and direction of flow of curved shapes.

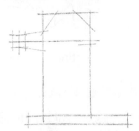

3 Lightly block in additional details.

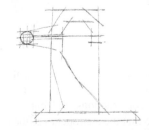

4 Darken the lines of the completed sketch.

GEOMETRIC METHODS FOR SKETCHING PLANE FIGURES

STEP by STEP

Sketching a Polygon by the Triangle Method

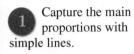

1 Divide the polygon into triangles as shown. Use the triangles as a visual aid to sketch the shape.

Sketching a Polygon by the Rectangle Method

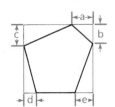

1 Imagine a rectangle drawn around the polygon as shown.

2 Sketch the rectangle and then locate the vertices of the polygon (points *a, b, c,* and so on) along the sides of the rectangle.

3 Join the points to complete the shape.

Visual Aids for Sketching Irregular Figures

1 Visualize shapes made up of rectangular and circular forms by enclosing those features in rectangles.

2 Determine where the centers of arcs and circles are located relative to the rectangles as shown.

3 Sketch the features inside the rectangular shapes you have lightly blocked in and darken the final lines.

Creating Irregular Shapes by Offset Measurements

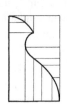

1 Enclose the shape in a rectangle.

2 Use the sides of the rectangle as a reference to make measurements that locate points along the curve.

Enlarging Shapes Using a Grid of Squares

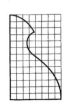

1 Complex curved shapes can be copied, enlarged, or reduced by hand, if necessary.

2 Draw or overlay a grid of squares on the original drawing.

3 To enlarge, draw the containing rectangle and grid of squares at the desired percentage and transfer the lines of shape through the corresponding points in the new set of squares.

 Use Worksheet 3 for practice.

5 ONE-VIEW DRAWINGS

Frequently, a single view supplemented by notes and dimensions is enough information to describe the shape of a relatively simple object.

In Figure 28, one view of the shim plus a note indicating the thickness as 0.25 mm is sufficient.

Nearly all shafts, bolts, screws, and similar parts should be represented by single views in this way.

Use Worksheet 4 to practice sketching.

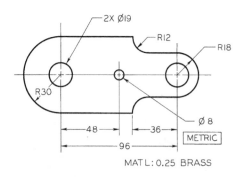

28   One-View Drawing of a Shim

SKETCHING A SINGLE-VIEW DRAWING

Follow the steps to sketch the single-view drawing of the shim shown in Figure 28.

1 Lightly sketch the centerlines for the overall width and height of the part. Estimate overall proportions by eye or, if you know the dimensions, use your scale to sketch accurately sized views. Space the enclosing rectangle equally from the margins of the sheet.

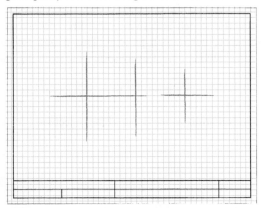

2 Block in all details lightly, keeping the drawing proportions in mind. Use techniques introduced in this chapter to help you.

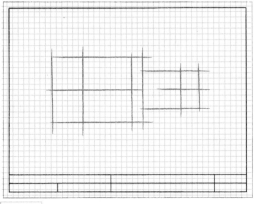

For practice, tear out Worksheet 5. Sketch the views shown.

3 Locate the centers of circles and arcs. Block in where they will fit using rectangles. Then sketch all arcs and circles lightly.

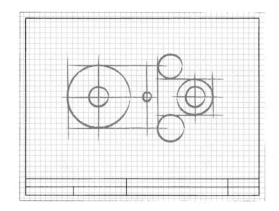

4 Darken your final lines.

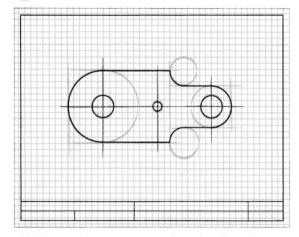

5 Add annotation to the drawing using neat lettering. Fill in the title block or title strip. Note the scale for the sketch if applicable. If not, letter NONE in the Scale area of the title block.

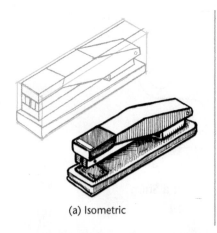

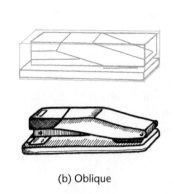

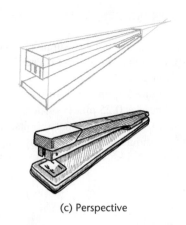

(a) Isometric   (b) Oblique   (c) Perspective

29   Three Types of Pictorial Sketches. *Reprinted by permission of Pearson Education, Inc., Upper Saddle River, NJ.*

6 PICTORIAL SKETCHING

A **pictorial sketch** represents a 3D object on a sheet of 2D paper by orienting the object so you can see its width, height, and depth in a single view.

Pictorial sketches are used frequently during the ideation phase of engineering design to quickly record ideas and communicate them to others. Their similarity to how the object is viewed in the world around us makes them useful for communicating engineering designs to nonengineers. Later in the design process, pictorial drawings are also often used to show how parts fit together in an assembly and in part catalogs and manuals to make it easy to identify the objects.

This chapter discusses three common methods used to sketch pictorials: isometric sketching, oblique sketching, and perspective sketching. Figure 29 shows perspective, isometric, and oblique sketches of a stapler.

Each of the pictorial methods differs in the way points on the object are located on the 2D viewing plane (the piece of paper).

A perspective sketch presents the most realistic looking view. It shows the object much as it would appear in a photograph—portions of the object that are farther from the viewer appear smaller, and lines recede into the distance.

An isometric sketch is drawn so that lines do not recede into the distance, but remain parallel. This makes isometric views easy to sketch but takes away somewhat from the realistic appearance.

An oblique sketch shows the front surface of the object looking straight on and is easy to create, but it presents the least realistic representation, as the depth of the object appears to be out of proportion.

7 UNDERSTANDING AXONOMETRIC DRAWINGS

Various types of pictorial drawings are used extensively in catalogs, sales literature, and technical work. They are often used in patent drawings; piping diagrams; machine, structural, architectural design, and furniture design; and for ideation sketching. The sketches for a wooden shelf in Figure 30 are examples of axonometric, orthographic, and perspective sketches.

The most common axonometric projection is **isometric,** which means "equal measure." When a cube is drawn in isometric, the axes are equally spaced (120° apart). Though not

as realistic as perspective drawings, isometric drawings are much easier to draw. CAD software often displays the results of 3D models on the screen as isometric projections. Some CAD software allows you to choose between isometric, dimetric, trimetric, or perspective representation of your 3D models on the 2D computer screen. In sketching, dimetric and trimetric sometimes produce a better view than isometric but take longer to draw and are therefore used less frequently.

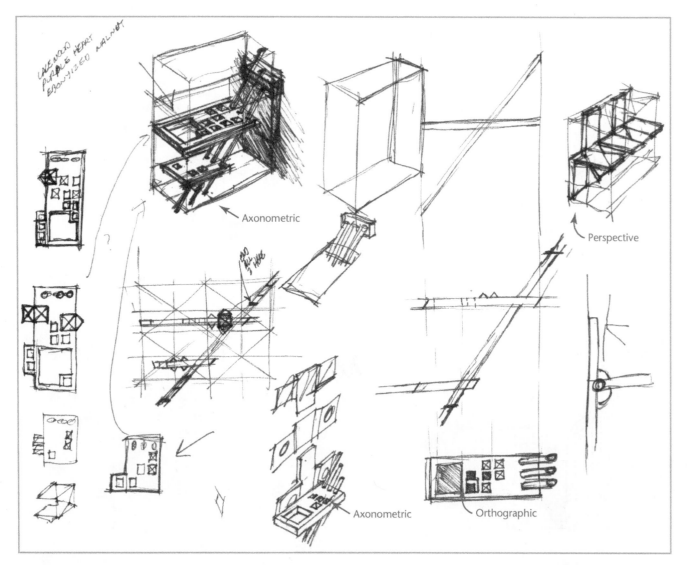

30 Sketches for a Wooden Shelf Using Axonometric, Orthographic, and Perspective Drawing Techniques. The axonometric projections in this sketch are drawn in isometric. *Coursesy of Douglas Wintin.*

Projection Methods

The four principal types of projection are illustrated in Figure 31. All except the regular multiview projection (Figure 31a) are **pictorial** types since they show several sides of the object in a single view. In both **multiview projection** and **axonometric projection** the visual rays are parallel to each other and perpendicular to the plane of projection. Both are types of **orthographic projections** (Figure 31b).

In **oblique projection** (Figure 31c), the visual rays are parallel to each other but at an angle other than 90° to the plane of projection.

In **perspective** (Figure 31d), the visual rays extend from the observer's eye, or station point (SP), to all points of the object to form a "cone of rays," so that the portions of the object that are farther away from the observer appear smaller than the closer portions of the object.

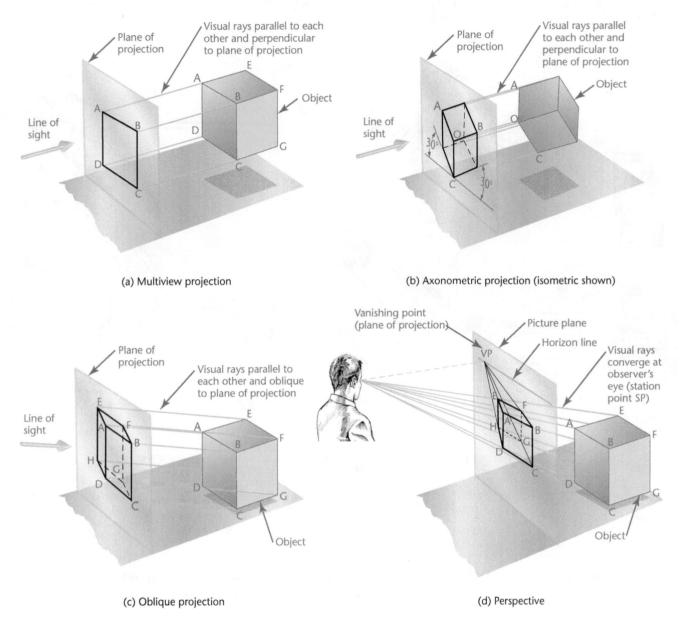

(a) Multiview projection

(b) Axonometric projection (isometric shown)

(c) Oblique projection

(d) Perspective

31 Four Types of Projection

Types of Axonometric Projection

The feature that distinguishes axonometric projection from multiview projection is the inclined position of the object with respect to the planes of projection. When a surface or edge of the object is not parallel to the plane of projection, it appears foreshortened. When an angle is not parallel to the plane of projection, it appears either smaller or larger than the true angle.

To create an axonometric view, the object is tipped to the planes of projection so that all the principal faces show in a single view. This produces a pictorial drawing that is easy to visualize, but since the principal edges and surfaces of the object are inclined to the plane of projection, the lengths of the lines are foreshortened. The angles between surfaces and edges

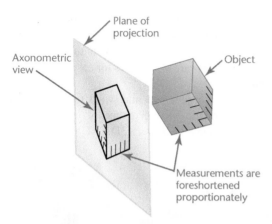

32 Measurements are foreshortened proportionately based on the amount of incline.

appear either larger or smaller than the true angle. There are an infinite variety of ways that the object may be oriented with respect to the plane of projection.

The degree of **foreshortening** of any line depends on its angle to the plane of projection. The greater the angle, the greater the foreshortening. If the degree of foreshortening is determined for each of the three edges of the cube that meet at one corner, scales can be easily constructed for measuring along these edges or any other edges parallel to them (Figure 32).

Use the three edges of the cube that meet at the corner nearest your view as the axonometric axes. Figure 33 shows three axonometric projections.

Isometric projection (Figure 33a) has equal foreshortening along each of the three axis directions.

Dimetric projection (Figure 33b) has equal foreshortening along two axis directions and a different amount of foreshortening along the third axis. This is because it is not tipped an equal amount to all of the principal planes of projection.

Trimetric projection (Figure 33c) has different foreshortening along all three axis directions. This view is produced by an object that is not equally tipped to any of the planes of projection.

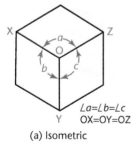

$La = Lb = Lc$
$OX = OY = OZ$

(a) Isometric

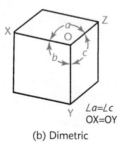

$La = Lc$
$OX = OY$

(b) Dimetric

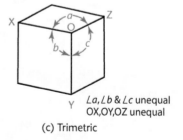

La, Lb & Lc unequal
OX, OY, OZ unequal

(c) Trimetric

33 Axonometric Projections

Axonometric Projections and 3D Models

When you create a 3D CAD model, the object is stored so that vertices, surfaces, and solids are all defined relative to a 3D coordinate system. You can rotate your view of the object to produce a view from any direction. However, your computer screen is a flat surface, like a sheet of paper. The CAD software uses similar projection to produce the view transformations, creating the 2D view of the object on your computer screen. Most 3D CAD software provides a variety of preset isometric viewing directions to make it easy for you to manipulate the view. Some CAD software also allows for easy perspective viewing on screen.

After rotating the object you may want to return to a preset typical axonometric view like one of the examples shown in Figure 34. Figure 35 shows a 3D CAD model.

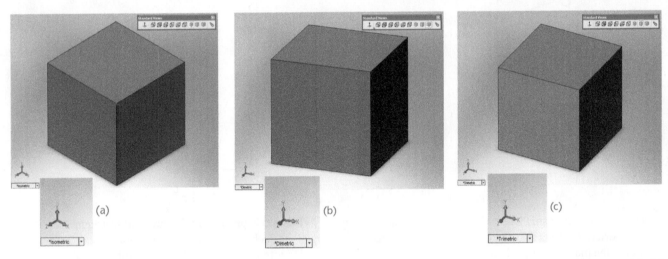

34 (a) Isometric View of a 1-Inch Cube Shown in SolidWorks, (b) Dimetric View, (c) Trimetric View. *Courtesy of Solidworks Corporation.*

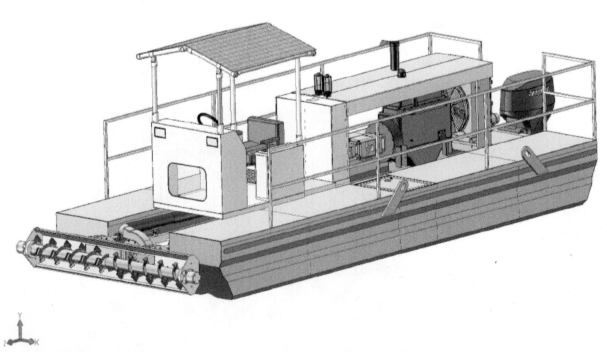

35 Complicated 3D CAD models such as this dredge from SRS Crisafulli Inc., are often viewed on-screen using pictorial projection. Notice the coordinate system display in the lower left. *Courtesy of SRS Crisafulli, Inc.*

8 ISOMETRIC PROJECTION

In an isometric projection, all angles between the axonometric axes are equal. To produce an isometric projection (isometric means "equal measure"), you orient the object so that its principal edges (or axes) make equal angles with the plane of projection and are therefore foreshortened equally. Oriented this way, the edges of a cube are projected so that they all measure the same and make equal angles with each other (of 120°) as shown in Figure 36.

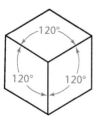

36   Isometric Projection

9 ISOMETRIC AXES

The projections of the edges of a cube make angles of 120° with each other. You can use these as the **isometric axes** from which to make measurements. Any line parallel to one of these is called an *isometric line*. The angles in the isometric projection of the cube are either 120° or 60°, and all are projections of 90° angles. In an isometric projection of a cube, the faces of the cube, and any planes parallel to them, are called *isometric planes*. See Figure 37.

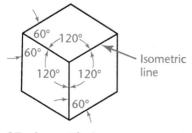

37   Isometric Axes

10 NONISOMETRIC LINES

Lines of an isometric drawing that are not parallel to the isometric axes are called **nonisometric lines** (Figure 38). Only lines of an object that are drawn parallel to the isometric axes are equally foreshortened. Nonisometric lines are drawn at other angles and are not equally foreshortened. Therefore the lengths of features along nonisometric lines cannot be measured directly with the scale.

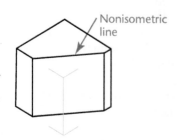

38   Nonisometric Edges

11 ISOMETRIC SCALES

An **isometric scale** can be used to draw correct isometric projections. All distances in this scale are $\sqrt{\frac{2}{3}} \times$ true size, or approximately 80 percent of true size. Figure 39a shows an isometric scale. More commonly, an isometric sketch or drawing is created using a standard scale, as in Figure 39b, disregarding the foreshortening that the tipped surfaces would produce in a true projection.

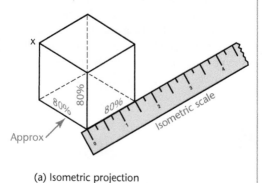

(a) Isometric projection

(b) Isometric drawing

39   Isometric and Ordinary Scales

---- TIP ----
Making an Isometric Scale

You can make an isometric scale from a strip of paper or cardboard as shown here by placing an ordinary scale at 45° to a horizontal line and the paper scale at 30° to the horizontal line. To mark the increments on the isometric scale, draw straight lines (perpendicular to the horizontal line) from the division lines on the ordinary scale.

Alternatively, you can approximate an isometric scale. Scaled measurements of 9" = 1'–0, or three-quarter-size scale (or metric equivalent) can be used as an approximation.

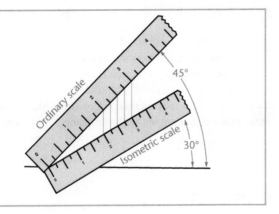

12 ISOMETRIC DRAWINGS

When you make a drawing using fore-shortened measurements, or when the object is actually projected on a plane of projection, it is called an **isometric projection** (Figure 40a). When you make a drawing using the full length measurements of the actual object, it is an **isometric sketch** or **isometric drawing** (Figure 40b) to indicate that it lacks fore-shortening.

The isometric drawing is about 25 percent larger than the isometric projection, but the pictorial value is obviously the same in both. Since isometric sketches are quicker, as you can use the actual measurements, they are much more commonly drawn.

Positions of the Isometric Axes

The first step in making an isometric drawing is to decide along which axis direction to show the height, width, and depth, respectively. Figure 40 shows

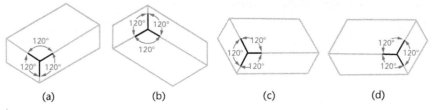

(a)   (b)   (c)   (d)

40   Positions of Isometric Axes

four different orientations that you might start with to create an isometric drawing of the block shown. Each is an isometric drawing of the same block, but with a different corner facing your view. These are only a few of many possible orientations.

You may orient the axes in any desired position, but the angle between them must remain 120°. In selecting an orientation for the axes, choose the position from which the object is usually viewed, or determine the position that

best describes the shape of the object or better yet, both.

If the object is a long part, it will look best with the long axis oriented horizontally.

---- TIP ----
Some CAD software will notify you about the lack of foreshortening in isometric drawings when you print or save them or allow you to select for it.

13 MAKING AN ISOMETRIC DRAWING

Rectangular objects are easy to draw using **box construction,** which consists of imagining the object enclosed in a rectangular box whose sides coincide with the main faces of the object.

For example, imagine the object shown in the two views in Figure 41 enclosed in a construction box, then locate the irregular features along the edges of the box as shown.

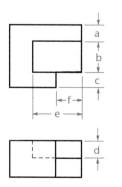

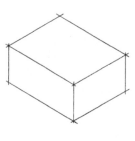

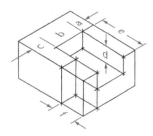

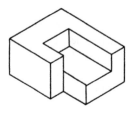

1. Lightly draw the overall dimensions of the box

2. Draw the irregular features relative to the sides of the box

3. Darken the final lines

41   Box Construction

Figure 42 shows how to construct an isometric drawing of an object composed of all "normal" surfaces. **Normal** is used technically to mean "at right angles." A normal surface is any surface that is parallel to the sides of the box. Notice that all measurements are made parallel to the main edges of the enclosing box—that is, parallel to the isometric axes. No measurement along a nonisometric line can be measured directly with the scale as these lines are not foreshortened equally to the normal lines. Start at any one of the corners of the bounding box and draw along the isometric axis directions.

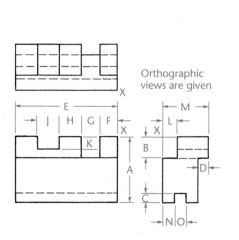

Orthographic views are given

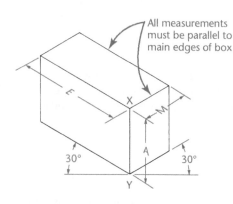

All measurements must be parallel to main edges of box

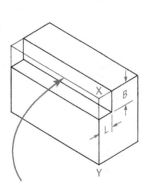

1. Select axes along which to block in height, weight and depth dimensions

2. Locate main areas to be removed from the overall block lightly sketch along isometric axes to define portion to be removed

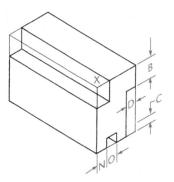

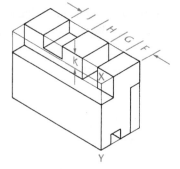

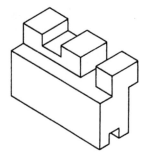

3. Lightly block in any remaining major portions to be removed through the whole block

4. Lightly block in features to be removed from the remaining shape along isometric axes

5. Darken final lines

42   Steps in Making an Isometric Drawing of Normal Surfaces

14 OFFSET LOCATION MEASUREMENTS

Use the method shown in Figure 43a and b to locate points with respect to each other. First, draw the main enclosing block, then draw the offset lines (*CA* and *BA*) full size in the isometric drawing to locate corner *A* of the small block or rectangular recess. These measurements are called **offset measurements**.

Since they are parallel to edges of the main block in the multiview drawings, they will be parallel to the same edges in the isometric drawings (using the rule of parallelism).

Tear out Worksheet 6. Use it to practice using offset measurements to create an isometric drawing.

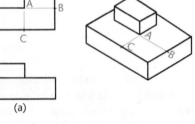
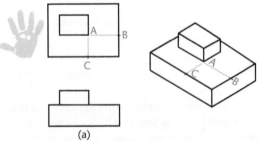
(a)

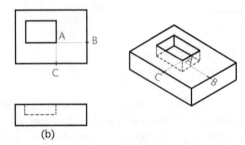
(b)

43 Offset Location Measurements

DRAWING NONISOMETRIC LINES

STEP by STEP

How to Draw Nonisometric Lines

The inclined lines *BA* and *CA* are shown true length in the top view (54 mm), but they are not true length in the isometric view. To draw these lines in the isometric drawing use a construction box and offset measurements.

1 Directly measure dimensions that are along isometric lines (in this case, 44 mm, 18 mm, and 22 mm).

2 Since the 54 mm dimension is not along an isometric axis, it cannot be used to locate point *A*.

Use trigonometry or draw a line parallel to the isometric axis to determine the distance to point *A*.

Since this dimension is parallel to an isometric axis, it can be transferred to the isometric.

3 The dimensions 24 mm and 9 mm are parallel to isometric lines and can be measured directly.

Transfer distance

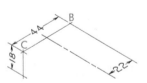
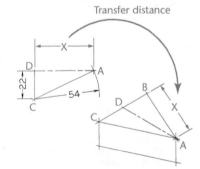
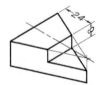

TIP

To convince yourself that nonisometric lines will not be true length in the isometric drawing, use a scrap of paper and mark the distance *BA* (II) and then compare it with *BA* on the given top view in Figure 44a. Do the same for line *CA*. You will see that *BA* is shorter and *CA* is longer in the isometric than the corresponding lines in the given views.

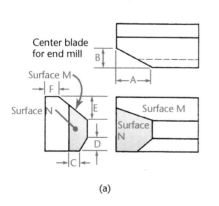

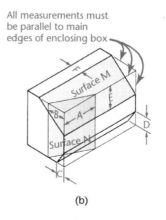

All measurements must be parallel to main edges of enclosing box

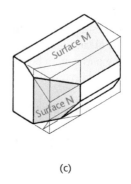

(a) (b) (c)

44   Inclined Surfaces in Isometric

Isometric Drawings of Inclined Surfaces

Figure 44 shows how to construct an isometric drawing of an object that has some inclined surfaces and oblique edges. Notice that inclined surfaces are located by offset or coordinate measurements along the isometric lines. For example, dimensions E and F are measured to locate the inclined surface M, and dimensions A and B are used to locate surface N.

OBLIQUE SURFACES IN ISOMETRIC

How to Draw Oblique Surfaces in Isometric

1 Find the intersections of the oblique surfaces with the isometric planes. Note that for this example, the oblique plane contains points A, B, and C.

2 To draw the plane, extend line AB to X and Y, in the same isometric plane as C. Use lines XC and YC to locate points E and F.

3 Finally, draw AD and ED using the rule that parallel lines appear parallel in every orthographic or isometric view.

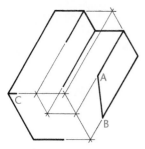

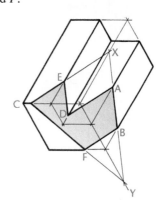

STEP by STEP

15 HIDDEN LINES AND CENTERLINES

Hidden lines in a drawing represent the edges where surfaces meet but are not directly visible. Hidden lines are omitted from pictorial drawings unless they are needed to make the drawing clear. Figure 45 shows a case in which hidden lines are needed because a projecting part cannot be clearly shown without them. Sometimes it is better to include an isometric view from another direction than to try to show hidden features with hidden lines.

Draw centerlines locating the center of a hole only if they are needed to indicate symmetry or for dimensioning. In general, use centerlines sparingly in isometric drawings. If in doubt, leave them out, as too many centerlines will look confusing.

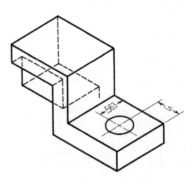

45   Using Hidden Lines

16 ANGLES IN ISOMETRIC

Angles project true size only when the plane containing the angle is parallel to the plane of projection. An angle may project to appear larger or smaller than the true angle depending on its position.

Since the various surfaces of the object are usually inclined to the front plane of projection, they generally will not be projected true size in an isometric drawing.

17 IRREGULAR OBJECTS

You can use the construction box method to draw objects that are not rectangular (Figure 46). Locate the points of the triangular base by offsetting a and b along the edges of the bottom of the construction box. Locate the vertex by offsetting lines OA and OB using the top of the construction box.

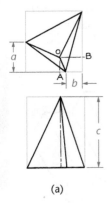

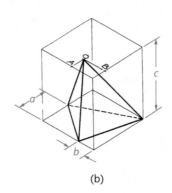

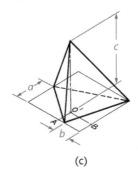

(a)   (b)   (c)

46   Irregular Object in Isometric

TIP

It is not always necessary to draw the complete construction box as shown in Figure 46b. If only the bottom of the box is drawn, the triangular base can be constructed as before. The orthographic projection of the vertex O' on the base can be drawn using offsets $O'A$ and $O'B$, as shown, and then the vertical line $O'O$ can be drawn, using measurement C.

HOW TO DRAW ANGLES IN ISOMETRIC

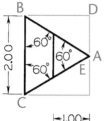

The multiview drawing at left shows three 60° angles. None of the three angles will be 60° in the isometric drawing.

1 Lightly draw an enclosing box using the given dimensions, except for dimension *X*, which is not given.

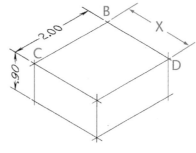

2 To find dimension *X*, draw triangle *BDA* from the top view full size, as shown.

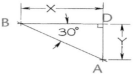

3 Transfer dimension *X* to the isometric to complete the enclosing box. Find dimension *Y* by a similar method and then transfer it to the isometric.

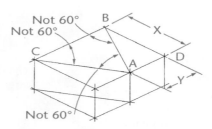

4 Complete the isometric by locating point *E* by using dimension *K*, as shown. A regular protractor cannot be used to measure angles in isometric drawings. Convert angular measurements to linear measurements along isometric axis lines.

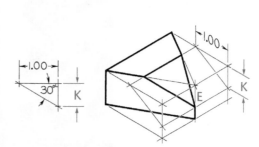

STEP by STEP

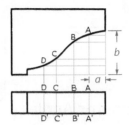

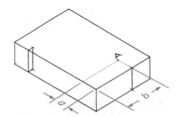

1. Use offset measurements *a* and *b* in the isometric to locate point A on the curve

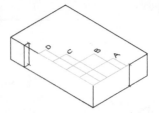

2. Locate points B, C, and D, and so on

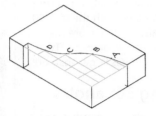

3. Sketch a smooth light freehand curve through the points

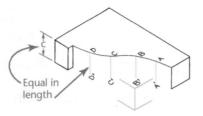

4. Draw a line vertically from point A to locate point A', and so on, making all equal to the height of block (c) then draw a light curve through the points

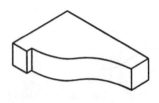

5. Darken the final lines

47   Curves in Isometric

18 CURVES IN ISOMETRIC

You can draw curves in isometric using a series of offset measurements similar to those discussed in Section 14. Select any desired number of points at random along the curve in the given top view, such as points *A*, *B*, and *C* in Figure 47. Choose enough points to accurately locate the path of the curve (the more points, the greater the accuracy). Draw offset grid lines from each point parallel to the isometric axes and use them to locate each point in the isometric drawing as in the example shown in Figure 47.

Tennis Ball (Factory Reject). Cartoon by Roger Price.
Courtesy of Droodles, "The Classic Collection."

19 TRUE ELLIPSES IN ISOMETRIC

If a circle lies in a plane that is not parallel to the plane of projection, the circle
projects as an ellipse. The ellipse can be constructed using offset measurements.

DRAWING AN ISOMETRIC ELLIPSE BY OFFSET MEASUREMENTS

Random Line Method

1 Draw parallel lines spaced at random across the circle.

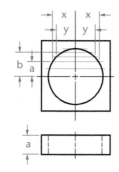

2 Transfer these lines to the isometric drawing. Where the hole exits the bottom of the block, locate points by measuring down a distance equal to the height d of the block from each of the upper points. Draw the ellipse, part of which will be hidden, through these points. Darken the final drawing lines.

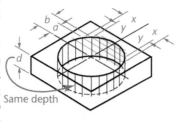

Same depth

Eight-Point Method

1 Enclose the given circle in a square, and draw diagonals. Draw another square through the points of intersection of the diagonals and the circle as shown.

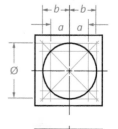

2 Draw this same construction in the isometric, transferring distances a and b. (If more points are desired, add random parallel lines, as above.) The centerlines in the isometric are the conjugate diameters of the ellipse. The 45° diagonals coincide with the major and minor axes of the ellipse. The minor axis is equal in length to the sides of the inscribed square.

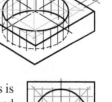

When more accuracy is required, divide the circle into 12 equal parts, as shown.

12 point method

Nonisometric Lines

If a curve lies in a nonisometric plane, not all offset measurements can be applied directly. The elliptical face shown in the auxiliary view lies in an inclined nonisometric plane.

1 Draw lines in the orthographic view to locate points.

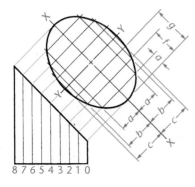

8 7 6 5 4 3 2 1 0

2 Enclose the cylinder in a construction box and draw the box in the isometric drawing. Draw the base using offset measurements and construct the inclined ellipse by locating points and drawing the final curve through them.

Measure distances parallel to an isometric axis (a, b, etc.) in the isometric drawing on each side of the centerline X–X. Project those not parallel to any isometric axis (e, f, etc.) to the front view and down to the base, then measure along the lower edge of the construction box, as shown.

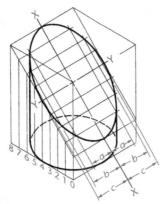

3 Darken final lines.

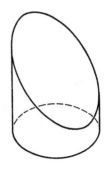

STEP by STEP

20 ORIENTING ELLIPSES IN ISOMETRIC DRAWINGS

Figure 48 shows four-center ellipses constructed on the three visible faces of a cube. Note that all of the diagonals are horizontal or at 60° with horizontal. Realizing this makes it easier to draw the shapes.

Approximate ellipses such as these, constructed from four arcs, are accurate enough for most isometric drawings. The four-center method can be used only for ellipses in isometric planes. Earlier versions of CAD software, such as AutoCAD Release 10, used this method to create the approximate elliptical shapes available in the software. Current releases use an accurate ellipse.

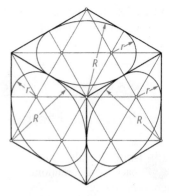

48   Four-Center Ellipse

DRAWING A FOUR-CENTER ELLIPSE

STEP by STEP

1 Draw or imagine a square enclosing the circle in the multiview drawing. Draw the isometric view of the square (an equilateral parallelogram with sides equal to the diameter of the circle).

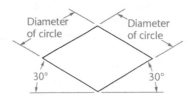

2 Mark the midpoint of each line.

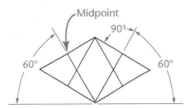

— TIP —

Here is a useful rule. The major axis of the ellipse is always at right angles to the centerline of the cylinder, and the minor axis is at right angles to the major axis and coincides with the centerline.

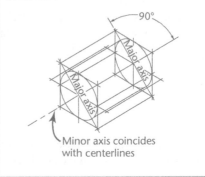

3 Draw the two large arcs, with radius *R*, from the intersections of the perpendiculars in the two closest corners of the parallelogram.

4 Draw the two small arcs, with radius *r*, from the intersections of the perpendiculars within the parallelogram, to complete the ellipse.

— TIP —

As a check on the accurate location of these centers, you can draw a long diagonal of the parallelogram as shown in Step 4. The midpoints of the sides of the parallelogram are points of tangency for the four arcs.

More Accurate Ellipses

The four-center ellipse deviates considerably from a true ellipse. As shown in Figure 49a, a four-center ellipse is somewhat shorter and "fatter" than a true ellipse. When the four-center ellipse is not accurate enough, you can use a closer approximation called the Orth four-center ellipse to produce a more accurate drawing.

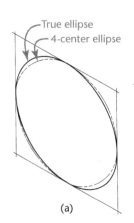

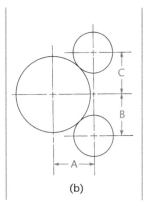

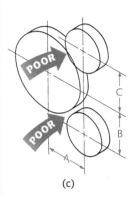

(a)   (b)   (c)

49 Inaccuracy of the Four-Center Ellipse

DRAWING AN ORTH FOUR-CENTER ELLIPSE

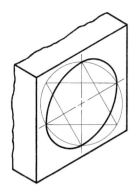

To create a more accurate approximate ellipse using the Orth method, follow the steps for these methods. The centerline method is convenient when starting from a hole or cylinder.

Centerline Method

1 Draw the isometric centerlines. From the center, draw a construction circle equal to the actual diameter of the hole or cylinder. The circle will intersect the centerlines at four points, *A*, *B*, *C*, and *D*.

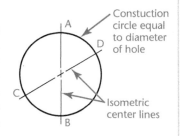

Constuction circle equal to diameter of hole

Isometric center lines

2 From the two intersection points on one centerline, draw perpendiculars to the other centerline. Then draw perpendiculars from the two intersection points on the other centerline to the first centerline.

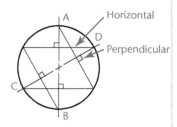

Horizontal

Perpendicular

3 With the intersections of the perpendiculars as centers, draw two small arcs and two large arcs.

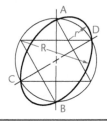

Enclosing Rectangle Method

1 Locate center and block in enclosing isometric rectangle.

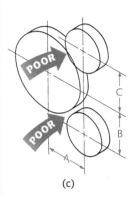

Diameter of circle   Diameter of circle

30°   30°

2 Use the midpoint of the isometric rectangle (the distance from *A* to *B*) to locate the foci on the major axis.

Major Axis

3 Draw lines at 60° from horizontal through the foci (points *C* and *D*) to locate the center of the large arc *R*.

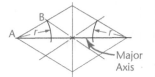

60°   60°

Center of large arc

4 Draw the two large arcs *R* tangent to the isometric rectangle. Draw two small arcs *r*, using foci points *C* and *D* as centers, to complete the approximate ellipse.

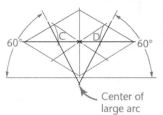

Note that these steps are exactly the same as for the regular four-center ellipse, except for the use of the isometric centerlines instead of the enclosing parallelogram. (When sketching, it works fine to just draw the enclosing rectangle and sketch the arcs tangent to its sides.)

STEP by STEP

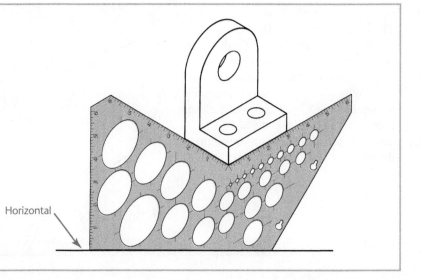

TIP

Isometric Templates

Special templates like this isometric template with angled lines and ellipses oriented in various isometric planes make it easy to draw isometric sketches.

The ellipses are provided with markings to coincide with the isometric centerlines of the holes—a convenient feature in isometric drawing.

You can also draw ellipses using an appropriate ellipse template selected to fit the major and minor axes.

Horizontal

---

21 DRAWING ISOMETRIC CYLINDERS

A typical drawing with cylindrical shapes is shown in Figure 50. Note that the centers of the larger ellipse cannot be used for the smaller ellipse, though the ellipses represent concentric circles. Each ellipse has its own parallelogram and its own centers. Notice that the centers of the lower ellipse are drawn by projecting the centers of the upper large ellipse down a distance equal to the height of the cylinder.

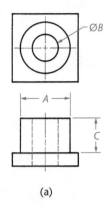
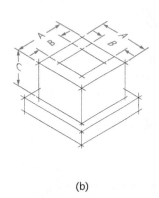
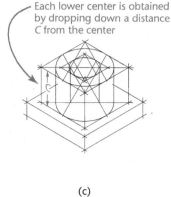
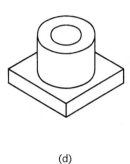

Each lower center is obtained by dropping down a distance C from the center

(a)   (b)   (c)   (d)

50   Isometric Drawing of a Bearing

---

22 SCREW THREADS IN ISOMETRIC

Parallel partial ellipses equally spaced at the symbolic thread pitch are used to represent only the crests of a screw thread in isometric (Figure 51). The ellipses may be sketched, drawn by the four-center method, or created using an ellipse template.

51   Screw Threads in Isometric

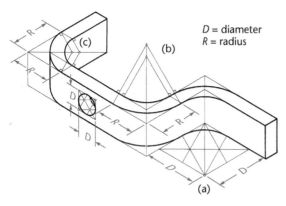

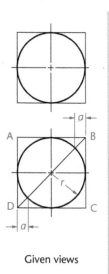

52 Arcs in Isometric

23 ARCS IN ISOMETRIC

The four-center ellipse construction can be used to sketch or draw circular arcs in isometric. Figure 52a shows the complete construction. It is not necessary to draw the complete constructions for arcs, as shown in Figure 52b and c. Measure the radius R from the construction corner; then at each point, draw perpendiculars to the lines. Their intersection is the center of the arc. Note that the R distances are equal in Figure 52b and c, but that the actual radii used are quite different.

Tear out Worksheet 7. Practice blocking in and sketching isometric arcs.

D = diameter
R = radius

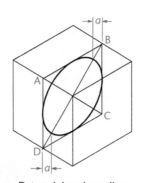

Determining the radius

1. Draw the the isometric of a great circle parallel to one face of the cube; then determine the radius of the sphere by locating points on the diagonal using measurement a to establish the ends of the major axis

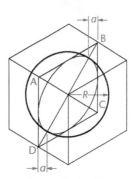

Isometric drawing

2. The diameter of the circle in the isometric drawing is $\sqrt{\frac{2}{3}} \times$ the diameter of the sphere

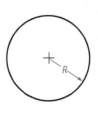

Isometric projection

3. The diameter of the circle in the isometric projection is equal to the true diameter of the sphere

Given views

53   Isometric of a Sphere

24 SPHERES IN ISOMETRIC

The isometric drawing of any curved surface is the envelope of all lines that can be drawn on that surface. For spheres, select the great circles (circles cut by any plane through the center) as the lines on the surface. Since all great circles, except those that are perpendicular or parallel to the plane of projection, are shown as ellipses having equal major axes, their envelope is a circle whose diameter is the major axis of the ellipse.

Figure 53 shows two views of a sphere enclosed in a construction cube. Next, an isometric of a great circle is drawn in a plane parallel to one face of the cube. There is no need to draw the ellipse, since only the points on the diagonal located by measurements a are needed to establish the ends of the major axis and thus to determine the radius of the sphere.

In the resulting isometric drawing the diameter of the circle is $\sqrt{\frac{2}{3}}$ times the actual diameter of the sphere. The isometric projection is simply a circle whose diameter is equal to the true diameter of the sphere.

ISOMETRIC SKETCHING FROM AN OBJECT

Positioning the object

To make an isometric sketch from an actual object, first hold the object in your hand and tilt it toward you, as shown in the illustration. In this position the front corner will appear vertical. The two receding bottom edges and those edges parallel to them should appear to be at about 30° with horizontal. The steps for sketching the object follow:

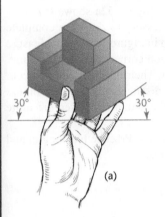

(a)

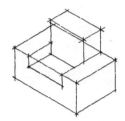

2 Block in the recess and the projecting block.

1 Sketch the enclosing box lightly, making *AB* vertical and *AC* and *AD* approximately 30° with horizontal. These three lines are the isometric axes. Make *AB*, *AC*, and *AD* approximately proportional in length to the actual corresponding edges on the object. Sketch the remaining lines parallel to these three lines.

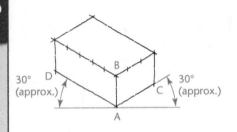

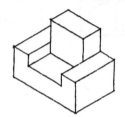

3 Darken all final lines.

ISOMETRIC SKETCHES USING AUTOCAD SOFTWARE

Need a quick isometric sketch? AutoCAD software has special drafting settings for creating an isometric style grid.

Figure A shows the Drafting Settings dialog box in AutoCAD. When you check the button for Isometric snap, the software calculates the spacing needed for an isometric grid. You can use it to make quick pictorial sketches like the example shown in Figure B. Piping diagrams are often done this way, although they can also be created using 3D tools.

Even though the drawing in Figure B looks 3D, it is really drawn in a flat 2D plane. You can observe this if you change the viewpoint so you are no longer looking straight onto the view.

The Ellipse command in AutoCAD has a special Isocircle option that makes drawing isometric ellipses easy. The isocircles are oriented in different directions depending on the angle of the snap cursor. Figure C shows isocircles and snap cursors for the three different orientations. In the software, you press CTRL and E simultaneously to toggle the cursor appearance.

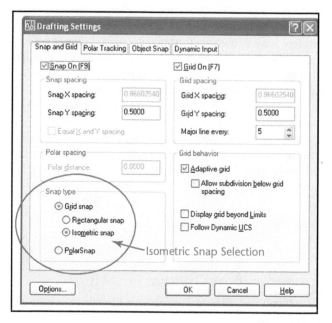

(A) Selecting Isometric Snap in the AutoCAD Drafting Settings Dialog Box

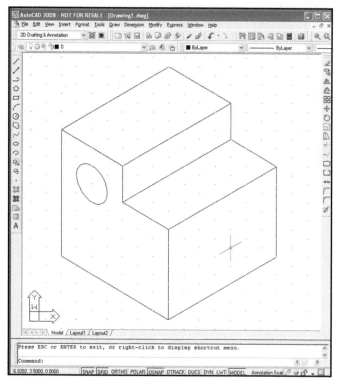

(B) A Pictorial Sketch Created from a Flat Drawing Using Isometric Snap

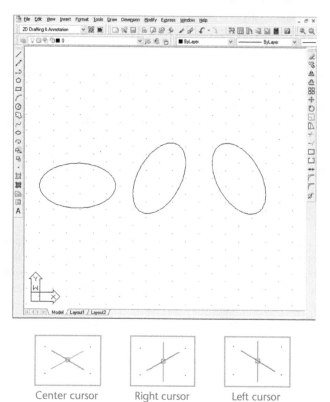

(C) Variously Oriented Isometric Circles and the Corresponding Snap Cursors Used to Create Them

25 OBLIQUE SKETCHES

Oblique drawing is an easy method for creating quick pictorials (Figure 54). In most oblique sketches, circles and angles parallel to the projection plane are true size and shape and are therefore easy to construct. Although circular shapes are easy to sketch in the front oblique plane, they would appear elliptical in the top or sides. Oblique views are primarily a sketching technique used when the majority of circular shapes appear in the front view or when the object can be rotated in order to position circles in the front view.

CAD is not typically used to create oblique views since better-appearing isometric or perspective drawings can be created easily from 3D CAD models.

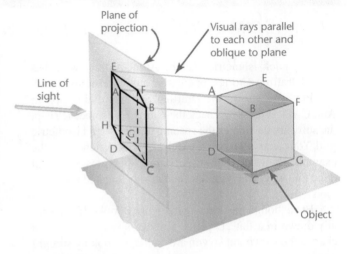

54   Oblique Projection Theory

Appearance of Oblique Drawings

Three things that affect the appearance of your oblique sketch are as follows:

1. The surface of the object you choose to show parallel to the projection plane
2. The angle and orientation you choose for the receding lines that depict the object's depth
3. The scale you choose for the receding lines depicting the object's depth (Figure 55)

Choosing the Front Surface

Think about which surface of the object would be the best one to think of as parallel to the plane of projection. For example, a cube has six different surfaces. As you are creating your sketch, any of those six surfaces could be oriented as the "front" of the part. Of course, with a cube it wouldn't matter which one you chose. But a cube with a hole through it will make a much better oblique sketch when the round hole is oriented parallel to the projection plane.

Angle of Receding Lines

An angle of 45° is often chosen for the angle of the receding lines because it makes oblique sketches quick and easy. You can use graph paper and draw the angled lines through the diagonals of the grid boxes. An angle of 30° is also a popular choice. It can look more realistic at times. Any angle can be used, but 45° is typical. As shown in Figure 56, you can produce different oblique drawings by choosing different directions for the receding lines.

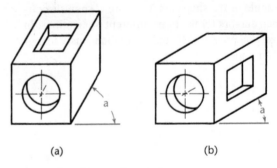

(a)   (b)

55   Angle of Receding Axis

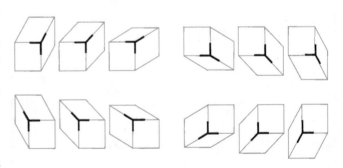

56   Variation in Direction of Receding Axis

Cavalier
projection

Cabinet
projection

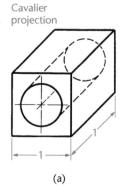
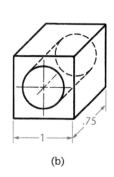
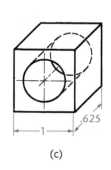
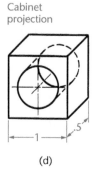
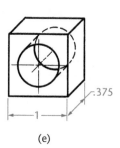

(a) .75(b) .625(c) .5(d) .375(e)

57   Foreshortening of Receding Lines

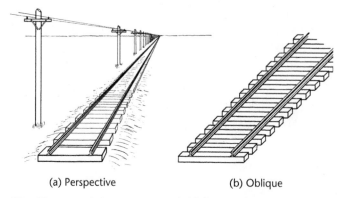

(a) Perspective   (b) Oblique

58   Unnatural Appearance of Oblique Drawing

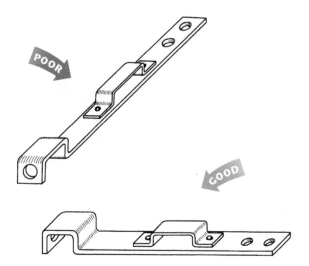

59   Long Axis Parallel to Plane of Projection

26 LENGTH OF RECEDING LINES

Theoretically, **oblique projectors** can be at any angle to the plane of projection other than perpendicular or parallel. The difference in the angle you choose causes **receding lines** of oblique drawings to vary in angle and in length from near zero to near infinity. However, many of those choices would not produce very useful drawings. Figure 57 shows a variety of oblique drawings with different lengths for the receding lines.

Since we see objects in perspective (where receding parallel lines appear to converge) oblique projections look unnatural to us. The longer the object in the receding direction, the more unnatural the object appears. For example, the object shown in Figure 57a is an isometric drawing of a cube in which the receding lines are shown full length. They appear to be too long and they appear to widen toward the rear of the block. Figure 58b shows how unnatural the familiar pictorial image of railroad tracks leading off into the distance would look if drawn in an oblique projection. To give a more natural appearance, show long objects with the long axis parallel to the view, as shown in Figure 59.

Cavalier Projection

When the receding lines are true length—(the projectors make an angle of 45° with the plane of projection)—the oblique drawing is called a **cavalier projection** (Figure 57a). Cavalier projections originated in the drawing of medieval fortifications and were made on horizontal planes of projection. On these fortifications the central portion was higher than the rest, so it was called cavalier because of its dominating and commanding position.

Cabinet Projection

When the receding lines are drawn to half size (Figure 57d), the drawing is known as a **cabinet projection**. This term is attributed to the early use of this type of oblique drawing in the furniture industries. Figure 60 shows a file drawer drawn in cavalier and cabinet projections.

USING BOX CONSTRUCTION TO CREATE AN OBLIQUE DRAWING

STEP by STEP

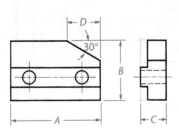

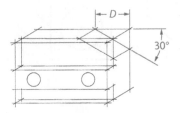

Follow these steps to draw a cavalier drawing of the rectangular object shown in the two orthographic views.

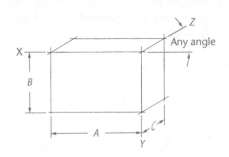

1 Lightly block in the overall width (*A*) and height (*B*) to form the enclosing rectangle for the front surface. Select an angle for the receding axis (*OZ*) and draw the depth (*C*) along it.

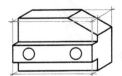

2 Lightly block in the details of the front surface shape including the two holes, which will appear round. Add the details of the right side surface shape. Extend lines along the receding axis connecting the edges to form the remaining surface edges.

3 Darken the final lines.

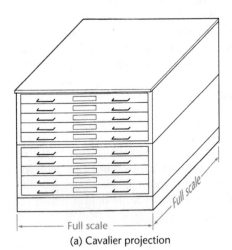

Full scale

Full scale

(a) Cavalier projection

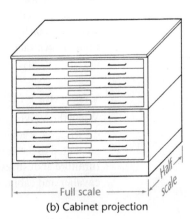

Half scale

Full scale

(b) Cabinet projection

60 Comparison of (a) Cavalier and (b) Cabinet Projections

27 CHOICE OF POSITION

Orient the view so that important shapes are parallel to the viewing plane as shown in Figure 61. In Figure 61a and c, the circles and circular arcs are shown in their true shapes and are easy to draw. In Figure 61b and d they are not shown in true shape and must be plotted as free curves or ellipses.

28 ELLIPSES FOR OBLIQUE DRAWINGS

Circular shapes that are parallel to the front plane of projection appear as circles in oblique view. In isometric views they appear elliptical. Figure 62 shows a comparison of a cylinder drawn in isometric and oblique views.

It is not always possible to orient the view of an object so that all its rounded shapes are parallel to the plane of projection. For example, the object shown in Figure 63a has two sets of circular contours in different planes. Both cannot be simultaneously placed parallel to the plane of projection, so in the oblique projection, one of them must be viewed as an ellipse.

If you are sketching, you can just block in the enclosing rectangle and sketch the ellipse tangent to its sides. Using CAD, you can draw the ellipse by specifying its center and major and minor axes. In circumstances where a CAD system is not available, if you need an accurate ellipse, you can draw it by hand using a four-center arc approximation.

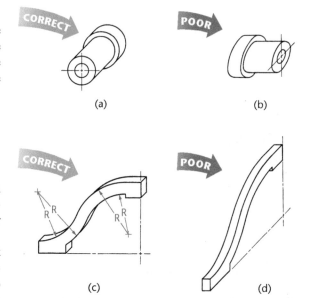

61 Essential Contours Parallel to Plane of Projection

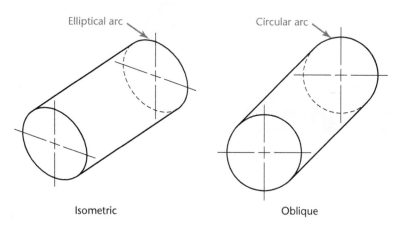

62 Comparison of Oblique and Isometric Projections for a Cylinder

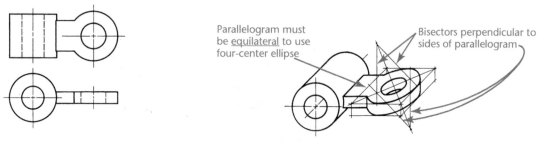

(a) Object with circles in different planes

(b) Use of four-center ellipse

63 Circles and Arcs Not Parallel to Plane of Projection

USING SKELETON CONSTRUCTION IN OBLIQUE DRAWING

STEP by STEP

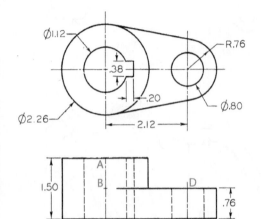

Oblique drawings are especially useful for showing objects that have cylindrical shapes built on axes or centerlines. Construct an oblique drawing of the part shown using projected centerlines using these steps.

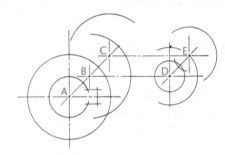

3 Build the drawing from the location of these centerlines.

1 Position the object in the drawing so that the circles shown in the given top view are parallel to the plane of projection. This will show true shape in the oblique view. Draw the circular shape in the front plane of the oblique view and extend the center axis along the receding axis of the oblique drawing.

Important: Determine all points of tangency

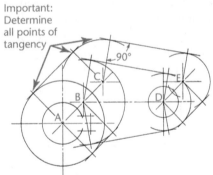

4 Construct all important points of tangency.

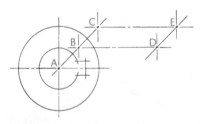

2 Add the centerline skeleton as shown.

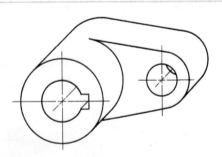

5 Darken the final cavalier drawing.

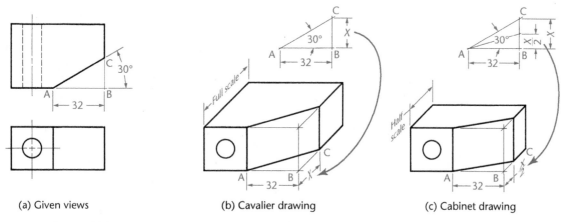

(a) Given views   (b) Cavalier drawing   (c) Cabinet drawing

64   Angles In Oblique Projection

29 ANGLES IN OBLIQUE PROJECTION

When an angle that is specified in degrees lies in a receding plane, convert the angle into linear measurements to draw the angle in an oblique drawing. Figure 64a shows a drawing with an angle of 30° specified.

To draw the angle in the oblique drawing, you will need to know distance X. The distance from point A to point B is given as 32 mm. This can be measured directly in the cavalier drawing (Figure 64b). Find distance X by drawing the right triangle ABC (Figure 64c) using the dimensions given, which is quick and easy using CAD.

You can also use a mathematical solution to find the length of the side: The length of the opposite side equals the tangent of the angle times the length of the adjacent side. In this case, the length is about 18.5 mm. Draw the angle in the cavalier drawing using the found distance.

Remember that all receding dimensions must be reduced to match the scale of the receding axis. In the cabinet drawing in Figure 64b, the distance BC must be half the side BC of the right triangle in Figure 64c.

Meat Cereals. *Courtesy of Randall Munroe, xkcd.com.*

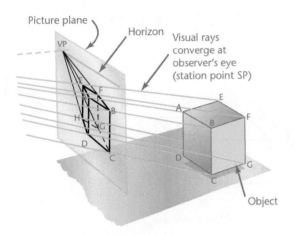

65   Perspective Drawing Theory

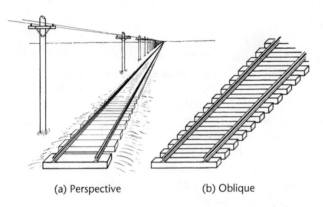

(a) Perspective   (b) Oblique

66   Perspective drawings appear more natural than oblique drawings.

30 SKETCHING PERSPECTIVES

Perspective pictorials most closely approximate the view produced by the human eye. Perspective views are the type of drawing most like a photograph. Examples of a perspective drawing can be seen in Figures 65, 66a, and 68. Although complex perspective views are time consuming to sketch, they are easy to create from 3D CAD models.

Unlike parallel types of projection, perspective projectors converge. The point at which the projectors converge is called the **vanishing point.** This is clearly seen in Figure 66a.

The first rule of perspective is that all parallel lines that are not parallel to the picture plane vanish at a single vanishing point, and if these lines are parallel to the ground, the vanishing point will be on the horizon. Parallel lines that are also parallel to the picture plane remain parallel and do not converge toward a vanishing point. (Figures 67 and 68.)

When the vanishing point is placed above the view of the object in the picture plane, the result is a bird's eye view, looking down onto the object. When the vanishing point is placed below the view of the object, the result is a worm's eye view looking up at the object from below.

There are three types of perspective: one-point, two-point, and three-point perspective, depending on the number of vanishing points used.

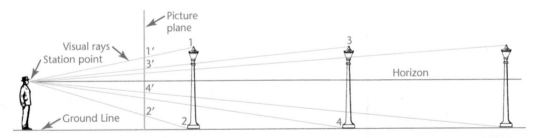

67   Looking through the Picture Plane

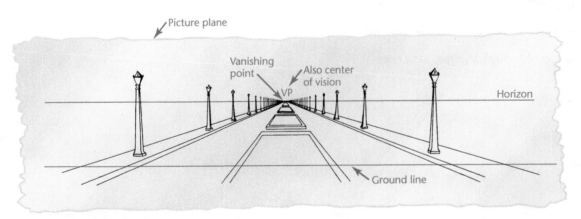

68   A Perspective

The Three Types Of Perspectives

Perspective drawings are classified according to the number of vanishing points required, which in turn depends on the position of the object with respect to the picture plane.

If the object sits with one face parallel to the plane of projection, only one vanishing point is required. The result is a **one-point perspective,** or **parallel perspective.**

If the object sits at an angle with the picture plane but with vertical edges parallel to the picture plane, two vanishing points are required, and the result is a **two-point perspective,** or an **angular perspective.** This is the most common type of perspective drawing.

If the object sits so that no system of parallel edges is parallel to the picture plane, three vanishing points are necessary, and the result is a three-point perspective.

One-Point Perspective

To sketch a one-point perspective view, orient the object so that a principal face is parallel to the picture plane. If desired, this face can be placed in the picture plane. The other principal face is perpendicular to the picture plane, and its lines will converge toward a single vanishing point.

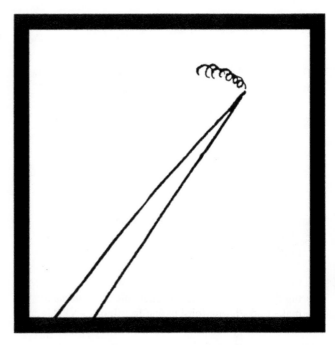

8:12 Train as Seen by 8:12 1/2 Commuter. By *Roger Price, reprinted from "Droodles, The Classic Collection."*

ONE-POINT PERSPECTIVE

To sketch the bearing in one-point perspective—that is, with one vanishing point—follow these steps illustrated below.

1 Sketch the true front face of the object, just as in oblique sketching. Select the vanishing point for the receding lines. In many cases it is desirable to place the vanishing point above and to the right of the picture, as shown, although it can be placed anywhere in the sketch. However, if the vanishing point is placed too close to the center, the lines will converge too sharply and the picture will be distorted.

VP
+

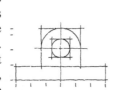

3 Estimate the depth to look good and sketch in the back portion of the object. Note that the back circle and arc will be slightly smaller than the front circle and arc.

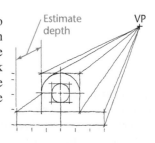

2 Sketch the receding lines toward the vanishing point.

VP

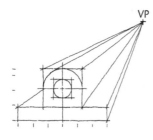

4 Darken all final lines. Note the similarity between the perspective sketch and the oblique sketch earlier in the chapter.

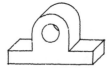

S T E P by **S T E P**

TWO-POINT PERSPECTIVE

To sketch a desk using two vanishing points, follow these steps:

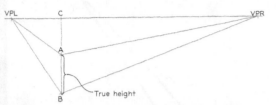

1 As shown above, sketch the front corner of the desk at height. Locate two vanishing points (VPL and VPR) on a horizon line (at eye level). Distance CA may vary—the greater it is, the higher the eye level will be and the more we will be looking down on top of the object. A rule of thumb is to make C–VPL one-third to one-fourth of C–VPR.

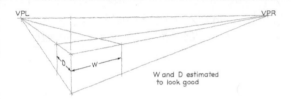

2 Estimate depth and width, and sketch the enclosing box.

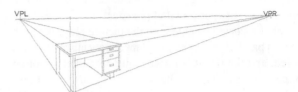

3 Block in all details. Note that all parallel lines converge toward the same vanishing point.

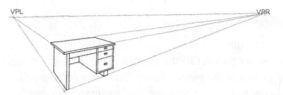

4 Darken all final lines. Make the outlines thicker and the inside lines thinner, especially where they are close together.

Two-Point Perspective

Two-point perspective is more true to life than one-point perspective. To sketch a two-point perspective, orient the object so that principal edges are vertical and therefore have no vanishing point; edges in the other two directions have vanishing points. Two-point perspective are especially good for representing building and large civil structures, such as dams or bridges.

Three-Point Perspective

In **three-point perspective,** the object is placed so that none of its principal edges is parallel to the picture plane. Each of the three sets of parallel edges has a separate vanishing point. In this case, use a picture plane that is approximately perpendicular to the centerline of the cone of visual rays. See Figure 69.

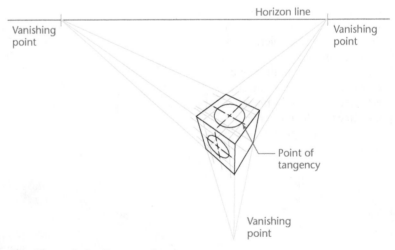

69 Three Point Perspective

Bird's-Eye versus Worm's-Eye View

The appearance of a perspective sketch depends on your viewpoint in relation to the object. Select some reachable object in the room and move so that you are looking at it from above and really notice its shape. Now gradually move so that you are looking at it from below. Notice how the change of viewpoint changes the appearance of its surfaces–which ones are visible and their relative size.

The **horizon line** in a perspective sketch is a horizontal line that represents the eye level of the observer. Locating the sketched object below the horizon line produces a view from above (or a bird's-eye view). Locating the sketched object above the horizon line produces a view from below (or a worm's-eye view). Figure 70 illustrates the horizon line in a drawing and the effect of placing the object above or below the horizon line.

31 CURVES AND CIRCLES IN PERSPECTIVE

If a circle is parallel to the picture plane, its perspective is a circle. If the circle is inclined to the picture plane, its perspective drawing may be any one of the conic sections where the base of the cone is the given circle, the vertex is the station point (SP), and the cutting plane is the picture plane (PP). The centerline of the cone of rays is usually approximately perpendicular to the picture plane, so the perspective will usually be an ellipse.

An ellipse may be drawn using a method of blocking in its center and a box tangent to the ellipse as shown in Figure 71a. A convenient method for determining the perspective of any planar curve is shown in Figure 71b.

32 SHADING

Shading can make it easier to visualize pictorial drawings, such as display drawings, patent drawings, and catalog drawings. Ordinary multiview and assembly drawings are not shaded. The shading should be simple, reproduce well, and produce a clear picture. Some of the common types of shading are shown in Figure 72. Two methods of shading fillets and rounds are shown in Figures 72c and 72d. Shading produced with dots is shown in Figure 72e, and pencil tone shading is shown in Figure 72f. Pencil tone shading used in pictorial drawings on tracing paper reproduces well only when making blueprints, not when using a copier.

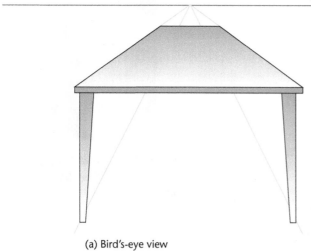

(a) Bird's-eye view

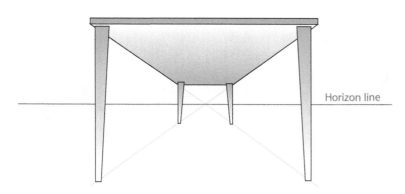

(b) Worm's-eye view

70   (a) Object below the Horizon Line (b) Object above the Horizon Line

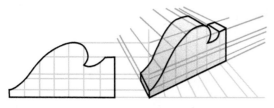

71   (a) Blocking in an Isometric Ellipse (b) Curves in Perspective

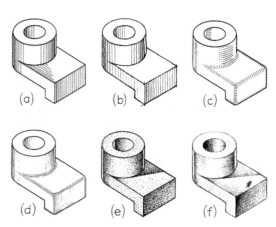

72   Methods of Shading

33 COMPUTER GRAPHICS

Pictorial drawings of all sorts can be created using 3D CAD (Figures 73, 74). To create pictorials using 2D CAD, use projection techniques similar to those presented in this chapter. The advantage of 3D CAD is that once you make a 3D model of a part or assembly, you can change the viewing direction at any time for orthographic, isometric, or perspective views. You can also apply different materials to the drawing objects and shade them to produce a high degree of realism in the pictorial view.

73 Shaded Dimetric Pictorial View from a 3D Model. *Courtesy of Robert Kincaid.*

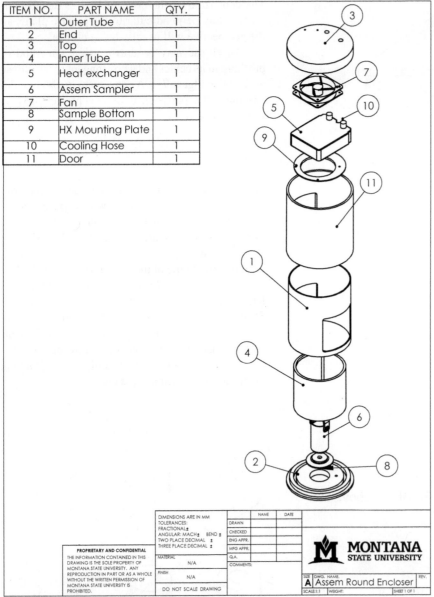

ITEM NO.	PART NAME	QTY.
1	Outer Tube	1
2	End	1
3	Top	1
4	Inner Tube	1
5	Heat exchanger	1
6	Assem Sampler	1
7	Fan	1
8	Sample Bottom	1
9	HX Mounting Plate	1
10	Cooling Hose	1
11	Door	1

DIMENSIONS ARE IN MM
TOLERANCES:
FRACTIONAL±
ANGULAR: MACH±   BEND ±
TWO PLACE DECIMAL ±
THREE PLACE DECIMAL ±

NAME   DATE
DRAWN
CHECKED
ENG APPR.
MFG APPR.
Q.A.
COMMENTS:

MATERIAL   N/A
FINISH   N/A
DO NOT SCALE DRAWING

MONTANA
STATE UNIVERSITY

SIZE DWG. NAME.
A Assem Round Encloser
REV.
SCALE:1:1   WEIGHT: SHEET 1 OF 1

74 Isometric Assembly Drawing. *Courtesy of PTC.*

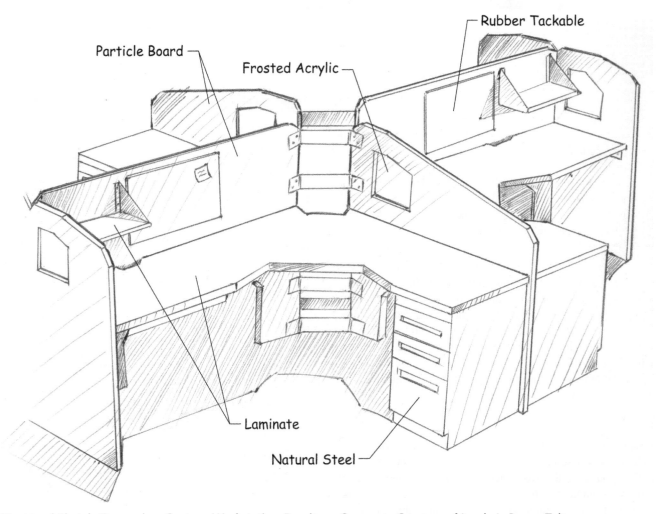

Particle Board

Frosted Acrylic

Rubber Tackable

Laminate

Natural Steel

75 Hand Sketch Conveying Custom Workstation Furniture Concept. *Courtesy of Jacob A. Baron-Taltre.*

34 DRAWING ON DRAWING

Because CAD helps people produce accurate drawings that are easy to alter, store, and repurpose, computer automation has made the painstaking aspects of hand-rendering technical drawings nearly obsolete. Still, the ability to sketch with clarity is an immediate and universal way to record and communicate ideas.

The ability to think of complex objects in terms of their basic solid components and to identify relationships between various surfaces, edges and vertices is basic to creating both hand-drawn (Figure 75) and computer-generated technical drawings. By understanding how to represent objects accurately, you can communicate efficiently as part of a team and increase your constructive visualization ability, or your ability to "think around corners."

"... I want to be able to draw any kind of line I want."

Jacob Baron-Taltre works as a product designer for a midsized furniture manufacturer in the Seattle region. He sketches nearly every day at work.

"Sometimes the sketches are very loose . . . just tools for me to work out some detail that I am designing. Other times they are more elaborate and crisp because they will likely be part of a conversation or presentation."

A computer is not the first tool he reaches for when beginning a project.

"Scribbling notes or quick sketches on paper is the fastest way to document the most ideas in the least time. Later, I'll develop some of those ideas more fully by hand and only then begin to use the computer to document the concepts as 2D or 3D CAD work. If a can't draw an idea by hand, I won't likely have more success (if any) using CAD."

Baron-Taltre said he sketches to explore various forms, sizes, and materials.

"CAD is more precise and that precision can be somewhat limiting. When I want to draw a line I want to be able to draw any kind of line I want. In CAD I have to use a specific tool for each line type."

"CAD is a great way to communicate finished thoughts and explore precise relationships. It's also great for quickly building accurate environments and models that can be rotated and examined. You can share these files and edit without having to redraw. Drawing by hand is faster for depicting specific ideas and can be used to communicate with someone in front of you. Plus, you can add detail to key areas of the drawing and leave out detail in areas needed just for context."

SKETCHING AND PARAMETRIC MODELING

The Design Process

Using CAD parametric modeling in many ways mirrors the design process. To get the rough ideas down, the designer starts by making hand sketches. Then as the ideas are refined, more accurate drawings are created either with instruments or using CAD. Necessary analysis is performed, and in response the design may change. The drawings are revised as needed to meet the new requirements. Eventually the drawings are approved so that the parts may be manufactured.

Rough Sketches

Using parametric modeling software, initially the designer roughly sketches the basic shapes on the screen. These sketches do not have to have perfectly straight lines or accurate corners. The software interprets the sketch much as you would interpret a rough sketch given to you by a colleague. If the lines are nearly horizontal or vertical, the software assumes that you meant them thus. If the line appears to be perpendicular it is assumed that it is.

Constraining the Sketch

Using a parametric CAD system, you can start by sketching on the computer screen as though you were sketching freehand. Then you refine the two-dimensional sketch by adding geometric constraints, which tell how to interpret the sketch and by adding parametric dimensions, which control the size of sketch geometry. Once the sketch is refined, you can create it as a 3D feature to which other features can be added. As the design changes, you can change the dimensions and constraints that control the sketch geometry, and the parametric model will be updated to reflect the new design.

When you are creating sketches by hand or for parametric modeling, think about the implications of the geometry you are drawing. Does the sketch imply that lines are perpendicular? Are the arcs that you have drawn intended to be tangent or intersecting? When you create a parametric model, the software applies rules to constrain the geometry, based on your sketch. You can remove, change, or add new constraints, but to use the software effectively you need to accurately depict the geometry you want formed.

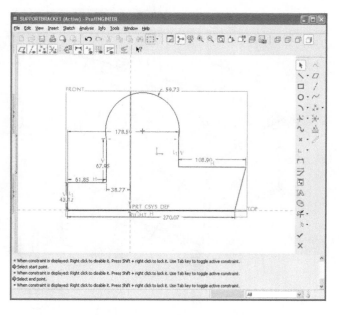

A Rough Sketch in Pro/Engineer Sketcher

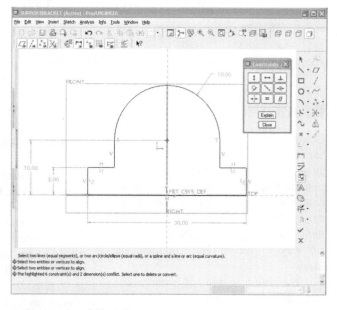

A Constrained Sketch

PERSPECTIVE VIEWS IN AUTOCAD

AutoCAD software uses an interactive command called Dview (dynamic viewing) that you can use to show 3D models and drawings in perspective. The Dview command uses a camera and target to create parallel and perspective views. You can use the camera option to select a new camera position with respect to the target point at which the camera is aimed. The Dview distance option is used to create a perspective view such as the one shown in Figure A by increasing the distance between the camera and the object to calculate a new view. The Off option of the command turns perspective viewing off again.

Notice that the grid squares in the figure appear larger closer to the viewing direction and smaller when they are farther away. Specifying a distance that is too close can fill up the entire view with the object.

The Zoom option of the Dview command acts like a normal zoom command when perspective viewing is off. When perspective viewing is on, you use the zoom dynamically by moving the slider bar shown in Figure B to adjust the camera lens to change the field of view. The default is to show the view similar to what you would see through a 35 mm camera with a 50 mm lens.

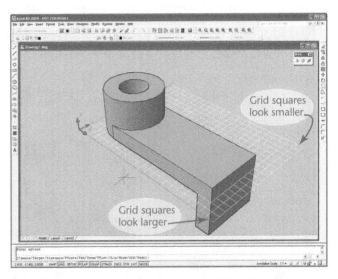

(A) A Perspective View Created Using the DView Command in AutoCAD. *With permission of Autodesk, Inc. © 2006–2007. All rights reserved.*

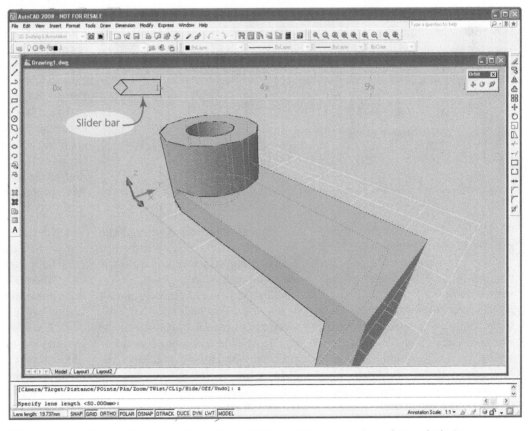

(B) Using the Zoom Slider to Adjust Field of View. *With permission of Autodesk, Inc. © 2006–2007. All rights reserved.*

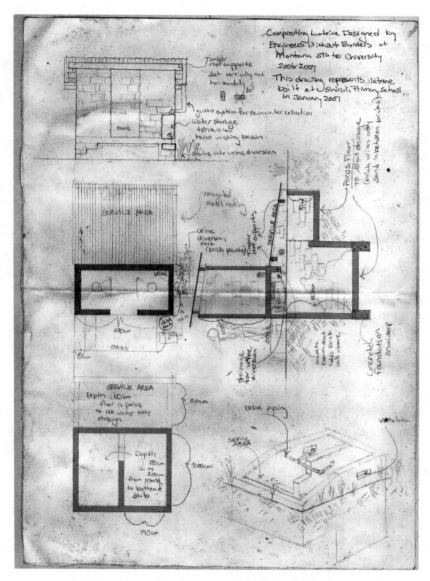

Sketch for a Composting Latrine. The student chapter of Engineers Without Borders at Montana State University is collaborating with 57 schools in the Khwisero Division of southwestern Kenya to provide sustainable sanitary improvements including wells and composting latrines. *Sketch courtesy of Andrea Orr, Engineers Without Borders, MSU.*

Andrea Orr was a student in environment design at Montana State University and a co-fundraiser and co–project designer in the MSU chapter of Engineers Without Borders.

She created the sketch above during the building of a composting latrine that she and Chris Allen designed for a school in the Khwisero Division of southwestern Kenya. The sketch showed instructors and local government officials how the latrine would work.

Though they had done multiple sketches ahead of time, she and Allen did this complied sketch to clarify their ideas into one concept.

Orr did the sketch outdoors, sitting next to the school building. There was no computer available, because at the remote location, electricity was rarely available. She also did a drawing explaining how to use and maintain the latrine, which was posted inside the finished structure.

Orr said that when she is not working in the field, she still sketches by hand before transferring to CAD.

"There's little bit of vagueness in a hand drawn sketch that keeps it open to creativity," said Orr.

"If you show a sketch to someone they are more likely to offer input and ideas than if it looks like a finished CAD rendering. That's one of the reasons I don't work in CAD until quite a few versions into the project."

KEY WORDS

Solids

Surfaces

Planar

Single-Curved

Double-Curved

Warped

Polyhedra

Regular Polyhedron

Prism

Pyramid

Cylinder

Cone

Sphere

Torus

Ellipsoid

Construction Lines

Contours

Negative Space

Viewpoint

Shading

Hatching

Edge

Vertex

Point

Line

Angle

Freehand Sketch

Line Patterns

Proportion

Pictorial Sketch

Oblique Drawing

Cavalier Projection

Cabinet Projection

Perspective

Vanishing Point

CHAPTER SUMMARY

- Sketching is a quick way of visualizing and solving a drawing problem. It is an effective way of communicating with all members of the design team.
- There are special techniques for sketching lines, circles, and arcs. These techniques should be practiced so they become second nature.
- Using a grid makes sketching in proportion an easy task.
- You can sketch circles by constructing a square and locating the four tangent points where the circle touches the square.
- A sketched line does not need to look like a CAD or mechanical line. The main distinction between CAD and instrumental drawing and freehand sketching is the character or technique of the line work.
- Freehand sketches are made to proportion, but not necessarily to a particular scale.
- Sketching is one of the most important skills for accurately recording ideas.
- Isometric, oblique, and perspective are three methods used to create pictorial sketches.

REVIEW QUESTIONS

1. What are the advantages of using grid paper for sketching?
2. What is the correct technique for sketching a circle or arc?
3. Sketch the alphabet of lines. Which lines are thick? Which are thin? Which are very light and will not reproduce when copied?
4. What type of 3D drawing can easily be drawn on square grid paper?
5. What is the advantage of sketching an object first before drawing it using CAD?
6. What is the difference between proportion and scale?

EXERCISES

SKETCHING EXERCISES

Exercise 1 Sketch the objects shown using isometric, oblique, and one- or two-point perspective.

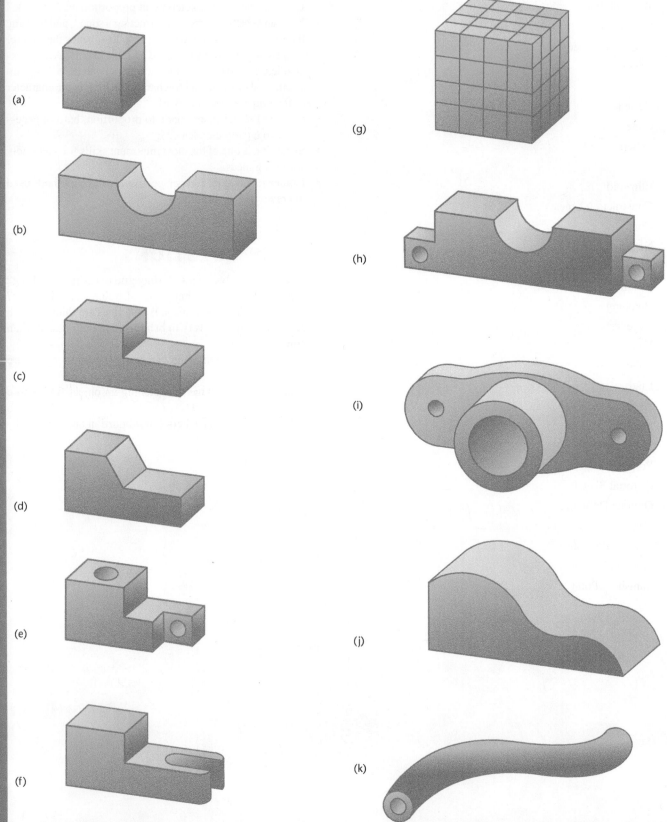

(a)

(b)

(c)

(d)

(e)

(f)

(g)

(h)

(i)

(j)

(k)

Exercise 2 Quick Sketch. © 2007 Jupiterimages Corporation.

1. Practice the sketching skills and techniques you have learned for construction lines and ellipses. Set a timer for 10 minutes and make quick sketches of these nine different cups.
2. Select one cup and create isometric, oblique, and perspective drawings.
3. Design a new piece of drinkware, using your sketching skills.
4. Select one cup. Draw an enclosing box and shade in the negative space so that the contour of the cup remains white.

(a) (b) (c)

(d) (e) (f)

(g) (h) (i)

Exercise 3 Quick Sketch. © 2007 Jupiterimages Corporation.
See instructions for Exercise 2, part 1.

(a)

(b)

(c)

(d)

(e)

(f)

Exercise 4 Quick Sketch. © *Jupiterimages Corporation.*
See instructions for Exercise 2, part 1.

(a)

(b)

(c)

(d)

(e)

(f)

Exercise 5 Sketching.
© *Jupiterimages Corporation.*
See instructions for Exercise 2, part 1.

(a)

(b)

(c)

(d)

(e)

Exercise 6 Divide working space into six equal rectangles and draw visible lines, as shown. Draw construction lines *AB* through centers *C* at right angles to required lines; then along each construction line, set off 0.50" spaces and draw required visible lines. Omit dimensions and instructional notes.

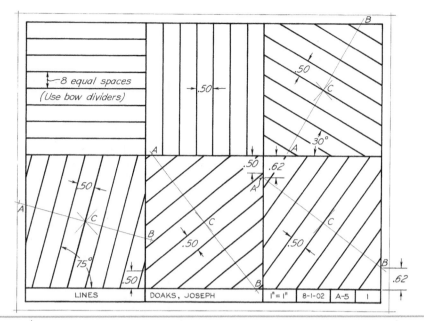

Exercise 7 Divide working space into six equal rectangles and draw lines as shown. In the first two spaces, draw conventional lines to match those in Figure 23. In remaining spaces, locate centers *C* by diagonals, and then work constructions out from them. Omit the metric dimensions and instructional notes.

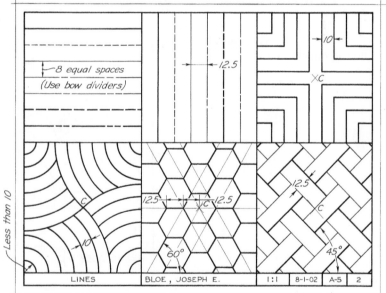

Exercise 8 Draw views in pencil, as shown. Omit all dimensions.

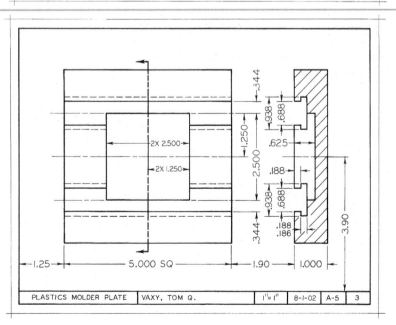

Exercise 9 Draw the figures in pencil, as shown. Omit all dimensions.

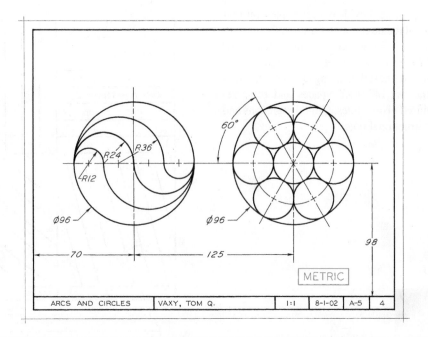

Exercise 10 Draw the views in pencil, as shown. Omit all dimensions.

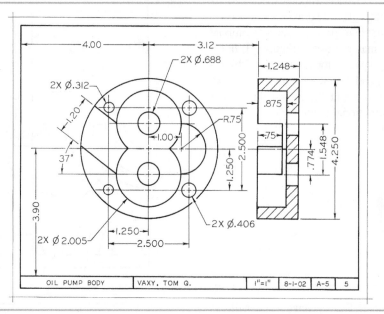

Exercise 11 Draw the friction plate using pencil. Omit dimensions and notes.

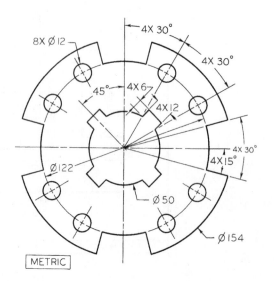

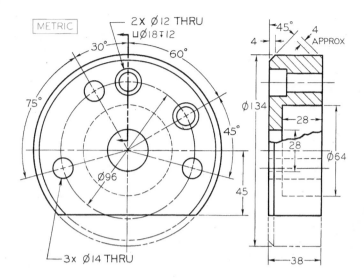

Exercise 12 Draw views of the seal cover using pencil. Omit the dimensions and notes.

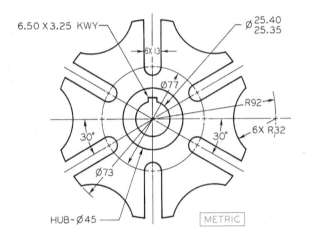

Exercise 13 Draw the Geneva cam using pencil. Omit dimensions and notes.

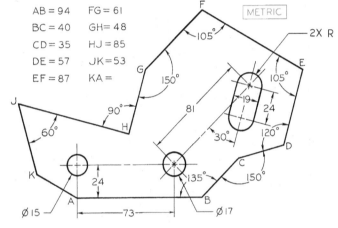

AB = 94	FG = 61
BC = 40	GH = 48
CD = 35	HJ = 85
DE = 57	JK = 53
EF = 87	KA =

Exercise 14 Draw accurately in pencil the shear plate. Give the length of *KA*. Omit the other dimensions and notes.

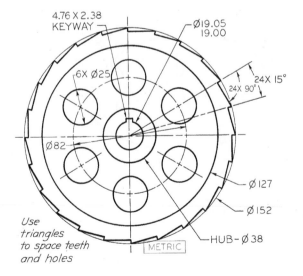

Exercise 15 Draw the ratchet wheel using pencil. Omit the dimensions and notes.

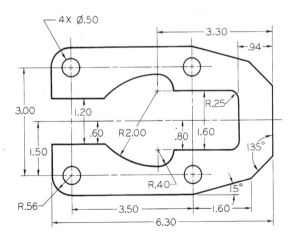

Exercise 16 Draw the latch plate using pencil. Omit the dimensions and notes.

Exercise 17 Parking Meter

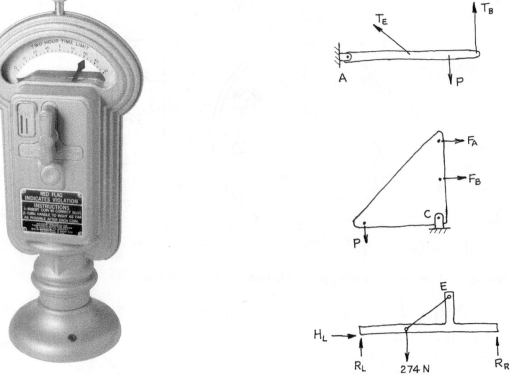

Exercise 18 Free-Body Diagram Sketches

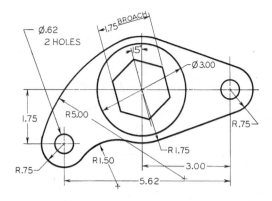

Exercise 19 Rocker Arm

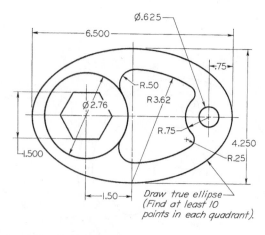

Exercise 20 Special Cam

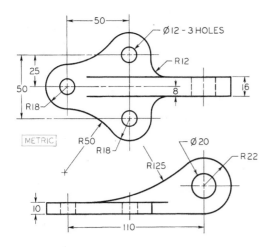

Exercise 21 Boiler Stay

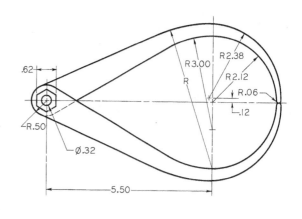

Exercise 22 Outside Caliper

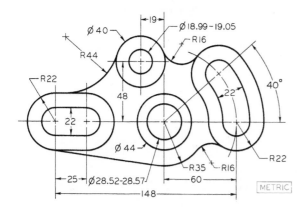

Exercise 23 Gear Arm

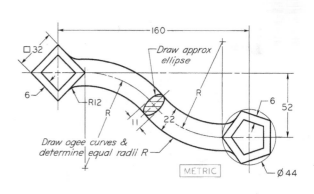

Exercise 24 Special S-Wrench

NEGATIVE SPACE

Use negative space techniques to redraw the figure shown in white in the space below. Start your sketch by drawing the outer boundary and then lightly blocking in the areas shown in color.

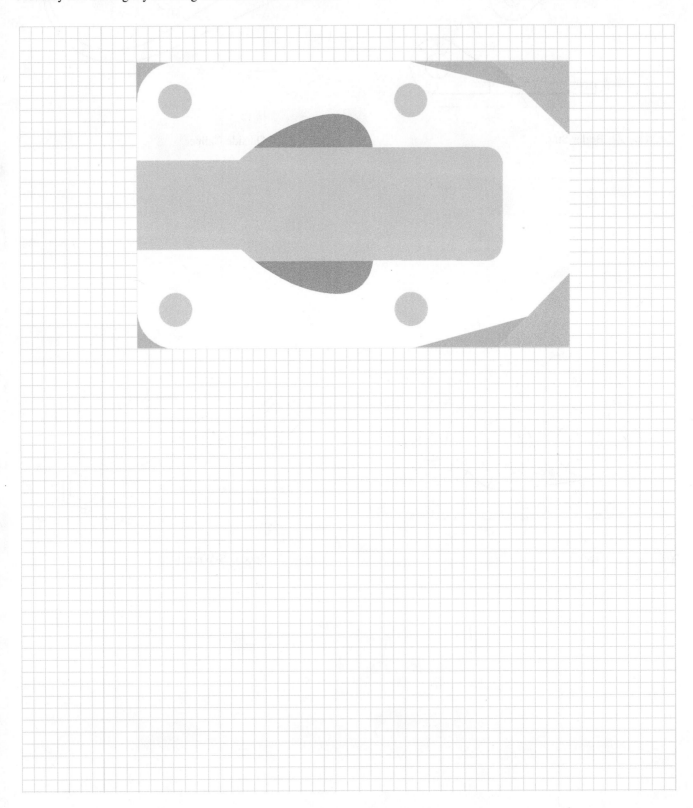

PRACTICE SKETCHING LINES AND ARROWS

Redraw the line patterns shown in the space provided.

Examples:

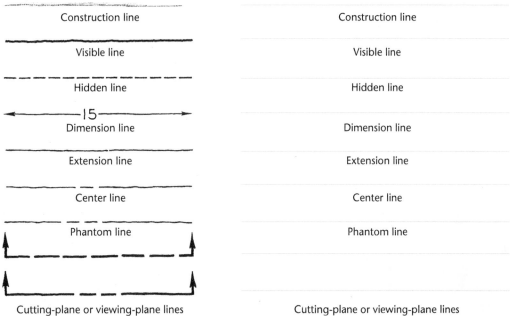

Construction line	Construction line
Visible line	Visible line
Hidden line	Hidden line
—— 15 —— Dimension line	Dimension line
Extension line	Extension line
Center line	Center line
Phantom line	Phantom line
Cutting-plane or viewing-plane lines	Cutting-plane or viewing-plane lines

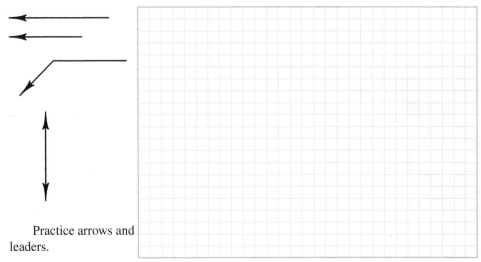

Practice arrows and leaders.

When using the arrowhead method in which both strokes are directed toward the point, it is easier to make the strokes toward yourself.

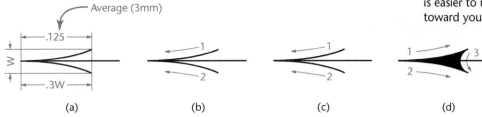

Average (3mm)

.125

W

.3W

(a)   (b)   (c)   (d)

SKETCHING TO SCALE

Measure the dimensions of the objects below in metric units. Sketch each object at the scale listed below. Specify the scale correctly on your drawings. Before you sketch, choose which of the boxes at right will best fit each item when it is sketched to the specified scale.

- Sketch the pushpin at 5:1 scale.
- Sketch the drink cup at 1:2 scale.

BLOCK IN THE IRREGULAR OBJECT

Block in the part at right using the steps:

1. Capture the main proportions with simple lines.
2. Block in the general sizes and direction of flow of curved shapes.
3. Lightly block in additional details.
4. Darken the lines of the completed sketch.

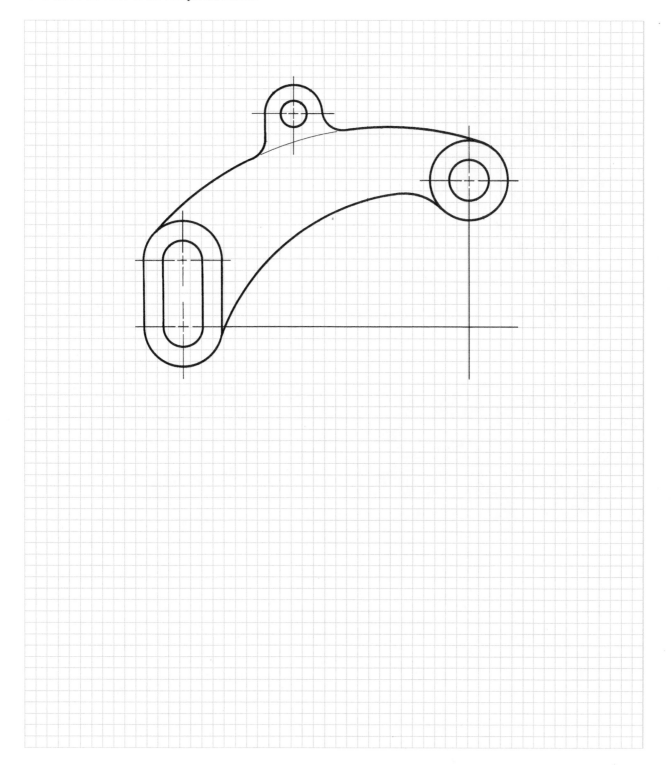

SINGLE-VIEW ORTHOGRAPHIC DRAWING

Objects that have a uniform thickness can usually be sketched using a single orthographic view.
Orient the object so that the circular shape is facing directly toward you.

1. Lightly block in the front surface of the bearing.
2. Darken the final lines.
3. Add thin centerlines to locate the hole center.

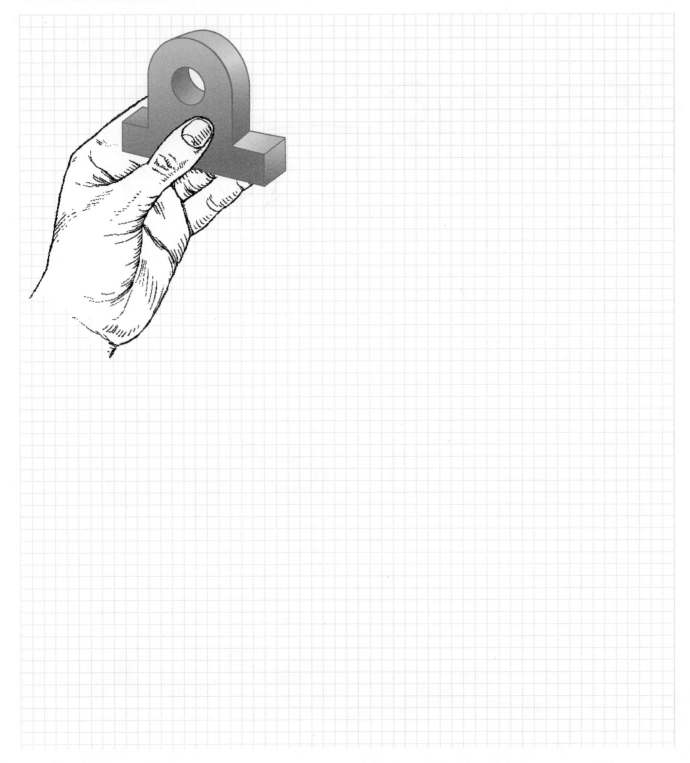

BOX CONSTRUCTION

Rectangular objects are easily drawn using box construction, in which you imagine the object to be enclosed in a rectangular box whose sides coincide with the main faces of the object.

Sketch the object shown in two views by imagining it is enclosed in a construction box.

- A construction box and distances *a, b, c, d, e,* and *f* have been blocked in for you.
- Refer to the given views and finish constructing the features of the object.
- Darken your final lines.

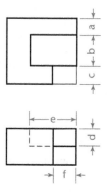

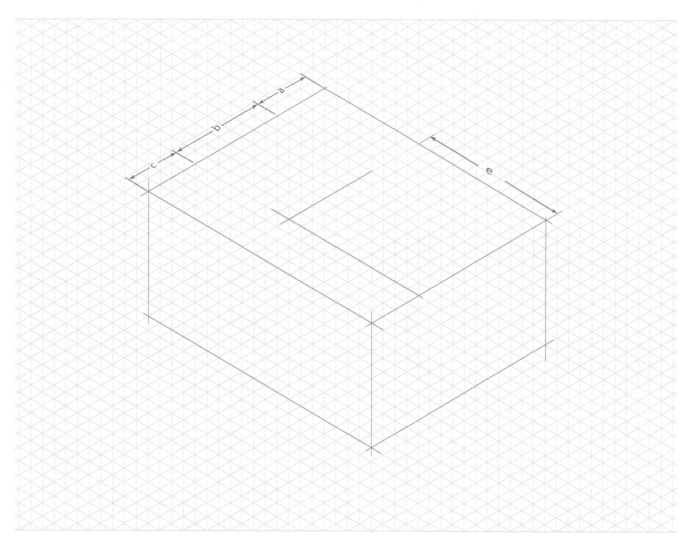

ANGLES IN ISOMETRIC

Two views of an object to be drawn in isometric are given.

Point *A* can easily be located in the isometric by measuring .88" down from point O, as shown.

However, point *B* is dimensioned by the 30° angle. To locate *B* in isometric you must find dimension *X*.

You can solve this problem graphically by using CAD to draw a triangle with angles of 30° and 90° and a side of .88" and then listing the length for dimension *X*.

Measure distance *X* in the true-size graphical solution shown at right, or use trigonometry to find the distance. Once you have found dimension *X*, use it to locate point *B* in the isometric sketch as shown and finish the sketch the bottom of the page.

You can also sketch the isometric so that it appears proportionate and, if necessary, dimension the angle as 30° to call attention to it.

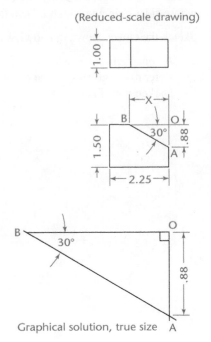

(Reduced-scale drawing)

Graphical solution, true size   A

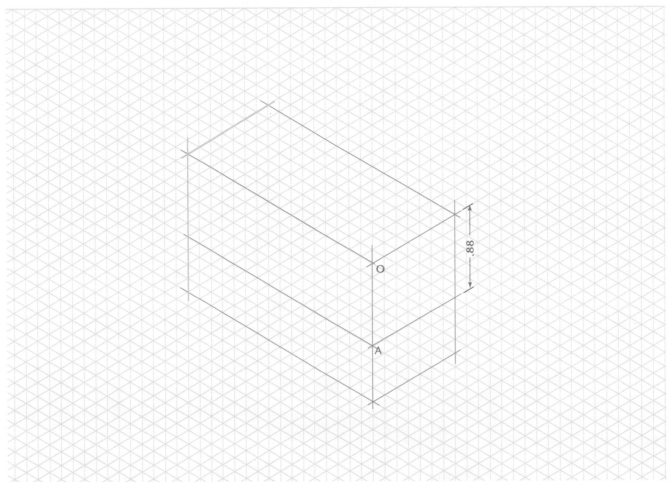

CREATE AN OBLIQUE SKETCH
OF AN OBJECT

Hold the object in your hand.

Orient the object so that most or all of the circular shapes are toward you. This way they will appear as true circles and arcs in the oblique sketch.

1. Block in the front face of the bearing as if you were sketching a front view.
2. Sketch receding lines parallel to each other and at any convenient angle (say 30° or 45°). Decide on the depth you

will show. The depth lines may be shown full length, but three-quarters or one-half size produces a more natural appearance. Block in the back shape of the object.
3. Darken the final lines.

Use the grid space to create an oblique sketch of a household object such as your clock, doorknob, or microwave, or sketch another object as provided by your instructor.

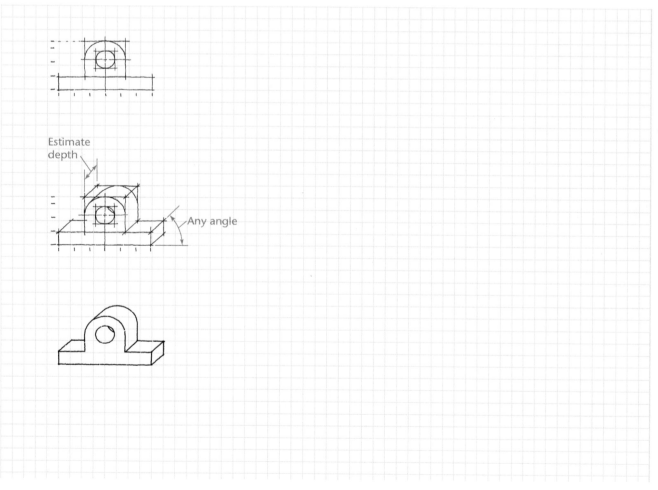

140

WORSHEET 1 | PRACTICE SKETCHING FREEHAND LINES

Use the spaces at right to practice sketching freehand lines of each type shown below.

Construction line

Visible line

Hidden line

—|5— Dimension line

Extension line

Center line

Phantom line

Cutting-plane lines

Construction line	Construction line
Visible line	Visible line
Hidden line	Hidden line
Dimension line	Dimension line
Extension line	Extension line
Center line	Center line
Phantom line	Phantom line
Cutting-plane lines	Cutting-plane lines

SKETCHING INCLINED LINES

For inclined lines, shift position with relation to the paper or turn the paper slightly. Use the same movements as for horizontal or vertical lines.

Complete the series of inclined lines below.

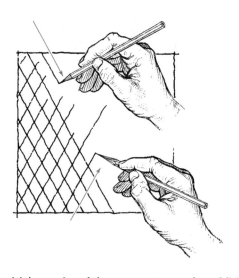

Make copies of these pages to use for additional practice.

WORKSHEET 2   SKETCHING CIRCLES AND ELLIPSES

Use the construction lines provided below to begin sketching circles and ellipses. Practice this technique and the others you have learned for creating circles and ellipses on your own unlined paper.

Make copies of these pages to use for additional practice.

WORSHEET 3   APPLYING THE SQUARES METHOD

Transfer the drawing of the car shown at right to the larger grid below using the squares method.

Match how the lines enter and exit each grid square.

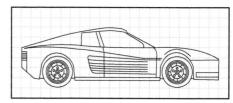

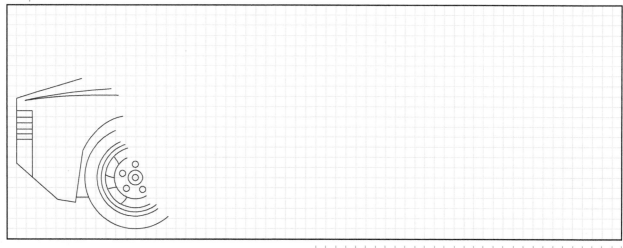

Cut a small picture out of a magazine or newspaper and fix it in the box at right.

Using the tickmarks as guides, draw a 1/8" grid over the picture.

Use the same process you used above to transfer and enlarge the picture to the grid below.

Place an overlay grid over any picture and sketch it on grid paper. Use the overlay grid to aid in proportions.

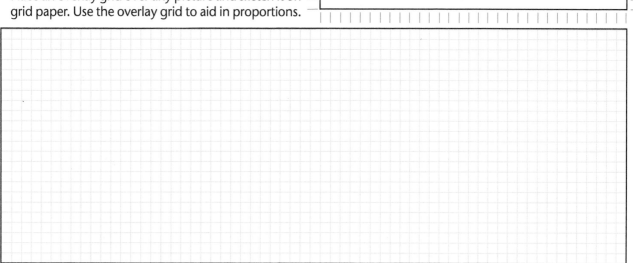

Make copies of these pages to use for additional practice.

WORKSHEET 4 PRACTICE LINE AND CURVE TECHNIQUE

Sketch the figures below on the grid provided.

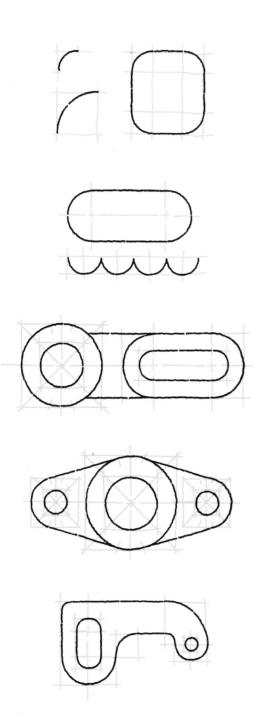

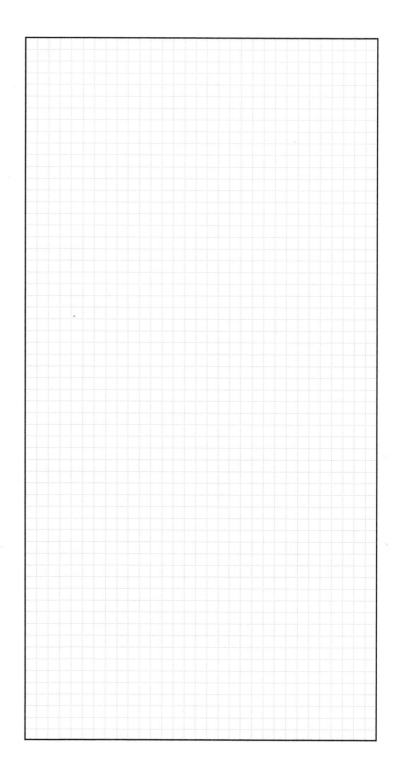

Make copies of these pages to use for additional practice.

148

WORKSHEET 5   STARTING WITH ISOMETRIC PICTORIALS

Sketch an isometric pictorial of the object shown in the orthographic views. A block with the correct overall dimensions has been provided to get you started.

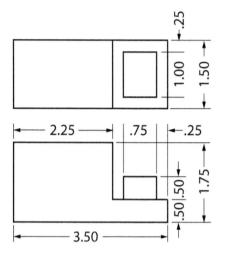

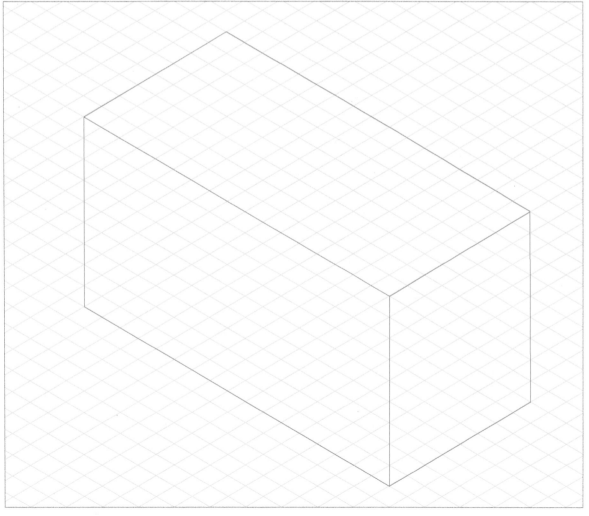

Make copies of these pages to use for additional practice.

WORKSHEET 6   SKETCHING TANGENT ARCS

Use sketching techniques to block in tangent arcs as shown in the example drawing. Remember, a radial line (one through the center of the circle) is perpendicular to the line at the point of tangency.

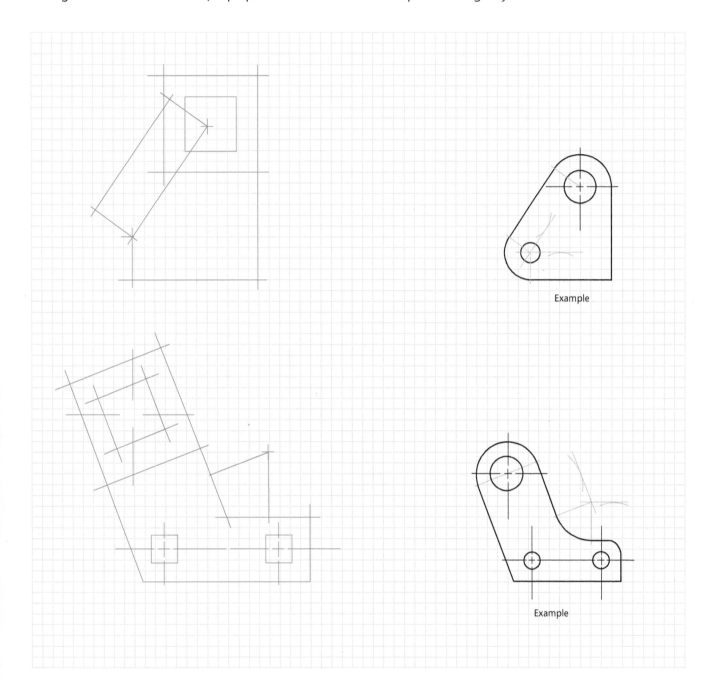

Example

Example

Make copies of these pages to use for additional practice.

152

WORKSHEET 7

SKETCHING CURVED SHAPES IN ISOMETRIC

Finish the isometric sketch of the object shown in the orthographic views.

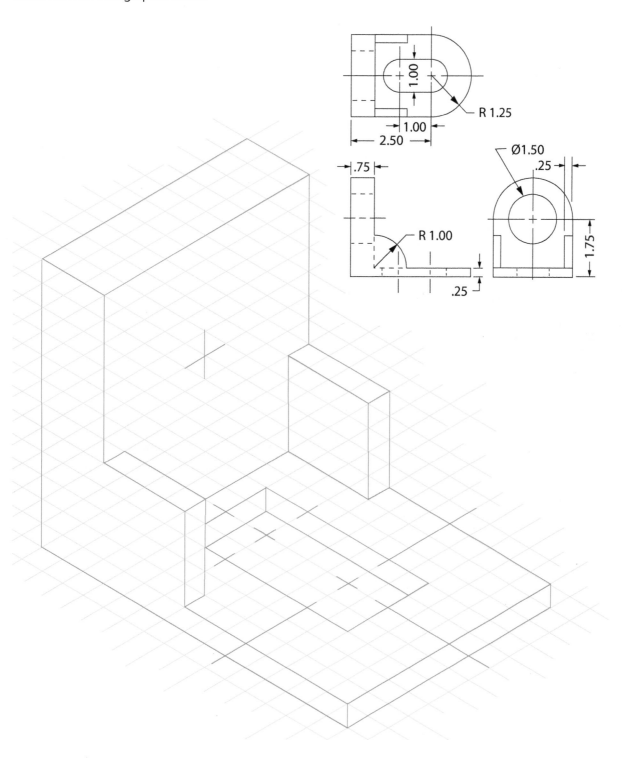

R 1.25

1.00

1.00

2.50

Ø1.50

.25

1.75

.75

R 1.00

.25

Make copies of these pages
to use for additional practice.

ORTHOGRAPHIC PROJECTION

ORTHOGRAPHIC PROJECTION

OBJECTIVES

After studying the material in this chapter, you should be able to:

1. Recognize and sketch the symbol for third-angle projection.

2. List the six principal views of projection.

3. Sketch the top, front, and right-side views of an object with normal, inclined, and oblique surfaces.

4. Understand which views show depth in a drawing that shows top, front, and right-side views.

5. Know the meaning of normal, inclined, and oblique surfaces.

6. Compare and contrast using a CAD program to sketching on a sheet of paper to create 2D drawing geometry.

7. List the dimensions that transfer between top, front, and right-side views.

8. Transfer depth between the top and right-side views.

9. Label points where surfaces intersect.

Refer to the following standard:
- ANSI/ASME Y14.3—2003 Multiview and Sectional View Drawings

The companion website for this text is www.prenhall.com/chet_giesecke_modgraphic_4.

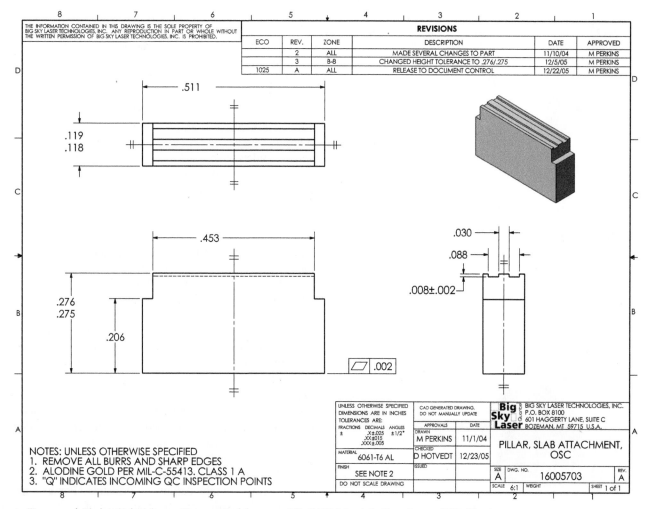

Front, Top, and Right-Side Views Generated from a 3D CAD Model. *Courtesy of Big Sky Laser.*

OVERVIEW

A view of an object is called a projection. By projecting multiple views from different directions in a systematic way, you can completely describe the shape of 3D objects.

There are certain standard practices that you must know in order to create sketches and drawings that can be accurately interpreted. For example, you need to know which views to show, how they should be oriented in your drawing, and how to represent key information such as edges, surfaces, vertices, hidden lines, centerlines, and other crucial details.

The standard published in ANSI/ASME Y14 3M-1994 is common in the United States where third-angle projection is used. Europe, Asia, and many other places use the first-angle projection system.

Search the following Web sites to learn more about orthographic projections (geomancy) and a biography of Gaspard Mongl (bib math).

- http://www.geomancy.org
- http://www.bibmath.net

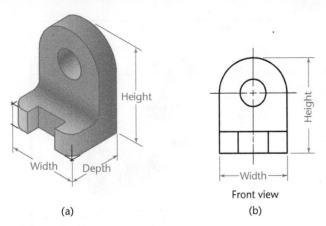

Height

Width   Depth

(a)

Height

Width

Front view

(b)

1   Front View of an Object

UNDERSTANDING PROJECTIONS

In order to make and interpret drawings you need to know how to create projections and understand the standard arrangement of views. You also need to be familiar with the geometry of solid objects and be able to visualize a 3D object that is represented in a 2D sketch or drawing. The ability to identify whether surfaces are normal, inclined, or oblique in orientation can help you to visualize objects. Common features such as vertices, edges, contours, fillets, holes, and rounds are shown in a standard way, which makes drawings simpler to create and helps to prevent them from being misinterpreted.

Views of Objects

A photograph shows an object as it appears to the observer, but not necessarily as it is. It cannot describe the object accurately, no matter what distance or which direction it is taken from, because it does not show the exact shapes and sizes of the parts. It would be impossible to create an accurate three-dimensional model of an object using only a photograph for reference because it shows only one view. It is a 2D representation of a 3D object.

Drawings are two dimensional representations as well, but unlike photos, they allow you to record sizes and shapes precisely. In engineering and other fields, a complete and clear description of the shape and size of an object is necessary to be sure that it is manufactured exactly as the designer intended. To provide this information about a 3D object, a number of systematically arranged views are used.

The system of views is called **multiview projection.** Each view provides certain definite information. For example, a front view shows the true shape and size of surfaces that are parallel to the front of the object. An example showing the direction of sight and the resulting front view projection is shown in Figure 1. Figure 2 shows the same part and the six principal viewing directions, as will be discussed in the next section. Figure 3 shows the same six views of a house.

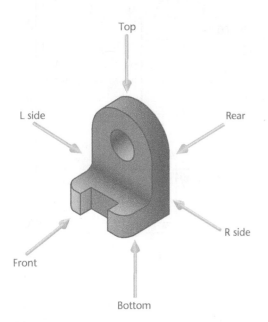

Top

L side

Rear

Front

R side

Bottom

2   The Six Principal Views

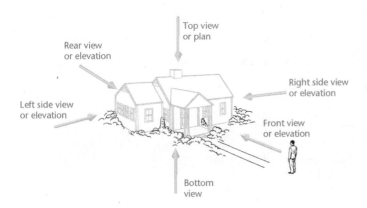

Rear view
or elevation

Top view
or plan

Right side view
or elevation

Left side view
or elevation

Front view
or elevation

Bottom
view

Top view
or plan

Rear view
or elevation

Left side view
or elevation

Front view or elevation

Rear view
or elevation

Bottom view

3   Six Views of a House

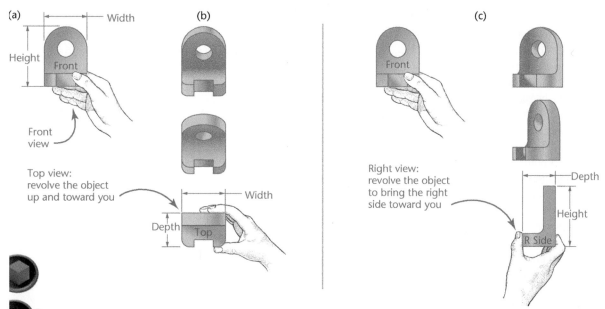

(a) Width / Height / Front / Front view / Top view: revolve the object up and toward you / Depth / Top / Width

(b)

(c) Front / Right view: revolve the object to bring the right side toward you / Depth / Height / R Side

4   Revolving the Object to Produce Views. You can experience different views by revolving an object, as shown. (a) First, hold the object in the front view position. (b) To get the top view, tilt the object toward you to bring the top of the object into your view. (c) To get the right-side view, begin with the object's front view facing you and revolve it to bring the right side toward you. To see views of the rear, bottom, or right side, you would simply turn the object to bring those sides toward you.

The Six Standard Views

Any object can be viewed from six mutually perpendicular directions, as shown in Figure 2. These are called the six **principal views.**

You can think of the six views as what an observer would see by moving around the object. As shown in Figure 3, the observer can walk around a house and view its front, sides, and rear. You can imagine the top view as seen by an observer from an airplane and the bottom, or "worm's-eye view," as seen from underneath. The term "plan" may also be used for the top view. The term "elevation" is used for all views showing the height of the building. These terms are regularly used in architectural drawing and occasionally in other fields.

To make drawings easier to read, the views are arranged on the paper in a standard way. The views in Figure 3 show the American National Standard arrangement. The top, front, and bottom views align vertically. The rear, left-side, front, and right-side views align horizontally. To draw a view out

of place is a serious error and is generally regarded as one of the worst mistakes in drawing. See Figure 4 for a demonstration of how to visualize the different views.

Principal Dimensions

The three principal dimensions of an object are **width, height,** and **depth** (Figure 5). In technical drawing, these fixed terms are used for dimensions shown in certain views, regardless of the shape of the object. The terms "length" and "thickness" are not used because they cannot be applied in all cases.

The front view shows only the height and width of the object and not the depth. In fact, any principal view of a 3D object shows only two of the three principal dimensions; the third is found in an adjacent view. Height is shown in the rear, left-side, front, and right-side views. Width is shown in the rear, top, front, and bottom views. Depth is shown in the left-side, top, right-side, and bottom views.

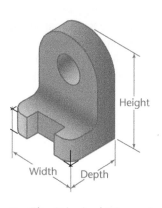

Height / Width / Depth

5   The Principal Dimensions of an Object

159

Projection Method

Figure 6 shows how to understand the front view of an object drawn using an orthographic projection. Imagine a sheet of glass parallel to the front surfaces of the object. This represents the **plane of projection.** The outline on the plane of projection shows how the object appears to the observer. In orthographic projection, rays (or projectors) from all points on the edges or contours of the object extend parallel to each other and perpendicular to the plane of projection. The word **orthographic** essentially means to draw at right angles.

Examples of top and side views are shown in Figure 7. The plane on which the front view is projected is called the **frontal plane.** The plane upon which the top view is projected is the **horizontal plane.** The plane upon which the side view is projected is called the **profile plane.**

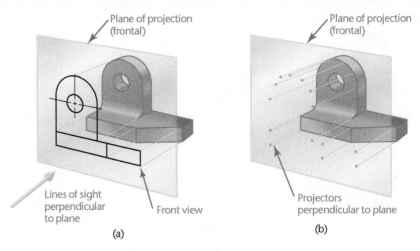

(a)

Lines of sight perpendicular to plane

Front view

(b)

Projectors perpendicular to plane

6 Projection of an Object

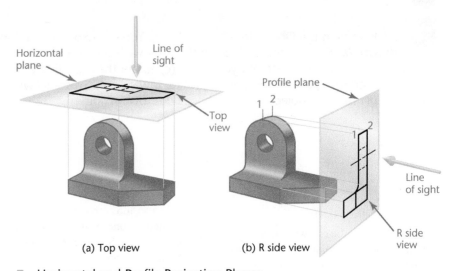

(a) Top view

(b) R side view

7 Horizontal and Profile Projection Planes

The Glass Box

One way to understand the standard arrangement of views on the sheet of paper is to envision a **glass box.** If planes of projection were placed parallel to each principal face of the object, they would form a box, as shown in Figure 8. The outside observer would see six standard views (front, rear, top, bottom, right side, left side) of the object through the sides of this imaginary glass box.

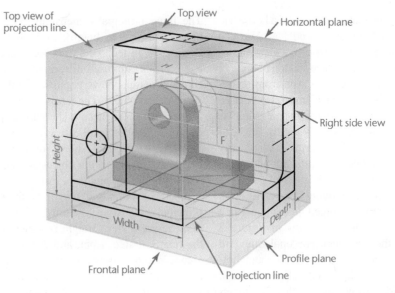

8 The Glass Box

To organize the views of a 3D object on a flat sheet of paper, imagine the six planes of the glass box being unfolded to lie flat, as shown in Figure 9. Think of all planes except the rear plane as hinged to the frontal plane. The rear plane is usually hinged to the left-side plane. Each plane folds out away from the frontal plane. The representation of the hinge lines of the glass box in a drawing are known as **folding lines.** The positions of these six planes after they have been unfolded are shown in Figure 10.

Carefully identify each of these planes and corresponding views with the planes' original position in the glass box.

In Figure 10, lines extend around the glass box from one view to another on the planes of projection. These are the projectors from a point in one view to the same point in another view. The size and position of the object in the glass box does not change. This explains why the top view is the same width as the front view and why it is placed directly above the front view. The same relation exists between the front and bottom views. Therefore, the front, top, and bottom views all line up vertically and are the same width. The rear, left-side, front, and right-side views all line up horizontally and are the same height.

Objects do not change position in the box, so the top view must be the same distance from the folding line OZ as the right side view is from the folding line OY. The bottom and left-side views are the same distance from their respective folding lines as are the right-side and the top views. The top, right-side, bottom, and left-side views are all the same distance from the respective folding lines and show the same depth.

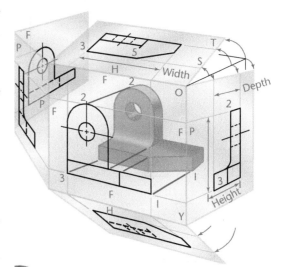

9   Unfolding the Glass Box

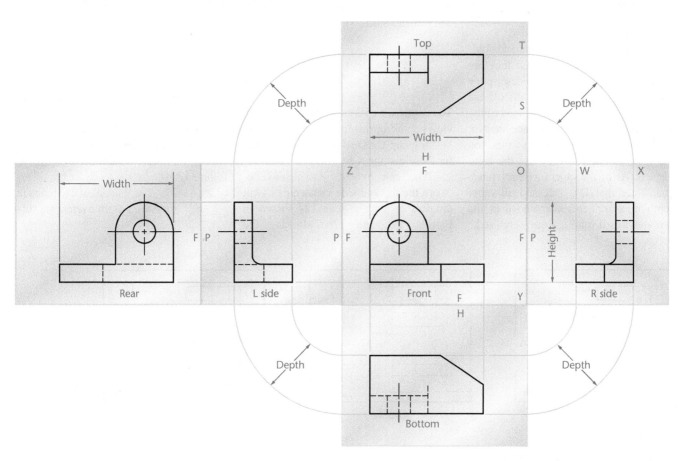

10   The Glass Box Unfolded

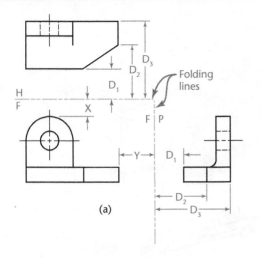

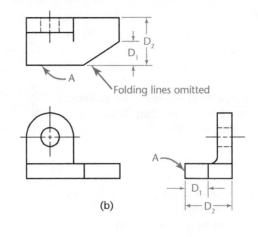

(a)

(b)

11   Views Shown with and without Folding Lines

The front, top, and right-side views of the object shown in the previous figures are shown in Figure 11a, but instead of a glass box, folding lines are shown between the views. These folding lines correspond to the hinge lines of the glass box.

The H/F folding line, between the top and front views, is the intersection of the horizontal and frontal planes. The F/P folding line, between the front and side views, is the intersection of the frontal and profile planes.

While you should understand folding lines, particularly because they are useful in solving problems in descriptive geometry, they are usually left off the drawing, as in Figure 11b. Instead of using the folding lines as reference lines for marking depth measurements in the top and side views, you may use the front surface (A) of the object as a reference line. Note that D1, D2, and all other depth measurements correspond in the two views as if folding lines were used.

 Use Worksheet 1 to practice transferring depth dimensions.

Spacing between Views

Spacing between views is mainly a matter of appearance. Views should be spaced well apart, but close enough to appear related to each other. You may need to leave space between the views to add dimensions.

Transferring Depth Dimensions

The depth dimensions in the top and side views must correspond point-for-point. When using CAD or instruments, transfer these distances accurately.

You can transfer dimensions between the top and side views either with dividers or with a scale, as shown in Figures 12a and 12b. Marking the

distances on a scrap of paper and using it like a scale to transfer the distance to the other view is another method that works well when sketching.

You may find it convenient to use a 45° miter line to project dimensions between top and side views, as shown in Figure 12c. Because the miter line is drawn at 45°, depths shown vertically in the top view Y can be transferred to be shown as horizontal depths in the side view X and vice versa.

Measuring from a Reference Surface

To transfer a dimension from one view to a related view (a view that shares that dimension) you can think of measuring from the edge view of a plane which shows on edge in both views as in Figure 13.

 Use Worksheet 2 to practice measuring from a reference surface.

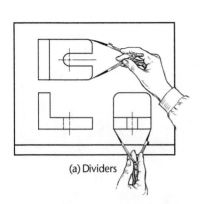

(a) Dividers

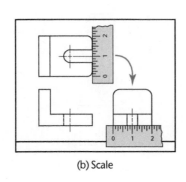

(b) Scale

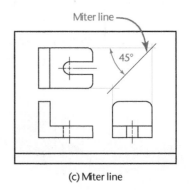

(c) Miter line

12   Transferring Depth Dimensions

Necessary Views

Figure 14 shows that right- and left-side views are essentially mirror images of each other, only with different lines appearing hidden. Hidden lines use a dashed-line pattern to represent portions of the object that are not directly visible from that direction of sight. Both the right and left views do not need to be shown, so usually the right-side view is drawn. This is also true of the top and bottom views, and of the front and rear views. The top, front, and right-side views, arranged together, are shown in Figure 15. These are called the **three regular views** because they are the views most frequently used.

A sketch or drawing should only contain the views needed to clearly and completely describe the object. These minimally required views are referred to as the **necessary views.** Choose the views that have the fewest hidden lines and show essential contours or shapes most clearly. Complicated objects may require more than three views or special views such as partial views.

Many objects need only two views to clearly describe their shape. If an object requires only two views and the left-side and right-side views show the object equally well, use the right-side view. If an object requires only two views and the top and bottom views show the object equally well, choose the top view. If only two views are necessary and the top view and right-side view show the object equally well, choose the combination that fits best on your paper. Some examples are shown in Figure 16.

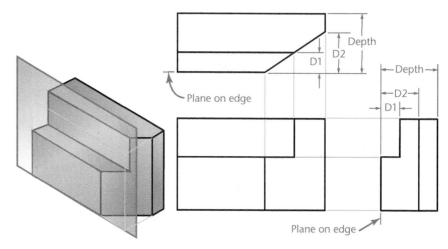

13 Transferring Depth Dimensions from a Reference Surface

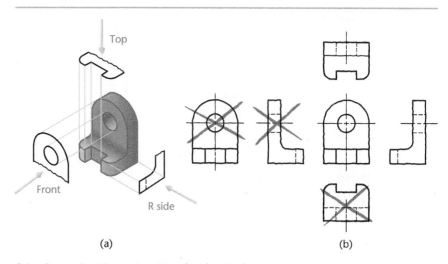

(a)   (b)

14 Opposite Views Are Nearly Identical

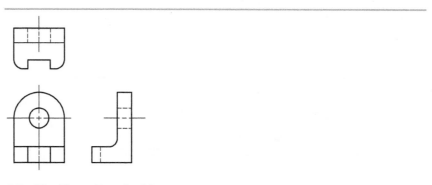

15 The Three Regular Views

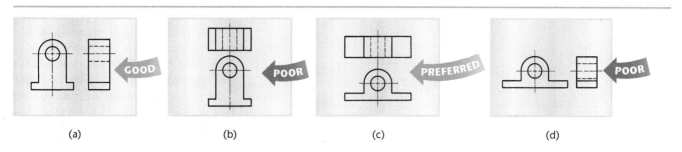

(a)   (b)   (c)   (d)

16 Choice of Views to Fit Paper

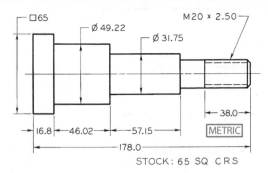

17 One-View Drawing of a Connecting Rod

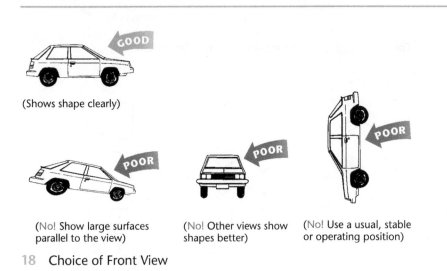

GOOD

(Shows shape clearly)

POOR

(No! Show large surfaces parallel to the view)

POOR

(No! Other views show shapes better)

POOR

(No! Use a usual, stable or operating position)

18 Choice of Front View

19 A long part looks best oriented with the long axis horizontal on the sheet. *Courtesy of Dynojet Research, Inc.*

Often, a single view supplemented by a note or by lettered symbols is enough, as shown in Figure 17. Objects that can be shown using a single view usually have a uniform thickness. This connecting rod is an exception. It is possible to show it in a single view due to the way it is dimensioned.

Orientation of the Front View

Four views of a compact automobile are shown in Figure 18. The view chosen for the front view in this case is the side, not the front, of the automobile.

- The front view should show a large surface of the part parallel to the front viewing plane.
- The front view should show the shape of the object clearly.
- The front view should show the object in a usual, stable, or operating position, particularly for familiar objects.
- When possible, a machine part is drawn in the orientation it occupies in the assembly.
- Usually screws, bolts, shafts, tubes, and other elongated parts are drawn in a horizontal position as shown in Figure 19.

CAD software can be used to generate orthographic views directly from a 3D model as shown in Figure 20. The pictorial view of this model is shown in Figure 21. When using CAD you still need to select a good orientation so that the part shows clearly in the front view. The standard arrangement of views shown in Figure 15 should be used. Do not be tempted to rearrange the views of your CAD drawing to fit the sheet better.

First- and Third-Angle Projection

As you saw earlier in this chapter, you can think of the system of projecting views as unfolding a glass box made from the viewing planes. There are two main systems used for projecting and unfolding the views: **third-angle projection,** which is used in the United States, Canada, and some other countries, and **first-angle projection,** which is primarily used in

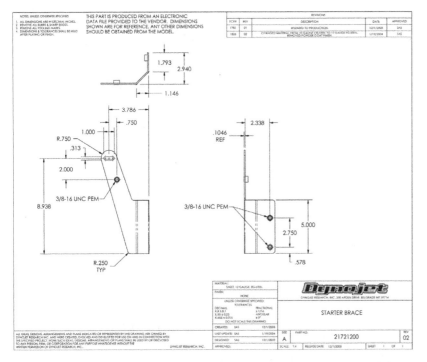

20 Computer-Generated Multiview Drawing from a CAD Model. *Courtesy of Dynojet Research, Inc.*

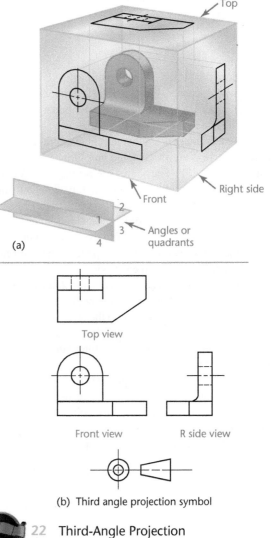

21 Pictorial View of the CAD Model Shown in Figure 20. *Courtesy of Dynojet Research, Inc.*

Europe and Asia. Difficulty in interpreting the drawing and manufacturing errors can result when a first-angle drawing is confused with a third-angle drawing.

Because of the global nature of technical drawings, you should thoroughly understand both methods. However, since it can be confusing to try to learn both methods intermixed, this text presents third-angle projection throughout. When you are comfortable with creating third-angle projection drawings, re-visit this section. You will see that the two drawing methods are very similar and you should be able to extend the same skills to either type of drawing.

Third-Angle Projection

Figure 22a shows the concept of third-angle orthographic pro-jection. To avoid misunderstanding, international **projection symbols** have been developed to distinguish between first-angle and third-angle projections on drawings. The symbol in Figure 22b shows two views of a truncated cone. You can exam-ine the arrangement of the views in the symbol to determine whether first- or third-angle projection was used. On interna-tional drawings you should be sure to include this symbol.

To understand the two systems, think of the vertical and horizontal planes of projection, shown in Figure 22a, as indef-inite in extent and intersecting at 90° with each other; the four angles produced are called the first, second, third, and fourth angles (similar to naming quadrants on a graph.) If the object to be drawn is placed below the horizontal plane and behind the vertical plane, as in the glass box you saw earlier, the object is said to be in the third angle. In third-angle projection, the views are produced as if the observer is outside, looking in.

(a)

Top

Right side

Front

Angles or quadrants

Top view

Front view   R side view

(b) Third angle projection symbol

22 Third-Angle Projection

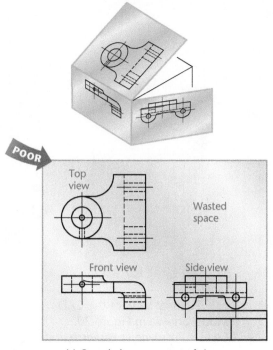

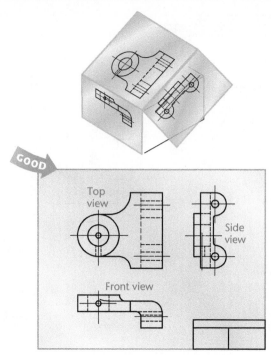

(a) Crowded arrangement of views

(b) Approved alternate arrangement of views

 23   Position of Side View

Alternative Arrangements for Third-Angle Projection

Sometimes drawing three views using the conventional arrangement wastes space. (For example, see the wide flat object in Figure 23a.) Using the space on the paper efficiently may prevent the need to use a reduced scale.

For these cases, there is another acceptable arrangement of third-angle projection views. Imagine unfolding the glass box as shown in Figure 23b. The views are arranged differently, with the right-side view aligned with the top view, but these views are still using third-angle projection.

In this case, think of the profile (side view) hinged to the horizontal plane (top view) instead of to the frontal plane (front view) so that the side view is beside the top view when unfolded, as shown in Figure 23b. Notice the side view is rotated 90° from the orientation shown in the side view in Figure 23a when it is in this placement. Note also that you can now directly project the depth dimension from the top view into the side view.

If necessary, you may place the side view horizontally across from the bottom view (so the profile plane is hinged to the bottom plane of the projection).

Similarly, the rear view may be placed directly above the top view or under the bottom view. In this case, the rear plane is considered hinged to the horizontal or bottom plane and rotated to coincide with the frontal plane.

Use Worksheets 3 and 4 to practice projecting views.

--- TIP ---
You can experiment with these alternative arrangements by trying them out on Worksheet 1 or on a paper box.

First-Angle Projection

If the object is placed above the horizontal plane and in front of the vertical plane, the object is in the first angle. In first-angle projection the observer looks through the object to the planes of projection. The right-side view is still obtained by looking toward the right side of the object, the front by looking toward the front, and the top by looking down toward the top; but the views are projected from the object onto a plane in each case.

The biggest difference between third-angle projection and first-angle projection is in how the planes of the glass box are unfolded, as shown in Figure 24. In first-angle projection, the right-side view is to the left of the front view, and the top view is below the front view, as shown.

You should understand the difference between the two systems and know the symbol that is placed on drawings to indicate which has been used. Keep in mind that you will use third-angle projection throughout this text.

Projection System Drawing Symbol

The symbol shown in Figure 25 is used on drawings to indicate which system of projection is used. Whenever drawings will be used internationally you should include this symbol in the title block area.

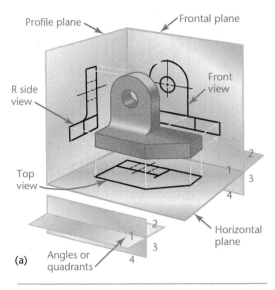

Profile plane

Frontal plane

Front view

R side view

Top view

Horizontal plane

Angles or quadrants

(a)

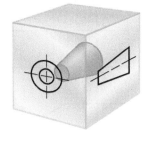

R side view

Front view

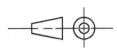

Top view

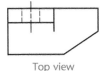

(b) First angle projection symbol

24 First-Angle Projection. *An object that is above the horizontal plane and in front of the vertical plane is in the first angle. An observer looks through the object to the planes of projection.*

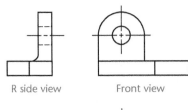

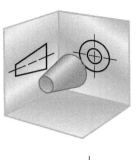

First Angle Projection

Third Angle Projection

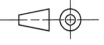

25 Drawing Symbols for First- and Third-Angle Projection

Hidden Lines

One advantage of orthographic views over photographs is that each view can show the entire object from that viewing direction. A photograph shows only the visible surface of an object, but an orthographic view shows the object all the way through, as if it were transparent.

Thick, dark lines represent features of the object that are directly visible. Dashed lines represent features that would be hidden behind other surfaces.

Figure 26 shows a part that has internal features. When a 3D view of this model is rendered using a transparent material, as shown in Figure 27, you can see the internal features. Figure 28 shows this part from the front as it would be oriented in an orthographic drawing. The features that are hidden from view are shown in orthographic views using the hidden line pattern as shown in Figure 29.

Whenever possible, choose views that show features with visible lines. Use hidden lines where they are needed to make the drawing clear.

Some practices for representing intersections of hidden lines with other lines may be difficult to follow when using CAD. In CAD, adjust the line patterns so that the hidden lines in your drawing have the best appearance possible.

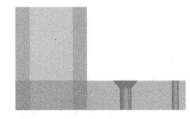

26 Shaded Model with Hidden Features

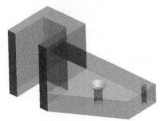

27 Transparent Model Showing Hidden Features

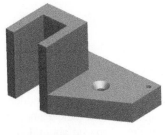

28 Front View of Transparent Model

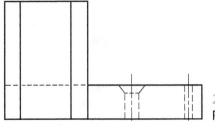

29 Front View Projection

167

CENTERLINES

The centerline pattern is used to:

- show the axis of symmetry for a feature or part
- indicate a path of motion
- show the location for bolt circles and other circular patterns

The centerline pattern is composed of three dashes: one long dash on each end with a short dash in the middle. In the drawing, centerlines are shown as thin and black. Because a centerline is not an actual part of the object, it extends beyond the symmetric feature as shown in Figure 30.

The most common shape that needs a centerline is a cylindrical hole. Figure 31 shows centerlines in a drawing. In the circular view of a hole, the centerline should form a cross to mark the center location. When a feature is too small for the centerline pattern to be shown with the long-short-long dash pattern, it is acceptable to use a straight line. You will learn more about showing hidden and centerlines in the technique sections.

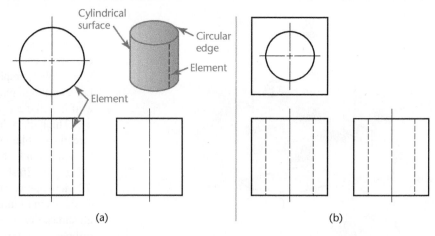

30   Cylindrical Surfaces

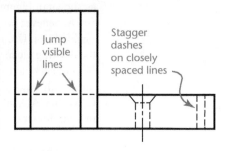

31   Hidden Lines

---

1 HIDDEN LINE TECHNIQUE

You can save time and reduce clutter by leaving out hidden lines that aren't necessary as long as you are certain that the remaining lines describe the object clearly and completely. If you omit unnecessary hidden lines, add a note to let the reader know that the lines were left out intentionally and that it is not an error in the drawing.

Sketch hidden lines by eye, using thin dark dashes about 5 mm long and spaced about 1 mm apart. Hidden lines should be as dark as other lines in the drawing, but should be thin.

When hidden lines intersect each other in the drawing, their dashes should meet. In general, hidden lines should

intersect neatly with visible lines at the edge of an object. Leave a gap when a hidden line aligns with a visible line, so that the visible line's length remains clear.

Use Worksheet 5 for practice hidden line technique.

---

2 PRECEDENCE OF LINES

Visible lines, hidden lines, and centerlines (which are used to show the axis of symmetry for contoured shapes, like holes) often coincide on a drawing. There are rules for deciding which line to show. A visible line always takes precedence over and covers up a centerline or a hidden line when they coincide in a view, as shown at A and B in Figure 32. A hidden line takes precedence over a centerline, as shown at C. At A and C the ends of the centerline are shown separated from the view by short gaps, but the centerline can be left off entirely. Figure 33 shows examples of correct and incorrect hidden lines.

Use Worksheet 6 for practice line precedence.

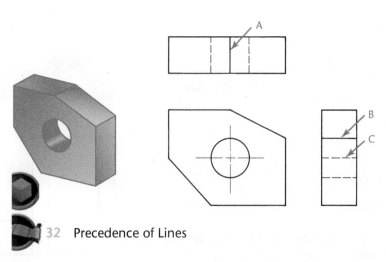

32   Precedence of Lines

Correct and incorrect practices for hidden lines

Make a hidden line join a visible line, except when it causes the visible line to extend too far, as shown here.

Leave a gap whenever a hidden line is a continuation of a visible line.

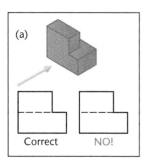

(a)

Correct   NO!

When two or three hidden lines meet at a point, join the dashes, as shown for the bottom of this drilled hole.

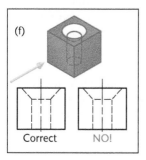

(f)

Correct   NO!

Make hidden lines intersect at L and T corners.

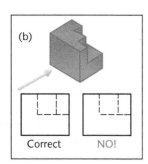

(b)

Correct   NO!

The same rule of joining the dashes when two or three hidden lines meet at a point applies for the top of this countersunk hole.

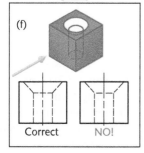

(f)

Correct   NO!

Make a hidden line "jump" a visible line when possible.

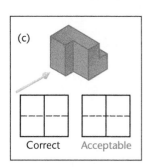

(c)

Correct   Acceptable

Hidden lines should not join visible lines when this makes the visible line extend too far.

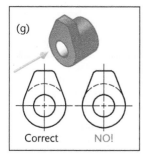

(g)

Correct   NO!

Draw parallel hidden lines so that the dashes are staggered, as in bricklaying.

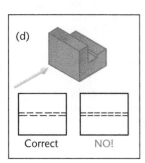

(d)

Correct   NO!

Draw hidden arcs with the arc joining the centerline, as in upper example. There should not be a gap between the arc and the centerline, as in the example below with the straightaway joining the centerline.

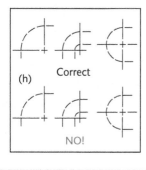

(h)   Correct

NO!

33   Correct and Incorrect Practices for Hidden Lines

TIP

Accent the beginning and end of each dash by pressing down on the pencil. Make hidden lines as tidy as you can so they are easy to interpret. Be sure to make hidden line dashes longer than gaps so they clearly represent lines.

3 CENTERLINES

Centerlines (symbol: ₵) are used to indicate symmetrical axes of objects or features, bolt circles, and paths of motion as shown in Figure 34. Centerlines are useful in dimensioning. They are not needed on unimportant rounded or filleted corners or on other shapes that are self-locating.

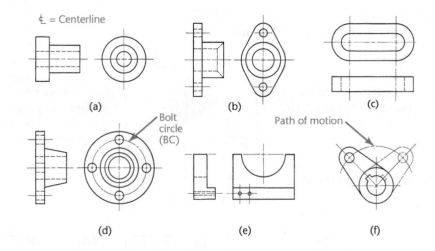

₵ = Centerline

(a) (b) (c)

Bolt circle (BC)

Path of motion

(d) (e) (f)

34 Centerlines

4 LAYING OUT A DRAWING

If you use 2D CAD, you can move the views later, keeping them in alignment, so you do not need to give as much attention to placement of the views in the beginning as if you were laying them out by hand. When using 3D CAD to generate views, you should still plan how the sheet will show the information clearly and select the necessary views to best represent the shape of the part. While you can easily change the scale of a CAD drawing after it is created, placing the dimensions and views on the sheet requires some planning. If you consider the purpose of the drawing, the planned scale, and the space that will be required for adding notes and dimensions, you will save the time of having to rearrange their placement later.

LAYING OUT A METRIC THREE-VIEW DRAWING

1 Determine space desired between the front and right side views, say 32 mm, C. Add this space to the sum of the length of the views that will be aligned along the long edge of the sheet. (108 + 58 + 32 = 198) To set equal distances to the paper edge, subtract this total from the sheet width, then divide the remaining number by two (266 − 198 = 70, and 70 ÷ 2 = 35). Do the same for the views to be aligned along the short side of the paper, selecting a desired space between the views. Space D need not match C. Remember to leave space for dimensions as you plan your sheet.

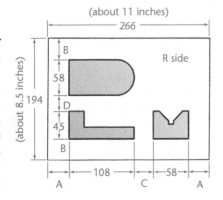

2 Set off vertical and horizontal spacing measurements with light tick marks along the edge of the sheet as shown. Locate centerlines from these spacing marks and construct arcs and circles.

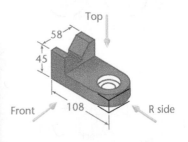

3 Construct the views, drawing horizontal, vertical, and then inclined construction lines in the order shown above.

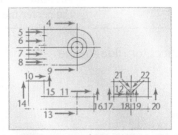

4 Add hidden lines and darken final lines.

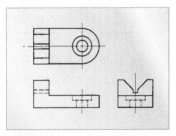

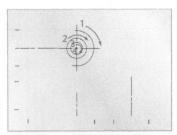

5 VISUALIZATION

Along with a basic understanding of the system for projecting views, you must be able interpret multiple views to picture the object that they show. In addition to being an indispensable skill to help you capture and communicate your ideas, technical sketching is also a way for others to present their ideas to you.

Even experienced engineers, technicians, and designers can't always look at a multiview sketch and instantly visualize the object represented. You will learn to study the sketch and interpret the lines in a logical way in order to piece together a clear idea of the whole. This process is sometimes called visualization.

Surfaces, Edges, and Corners

To effectively create and interpret multiview projections, you have to consider the elements that make up most solids. **Surfaces** form the boundaries of solid objects. A **plane** (flat) surface may be bounded by straight lines, curves, or a combination of the two. It takes practice to envision flat representations as 3D objects. Take a moment to examine the views shown in Figure 35 and try to picture the object.

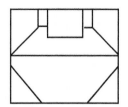
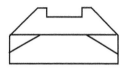
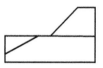

35   Three Views of an Object

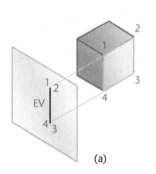
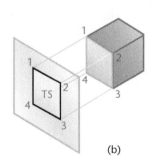
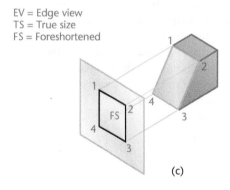

EV = Edge view
TS = True size
FS = Foreshortened

(a)   (b)   (c)

36   Projections of Surfaces

─── TIP ───

Using Numbers to Identify Vertices

Add lightly drawn numbers to your sketches to keep track of each vertex on the surface you are considering. Each vertex is unique on the part, so each numbered vertex will appear only once in each view. Sometimes two vertices will line up one behind the other as in 36a. When this happens you can list them in order with the closest first, as in 1, 2, or sometimes it is useful to put numbers for the closest visible vertex outside the shape, and the farthest hidden vertex inside the shape outline.

6 VIEWS OF SURFACES

A plane surface that is perpendicular to a plane of projection appears on edge as a straight line (Figure 36a). If it is parallel to the plane of projection, it appears true size (Figure 36b). If it is angled to the plane of projection, it appears foreshortened or smaller than its actual size (Figure 36c). A plane surface always projects either on edge (appearing as a single line) or as a surface (showing its characteristic shape) in any view. It can ap-

pear foreshortened, but it can never appear larger than its true size in any view.

There are terms used for describing a surface's orientation to the plane of projection. The three orientations that a plane surface can have to the plane of projection are *normal*, *inclined*, and *oblique*. Understanding these terms will help you picture and describe objects.

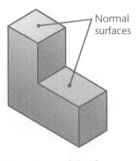

Normal
surfaces

37   Normal Surfaces

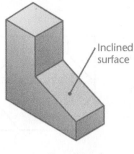

Inclined
surface

38   Inclined Surface

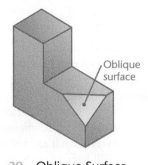

Oblique
surface

39   Oblique Surface

7 NORMAL SURFACES

A **normal surface** is parallel to a plane of projection. It appears true size and true shape on the plane to which it is parallel, and it appears as a true-length vertical or a horizontal line on adjacent planes of projection. Figure 37 shows an illustration of normal surfaces.

Practice identifying normal surfaces on CAD drawings. You can download orthographic views of subjects that show many normal surfaces at the following Web sites:
- http://www.constructionsite.come/harlen/8001-81.htm
- http://www.user.mc.net/hawk/cad.htm

8 INCLINED SURFACES

An **inclined surface** is perpendicular to one plane of projection, but inclined (or tipped) to adjacent planes. An inclined surface projects an edge on the plane to which it is perpendicular. It appears foreshortened on planes to which it is inclined. An inclined surface is shown in Figure 38. The degree of foreshortening is proportional to the inclination. While the surface may not appear true size in any view, it will have the same characteristic shape and the same number of edges in the views in which you see its shape.

9 OBLIQUE SURFACES

An **oblique surface** is tipped to all principal planes of projection. Since it is not perpendicular to any projection plane, it cannot appear on edge in any standard view. Since it is not parallel to any projection plane, it cannot appear true size in any standard view. An oblique surface always appears as a foreshortened surface in all three standard views. Figure 39 and Figure 40 show oblique surfaces.

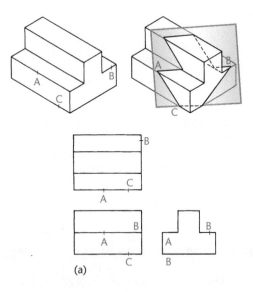

(a)

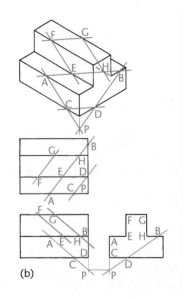

(b)

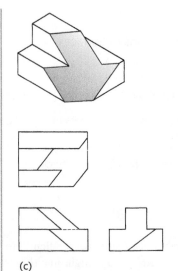

(c)

40   Oblique Surfaces

10 EDGES

The intersection of two plane surfaces of an object produces an **edge**, which shows as a straight line in the drawing. An edge is common to two surfaces, forming a boundary for each. If an edge is perpendicular to a plane of projection, it appears as a point; otherwise it appears as a line. If it is parallel to the plane of projection, it shows true length. If it is not parallel, it appears foreshortened. A straight line always projects as a straight line or as a point. The terms normal, inclined, and oblique describe the relationship of an edge to a plane of projection.

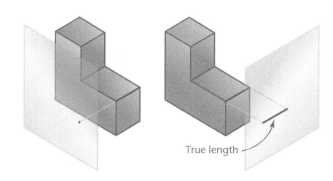

41 Projections of a Normal Edge

11 NORMAL EDGES

A **normal edge** is a line perpendicular to a plane of projection. It appears as a point on that plane of projection and as a true-length line on adjacent planes of projection (Figure 41).

12 INCLINED EDGES

An **inclined edge** is parallel to one plane of projection but inclined to adjacent planes. It appears as a true-length line on the plane to which it is parallel and as a foreshortened line on adjacent planes. The true-length view of an inclined line always appears as an angled line, but the foreshortened views appear as either vertical or horizontal lines (Figure 42).

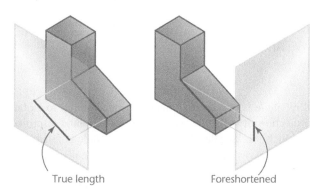

42 Projections of an Inclined Edge

13 OBLIQUE EDGES

An **oblique edge** is tipped to all planes of projection. Since it is not perpendicular to any projection plane, it cannot appear as a point in any standard view. Since it is not parallel to any projection plane, it cannot appear true length in any standard view. An oblique edge appears foreshortened and as an angled line in every view (Figure 43).

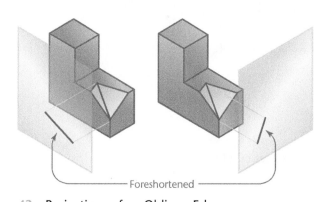

43 Projections of an Oblique Edge

14 PARALLEL EDGES

When edges are parallel to one another on the object, they will appear as parallel lines in every view, unless they align one behind the other. This information can be useful when you are laying out a drawing, especially if it has a complex inclined or oblique surface that has parallel edges. Figure 44 shows an example of parallel lines in drawing views.

(a) Parallel planes intersected by another plane

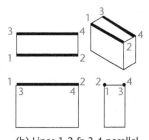

(b) Lines 1,2 & 3,4 parallel, and parallel to horizontal plane

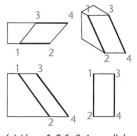

(c) Lines 1,2 & 3,4 parallel, & parallel to frontal plane

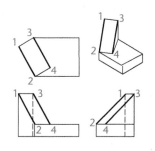

(d) Lines 1,2 & 3,4 parallel, and oblique to all planes

44 Parallel Lines

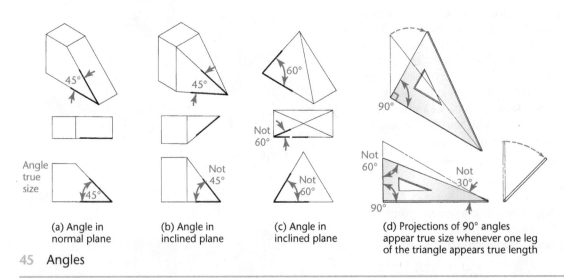

(a) Angle in normal plane

(b) Angle in inclined plane

(c) Angle in inclined plane

(d) Projections of 90° angles appear true size whenever one leg of the triangle appears true length

45 Angles

15 ANGLES

If an angle is in a normal plane (a plane parallel to a plane of projection) it will show as true size on the plane of projection to which it is parallel (Figure 45). If an angle is in an inclined plane, it may be projected either larger or smaller than the true angle, depending on its position. The 45° angle is shown oversize in the front view in Figure 45b, and the 60° angle is shown undersize in both views in Figure 45c.

A 90° angle will project as true size, even if it is in an inclined plane, provided that one leg of it is a normal line.

In Figure 45d the 60° angle is projected oversize and the 30° angle is projected undersize. Try this on your own using a 30° or 60° triangle as a model, or even the 90° corner of a sheet of paper. Tilt the triangle or paper to look at an oblique view.

16 VERTICES

A corner, or **point**, is the common intersection of three or more surfaces. A point appears as a point in every view. An example of a point on an object is shown in Figure 46.

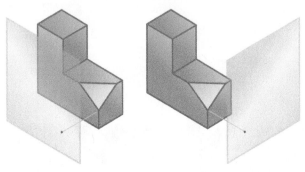

46 Views of a Point

17 INTERPRETING POINTS

A point located in a sketch can represent two things:

- A vertex
- The point view of an edge (two vertices lined up one directly behind the other)

18 INTERPRETING LINES

A straight visible or hidden line in a drawing or sketch has three possible meanings, as shown in Figure 47:

- An edge (intersection) between two surfaces
- The edge view of a surface
- The limiting element of a curved surface

Since no shading is used on orthographic views, you must examine all the views to determine the meaning of the lines. If you were to look at only the front and top views in Figure 46, you might believe line AB is the edge view of a flat surface. From the right-side view, you can see that there is a curved surface on top of the object.

If you look at only the front and side views, you might believe the vertical line CD is the edge view of a plane surface. The top view reveals that the line actually represents the intersection of an inclined surface.

47 Interpreting Lines

19 SIMILAR SHAPES OF SURFACES

If a flat surface is viewed from several different positions, each view will show the same number of sides and a similar shape. This consistency of shapes is useful in analyzing views. For example, the L-shaped surface shown in Figure 48 appears L-shaped in every view in which it does not appear as a line. A surface will have the same number of sides and vertices and the same characteristic shape whenever it appears as a surface. Note how the U-shaped, hexagonal, and T-shaped surfaces in Figure 49 are recognizable in different views.

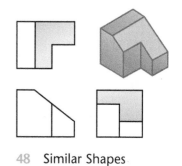

48 Similar Shapes

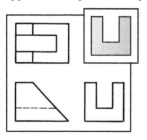 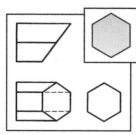 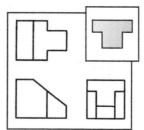

49 Similar Shapes

PRACTICE VISUALIZING

Look at the top view (a) and then examine some of the various objects it could represent. As you practice interpreting views, you will get better at visualizing three dimensional objects from projected views.

Notice that the top view alone does not provide all the information, but it does tell you that surfaces a, b and c are not in the same plane. There are many possibilities beyond those shown.

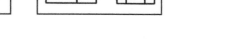

Top view

(a)   (b)   (c)   (d)

20 INTERPRETING VIEWS

One method of interpreting sketches is to reverse the mental process used in projecting them. The views of an angle bracket are shown in Figure 50a.

The front view (Figure 50b) shows the object's L-shape, its height and width, and the thickness of its members. The meanings of the hidden lines and centerlines are not yet clear, and you do not know the object's depth.

The top view (Figure 50c) shows the depth and width of the object. It also makes it clear that the horizontal feature is rounded at the right end and has a round hole. A hidden line at the left end indicates some kind of slot.

The right-side view (Figure 50d) shows the height and depth of the object. It reveals that the left end of the object has rounded corners at the top and

clarifies that the hidden line in the front view represents an open-end slot in a vertical position.

Each view provides certain definite information about the shape of the object, and all are necessary to visualize it completely.

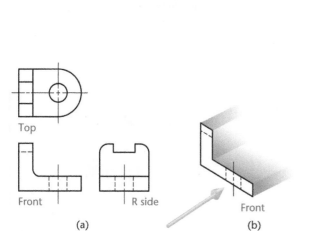

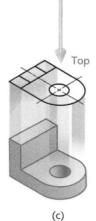

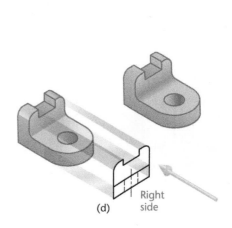

(a)   (b)   (c)   (d)

 50 Visualizing from Given Views

STEP by STEP

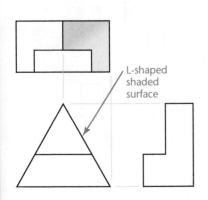

L-shaped shaded surface

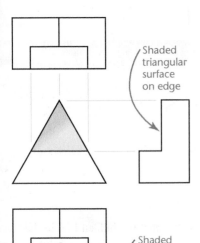

Shaded triangular surface on edge

Shaded trapezoidal surface on edge

READING A DRAWING

1 Visualize the object shown by the three views at left. Since no lines are curved, we know that the object is made up of plane surfaces.

The shaded surface in the top view is a six-sided L-shape. Since you do not see its shape in the front view—and every surface either appears as its shape or as a line—it must be showing on edge as a line in the front view. The indicated line in the front view also projects to line up with the vertices of the L-shaped surface.

Because we see its shape in the top view and because it is an angled line in the front view, it must be an inclined surface on the object. This means it will show its foreshortened shape in the side view as well, appearing L-shaped and six-sided. The L-shaped surface in the right-side view must be the same surface that was shaded in the top view.

2 In the front view we see the top portion as a triangular-shaped surface, but no triangular shapes appear in either the top or the side view. The triangular surface must appear as a line in the top view and in the side view.

Sketch projection lines from the vertices of the surface where you see its shape. The same surface in the other views must line up along the projection lines. In the side view, it must be the line indicated. That can help you to identify it as the middle horizontal line in the top view.

3 The trapezoidal-shaped surface shaded in the front view is easy to identify, but there are no trapezoids in the top and side views. Again the surface must be on edge in the adjacent views.

4 On your own, identify the remaining surfaces using the same reasoning. Which surfaces are inclined, and which are normal? Are there any oblique surfaces?

If you are still having trouble visualizing the object, try picturing the views as describing those portions of a block that will be cut away, as illustrated below.

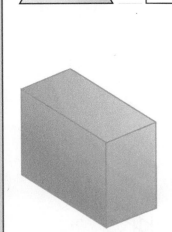

21 MODELS

One of the best aids to visualization is an actual model of the object. Models don't necessarily need to be made accurately or to scale. They may be made of any convenient material, such as modeling clay, soap, wood, wire, or Styrofoam, or any material that can easily be shaped, carved, or cut. Some examples of soap models are shown in Figure 51.

 Rules for Visualizing from a Drawing: Putting It All Together

Reading a multiview drawing is like unraveling a puzzle. When you interpret a drawing, keep these things in mind:

- The closest surface to your view must have at least one edge showing as a visible line.
- A plane surface has a similar shape in any view or appears on edge as a straight line.
- Lines of the drawing represent either an intersection between two surfaces, a surface perpendicular to your view that appears "on edge," or the limiting element of a curved surface.
- No two adjacent areas divided by a visible line in an orthographic view can lie on the same plane in the actual object. Areas not adjacent in a view may lie in the same plane on the object.
- If a line appears hidden, a closer surface is hiding it.
- Your interpretation must account for all of the lines of the drawing. Every line has a meaning.

Making a Model

Try making a soap or clay model from projected views:

First, look at the three views of the object. Make your block of clay to the same principal dimensions (height, width, and depth) as shown in the views.

Score lines on the frontal surface of your clay block to correspond with those shown on the front view in the drawing. Then do the same for the top and right-side views.

Slice straight along each line scored on the clay block to get a 3D model that represents the projected views.

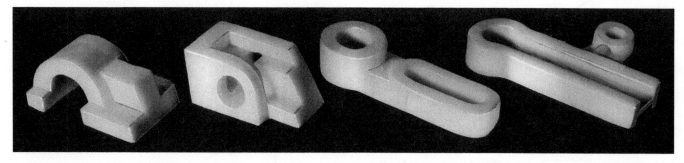

51   Soap Models

22 PROJECTING A THIRD VIEW

Ordinarily when you are designing a product or system, you have a good mental picture of what the object you are sketching will look like from different directions. However, skill in projecting a third view can be useful for two reasons. First, views must be shown in alignment in the drawing and projected correctly. Secondly, practice in projecting a third view from two given views is an excellent way to develop your visual abilities.

Numbering the vertices on the object makes projecting a third view easy. Points that you number on the drawing represent points on the object where three surfaces come together to form a vertex (and sometimes a point on a contour or the center of a curve).

Once you have located a point in two drawing views, its location in the third view is known. In other words, if a point is located in the front and top view, its location in the side view is a matter of projecting the height of the point in the glass box from the front view and the depth of the point in the glass box from the top view.

In order to number the points or vertices on the object and show those numbers in different views, you need to be able to identify surfaces on the object. Then project (or find) the points in each new view, surface by surface. You can use what you know about edges and surfaces to identify surfaces on the object when you draw views. This will help you to interpret drawings created by others as well as know how to project your own drawings correctly.

PROJECTING A THIRD VIEW

Follow the steps to project a third view.

The figure below is a pictorial drawing of an object to be shown in three views. It has numbers identifying each corner (vertex) and letters identifying some of the major surfaces. You are given the top and front view. You will use point numbers to project the side view.

1 To number points effectively, first identify surfaces and interpret the views that are given. Start by labeling visible surfaces whose shapes are easy to identify in one view. Then locate the same surface in the adjacent view. (The surfaces on the pictorial object have been labeled to make it easier.)

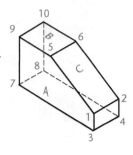

2 Surface A in the front view is a normal surface. It will appear as a horizontal line in the top view. The two rectangular surfaces B and C in the top view are a normal surface and an inclined surface. They will show as a horizontal line and an inclined line in the front view, respectively.

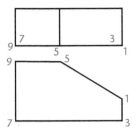

3 After identifying the surfaces, label the vertices of a surface that has an easily recognized shape, in this case, surface A.

Label its vertices with numbers at each corner as shown. If a point is directly visible in the view, place the number outside the corner.

If the point is not directly visible in that view, place the numeral inside the corner. Using the same numbers to identify the same points in different views will help you to project known points in two views to unknown positions in a third view.

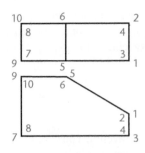

4 Continue on, surface by surface, until you have numbered all of the vertices in the given views as shown. Do not use two different numbers for the same vertex.

5 Try to visualize the right-side view you will create. Then construct the right-side view point by point, using very light lines. Locate point 1 in the side view by drawing a light horizontal projection line from point 1 in the front view. Use the edge view of surface A in the top view as a reference plane to transfer the depth location for point 1 to the side view as shown.

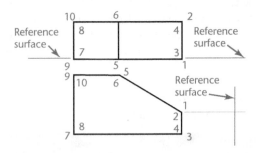

6 Project points 2, 3, and 4 in a similar way to complete the vertical end surface of the object.

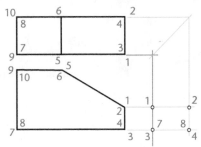

7 Project the remaining points using the same method, proceeding surface by surface.

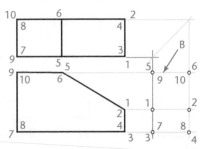

PROJECTING A THIRD VIEW

Continue the steps to project a third view.

8 Use the points that you have projected into the side view to draw the surfaces of the object as in this example.

If surface A extended between points 1-3-7-9-5 in the front view where you can see its shape clearly, it will extend between those same points in every other view.

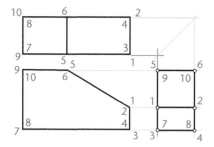

When you connect these points in the side view, they form a vertical line.

This makes sense, because A is a normal surface. As is the rule with normal surfaces, you will see its shape in one standard view (the front in this case) and it will appear as a horizontal or vertical line in the other views.

Continue connecting vertices to define the surfaces on the object, to complete the third view.

---

9 Inspect your drawing to see if all of the surfaces are shown and darken the final lines.

Consider the visibility of surfaces. Surfaces that are hidden behind other surfaces should be shown with hidden lines.

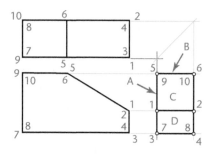

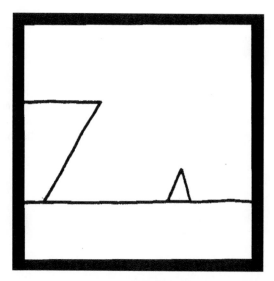

"Ship Arriving Too Late to Save Drowning Witch." This well-known drawing by artist Roger Price is an example of how a single orthographic view can be difficult to interpret. *Courtesy of "Droodles, The Classic Collection."*

23 BECOMING A 3D VISUALIZER

To the untrained person, orthographic projections might not convey the idea of a 3D shape, but with some practice you should now be able to look at projected front, top, and right-side views and envision that they represent the width, depth, and height of an object. Understanding how points, lines, and surfaces can be interpreted and how normal, inclined, or oblique surfaces appear from different views helps you interpret orthographic views to let you form a mental image of the 3D object they represent.

Having an understanding of how orthographic views represent an object gives you the power to start capturing your own 3D concepts on paper in a way that others can accurately interpret. Keep in mind the idea of an unfolded "glass box" to explain the arrangement of views. This clarifies how the views relate to one another and why you can transfer certain dimensions from adjacent views. Using standard practices to represent hidden lines and centerlines helps you further define surfaces, features, and paths of motion.

The better you understand the foundation concepts of projected views, the more fluent you will be in the language of 3D representation and the skill of spatial thinking, regardless of whether you sketch by hand or use CAD.

USING A MITER LINE

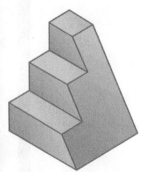

Given two completed views you can use a miter line to transfer the depths and draw the side view of the object shown at left.

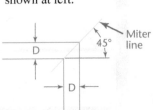

1 Locate the miter line a convenient distance away from the object to produce the desired spacing between views.

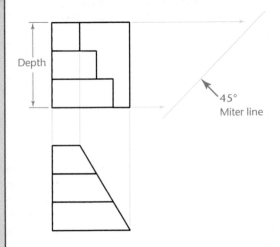

2 Sketch light lines projecting depth locations for points to the miter line and then down into side view as shown.

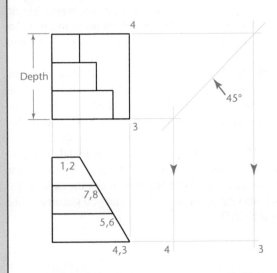

3 Project the remaining points.

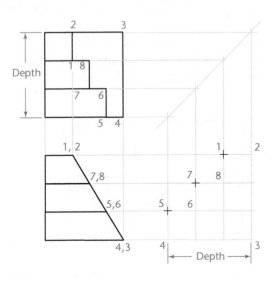

4 Draw view locating each vertex of surface on the projection line and the miter line. To move the right-side view to the right or left, move the top view upward or downward by moving the miter line closer to or farther from the view. You don't need to draw continuous lines between the top and side views via the miter line. Instead, make short dashes across the miter line and project from these. The 45° miter-line method is also convenient for transferring a large number of points, as when plotting a curve.

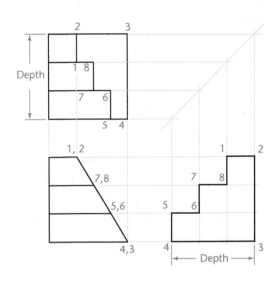

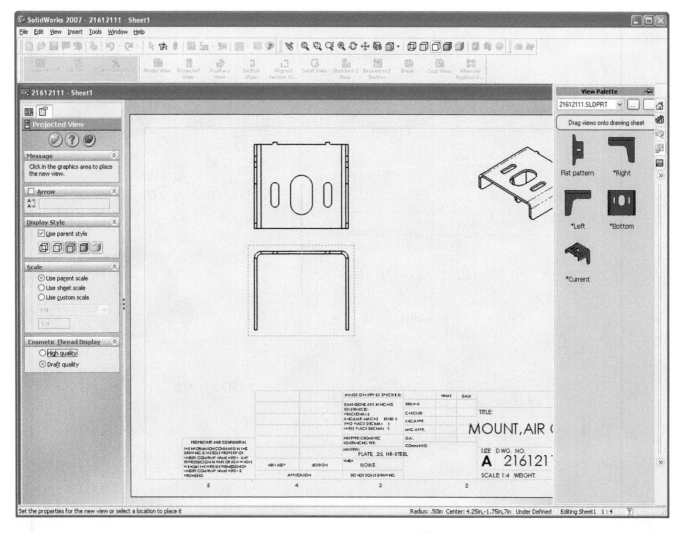

Orthographic Views Generated from a CAD Model. *Courtesy of Solidworks Corporation.*

Once a 3D model is created, most CAD packages allow you to place orthographic views generated from the model. To place a projected view is as easy as selecting the base view and then choosing where to place the projected view. You can also usually turn off hidden lines in each individual view based on whether or not they add useful information. Using CAD to place the 3D views also makes it easy to show views in alignment.

Most 3D CAD software allows you to configure it to show the views in either third-angle or first-angle projection.

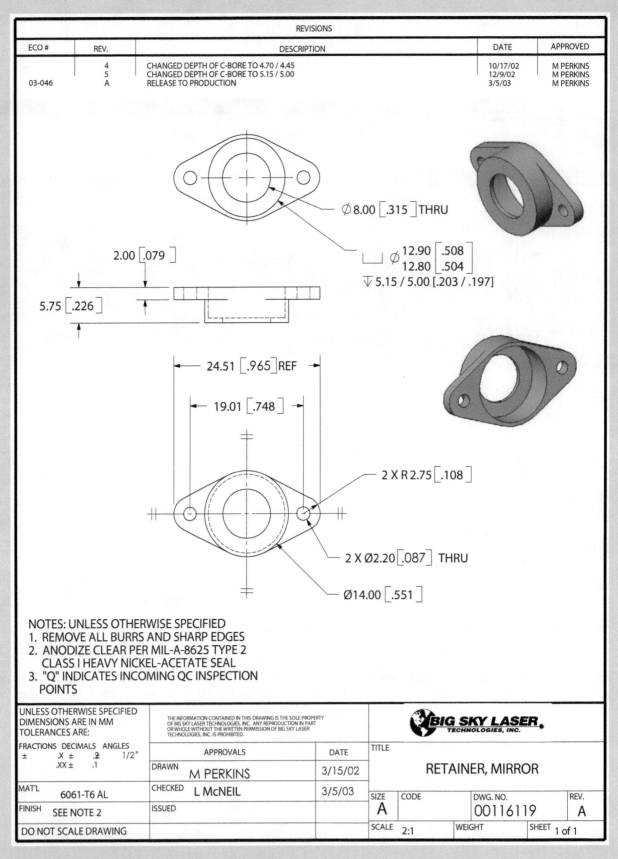

REVISIONS					
ECO #	REV.	DESCRIPTION		DATE	APPROVED
	4	CHANGED DEPTH OF C-BORE TO 4.70 / 4.45		10/17/02	M PERKINS
	5	CHANGED DEPTH OF C-BORE TO 5.15 / 5.00		12/9/02	M PERKINS
03-046	A	RELEASE TO PRODUCTION		3/5/03	M PERKINS

⌀ 8.00 [.315] THRU

⌀ 12.90 [.508]
   12.80 [.504]
▽ 5.15 / 5.00 [.203 / .197]

2.00 [.079]

5.75 [.226]

24.51 [.965] REF

19.01 [.748]

2 X R 2.75 [.108]

2 X ⌀2.20 [.087] THRU

⌀14.00 [.551]

NOTES: UNLESS OTHERWISE SPECIFIED
1. REMOVE ALL BURRS AND SHARP EDGES
2. ANODIZE CLEAR PER MIL-A-8625 TYPE 2
   CLASS I HEAVY NICKEL-ACETATE SEAL
3. "Q" INDICATES INCOMING QC INSPECTION
   POINTS

UNLESS OTHERWISE SPECIFIED
DIMENSIONS ARE IN MM
TOLERANCES ARE:

THE INFORMATION CONTAINED IN THIS DRAWING IS THE SOLE PROPERTY OF BIG SKY LASER TECHNOLOGIES, INC. ANY REPRODUCTION IN PART OR WHOLE WITHOUT THE WRITTEN PERMISSION OF BIG SKY LASER TECHNOLOGIES, INC. IS PROHIBITED.

BIG SKY LASER
TECHNOLOGIES, INC.

FRACTIONS	DECIMALS	ANGLES			
±	.X ± .2	1/2°	APPROVALS	DATE	TITLE
	.XX ± .1		DRAWN M PERKINS	3/15/02	RETAINER, MIRROR
MAT'L 6061-T6 AL			CHECKED L McNEIL	3/5/03	

SIZE A	CODE	DWG. NO. 00116119	REV. A

FINISH SEE NOTE 2 | ISSUED

| SCALE 2:1 | WEIGHT | SHEET 1 of 1 |

DO NOT SCALE DRAWING

Top, Front and Bottom Views of a Mirror Retainer. The bottom view is shown for ease of dimensioning.
Courtesy of Big Sky Laser.

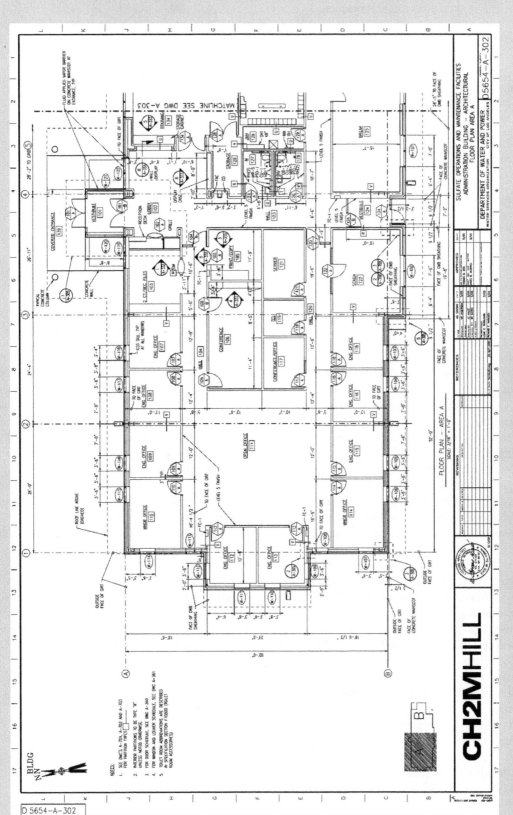

Architectural floor plans show the building as though the roof were cut off and you projected the top orthographic view. *Courtesy of CH2M HILL.*

KEY WORDS

Multiview Projection

Principal Views

Width

Height

Depth

Plane of Projection

Orthographic

Frontal Plane

Horizontal Plane

Profile Plane

Glass Box

Folding Lines

Three Regular Views

Necessary Views

Third-Angle Projection

First-Angle Projection

Projection Symbols

Surfaces

Plane

Normal Surface

Inclined Surface

Oblique Surface

Edge

Normal Edge

Inclined Edge

Oblique Edge

Point

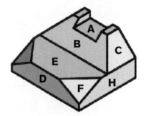

Key to Figure 35
Normal Surfaces: A, D, E, H
Inclined Surfaces: B, C
Oblique Surface: F

CHAPTER SUMMARY

- Orthographic drawings are the result of projecting the image of a 3D object onto one of six standard planes of projection. The six standard views are often thought of as an unfolded glass box. The arrangement of the views in relation to one another is important. Views must project to line up with adjacent views, so that any point in one view projects to line up with that same point in the adjacent view. The standard arrangement of views shows the top, front, and right side of the object.

- Visualization is an important skill for engineers. You can build your visual abilities through practice and through understanding terms describing objects. For example, surfaces can be normal, inclined, or oblique. Normal surfaces appear true size in one principal view and as an edge in the other two principal views. Inclined surfaces appear as an edge view in one of the three principal views. Oblique surfaces do not appear as an edge view in any of the principal views.

- Choice of scale is important for representing objects clearly on the drawing sheet.

- Hidden lines are used to show the intersections of surfaces, surfaces that appear on edge, and the limits of curved surfaces that are hidden from the viewing direction.

- Centerlines are used to show the axis of symmetry for features and paths of motion, and to indicate the arrangement for circular patterns.

- Creating CAD drawings involves applying the same concepts as paper drawing. The main difference is that drawing geometry is stored more accurately using a computer than in any hand drawing. CAD drawing geometry can be reused in many ways and plotted to any scale as necessary.

REVIEW QUESTIONS

1. Sketch the symbol for third-angle projection.
2. List the six principal views of projection.
3. Sketch the top, front, and right-side views of an object of your design having normal, inclined, and oblique surfaces.
4. In a drawing that shows the top, front, and right-side view, which two views show depth? Which view shows depth vertically on the sheet? Which view shows depth horizontally on the drawing sheet?
5. What is the definition of a normal surface? An inclined surface? An oblique surface?
6. What are three similarities between using a CAD program to create 2D drawing geometry and sketching on a sheet of paper? What are three differences?
7. What dimensions are the same between the top and front view: width, height, or depth? Between the front and right-side view? Between the top and right-side view?
8. List two ways of transferring depth between the top and right-side views.
9. If surface A contained corners 1, 2, 3, 4, and surface B contained corners 3, 4, 5, 6, what is the name of the line where surfaces A and B intersect?

MULTIVIEW PROJECTION EXERCISES

The following projects are intended to be sketched freehand on graph paper or plain paper. Use metric or decimal inch as assigned. The marks shown on some exercises indicate rough units of either 1/2" and 1/4" (or 10 mm and 5 mm). All holes are through holes. Use metric or decimal inch dimensions if assigned by the instructor.

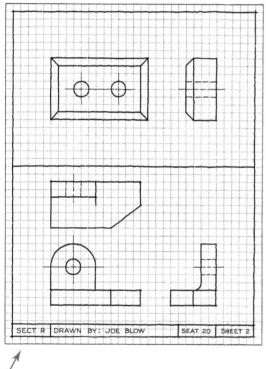

Example of two sketched solutions per 8.5 x 11" sheet

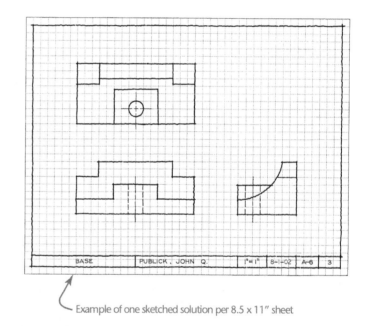
Example of one sketched solution per 8.5 x 11" sheet

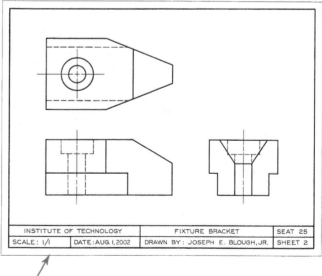
Example of one CAD/instrument solution per 8.5 x 11" sheet

Example Exercise

185

EXERCISES

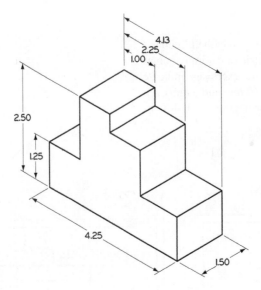

Exercise 1 Spacer. Draw and sketch all necessary views.

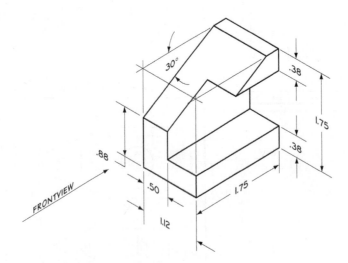

Exercise 2 Slide. Draw and sketch all necessary views.

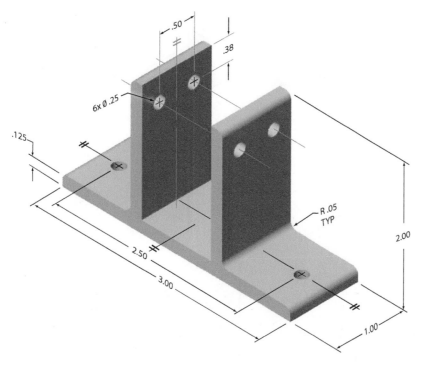

Exercise 3 Wall bracket
Create a drawing with the necessary orthographic views for the wall bracket.

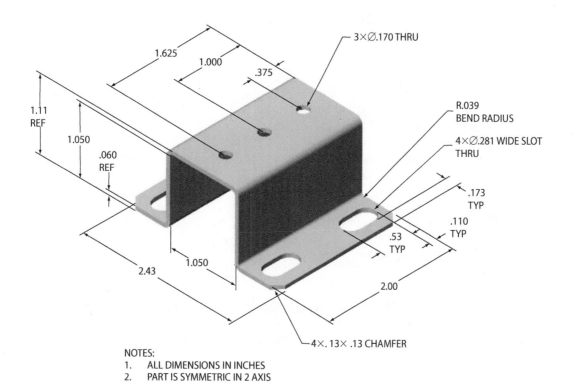

NOTES:
1. ALL DIMENSIONS IN INCHES
2. PART IS SYMMETRIC IN 2 AXIS
3. MAKE FROM .060" THICK SHEET METAL

Exercise 4 Sheet metal bracket
Create a drawing of the necessary orthographic views for the sheet metal bracket.

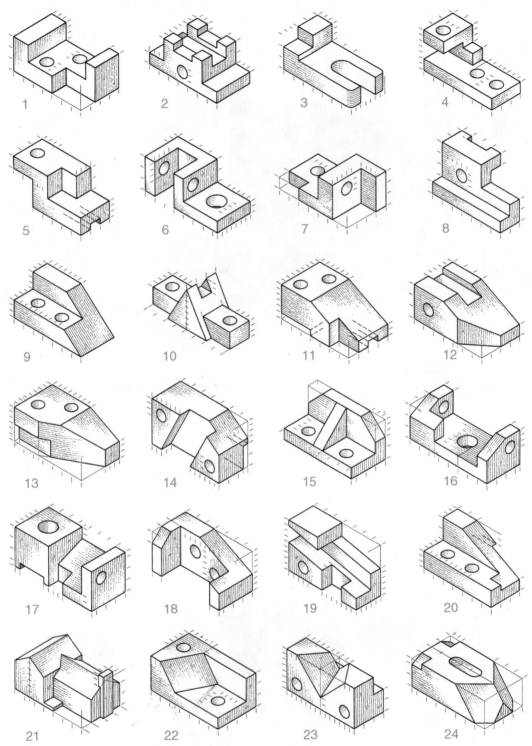

Exercise 5 Multiview Sketching Problems. Sketch necessary orthographic views on graph paper or plain paper, showing either one or two problems per sheet as assigned by your instructor. These exercises are designed to fit on 8½ × 11" size A, or metric A4 paper. The units shown may be either .500" and .250" or 10 mm and 5 mm. All holes are through holes.

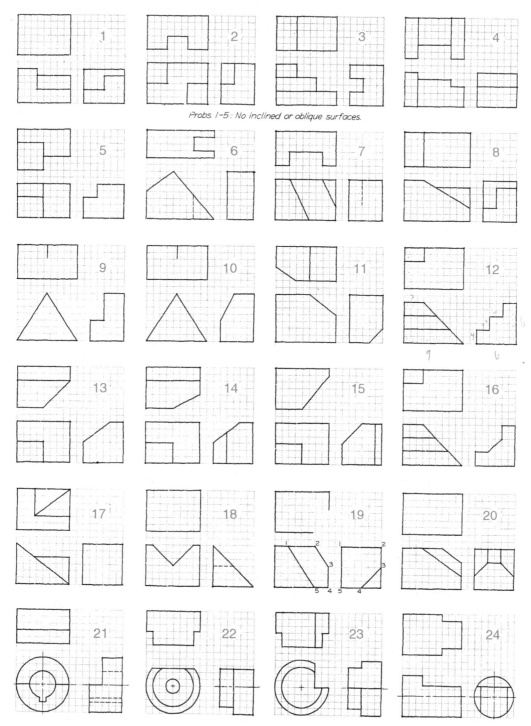

Probs. 1–5: No inclined or oblique surfaces.

Exercise 6 Missing-Line Sketching Problems. (1) Sketch given views on graph paper or plain paper showing either one or two problems per sheet as assigned by your instructor. These exercises are designed to fit on 8½ × 11" size A or metric A4 paper. Add missing lines. The squares may be either .250" or 5 mm. (2) Sketch in isometric on isometric paper or in oblique on cross-section paper, if assigned.

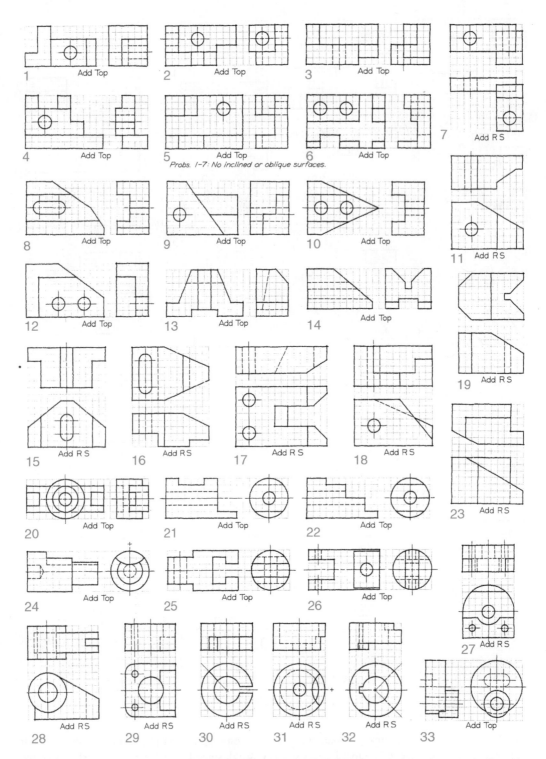

Exercise 7 Third-View Sketching Problems. Sketch the given views and add the missing views as indicated on graph paper or plain paper. These exercises are designed to fit on 8½ × 11" size A or metric A4 paper. The squares may be either .25" or 5 mm. The given views are either front and right-side views or front and top views. Hidden holes with centerlines are drilled holes.

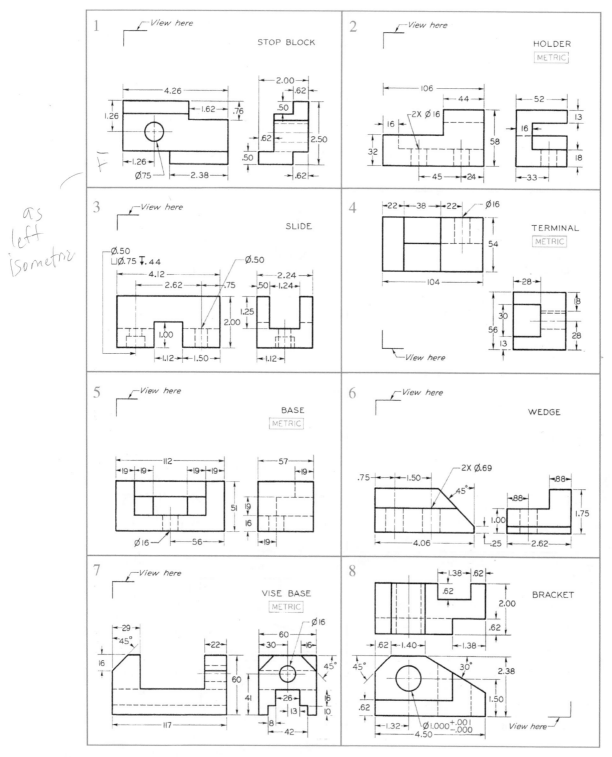

Exercise 8 Missing-View Problems. Sketch or draw the given views, and add the missing view. These exercises are designed to fit on 8½ × 11" size A or metric A4 paper. Use metric or decimal inch dimensions as assigned by the instructor. Move dimensions to better locations where possible. In Exercises 1–5, all surfaces are normal surfaces.

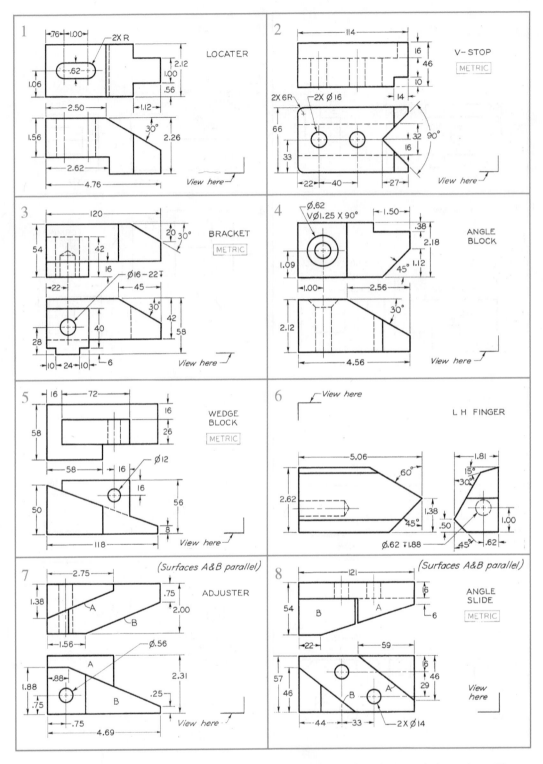

Exercise 9 Missing-View Problems. Sketch or draw the given views, and add the missing view. These exercises are designed to fit on 8½ × 11" size A or metric A4 paper. Use metric or decimal inch dimensions as assigned by the instructor. Move dimensions to better locations where possible.

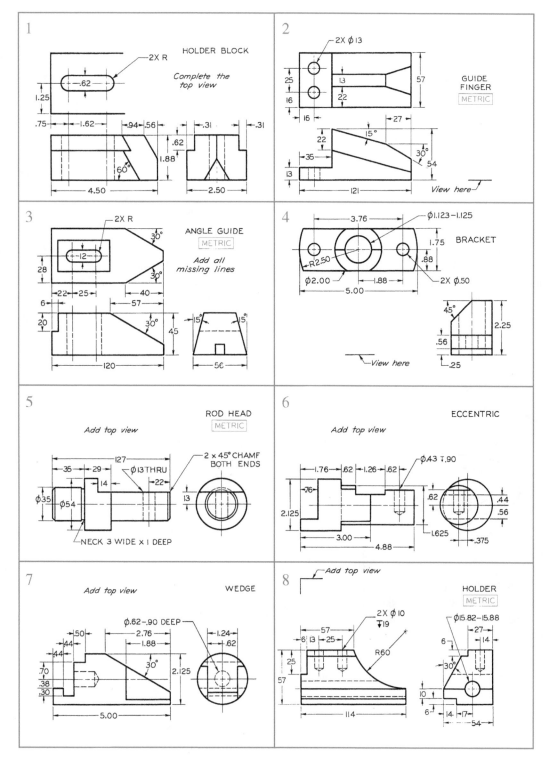

Exercise 10 Missing-View Problems. Sketch or draw the given views, and add the missing view. These exercises are designed to fit on 8½ × 11" size A or metric A4 paper. Use metric or decimal inch dimensions as assigned by the instructor. Move dimensions to better locations where possible.

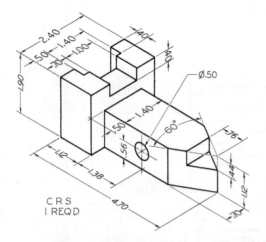

Exercise 11 Safety Key. Draw the necessary orthographic views on 8½ × 11" size A or metric A4 paper. Use a title block or title strip as assigned by your instructor.

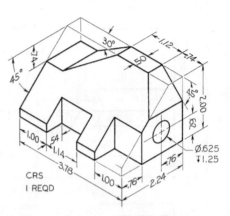

Exercise 12 Tool Holder. Draw the necessary orthographic views on 8½ × 11" size A or metric A4 paper. Use a title block or title strip as assigned by your instructor.

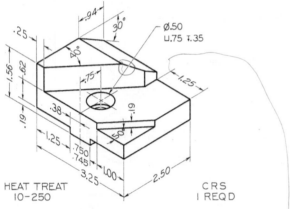

Exercise 13 Index Feed. Draw the necessary orthographic views on 8½ × 11" size A or metric A4 paper. Use a title block or title strip as assigned by your instructor.

look at
Front
Viewagain

194

SELECTING THE BEST FRONT VIEW

1. Shows shape clearly.
2. Usual, stable, or operating position.
3. Orient long shapes horizontally.
4. The right and top views are generally preferred to the bottom and left views.

For the drawings below, six views of the part are shown. In each problem, circle the best choice for the front view. Given your choice of front view, list the letter for the following views.

Tape Dispenser		Base block	
Top	_____	Top	_____
Right	_____	Right	_____
Left	_____	Left	_____
Bottom	_____	Bottom	_____
Rear	_____	Rear	_____

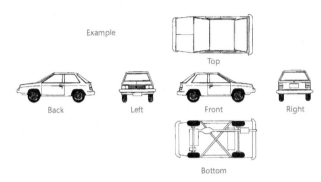

Example

Top

Back Left Front Right

Bottom

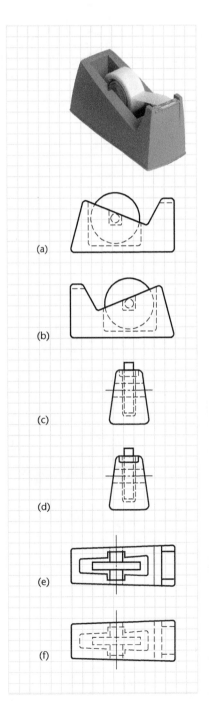

(a)

(b)

(c)

(d)

(e)

(f)

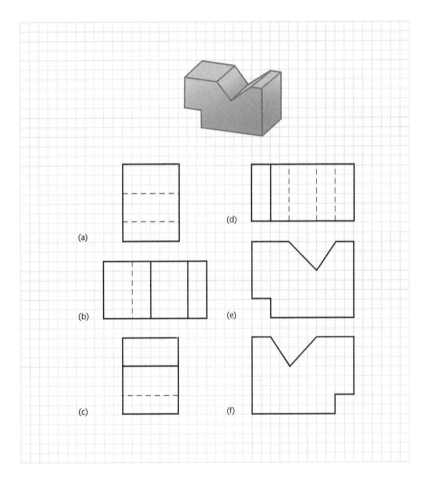

(a)

(b)

(c)

(d)

(e)

(f)

ADJACENT VIEWS

In the top view shown here, lines divide the view into three adjacent areas. No two adjacent areas lie in the same plane because each line represents an edge (or intersection) between surfaces. While each area represents a surface at a different level, you can't tell whether *A*, *B*, or *C* is the highest surface or what shape the surfaces may be until you see the other necessary views of the object.

The same reasoning applies to the adjacent areas in any given view. Since an area or surface in a view can be interpreted in different ways, other views are necessary to determine which interpretation is correct.

Below is one shape that the top view above might represent. Make a rough sketch of the front view for each description. Sketch two more possible interpretations for this top view and write their descriptions.

- Surface *B* is highest, and *C* and *A* are both lower.
- One or more surfaces are inclined.
- Surface *B* is highest, and surfaces *A* and *C* are lower.
- Surface *C* is highest, and *B* is lower than *A*.

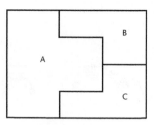

Top view

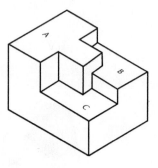

NORMAL AND OBLIQUE SURFACES

Oblique surface *C* appears in the top view and front view with its vertices labeled 1-2-3-4.

- Locate the same vertices and number them in the side view.
- Shade oblique surface *C* in the side view. (Note that any surface appearing as a line in any view cannot be an oblique surface.)
- How many inclined surfaces are there on the part shown?_____
- How many normal surfaces?_____

Control level for hydraulic pump

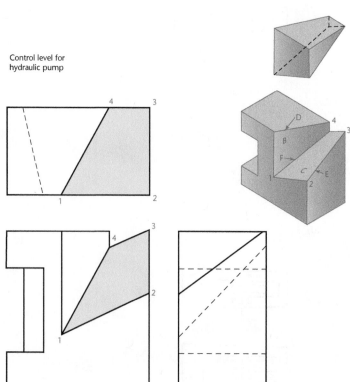

SKETCHING THREE VIEWS

A pictorial sketch of a lever bracket that requires three views is shown. Follow the steps to sketch the three views:

1. Block in the enclosing rectangles for the three views. You can either use overall proportions by eye or if you know the dimensions you can use your scale to sketch accurately sized views. Spacing your views equally from the edge of the rectangle and from each other, sketch horizontal lines to establish the height of the front view and the depth of the top view. Sketch vertical lines to establish the width of the top and front views and the depth of the side view. Make sure that this is in correct proportion to the height, and remember to maintain a uniform space between views. Remember that the space between the front and right-side view is not necessarily equal. Transfer the depth dimension from the top view to the side view; use the edge of a strip of paper or a pencil as a measuring stick. The depth in the top and side views should always be equal.
2. Block in all details lightly.
3. Sketch all arcs and circles lightly.
4. Darken all final lines.

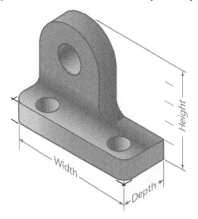

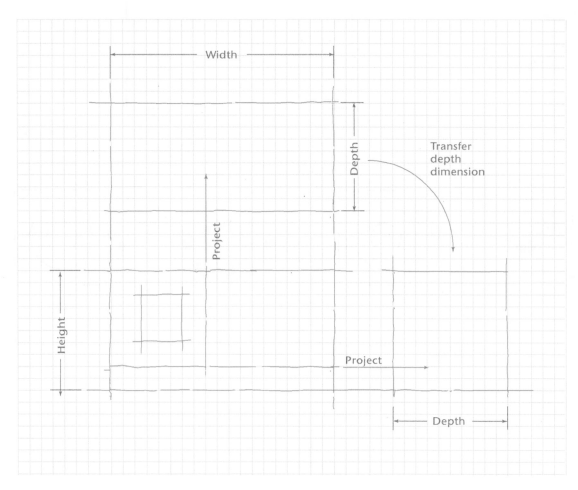

PRACTICE SKETCHING HIDDEN AND CENTERLINES

Practice sketching centerlines on the features shown.

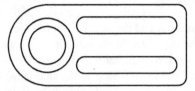 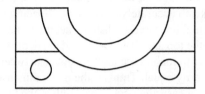 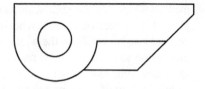

Draw the hidden and centerlines for the parts shown.

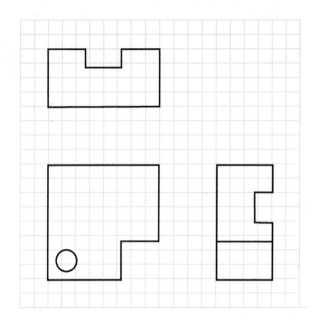

 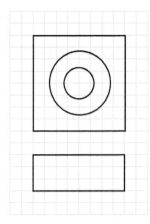  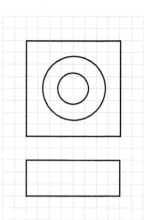

WORKSHEET 1   THE GLASS BOX

DIRECTIONS

The pattern at right shows the viewing planes for the six regular views unfolded. Cut on the solid lines and fold on the dashed fold lines to make a box. The front and rear viewing planes are labeled for you. Label the top, right-side, left-side, and bottom views.

1. Label the viewing planes with the principal dimensions that will show in each view. (For example, the front view will show the height and width of an object placed inside the box.)

2. Can you think of a different way to cut and fold the box so that the top and right-side views would align?

Rear

Front

Make copies of these pages to use for additional practice.

WORKSHEET 2   TRANSFERRING DEPTH DIMENSIONS

Two views of a triangular plane are shown projected onto the glass box below. Vertex B has already been projected into the side view for you. Finish projecting vertices A and C and draw the side view of the triangular plane. Cut out and fold up the "glass box" to help you visualize how to transfer the vertices to the side view. Cut out a triangular piece of paper the true size of the triangle and orient it inside the "glass box."

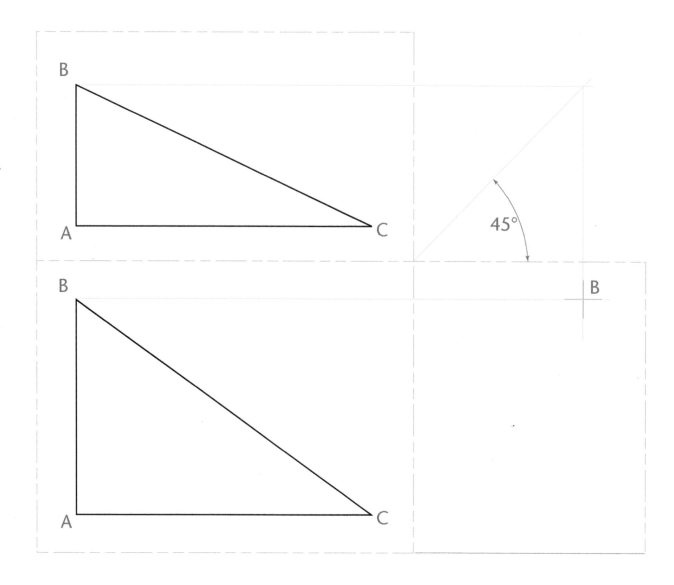

Make copies of these pages to use for additional practice.

WORKSHEET 3 BLOCKING A MULTIVIEW DRAWING

Construction lines are provided below to help you to create the orthographic views of the part shown. Show all features in each view. Darken the final drawing lines.

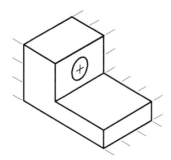

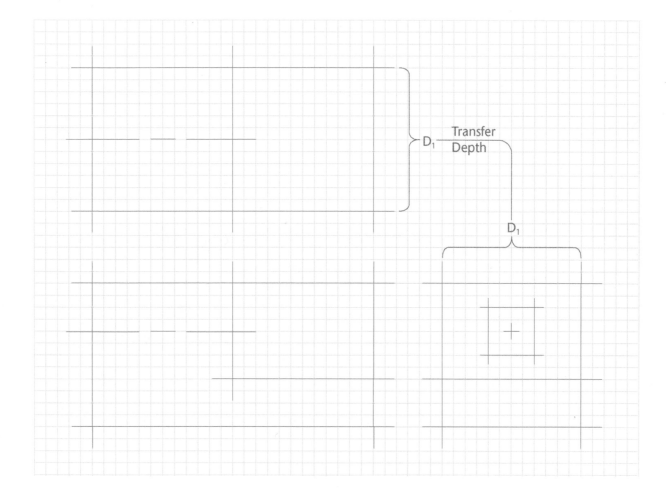

Make copies of these pages to use for additional practice.

WORKSHEET 4   PROJECTING INCLINED SURFACES

Construction lines have been drawn for you to help you sketch the orthographic views of the block shown. Surface B shows on edge in the top view. Surface A shows on edge in the front view. Finish projecting the points to the side view and complete the drawing in the right-side view. Darken all final lines.

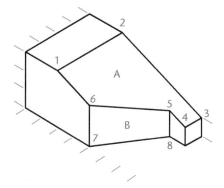

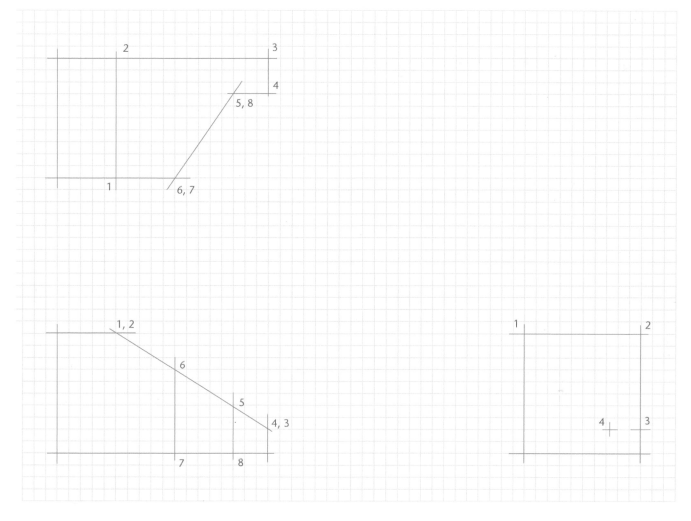

Make copies of these pages to use for additional practice.

WORKSHEET 5 | PRACTICE WITH HIDDEN LINES

Add hidden lines to the drawing of the part below. Use good line quality and proper hidden line technique. Estimate the depth for the counterbored hole.

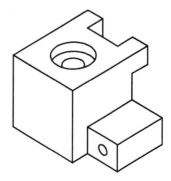

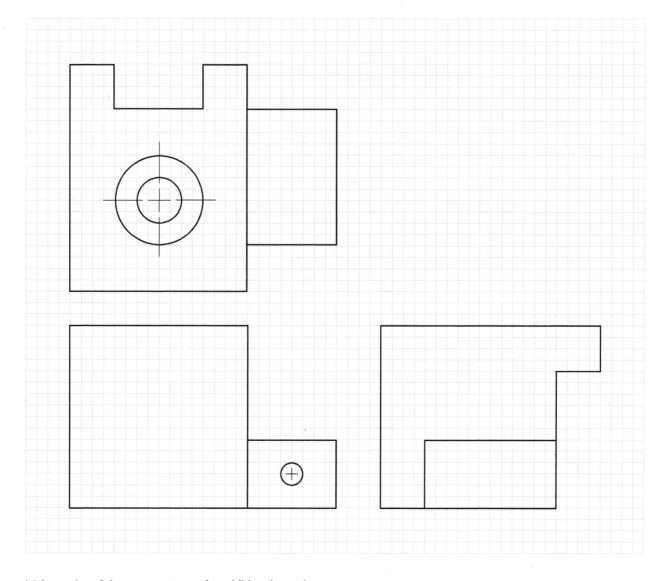

Make copies of these pages to use for additional practice.

WORKSHEET 6   PRACTICE WITH CENTERLINES

Lines are missing from the views shown below. Add the missing lines, including centerlines. Use good centerline practices.

Fold between views to aid in visualization.

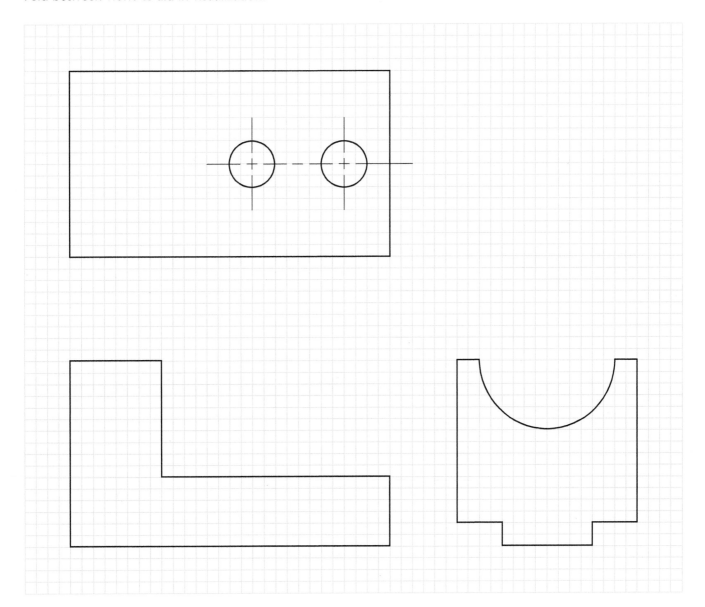

Make copies of these pages to use for additional practice.

2D DRAWING
REPRESENTATION

From Chapter 5 of *Modern Graphics Communication*, Fourth Edition, Frederick E. Giesecke, Alva Mitchell, Henry Cecil Spencer, Ivan Leroy Hill, John Thomas Dygdon, James E. Novak, Shawna Lockhart. Copyright © 2010 by Pearson Education, Inc. Published by Pearson Prentice Hall.

2D DRAWING REPRESENTATION

2D DRAWING REPRESENTATION

--------- OBJECTIVES ---------

After studying the material in this chapter, you should be able to:

1. Represent curved surfaces in multiview drawings

2. Show intersections and tangencies of curved and planar surfaces

3. Represent common types of holes

4. Show fillets, rounds, and runout in a 2D drawing

5. Use partial views

6. Apply revolution conventions when necessary for clarity

7. Draw removed views and projected views

8. Show right- and left-hand parts

9. Project curved surfaces by points

10. Show and label an enlarged detail

11. Show conventional breaks

Refer to the following standard:
- ANSI/ASME Y14.3—2003 Multiview and Sectional View Drawings

The companion website for this text is www.prenhall.com/chet_giesecke_modgraphic_4.

The CoWorker robot is a 3-feet-high Pentium powered robot that can provide a mobile telepresence in remote locations. The CoWorker is made by the iRobot Corporation. *Courtesy of Sam Ogden/Photo Researchers, Inc.*

OVERVIEW

An object that has molded plastic parts like the one shown above has curved surfaces on inside and outside corners in order to make it easier to remove the part from the mold. There are a number of practices for showing curved surfaces in your drawings.

Learning the names of typical features and types of holes that are used in part design and how they are represented in drawing views will make it easier for you to communicate about designs and to understand their documentation requirements.

At times conventional practices are used that are not standard orthographic projections. This is to make it easier to draw or represent objects in your drawings. An example is revolving certain features when it adds to the clarity of the drawing. Another example is

showing "breaks" when a part does not fit well on the sheet because of its long shape, or to avoid unecessary detail.

There is an art to creating drawings that show the information clearly and provide all of the detail necessary to manufacture it. People can read drawings more easily when the least, but still sufficient, information is provided clearly.

The following Web sites show a community for architectural and building systems with cartoons (archmaaik), a drawing archive of architect and sculptor Amancio d'Alpoim Miranda Guedes (guedes), and free electronic publication for steel construction (search aisc):

- http://archmaaik.net
- http://www.guedes.info/drawings/index.htm
- http://www.aisc.org

PRACTICES FOR 2D DOCUMENTATION DRAWINGS

Now that you are familiar with the basics of orthographic projection and visualizing objects from the information presented in orthographic views, you are ready to make and read more complex 2D drawings. While you might sketch complex designs by hand, it is more likely that you would create these types of drawings using CAD, either as 2D CAD drawings, or generating the 2D CAD drawing from a 3D solid model.

At times practices used to create drawings using 3D CAD differ from those used in creating hand-drawn or 2D CAD drawings. It is necessary to understand the standards and practices in order to create good drawings even when using 3D CAD. The software will not do everything for you.

Common Manufactured Features

Certain features are a part of many engineering designs. Learning their names and shapes, as shown in Figure 1 and detailed in Table 1, helps you visualize and communicate about them. Some CAD systems may even have prebuilt features that you can place onto a 3D part to create them quickly.

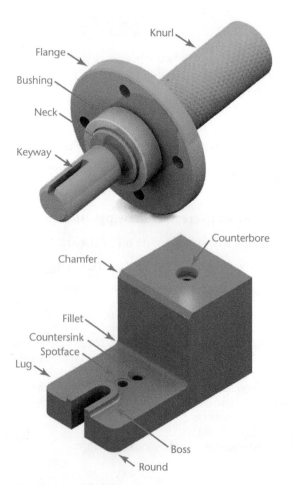

Table 1 Common Manufactured Features.

Feature/Description	Example
Fillet: A rounded interior blend between surfaces. Some uses are to strengthen adjoining surfaces or to allow a part to be removed from a mold.	
Round: A rounded exterior blend between surfaces; used to make edges and corners easier to handle, improve strength of castings, and allow for removal from a mold.	
Counterbore: A cylindrical recess around a hole, usually to receive a bolt head or nut.	
Countersink: A conical-shaped recess around a hole, often used to receive a tapered screw head.	
Spotface: A shallow recess like a counterbore, used to provide a good bearing surface for a fastener.	
Boss: A short raised protrusion above the surface of a part, often used to provide a strong flat bearing surface.	
Lug: A flat or rounded tab protruding from a surface usually to provide a method for attachment.	
Flange: A flattened collar or rim around a cylindrical part to allow for attachment.	
Chamfer: An angled surface, used on cylinders to make them easier to start into a hole, or plates to make them easier to handle.	
Neck: A small groove cut around the diameter of a cylinder, often where it changes diameter.	
Keyway/Keyseat: A shaped depression cut along the axis of a cylinder or hub to receive a key, used to attach hubs, gears, and other parts to a cylinder so they won't turn on it.	
Knurl: A pattern form on a surface to provide for better gripping or more surface area for attachment, often used on knobs and tool handles.	
Bushing: A hollow cylinder that is often used as a protective sleeve or guide, or as a bearing.	

Conventional Representations

Standard orthographic projections don't always show complex shapes as clearly and simply as you may wish, so certain alternative practices, refered to as conventions, are accepted. While "convention" is usually a general term for an accepted method, in the case of conventional representations in technical drawing, it refers particularly to simplified representations that enhance economy and clarity in a drawing. While conventional representations do deviate from true orthographic projection, their methods of simplification are generally recognized and accepted. (See ASME Y14.3-2003.) In other words, conventions are like rules for breaking the rules.

Intersections and Tangencies

To represent complex objects, multiview drawings use standard methods for depicting the way planar and curved surfaces meet. A plane surface can **intersect** or be **tangent** to a contoured surface as shown in Figures 2 and 3. When a plane surface intersects the contoured surface, a line is drawn to represent the edge formed by that interesection. When the plane surface is tangent to the contoured surface, no line or a thin phantom line pattern is drawn where the surfaces meet, depending on whether the phantom line is needed to aid in visualization.

Removed Views

It is not always possible to show all of the drawing views in alignment on the sheet. This is particularly true of civil and architectural drawings where the size and complexity of the object make it hard to show the level of detail necessary and still fit the views all on one sheet. When this is the case, a removed view can be used. There are two different ways to indicate the viewing direction for removed views. One is to use a view indicator arrow to show the direction of sight as shown in Figure 4a. The other is to use a viewing plane line as shown in Figure 4b. Clearly label the removed view.

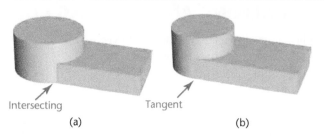

(a) (b)

2 Intersecting and Tangent Surfaces

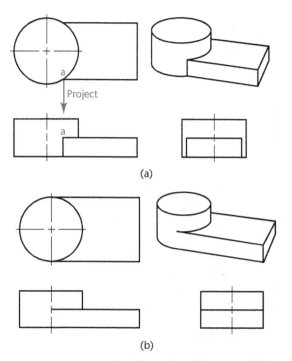

(a)

(b)

3 Orthographic Views of Intersecting and Tangent Surfaces

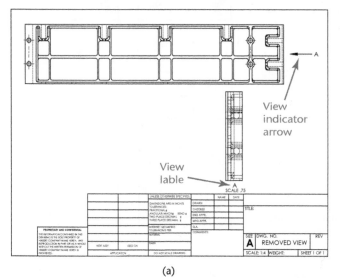

(a)

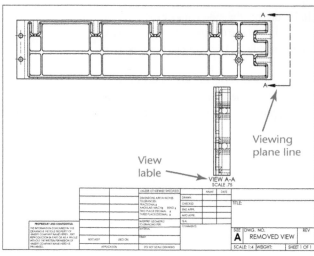

(b)

4 Indicating Removed Views

1 VISUALIZING AND DRAWING COMPLEX CYLINDRICAL SHAPES

The illustrations in Figure 5 show how to visualize cylindrical features being cut from a rectangular block (prism). Compare each illustration showing the material being removed with the drawing.

In Figure 5a there is no line where the contoured surface of the rounded top joins the straight planar sides. The top view appears as a rectangle. The centerline for the rounded top is shown in all three views. Consider these questions as you look at Figure 5a:

- In this drawing, how many views are necessary?
- Which views are repetitive?
- Is the centerline required to locate the rounded top?

In Figure 5b, the material for the center hole is removed. Now hidden lines are added to the top and side view showing the limiting elements of the cylindrical hole. As you look at Figure 5b, note:

- In the front view the hole appears round.
- The centerlines in the drawing locate the hole as well as the rounded top, since they are concentric.

In Figure 5c, the counterbored holes are created. As you look at Figure 5c ask yourself:

- How many lines are used to show the counterbore in the side and top views?
- How many views are necessary?

In Figure 5d a portion of the top surface is removed. Notice how those lines appear in the top and side views. How many views are necessary now?

In Figures 5a and 5b only one view is required.

In Figure 5c, the side view or top view or a note specifying the depth of the counterbore would be needed. The counterbore is five lines.

In Figure 5d the top or side view or a note is required. The side view is probably a better choice, because it shows more about the shape than the top view.

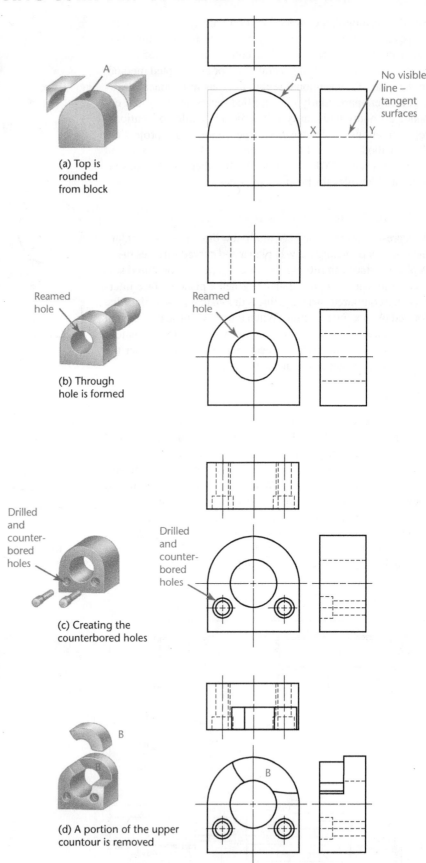

(a) Top is rounded from block

No visible line – tangent surfaces

Reamed hole

(b) Through hole is formed

Reamed hole

Drilled and counter- bored holes

(c) Creating the counterbored holes

Drilled and counter- bored holes

(d) A portion of the upper countour is removed

5 Visualizing and Drawing Cylindrical Shapes

2 CYLINDERS WHEN SLICED

Cylinders are often machined to form plane or other types of surfaces. Figure 6a shows a single machined cut that created two normal surfaces. Normal surfaces appear true shape in the view where the line of sight is perpendicular to the surface. In the two other views that normal surface appears on edge. The back half remains unchanged.

In Figure 6b, two stepped cuts form four normal surfaces. Note that surface 7–8 (top view) is through the center of the cylinder, producing in the side view line 21–24 and in the front view surface 11–14–16–15, which is equal in width to the diameter of the cylinder. Surface 15–16 (front view) is read in the top view as 7–8–ARC 4. Surface 11–14 (front view) is read in the top view as 5–6–ARC 3–8–7–ARC 2.

Figure 6c shows a part with two coaxial cylindrical features, which is cut to form a normal surface parallel to the axis of the cylinders.

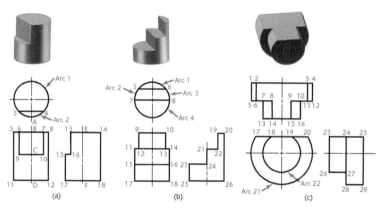

6 Showing Views of Cylinders with Planar Surfaces Cut Away

PLOTTING ELLIPSES BY HAND

Given the front and right-side view, project the correct view of the ellipse into the top view. Steps 1–3 apply to both illustrated examples.

Example 1

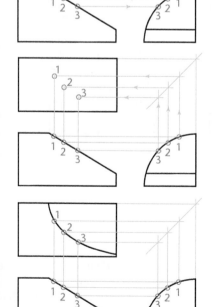

1 Break up the curve into several points and locate them in the adjacent view.

2 Project the points along projection lines into the top view from the front view. Transfer the depth from the side view, using the back surface as a reference plane.

3 Draw the curve through the points.

Example 2

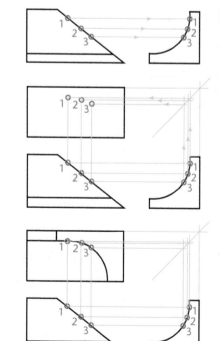

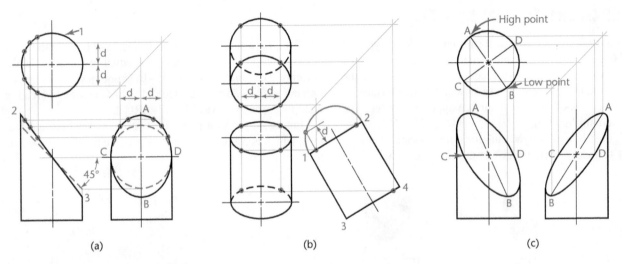

7   Elliptical Surfaces on Cylinders

3 CYLINDERS AND ELLIPSES

If a cylinder is cut by an inclined plane, as shown in Figure 7a, the inclined surface is bounded by an ellipse. This ellipse will appear as a circle in the top view, as a straight line in the front view, and as an ellipse in the side view. Note that circle 1 appears circular in the top view regardless of the angle of the cut. If the cut is at 45° from horizontal, it would also appear as a circle in the side view.

When a circular shape is shown inclined in another view and projected into the adjacent view as shown in Figure 7b it will appear as an ellipse, even though the shape is a circle. The inclined ellipse in Figure 7c is not shown true size and shape in any of the standard views given.

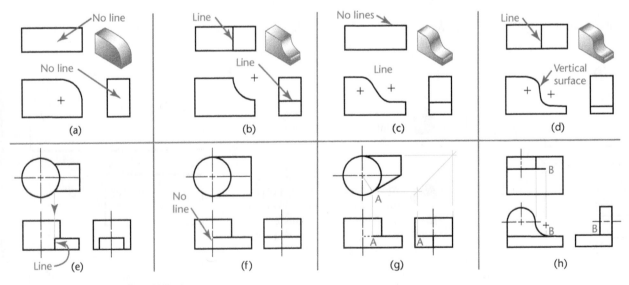

8   Intersections and Tangencies

4 INTERSECTIONS AND TANGENCIES

Where a curved surface is tangent to a plane surface (Figure 8a) no line is drawn, but when it intersects a plane surface, as in Figure 8b, a definite edge is formed.

Figure 8c shows that when curves join each other or plane surfaces smoothly (i.e., they are tangent), you do not draw a line to show where they come together. If a combination of curves creates a vertical surface, as in Figure 8d, the vertical surface is shown as a line (here in the top view).

When plane surfaces join a contoured surface, don't show a line if they are tangent, but do show a line if they intersect. Figures 8e–h show examples of planes joining contoured surfaces.

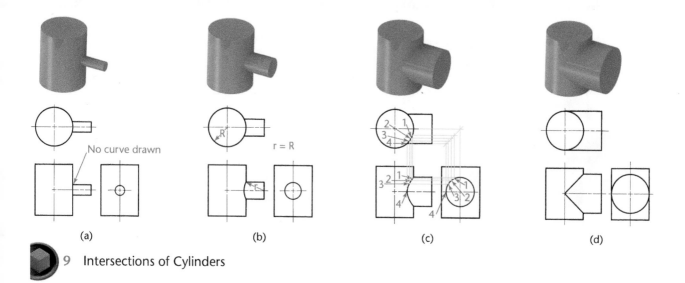

(a)   (b)   (c)   (d)

9   Intersections of Cylinders

Intersections of Cylinders

Figure 9a shows an example of a small cylinder intersecting a large cylinder. When the intersection is small, its curved shape is not plotted accurately because it adds little to the sketch or drawing for the time it takes. Instead it is shown as a straight line.

When the intersection is larger, it can be approximated by drawing an arc with the radius the same as that of the large cylinder, as shown in Figure 9b.

Large intersections can be plotted accurately by selecting points along the curve to project, as shown in Figure 9c.

When the cylinders are the same diameter, their intersections appear as straight lines in the adjoining view, as shown in Figure 9d. When you are using 3D modeling, the accurate intersection of the surfaces is typically represented. See Figure 10.

> ### TIP
>
> Using CAD tools you can locate the center and points on the major and minor axis and use the CAD software's ellipse tool to draw the whole ellipse through the points. Then trim off the extra portion.
>
> A similar technique works when using a template.

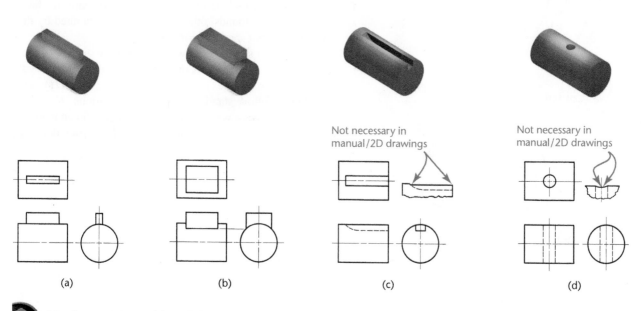

(a)   (b)   (c)   (d)

10   Intersections. (a) and (b) Examples of a narrow prism intersecting a cylinder. (c) and (d) Intersections of a keyseat and cylinder and a small hole and cylinder.

TO SHOW OR NOT TO SHOW:
TANGENT SURFACES IN SOLID MODELS

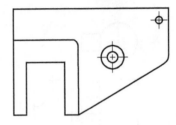

Orthographic drawing views
do not show tangent edges

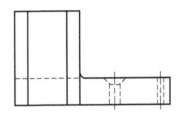

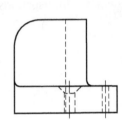

Best: Tangent edges shown as
phantom lines in pictorial view

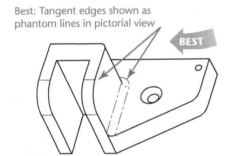

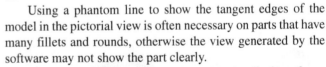

Okay: Tangent edges shown
as solid lines in pictorial view

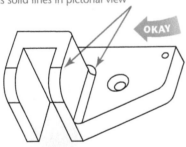

When you are creating solid models of contoured surfaces, it can be very useful to show the "tangent edges" where the contoured surface intersects the model. These lines that depict where the contoured surface ends and where the planar suface begins are not typically drawn in orthographic drawing views, unless the drawing might be confusing without them. When it is necessary to show the tangent edges, use a phantom line for them.

Using a phantom line to show the tangent edges of the model in the pictorial view is often necessary on parts that have many fillets and rounds, otherwise the view generated by the software may not show the part clearly.

Most CAD software allows you to set the display of tangent edges both for the entire drawing and for individual views.

Even when you are creating drawings using a CAD system you should follow standard drawing conventions. Knowing your CAD software well is important so that you can manage settings like those for tangent edges to show your drawing clearly.

Poor: View is unclear without
tangent edges in pictorial view

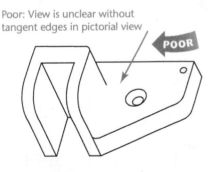

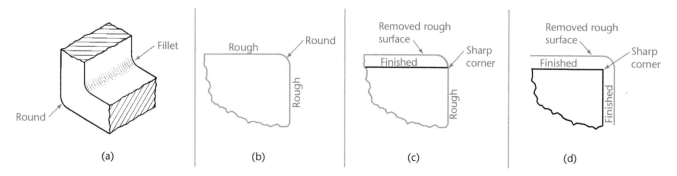

(a)   (b)   (c)   (d)

11 Rough and Finished Surfaces

5 FILLETS AND ROUNDS

A rounded interior corner is called a **fillet.** A rounded exterior corner is called a **round** (Figure 11a). Sharp corners are usually avoided in designing parts to be cast or forged because they are difficult to produce and can weaken the part.

Two intersecting rough surfaces produce a rounded corner (Figure 11b). If one of these surfaces is machined, as shown in Figure 11c, or if both surfaces are machined, as shown in Figure 11d, the corner becomes sharp. In drawings, a rounded corner means that both intersecting surfaces are rough. A sharp corner means that one or both surfaces are machined. Do not shade fillets and rounds on multiview drawings. The presence of the curved surfaces is indicated only where they appear as arcs, unless it is done to call attention to them.

3D CAD software varies in its ability to create complex blends for fillets and rounds. Figure 12 shows a CAD model with complex fillets. Figure 13 shows complex 3D CAD rounds.

12 Fillets on a CAD Model. *Courtesy of Ross Traeholt.*

13 Rounds on a CAD Model of a Design for a Three-Hole Punch. *Courtesy of Douglas Wintin.*

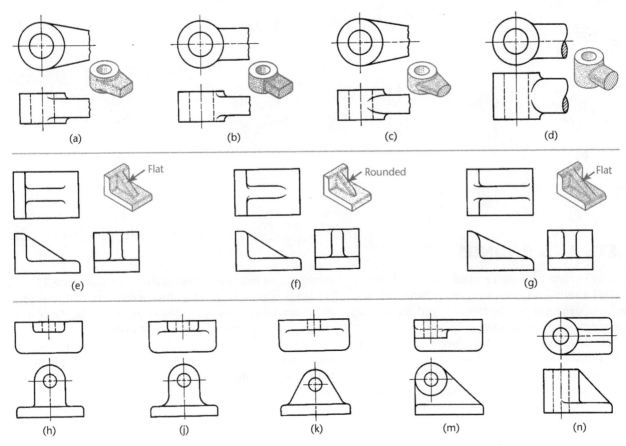

14   Conventional Fillets, Rounds, and Runouts

6 RUNOUTS

Small curves called **runouts** are used to represent fillets that connect with plane surfaces tangent to cylinders, as shown in Figures 14a–14d. The runouts, shown in Figure 14f, should have a radius equal to that of the fillet and a curvature of about one-eighth of a circle, as shown in Figure 15c.

Runouts from different filleted intersections will appear differently due to the shapes of the horizontal intersecting members. Figures 14a–14g show more examples of conventional representations for fillets, rounds, and runouts. In Figures 14e and 14f the runouts differ because the top surface of the web is flat in Figure 14e, while the top surface of the web in Figure 14f is considerably rounded.

When two different sizes of fillets intersect, the direction of the runout is dictated by the larger fillet, as shown in Figures 14g and 14j.

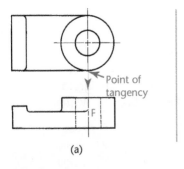

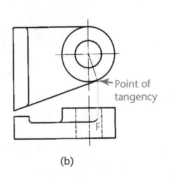

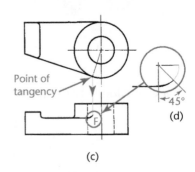

15   Runouts

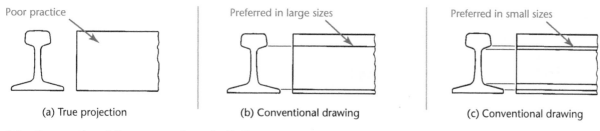

(a) True projection

(b) Conventional drawing

(c) Conventional drawing

16 Conventional Representation of a Rail

7 CONVENTIONAL EDGES

Rounded and filleted intersections eliminate sharp edges and can make it difficult to present the shape clearly. In some cases, as shown in Figure 16a, the true projection may be misleading. There is a conventional way of showing rounded and filleted edges for the sake of clarity. Added lines depicting rounded and filleted edges, as shown in Figures 16b and 16c, give a clearer representation, even though it is not the true projection. Project the added lines from the intersections of the surfaces as if the fillets and rounds were not present.

Figure 17 shows top views for each given front view. The first set of top views have very few lines, even though they are the true projection. The second set of top views, where lines are added to represent the rounded and filleted edges, are quite clear. Note the use of small Y shapes where rounded or filleted edges meet a rough surface. If an edge intersects a finished surface, no Y shape is shown.

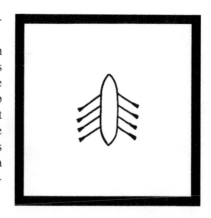

George Washington Crossing the Delaware as Seen by a Trout. *Cartoon by Roger Price. Courtesy of "Droodles, The Classic Collection."*

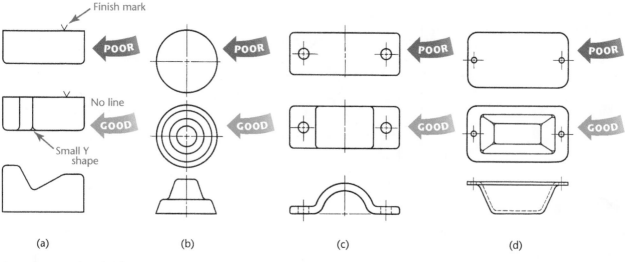

(a)   (b)   (c)   (d)

17 Conventional Edges

8 NECESSARY VIEWS

What are the absolute minimum views required to completely define an object?

As you have already seen, sometimes only a single view with a note about the part's thickness is enough to define the shape (Figure 18). Sometimes two views are required (Figure 19). For complex parts three or more views may be required (Figure 20).

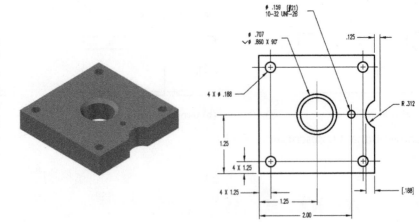

18 One-View Drawing

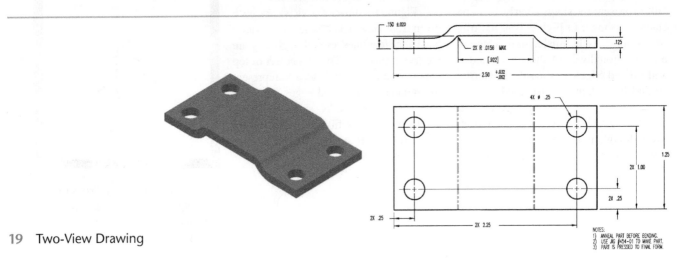

19 Two-View Drawing

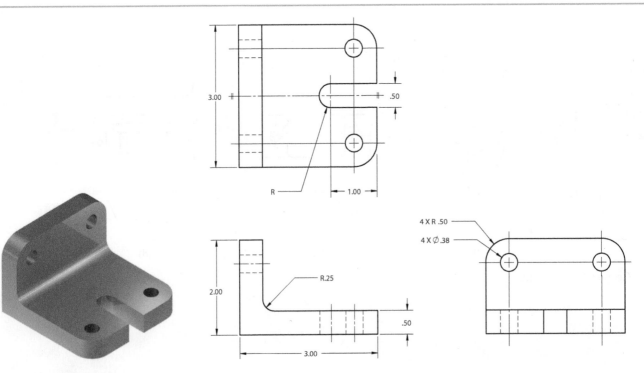

20 Three-View Drawing

21 Three-View Drawings Showing Unnecessary Views Eliminated

In each set of views shown in Figure 21 three views are shown, but only two of the three are required.

When deciding which views to show, keep in mind the following:

- Show sufficient views to completely describe the shape.

- Show the right-hand view instead of the left-hand view if both show the object equally well.
- Choose the top view rather than the bottom view.
- Show long parts horizontally on the sheet for two reasons: (1) they fit better, (2) they tend to appear even longer when shown vertically.

- Make it your goal to communicate the information clearly. If an additional view helps toward this goal, show it. Keep in mind that drawings are easier to read and update if they are simpler, rather than more complex.

9 PARTIAL VIEWS

A view may not need to be complete, but needs to show what is necessary to clearly describe the object. This is called a **partial view** and is used to save sketching time and make the drawing less confusing to read. You can use a break line to limit the partial view, as shown in Figure 22a, or limit a view by the contour of the part shown, as shown in Figure 22b. If the view is symmetrical, you can draw a half-view on one side of the centerline, as shown in Figure 22c, or break out a partial view, as shown in Figure 22d. The half-views should be the near side, as shown.

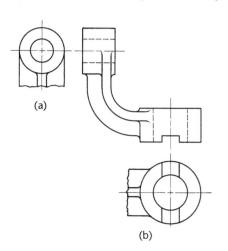

(a)

(b)

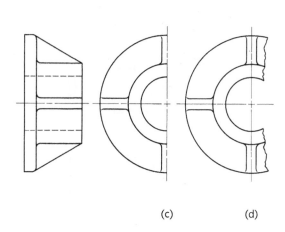

(c)   (d)

22 Partial Views

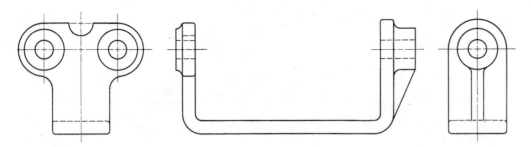

23   Partial Side Views

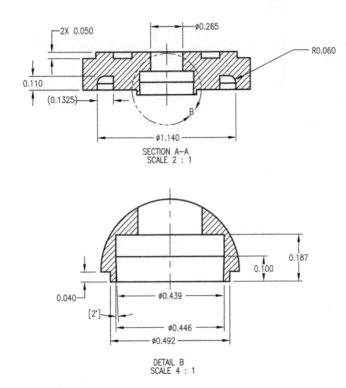

SECTION A—A
SCALE 2 : 1

DETAIL B
SCALE 4 : 1

24   Enlarged Detail

When you are drawing a partial view, do not place a break line where it will coincide with a visible or hidden line, as this may cause the drawing to be misinterpreted.

Occasionally the distinctive features of an object are on opposite sides. In either complete side view there will be a considerable overlapping of shapes. In cases like this, two side views are often the best solution, as shown in Figure 23. The views are partial views, and certain visible and hidden lines have been omitted for clarity.

Showing Enlarged Details

Figure 24 shows drawing details clearly by including detail views drawn at a larger scale. When adding a detail, draw a circle around the features that will be included in the detail as shown in Figure 24 (top). Place the detail view on the sheet similarly to a removed view. Label successive details with the word detail followed by letters as in DETAIL A, DETAIL B and so on and note the scale for the detail below its name.

Enlarged details are easy to generate using CAD software.

Conventional Breaks

To shorten the view of a long object, you can use break lines as shown in Figure 25. Figure 26 shows two views of a garden rake. When the long handle of the rake is shown to scale, the details of the drawing are small and hard to read. By using a break to leave out a portion of the handle, the scale for the ends can be increased to show the details clearly.

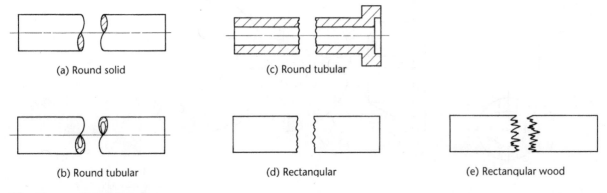

(a) Round solid

(c) Round tubular

(b) Round tubular

(d) Rectangular

(e) Rectangular wood

25   Conventional Break

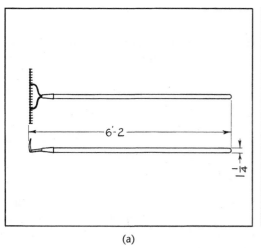

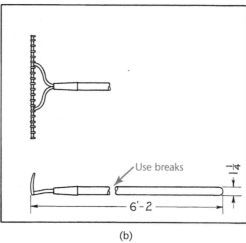

(a)

(b)

26 Conventional breaks allow for increased scale to show detail.

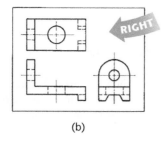

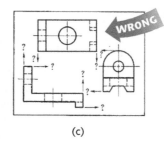

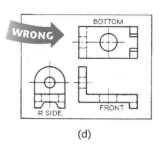

(a) Offset guide

(b)

(c)

(d)

27 Alignment of Views

10 ALIGNMENT OF VIEWS

Always draw views in the standard arrangement shown in Figure 27 to be sure that your drawings are not misinterpreted. Figure 27a shows an offset guide that requires three views. Their correct arrangement is shown in Figure 27b. The top view should be directly above the front view, and the right-side view directly to the right of the front view—not out of alignment, as in Figure 27c.

Never draw the views in reversed positions, with the bottom over the front view or the right side to the left of the front view, as shown in Figure 27d. Even though the views do line up with the front view, this arrangement could be misread.

Figure 28 shows three views in the correct alignment, but this drawing has a poor choice for the front view. The front view should show the shape of the object clearly. One way to consider this is that the front view shows the most information about the material that would have to be removed from a block.

After design sketches are completed, you will usually follow them with detailed CAD drawings. In finished CAD drawings you should apply the same rules for arranging views, clearly depicting the subject of the drawing, using the proper line patterns and line weights, and following all of the necessary standards as used in drawings created by hand. Many programs allow you to select a standard arrangement of views produced directly from your 3D CAD model.

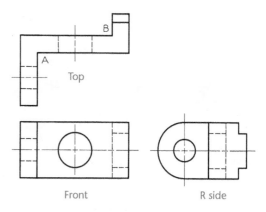

28 Three Views in Correct Alignment but Poor Choice of Front View

— **TIP** —

Because CAD makes it easy to move whole views, it is tempting to place views where they fit on the screen or plotted sheet and not in the standard arrangement. This is not acceptable.

3D CAD software that generates 2D drawing views as projections of the 3D object usually has a setting to select from third angle or first angle projection. Check your software if you are unsure which projection methods are available.

227

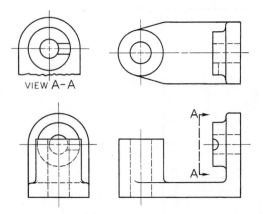

VIEW A–A

29 Removed View Using Viewing Plane Line

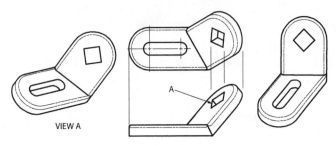

VIEW A

30 Removed View Using View Indicator Arrow

11 REMOVED VIEWS

A **removed view** is a complete or partial view removed to another place on the sheet so that it is no longer in direct projection with any other view, as shown in the upper left corner of Figure 29. A removed view may be used to show a feature of the object more clearly, possibly to a larger scale, or to save drawing a complete regular view. A viewing-plane line is used to indicate the part being viewed. The arrows at the corners show the direction of sight. The removed views should be labeled View A–A or View B–B and so on; the letters refer to those placed at the corners of the viewing-plane line. A view indicator arrow can also be used to show the viewing direction for the removed view, as shown in Figure 30. Be sure to label the removed view clearly and provide its scale if it is different from the overall drawing scale.

Architectural drawings often cannot fit even two standard views on the sheet. The sheets are typically labeled to indicate the standard views, as in Figure 31. Views are labeled, for example, "Plan" for the top view, "East Elevation" for the side view seen from the east compass direction, and so forth. Additional views use a viewing-plane line or arrow to indicate the direction of sight.

In large civil drawings and other complex drawings such as the electrical drawing in Figure 32, one entire view may not be able to be shown clearly on a single sheet. For projects that extend sheet to sheet, match lines are often drawn showing how one sheet matches to the previous one.

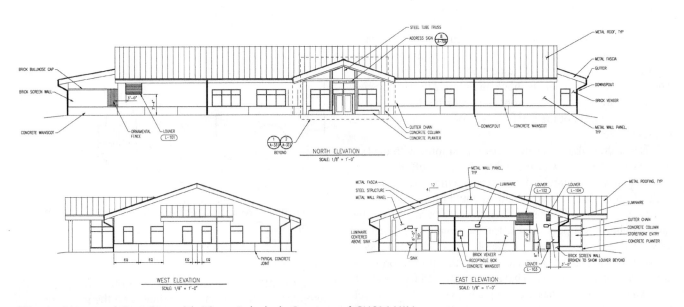

31 Architectural Drawing with Views Labeled. *Courtesy of CH2M HILL.*

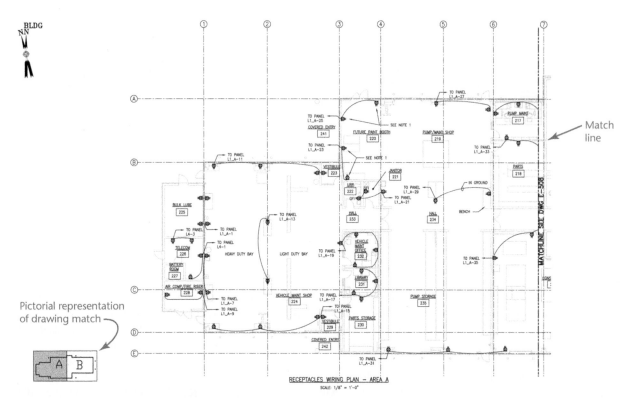

32 A Portion of a Building Systems Electrical Drawing Using Match Lines. *Courtesy of CH2M HILL.*

12 RIGHT-HAND AND LEFT-HAND PARTS

Often parts function in pairs of similar opposite parts. But opposite parts can rarely be exactly alike. For example, the right-front fender of an automobile cannot be the same shape as the left-front fender. A **left-hand part** is not simply a right-hand part turned around; the two parts are mirror images and are not interchangeable.

On sketches and drawings a left-hand part is noted as LH, and a **right-hand part** as RH. In Figure 33a, the part in front of the mirror is a right-hand part, and the image shows the left-hand part. No matter how the object is turned, the mirror image will show the left-hand part. Figures 33b and 33c show left-hand and right-hand drawings of the same object.

Ordinarily you draw only one of two opposite parts and label the one that is drawn with a note, such as LH PART SHOWN, RH OPPOSITE. If the opposite-hand shape is not clear, you should make a separate sketch or drawing to show it clearly and completely.

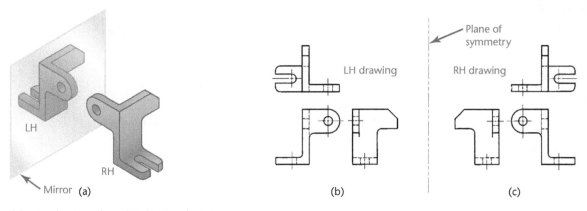

33 Right-Hand and Left-Hand Parts

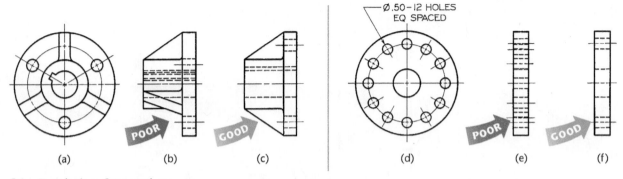

34 Revolution Conventions

13 REVOLUTION CONVENTIONS

Regular multiview projections are sometimes awkward, confusing, or actually misleading. For example, Figure 34a shows an object that has three triangular ribs, three holes equally spaced in the base, and a keyway. The right-side view is a regular projection, but is not recommended—the lower ribs appear in a foreshortened position, the holes do not appear in their true relation to the rim of the base, and the keyway is projected as a confusion of hidden lines.

The method shown in Figure 34c is preferred because it is simpler to read

and requires less time to sketch. Each of the features mentioned has been revolved in the front view to lie along the vertical centerline, from which it is projected to the correct side view.

Figures 34d and 34e show regular views of a flange with several small holes. The hidden holes are confusing and take unnecessary time to show. Figure 34f shows the holes revolved for clarity.

Figure 35 shows a regular projection with a confusing foreshortening of its inclined arm. In Figure 35b, the lower arm

is revolved to line up vertically in the front view so that it projects the true length in the side view and makes the object's symmetry clear.

Revolutions like these are frequently used in connection with sectioning. Revolved sectional views are called aligned sections.

In views generated from 3D CAD models, revolving the features to show their true size is not required, but it is preferred, especially in hand-drawn and 2D CAD drawings.

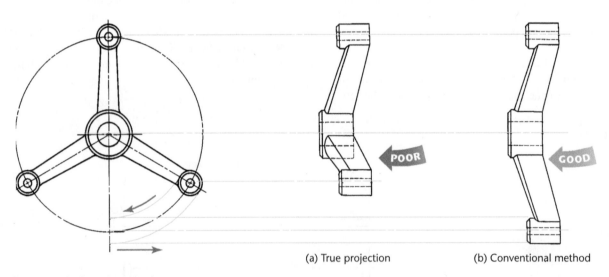

(a) True projection   (b) Conventional method

35 Revolution Conventions

Common Hole Features Shown in Orthographic Views

Orthographic views of common hole features are shown in Figure 36.
See Table 1 for descriptions of these common hole features.

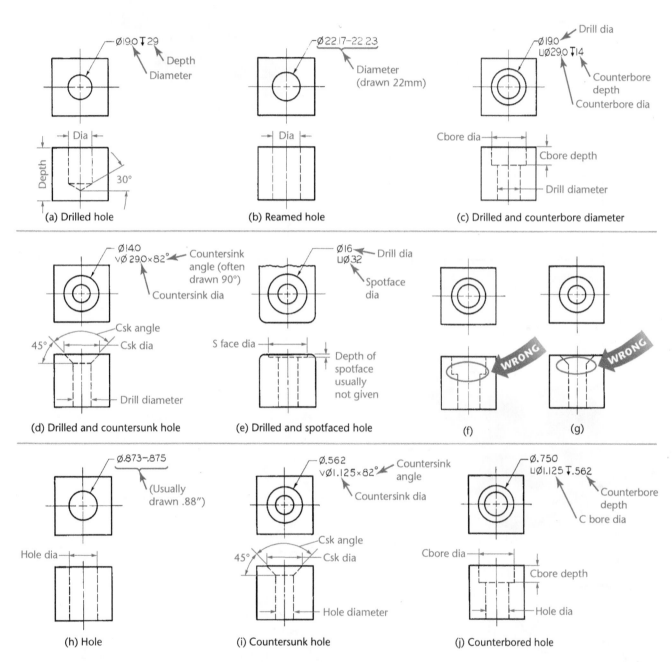

36 Representing Holes in Orthographic Views; Dimensions for (a)–(e) in Metric

Common Features Shown in Orthographic Views

Orthographic views of common features are shown in Figure 37. See Table 1 for descriptions of common features.

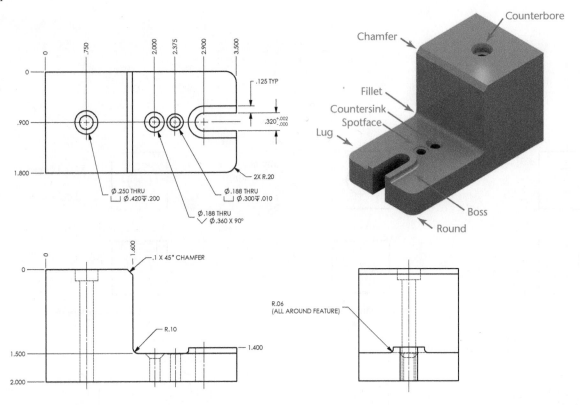

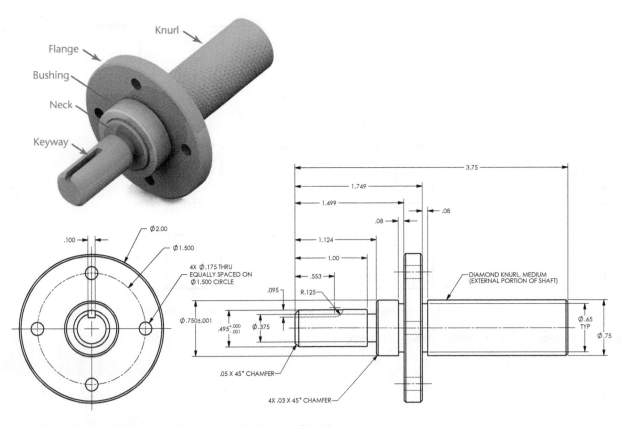

37   Representing Common Features in Orthographic Views

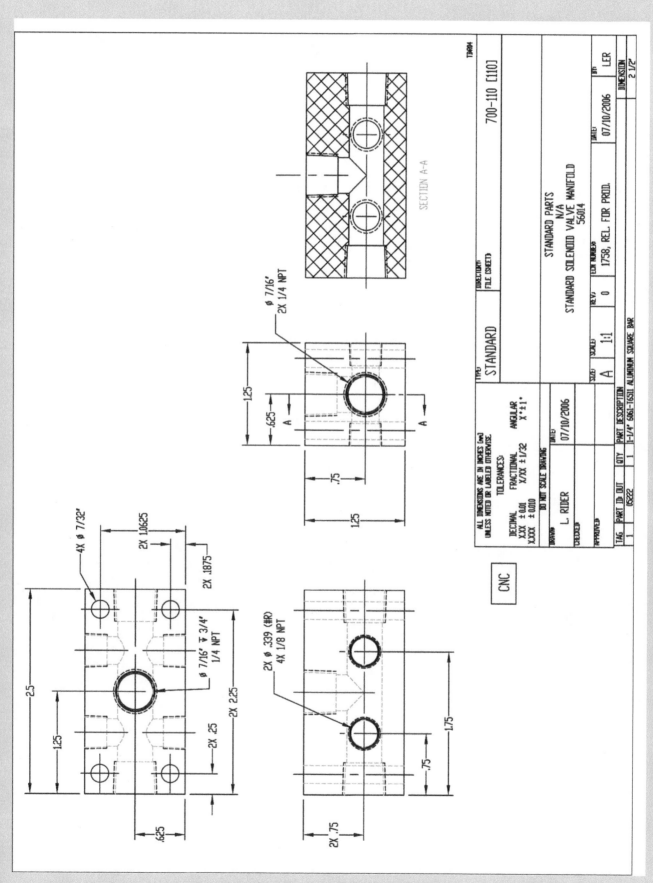

Orthographic Views of a Solenoid Valve Manifold. This drawing is for a part that has many intersecting holes. *Courtesy of Wood's Power-Grip Co., Inc.*

PORTFOLIO

PORTFOLIO

The views in this architectural drawing are too large to fit on a sheet in typical projection so removed views are used. Notice that each view is clearly labeled as to its direction of sight since they are not in projection. *Courtesy of Locati Architects.*

KEY WORDS

Fillet

Round

Counterbore

Countersink

Spotface

Boss

Lug

Flange

Chamfer

Neck

Keyway/Keyseat

Knurl

Bushing

Intersect

Tangent

Runouts

Partial View

Removed View

Left-Hand Part

Right-Hand Part

Revolutions

CHAPTER SUMMARY

1. Irregular curves can be plotted by identifying points on the object. The points can be projected to approximate the boundaries of the curved surface.
2. Drawing conventions define usual practices for the representation of features such as holes, bosses, ribs, webs, lugs, fillets, and rounds.
3. Use the same main practices to arrange drawing views on the sheet for both hand-drawn and CAD drawings. Show and label enlarged details and removed views. Use partial views and leave out hidden lines as long as the object is shown clearly.
4. When curved and planar surfaces intersect, an edge is formed that is represented by a line in the drawing. When curved and planar surfaces are tangent, no edge is formed, so no line is needed. If the drawing is not clear without it, use a phantom line to show tangencies.
5. Common types of holes are through, blind, countersunk, counterbored, and spotfaced.
6. Fillets, rounds, and runout are special types of tangent contours formed on parts with rounded edges.
7. When necessary for clarity, features are sometimes shown in a revolved position using revolution conventions.
8. Break lines can be used to leave out a section of a part where it is uniform or repetitive. Often this is done to enlarge the scale of the remaining portions of the part so that details can be seen clearly.

REVIEW QUESTIONS

1. If the top view of an object shows a drilled through hole, how many hidden lines would be necessary in the front view to describe the hole? How many if the hole is countersunk? Counterbored?
2. If a plane surface intersects a contoured surface, should you show a line in the drawing to represent that intersection? What about when the plane is tangent?
3. What is a fillet? A round? A lug? A boss? Knurling?
4. How do you show right-hand and left-hand parts?
5. Which is easier, creating an enlarged detail by hand or using a CAD system?

EXERCISES

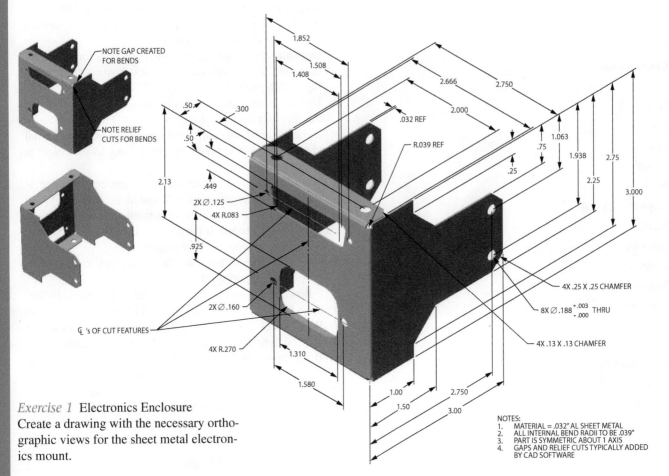

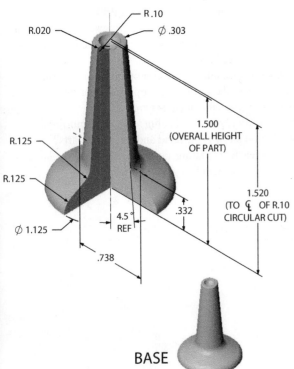

NOTE GAP CREATED FOR BENDS

NOTE RELIEF CUTS FOR BENDS

1.852
1.508
1.408
.50
.300
.50
.032 REF
R.039 REF
2.13
.449
2X ⌀.125
4X R.083
.925
2X ⌀.160
℄'s OF CUT FEATURES
4X R.270
1.310
1.580
2.666
2.750
2.000
1.063
.75
1.938
.25
2.25
2.75
3.000
4X .25 X .25 CHAMFER
8X ⌀.188 +.003/-.000 THRU
4X .13 X .13 CHAMFER
1.00
1.50
2.750
3.00

NOTES:
1. MATERIAL = .032" AL SHEET METAL
2. ALL INTERNAL BEND RADII TO BE .039"
3. PART IS SYMMETRIC ABOUT 1 AXIS
4. GAPS AND RELIEF CUTS TYPICALLY ADDED BY CAD SOFTWARE

Exercise 1 Electronics Enclosure
Create a drawing with the necessary orthographic views for the sheet metal electronics mount.

R.10
R.020
⌀ .303
1.500 (OVERALL HEIGHT OF PART)
R.125
R.125
1.520 (TO ℄ OF R.10 CIRCULAR CUT)
⌀ 1.125
4.5° REF
.332
.738

BASE

Exercise 2 Gyroscope Base
Create a drawing with the necessary orthographic view.

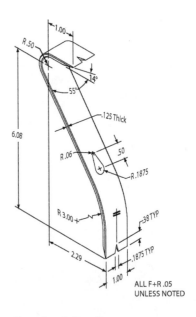

1.00
R.50
14°
55°
.125 Thick
6.08
R.06
.50
R.1875
R 3.00
.38 TYP
2.29
.1875 TYP
1.00
ALL F+R .05 UNLESS NOTED

Exercise 3 Pry Bar
Create a drawing with the necessary orthographic views for the pry bar.

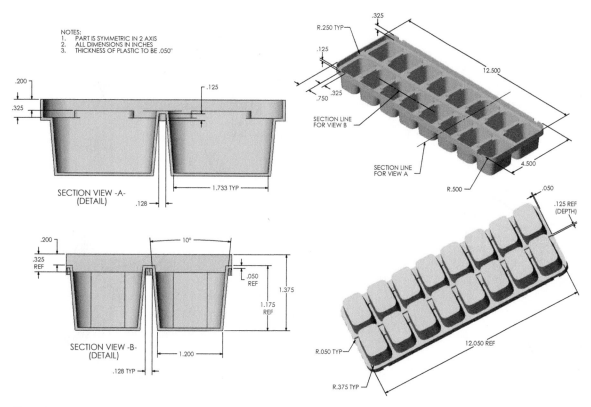

NOTES:
1. PART IS SYMMETRIC IN 2 AXIS
2. ALL DIMENSIONS IN INCHES
3. THICKNESS OF PLASTIC TO BE .050"

.200

.325

.125

SECTION VIEW -A-
(DETAIL)

.128

1.733 TYP

.200

.325
REF

10°

.050
REF

1.375

1.175
REF

SECTION VIEW -B-
(DETAIL)

1.200

.128 TYP

.325

R.250 TYP

.125

.325

.750

SECTION LINE
FOR VIEW B

SECTION LINE
FOR VIEW A

R.500

12.500

4.500

.050

.125 REF
(DEPTH)

R.050 TYP

R.375 TYP

12.050 REF

Exercise 4 Ice Cube Tray

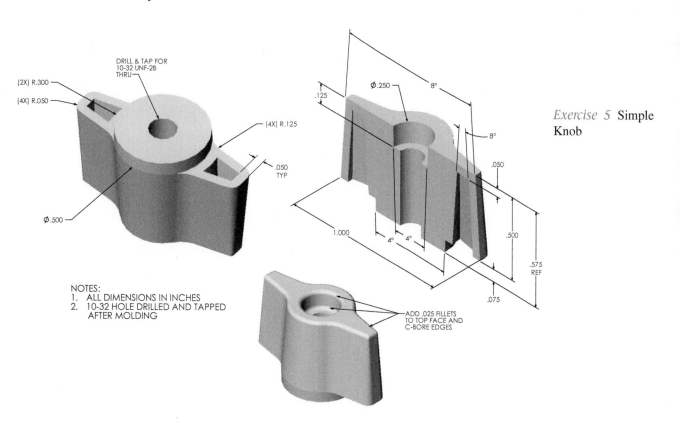

DRILL & TAP FOR
10-32 UNF-2B
THRU

(2X) R.300

(4X) R.050

(4X) R.125

.050
TYP

Ø .500

Ø.250

.125

8°

8°

.050

4°   4°

1.000

.500

.575
REF

.075

Exercise 5 Simple
Knob

ADD .025 FILLETS
TO TOP FACE AND
C-BORE EDGES

NOTES:
1. ALL DIMENSIONS IN INCHES
2. 10-32 HOLE DRILLED AND TAPPED
   AFTER MOLDING

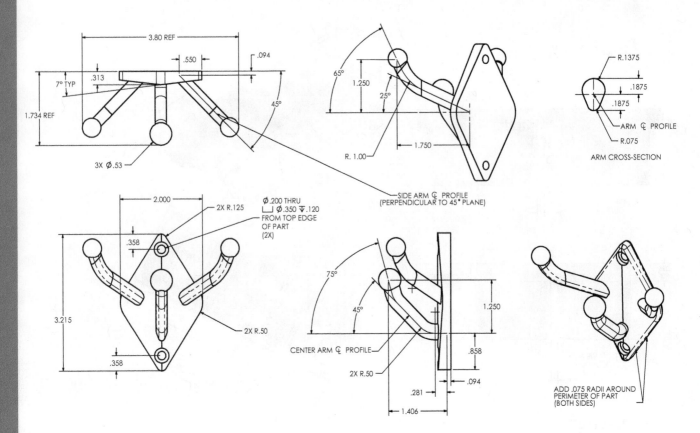

3.80 REF
.550
.094
.313
7° TYP
1.734 REF
45°
3X Ø.53

65°
1.250
25°
R. 1.00
1.750
SIDE ARM ₵ PROFILE
(PERPENDICULAR TO 45° PLANE)

R.1375
.1875
.1875
ARM ₵ PROFILE
R.075
ARM CROSS-SECTION

2.000
2X R.125
Ø.200 THRU
⌴ Ø.350 ▽.120
FROM TOP EDGE
OF PART
(2X)
.358
3.215
2X R.50
.358

75°
45°
1.250
.858
CENTER ARM ₵ PROFILE
2X R.50
.281
.094
1.406

ADD .075 RADII AROUND
PERIMETER OF PART
(BOTH SIDES)

Exercise 6 Wall Hanger

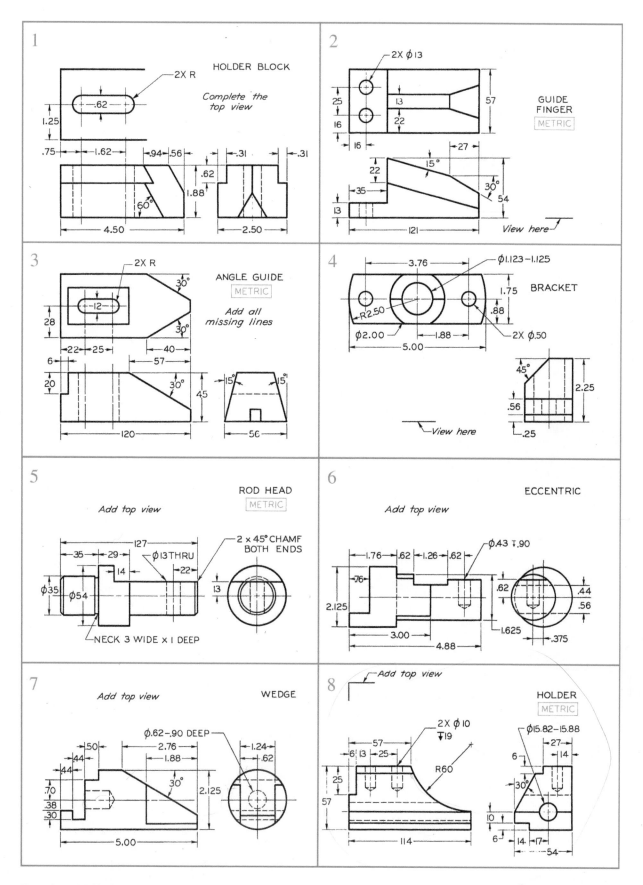

1 HOLDER BLOCK
Complete the top view
2X R
.62
1.25
.75 1.62 .94 .56 .31 .31
.62
1.88
60°
4.50 2.50

2 GUIDE FINGER
METRIC
2X ⌀13
25
16
13
22
57
16
27
22
15°
35
13
30°
54
121
View here

3 ANGLE GUIDE
METRIC
Add all missing lines
2X R
30°
12
30°
28
22 25 40
6
57
20
30°
45
120
15° 15°
56

4 BRACKET
3.76
⌀1.123–1.125
1.75
R2.50
.88
⌀2.00 1.88 2X ⌀.50
5.00
View here
45°
2.25
.56
.25

5 ROD HEAD
METRIC
Add top view
127
35 29
14
⌀13 THRU 22
2 x 45° CHAMF BOTH ENDS
13
⌀35
⌀54
13
NECK 3 WIDE x 1 DEEP

6 ECCENTRIC
Add top view
1.76 .62 1.26 .62
⌀.43 ⊤.90
.76
.62
.44
.56
2.125
3.00
1.625
4.88
.375

7 WEDGE
Add top view
⌀.62–.90 DEEP
.50
.44
.44
2.76
1.88
1.24
.62
.70
.38
.30
30°
2.125
5.00

8 HOLDER
METRIC
Add top view
2X ⌀10
⊤19
57
6 13 25
R60
25
57
114
⌀15.82–15.88
27
14
6
30°
10
6 14 17
54

Exercise 7 Missing-View Problems. Sketch or draw the given views, and add the missing view. These exercises are designed to fit on 8½ × 11" A-size or A4 metric size paper. Use a title block or title strip as assigned by your instructor. Use metric or decimal-inch dimensions as assigned by your instructor. Move dimensions to better locations where possible.

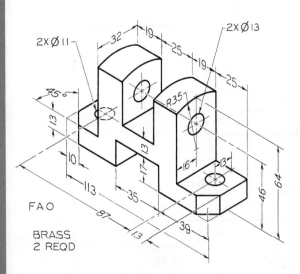

FAO

BRASS
2 REQD

Exercise 8 Rod Support*

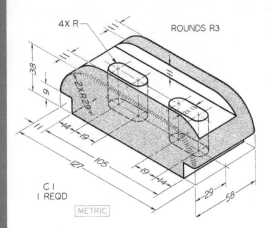

C I
I REQD

METRIC

Exercise 9 Tailstock*

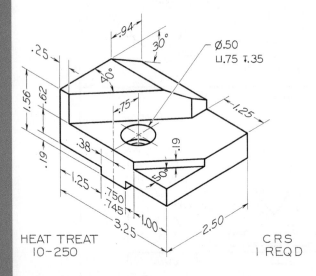

HEAT TREAT
10–250

CRS
I REQD

Exercise 10 Index Feed*

*Sketch or draw necessary views. These exercises are designed to fit on $8\frac{1}{2} \times 11$" A-size or A4 metric size paper. Use a title block or title strip as assigned by your instructor. Use metric or decimal-inch dimensions as assigned by your instructor. Move dimensions to better locations where possible.

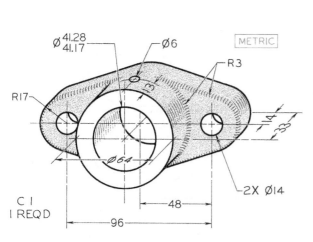

Exercise 11 Bearing*

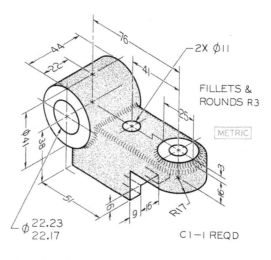

Exercise 14 Index Arm*

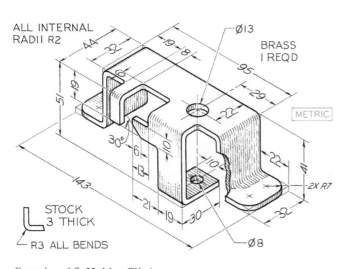

Exercise 12 Holder Clip*

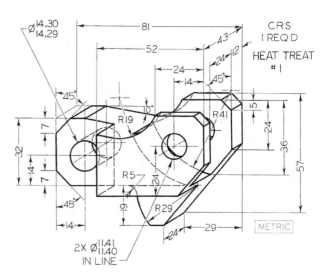

Exercise 15 Roller Lever*

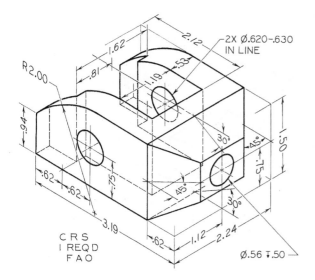

Exercise 13 Cam*

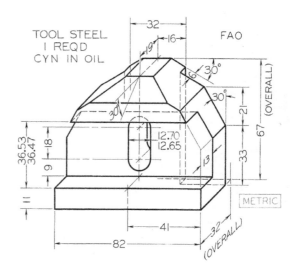

Exercise 16 Support*

*Sketch or draw necessary views. These exercises are designed to fit on 8½ × 11" A-size or A4 metric size paper. Use a title block or title strip as assigned by your instructor. Use metric or decimal-inch dimensions as assigned by your instructor. Move dimensions to better locations where possible.

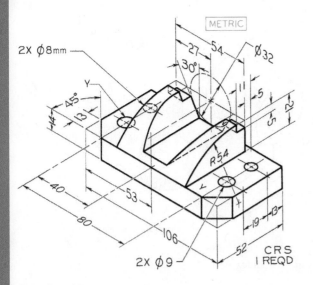

Exercise 17 Locating Finger*

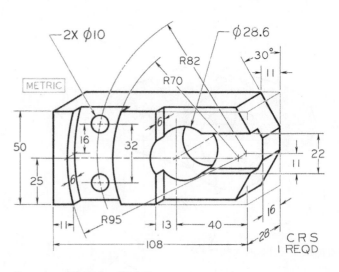

Exercise 20 Index Slide*

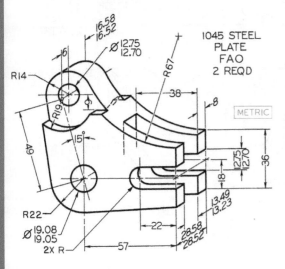

Exercise 18 Toggle Lever*

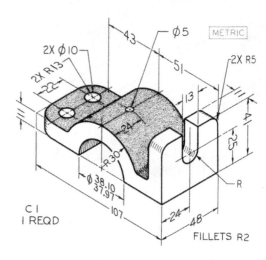

Exercise 21 Frame Guide*

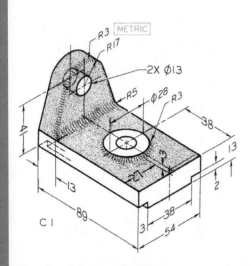

Exercise 19 Cut-off Holder*

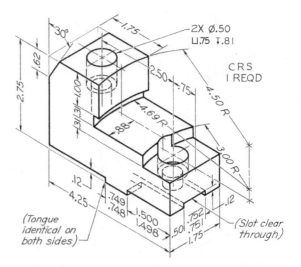

Exercise 22 Chuck Jaw*

*Sketch or draw necessary views. These exercises are designed to fit on 8½ × 11" A-size or A4 metric size paper. Use a title block or title strip as assigned by your instructor. Use metric or decimal-inch dimensions as assigned by your instructor. Move dimensions to better locations where possible.

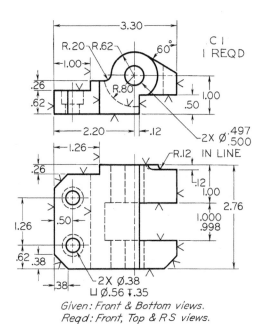

.C 1
I REQD

Given: Front & Bottom views.
Reqd: Front, Top & RS views.

Exercise 23 Hinge Bracket*

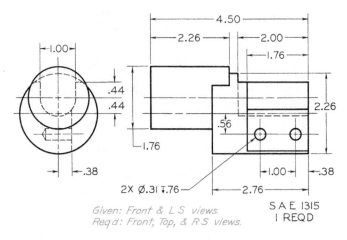

2X Ø.31 ⊤.76

S A E 1315
I REQD

Given: Front & L S views.
Reqd: Front, Top, & R S views.

Exercise 24 Tool Holder*

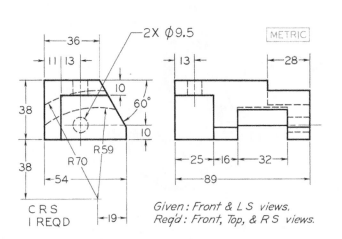

C R S
I REQD

Given: Front & L S views.
Reqd: Front, Top, & R S views.

Exercise 25 Shifter Block*

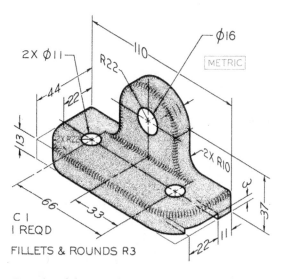

C 1
I REQD

FILLETS & ROUNDS R3

Exercise 26 Cross-feed Stop*

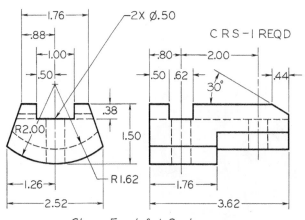

C R S – I REQD

Given: Front & L S views.
Reqd: Front, Top, & R S views.

Exercise 27 Cross Cam*

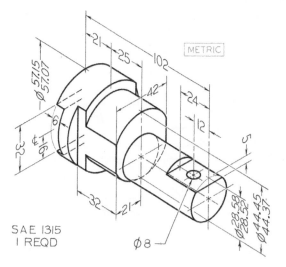

SAE 1315
I REQD

Exercise 28 Roller Stud*

*Sketch or draw necessary views. These exercises are designed to fit on 8½ × 11" A-size or A4 metric size paper. Use a title block or title strip as assigned by your instructor. Use metric or decimal-inch dimensions as assigned by your instructor. Move dimensions to better locations where possible.

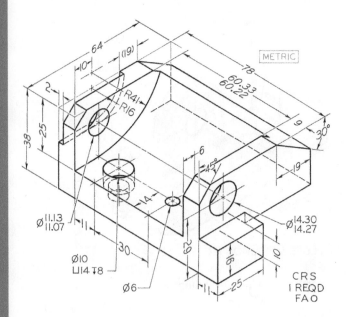

Exercise 29 **Hinge Block***

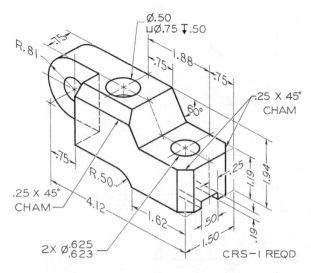

Exercise 32 Vibrator Arm*

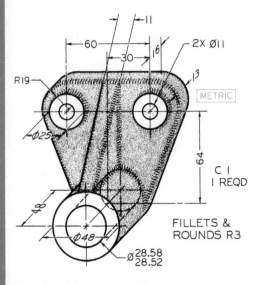

Exercise 30 Feed Rod Bearing*

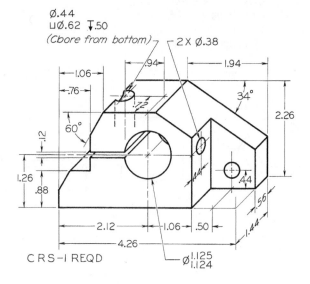

Exercise 33 Clutch Lever*

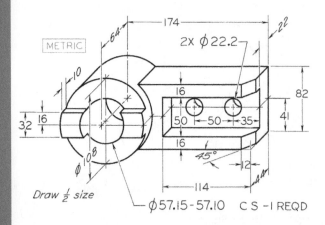

Exercise 31 Lever Hub*

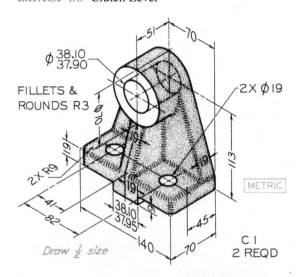

Exercise 34 Counter Bearing Bracket*

*Sketch or draw necessary views. These exercises are designed to fit on 8½ × 11" A-size or A4 metric size paper. Use a title block or title strip as assigned by your instructor. Use metric or decimal-inch dimensions as assigned by your instructor. Move dimensions to better locations where possible.

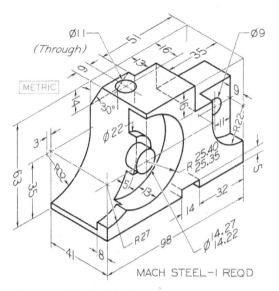

Exercise 35 Tool Holder*

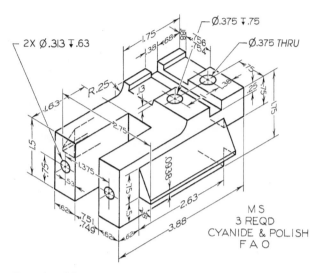

Exercise 38 Tool Holder*

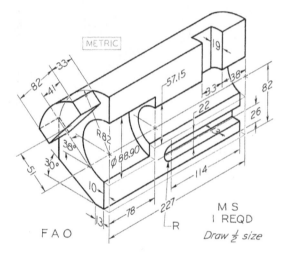

Exercise 36 Control Block*

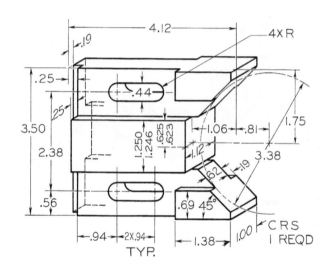

Exercise 39 Locating V-Block*

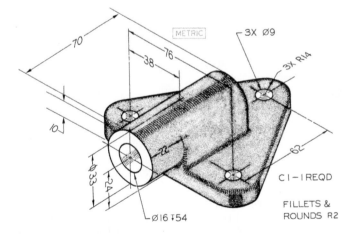

Exercise 37 Socket Bearing*

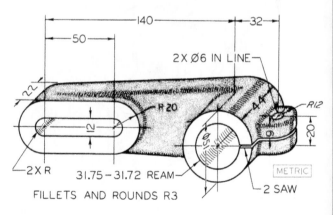

Exercise 40 Anchor Bracket*

*Sketch or draw necessary views. These exercises are designed to fit on 8½ × 11" A-size or A4 metric size paper. Use a title block or title strip as assigned by your instructor. Use metric or decimal-inch dimensions as assigned by your instructor. Move dimensions to better locations where possible.

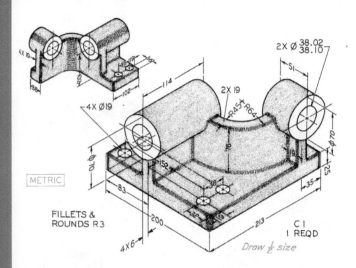

Exercise 41 Lead Screw Bracket*

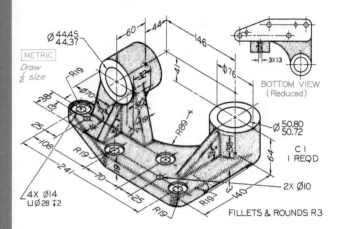

Exercise 42 Lever Bracket*

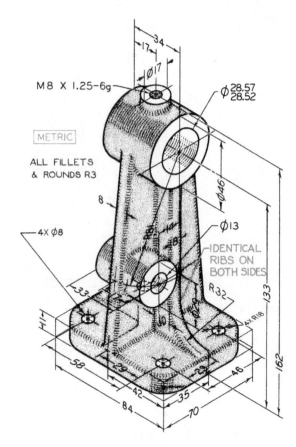

Exercise 44 Bearing Bracket*

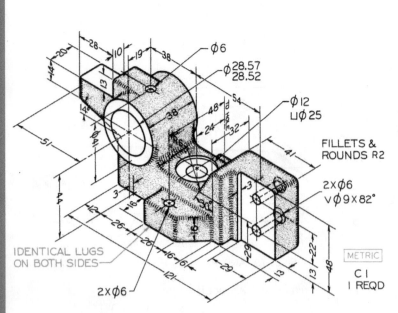

Exercise 43 Gripper Rode Center*

*Sketch or draw necessary views. Larger and more detailed parts show the details more clearly when drawn on larger sheet sizes. Consider using B, C, or A3 or A2 sheets. Use a title block or title strip as assigned by your instructor. Use metric or decimal-inch dimensions as assigned by your instructor. Move dimensions to better locations where possible.

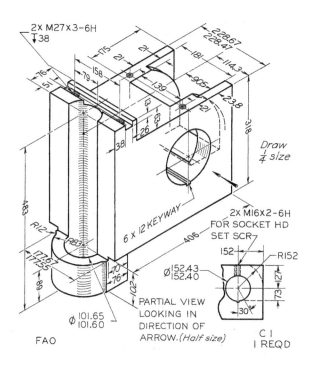

2X M27X3-6H
↧38

6 x 12 KEYWAY

2X M16X2-6H
FOR SOCKET HD
SET SCR

Draw
¼ size

PARTIAL VIEW
LOOKING IN
DIRECTION OF
ARROW.(Half size)

FAO

C I
I REQD

Exercise 45 Link Arm Connector*

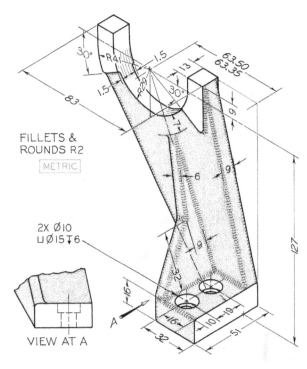

FILLETS &
ROUNDS R2

METRIC

2X Ø10
⌴Ø15↧6

VIEW AT A

Exercise 47 LH Shifter Fork*

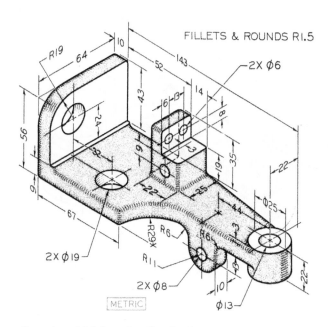

FILLETS & ROUNDS R1.5

2X Ø6

2X Ø19

R II

2X Ø8

Ø13

METRIC

Exercise 46 Mounting Bracket*

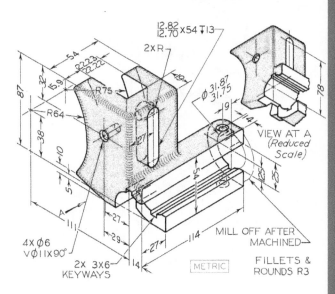

2X R

VIEW AT A
(Reduced
Scale)

MILL OFF AFTER
MACHINED

4X Ø6
∨Ø11X90°

2X 3X6
KEYWAYS

METRIC

FILLETS &
ROUNDS R3

Exercise 48 Gear Shift Bracket*

*Sketch or draw necessary views. Larger and more detailed parts show the details more clearly when drawn on larger sheet sizes. Consider using B, C, or A3 or A2 sheets. Use a title block or title strip as assigned by your instructor. Use metric or decimal-inch dimensions as assigned by your instructor. Move dimensions to better locations where possible.

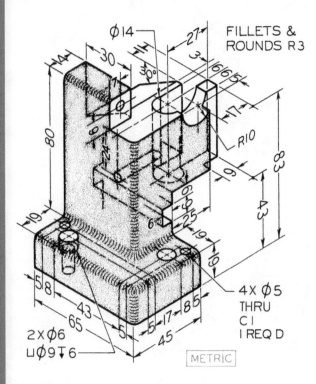

FILLETS &
ROUNDS R 3

Exercise 49 Fixture Base*

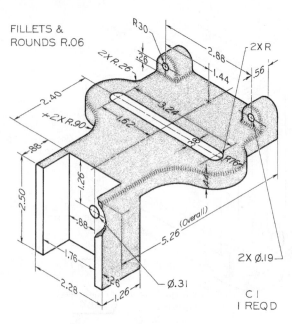

FILLETS &
ROUNDS R.06

Exercise 51 Tension Bracket*

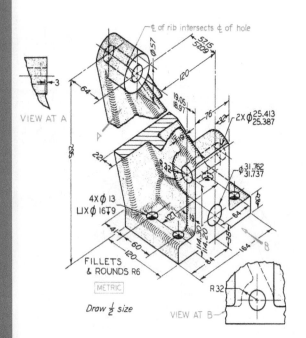

Exercise 50 Ejector Base*

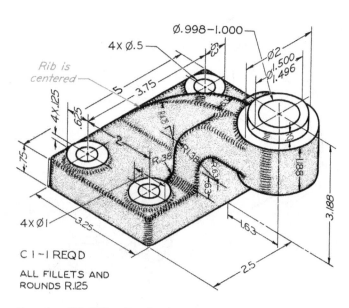

Exercise 52 Offset Bearing*

*Sketch or draw necessary views. Larger and more detailed parts show the details more clearly when drawn on larger sheet sizes. Consider using B, C, or A3 or A2 sheets. Use a title block or title strip as assigned by your instructor. Use metric or decimal-inch dimensions as assigned by your instructor. Move dimensions to better locations where possible.

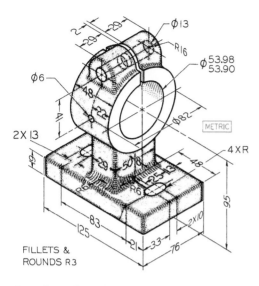

Exercise 53 Feed Guide*

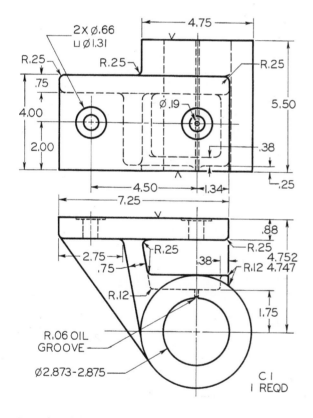

Exercise 54 Feed Shaft Bracket. Given: Front and top views. Required: Front, top, and right-side views, half size.*

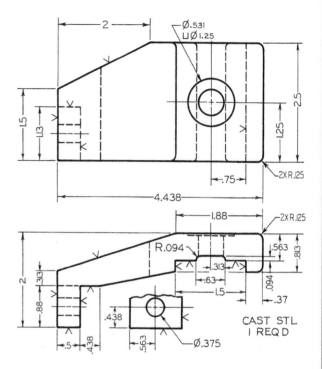

Exercise 55 Trip Lever. Given: Front, top, and partial side views. Required: Front, bottom, and left-side views, drawn completely.*

---

*Sketch or draw necessary views. Larger and more detailed parts show the details more clearly when drawn on larger sheet sizes. Consider using B, C, or A3 or A2 sheets. Use a title block or title strip as assigned by your instructor. Use metric or decimal-inch dimensions as assigned by your instructor. Move dimensions to better locations where possible.

SECTIONAL VIEWS

From Chapter 6 of *Modern Graphics Communication*, Fourth Edition, Frederick E. Giesecke, Alva Mitchell, Henry Cecil Spencer, Ivan Leroy Hill, John Thomas Dygdon, James E. Novak, Shawna Lockhart. Copyright © 2010 by Pearson Education, Inc. Published by Pearson Prentice Hall. All rights reserved.

SECTIONAL VIEWS

After studying the material in this chapter, you should be able to:

1. Understand sections and cutting-plane lines.

2. Apply correct section lining practices.

3. Recognize and draw section lining for ten different materials.

4. Draw a sectional view, given a two-view drawing.

5. Demonstrate correct hidden-line practices for sectional views.

6. Identify seven types of sections.

7. Apply section techniques to create clear interpretable drawings.

8. Demonstrate the proper techniques for sectioning ribs, webs, and spokes.

9. Use hatching when using conventional breaks to show elongated objects.

10. Interpret drawings that include sectional views.

Refer to the following standard:
- ANSI/ASME Y14.3—2003 Multiview and Sectional View Drawings

The companion website for this text is www.prenhall.com/chet_giesecke_modgraphic_4.

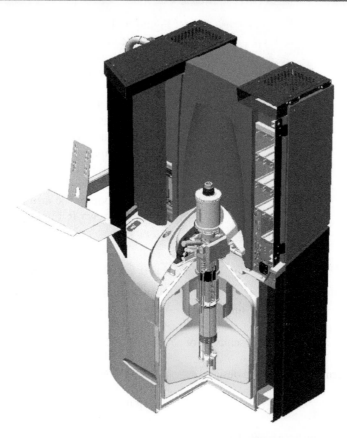

3D Section View of the Superconducting Quantum Interference Device (SQUID). This isometric section view shows the interior details. *Courtesy of Quantum Design.*

OVERVIEW

Technical drawings often represent a single part with a complex interior structure, or many different parts in a mechanical assembly, building, bridge, toy, or other product. When you are creating a drawing, if the interior structure cannot be shown clearly by using hidden lines, you should use a section view to reveal the internal features of the part.

To visualize a section view, think of slicing through the object as if you were cutting through an apple or melon. This familiar cutaway view—looking onto the cut portion of the object—is called a sectional view, or sometimes a cross section.

Special conventions, some that depart from the practices you have learned for orthographic projection, are used to make section views easier to understand.

3D CAD modeling software often cannot generate section views that meet all of these special conventions, so current practice allows for direct sections of the 3D model. 2D and 3D CAD users need to thoroughly understand sectional views to use them effectively.

Selecting the sectional view that best shows the drawing information is a skill that takes practice.

Search the following Web sites to learn more about standard steel beam cross sections (efunda), standard steel shapes (aisc), and a sample of cross sections from the Visible Human (nlm.nih):
- http://www.efunda.com
- http://www.aisc.org
- http://www.nlm.nih.gov

1   Full Section View of a Melon

UNDERSTANDING SECTIONS

Section views are used for three main purposes:

- To document the design and manufacture of single parts that are manufactured as one piece.
- To document how multiple parts are to be assembled or built.
- To aid in visualizing the internal workings of a design.

Sections of Single Parts

If you have ever cut a melon in half, you have created a full section in real life (Figure 1). To visualize a section of a single part is no different. Think of the part as being sliced through by the cutting plane, as if the plane were a giant cleaver. Once the object is cut, the closer half is pulled away, showing the inside construction of the part.

Full Sections

When the part is cut fully in half, the resulting view is called a **full section** as shown in Figure 2. Figure 3 shows a technical drawing of the part from Figure 2 that does not use a section view. Notice how confusing all of the hidden lines make it look.

Figure 4 shows the same drawing, but this time the typical right-side view is replaced with a right-side section view. Now it is much easier to understand.

In a drawing with a section view, the missing half is imagined to be removed and is not actually shown removed in any view except the section view. A line called the **cutting-plane line** provides the information necessary for understanding where the part was cut.

The cutting-plane line shows where the object was cut and from which direction the section is viewed. The arrows at the ends of the cutting-plane line indicate the direction of sight for the section view. The arrows point *toward the section being viewed* as shown in Figures 4 and 5, not away from it, as in Figure 6.

The Cutting Plane

The cutting-plane is shown in a view adjacent to the sectional view, in this case the front view. In this view, the cutting plane appears edgewise as a thick dashed line called the cutting-plane line. The arrows at the ends of the cutting-plane line indicate the direction of sight for the sectional view as shown in Figure 4.

In the section view, the areas that would have been in actual contact with the cutting plane (refer to the visual example shown in Figure 2), are shown with **section lining.** Those areas are cross-hatched with thin parallel section lines.

Lines behind the Cutting Plane

The visible edges of the object behind the cutting plane are generally shown because they are now visible, but they are not cross-hatched with section lining, because they were not cut. Figure 7 shows an example of object edges exposed by the cutting plane appearing as visible lines in the section view. In a full section, the location of the cutting plane is obvious from the section itself, so the cutting-plane line is often omitted. Cutting-plane lines should be used wherever necessary for clarity. You will learn about other types of sections that require the cutting plane line in order to be understood, later in this chapter.

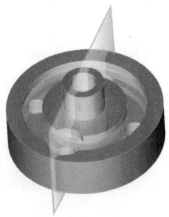

 2   Slicing a Single Part

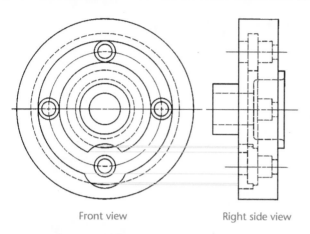

Front view

Right side view

3 Front and Right-Side Views. Parts with a lot of interior detail may have so many hidden lines that their views are confusing.

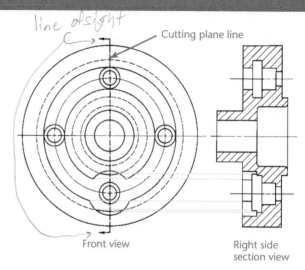

line of sight

Cutting plane line

Front view

Right side section view

4 Front and Right-Side View in Full Section. Using a section view makes it easier to see interior details.

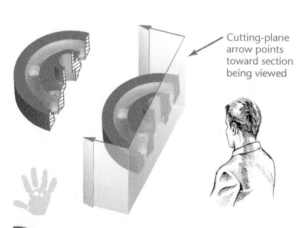

Cutting-plane arrow points toward section being viewed

5 Cutting-plane line indicates direction of sight.

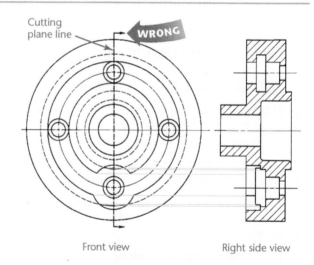

Cutting plane line

WRONG

Front view

Right side view

6 Arrows should not point to removed portion.

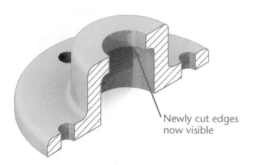

Newly cut edges now visible

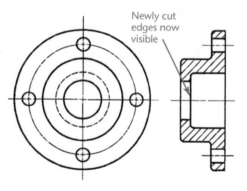

Newly cut edges now visible

7 Newly visible edges cut by cutting plane are cross-hatched with section lining.

VISUALIZING A FULL SECTION

Choose a Cutting Plane

1 This illustration shows a collar to be sectioned. It has a drilled and counterbored hole. To produce a clear section showing both the counterbored hole and the smaller hole near the top of the object, choose a cutting plane that will pass through the vertical center line in the front view and imagine the right half of the object removed.

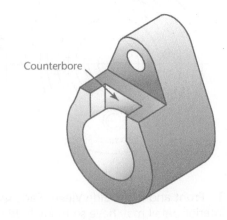

Counterbore

Identify the Surfaces

2 Below is a pictorial drawing of the remaining half. The first step in projecting the section view is making sure that you interpret the object correctly. Identifying the surfaces on the object can help.

Surfaces R, S, T, U, and V have been labeled on the given views and the pictorial view.

Which surface is R in the front view?
Which surface is U in the top view?
Are they normal, inclined, or oblique surfaces?

Can you identify the counterbore in each view?

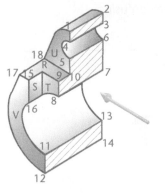

Draw the Section View

3 To draw the section view, omit the portion of the object in front of the cutting plane. You will only be drawing the portion that remains.

Determine which are solid parts of the object the cutting plane will pass through. *Hint: The outside of an object can never be a hole; it must be solid, unless the cutting plane passes through a slot to the exterior.*

The points which will be projected to create the section view have been identified for you in the example shown.

The three surfaces produced by the cutting plane are bounded by points 1-2-3-4 and 5-6-7-8-9-10 and 13-14-12-11. These are shown hatched.

Each sectioned area is completely enclosed by a boundary of visible lines. In addition to the cut surfaces, the sectional view shows all visible parts behind the cutting plane.

No hidden lines are shown. However, the corresponding section shown in this step is incomplete because visible lines are missing.

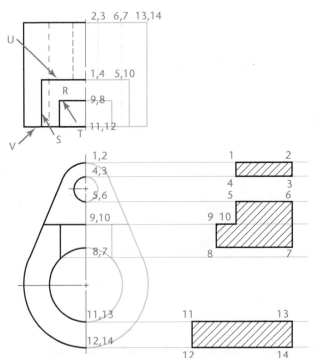

Project the Visible Lines

4 From the direction the section is viewed, the top surface (V) of the object appears in the section as a visible line (12-11-16-15-17).

The bottom surface of the object appears similarly as 14-13-7-6-3-2. The bottom surface of the counterbore appears in the section as line 19-20.

Also, the back half of the counterbore and the drilled hole will appear as rectangles in the section at 19-20-15-16 and 3-4-5-6. These points must also be projected. The finished view is shown at right.

Notice that since all cut surfaces are part of the same object, the hatching must all run in the same direction.

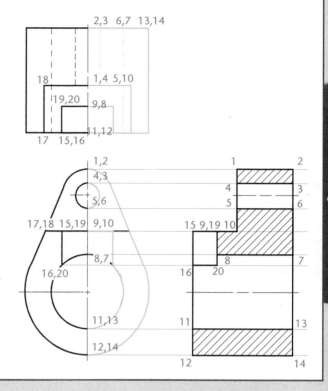

S T E P by S T E P

1 PLACEMENT OF SECTION VIEWS

Section views can replace the normal top, front, side, or other standard orthographic views in the standard view arrangement. Figure 8 shows an example. In this drawing, the front view of the object is shown in section. Only two views are necessary. The front view is shown as a section view and the cutting plane line is shown in the right-side view.

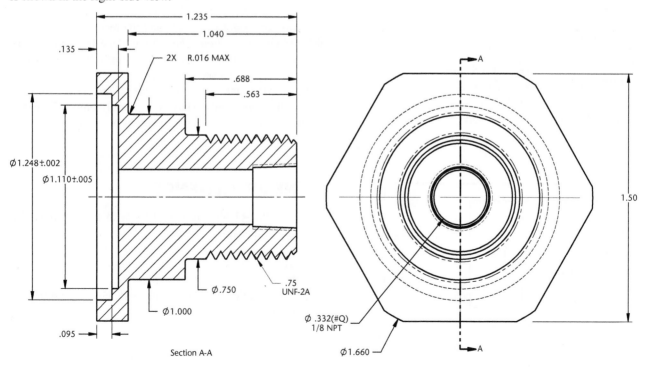

Section A-A

8 Section views can replace standard orthographic views. *Courtesy of Wood's Power-Grip. Co. Inc.*

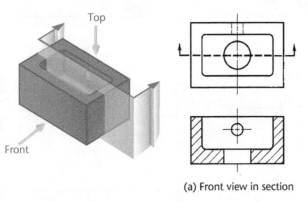

(a) Front view in section

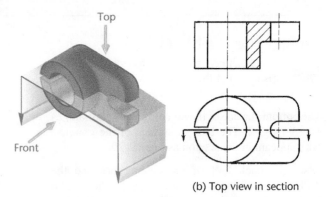

(b) Top view in section

9 Front and Top Views in Section

In Figure 9a, the object is cut through with a plane parallel to the front view. The front half of the object is imagined removed. The resulting full section may be referred to as the "front view in section" because it occupies the front view position.

In Figure 9b, the cutting plane is a horizontal plane (which would appear as a line in the front view). The upper half of the object is imagined removed. The resulting full section is shown in place of the top view.

When adding a section view to your drawing keep in mind that your purpose is to document and convey information about your design and show the information in the way that best achieves this.

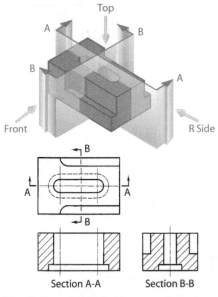

10 Front and Side Views in Section

2 LABELING CUTTING PLANES

In Figure 10, two cutting planes are shown, one a plane parallel to the front view and the other a plane parallel to the side view, both of which appear edgewise in the top view. Each section is completely independent of the other and drawn as if the other were not present.

For section A–A, the front half of the object is imagined removed. The back half is then viewed in the direction of the arrows for a front view, and the resulting section is a front view in section.

For section B–B, the right half of the object is imagined removed. The left half is then viewed in the direction of the arrows for a right-side view, and the resulting section is a right-side view in section. The cutting-plane lines are preferably drawn through an exterior view (in this case the top view, as shown) instead of a sectional view.

The cutting-plane lines in Figure 10 are shown for purposes of illustration only. They are generally omitted in cases where the location of the cutting plane is obvious.

3 LINE PRECEDENCE

When a cutting-plane line coincides with a centerline, the cutting-plane line takes precedence. When the cutting-plane line would obscure important details in the view, just the ends of the line outside the view and the arrows can be shown as in Figure 11. When you do this, be sure to leave a small but visible gap between the lines of the view and the small portion of the cutting-plane line.

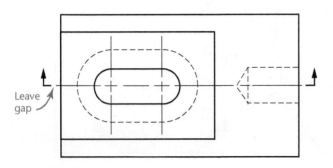

11 The cutting-plane line takes precedence over the centerline.

4 RULES FOR LINES IN SECTION VIEWS

When creating section views follow these general rules:

- Show *edges and contours which are now visible behind the cutting plane*; otherwise a section will appear to be made up of disconnected and unrelated parts. (Occasionally, visible lines behind the cutting plane may be omitted, particularly from those generated from 3D models.)

- Omit *hidden lines in section views*. Section views are used to show interior detail without a confusion of hidden lines, so add them only if necessary to understand the part.

- Sometimes hidden lines are necessary for clarity and should be used in such cases, especially if their use will make it possible to omit a view (Figure 12d).

- A sectioned area is always completely bounded by a visible outline—never by a hidden line, because in every case the cut surfaces will be the closest surface in the section view and therefore their boundary lines will be visible (Figure 12e).

- In a section view of an object, the section lines in all hatched areas for that object must be parallel, not as shown in Figure 12f. The use of section lining in opposite directions is an indication of different parts, as when two or more parts are adjacent in an assembly drawing.

- A visible line can never cross a sectioned area in a view of a single part. This would be impossible on the full section of a single part because the section lines are all in the same plane. A line across it would indicate a change of plane (Figure 12g). In an assembly section, this would be possible. You will learn about assemblies in a later part of the chapter.

TIP

Learning the rules for section lining saves time. Extra hidden lines and hatching that is denser than necessary take longer to draw and make drawings slower to print. They also make drawings harder to read.

TIP

In CAD, when views can be placed by projection from a 3D model, saving time by omitting a view is not a big concern, but saving space on the drawing sheet by leaving out a view may often be.

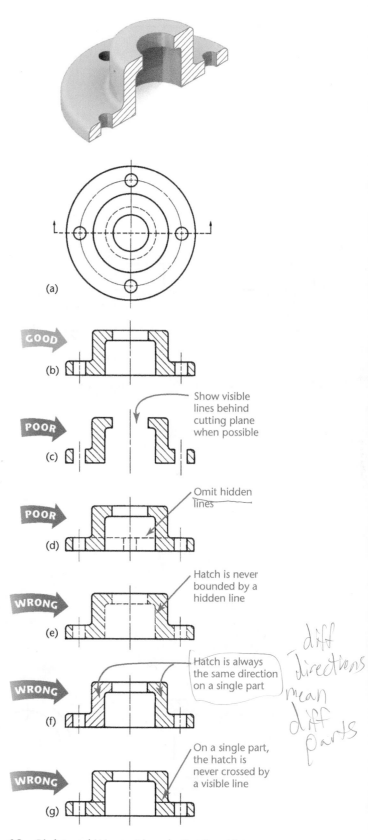

12   Right and Wrong Lines in Section Views

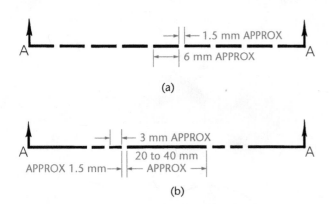

(a)

(b)

13 Cutting-Plane Lines (Full Size)

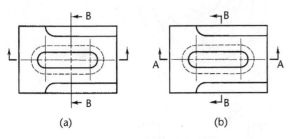

(a)   (b)

14 Alternative Methods for Showing a Cutting Plane

5 CUTTING-PLANE LINE STYLE

Figure 13a shows the preferred style of line to use for the cutting-plane line. It is made up of equal dashes, each about 6 mm (1/4″) long ending in arrowheads. This form works especially well for drawings. The alternative style, shown in Figure 13b, uses alternating long dashes and pairs of short dashes and ends with arrowheads. This style has been in general use for a long time, so you may still see it on drawings. Both lines are drawn the same thickness as visible lines. The arrowheads at the ends of the cutting-plane line indicate the direction in which the cutaway object is viewed (as was shown in Figure 5).

Use capital letters at the ends of the cutting-plane line when necessary to help the drawing's reader match each cutting-plane line to its section view. Figure 10 showed an example where the cutting plane is labeled and the resulting section view is labeled to match. This most often occurs in the case of multiple sections or removed sections, which are discussed later in the chapter.

An alternative method for showing the cutting plane is to draw the cutting-line pattern and then draw reference arrows pointing to it in the direction of sight (Figure 14a).

Especially on architectural drawings, the center of the cutting-plane line is often left out and stylized arrows are used to identify the cutting plane (Figure 14b).

Visualizing Cutting-Plane Direction

Correct and incorrect relations between cutting-plane lines and corresponding sectional views are shown in Figure 15.

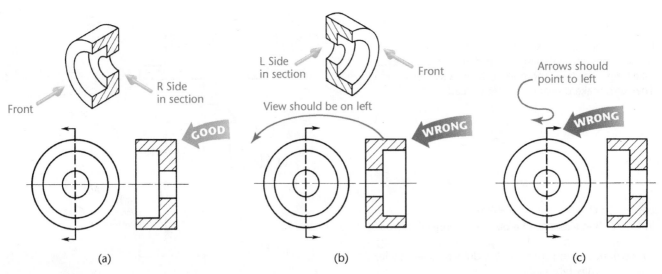

(a)   (b)   (c)

15 Correct and Incorrect Cutting-Plane Line Placement

6 SECTION-LINING TECHNIQUE

The correct method of drawing section lines is shown in Figure 16a. When drawing by hand, use a sharp, medium-grade pencil (H or 2H) to draw uniformly thin section lines, or **hatching** (a term meaning closely spaced parallel lines). There should be a marked contrast between the thin section lines and the thick visible outlines of the part.

Draw section lines at 45° from horizontal unless they would be parallel or perpendicular to major edges of the part, in which case use a different angle. Figure 16b shows an example of section lines drawn at a different angle to prevent them from being parallel or perpendicular to visible outlines.

Space the lines as evenly as possible by eye (for most drawings, about 2.5 mm (1/32″) apart). The spacing interval depends on the size of the drawing or of the sectioned area, with larger drawings having wider spacing. In a smaller drawing the spacing interval may be as small as 1.5 mm (1/16″) while in a large drawing, it may be 3 mm (1/8″) or more. As a rule, space the lines as generously as possible, yet close enough to clearly distinguish the sectioned areas.

Keep extension lines and dimension values off sectioned areas. If there is no alternative, omit the section lines behind the dimensions (Figure 16c).

Tear out Worksheet 1. Draw the right-side view.

> **TIP**
>
> Beginners tend to draw section lines too close together. This is tedious and makes small inaccuracies in spacing obvious. After the first few lines, look back repeatedly at the original spacing to avoid gradually increasing or decreasing the intervals between the lines.

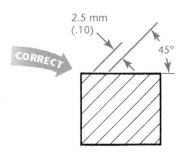

- Uniformly spaced by an interval of about 2.5mm
- Not too close together
- Uniformly thin, not varying in thickness
- Distinctly thinner than visible lines
- Do not run beyond or stop short of visible outlines

(a) Correctly drawn section lines

Spacing irregular

Lines too close

Varying line widths

Lines too thick

Lines short or overrunning

(b) Direction of Section Lines

If section lines drawn at 45° with horizontal would be parallel or perpendicular (or nearly so) to a prominent visible outline, the angle should be changed to 30°, 60°, or some other angle.

      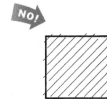

Angle of section lines is adjusted

Lines should not be parallel to outline

Lines should not be perpendicular to outline

(c) Dimensions and Section Lines

Keep extension lines and values for dimensions off crosshatched areas, but when this is unavoidable, the crosshatching should be omitted where the dimension figure is placed.

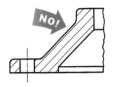 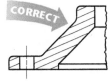 

O.K.

Extension lines and dimension values are not on hatched area

Section lines are omitted behind dimensioning

Dimensioning should not be on hatched area

16 Correct and Incorrect Section-Lining Technique

Section-Lining Large Areas

When adding section lines to a large area, use outline sectioning, where the center portion of the hatched area is left blank to save time and make the view more legible, as shown in Figure 17.

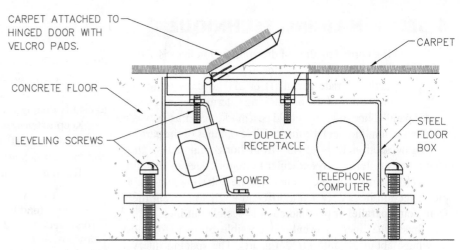

17 Outline Sectioning. *Courtesy of Associated Construction Engineering.*

Section-Lining Symbols

Section-lining symbols (Figure 18) may be used to indicate specific materials. These symbols represent general material types only, such as cast iron, brass, and steel. Because there are so many different types of materials (there are hundreds of types of steel, for example), a general name or symbol is not enough. A detailed specification listing the material must be lettered in the form of a note or in the title strip.

The general-purpose section lining (which is the same as that for cast iron) may be used to represent any material on the detail drawing for a single part.

Using different section-lining patterns helps you distinguish different materials, especially on assembly drawings, but it is acceptable to use the general-purpose symbol shown at different angles for different parts.

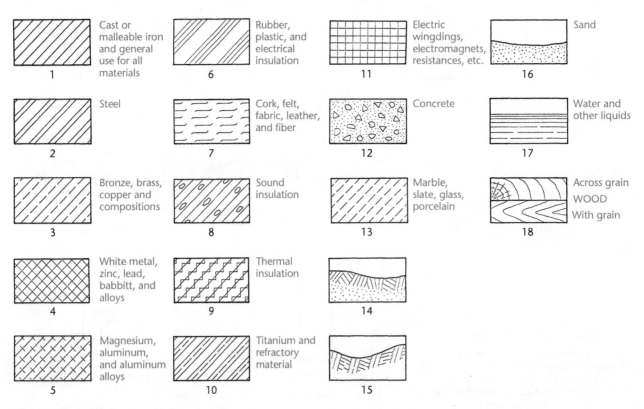

18 Symbols for Section Lining

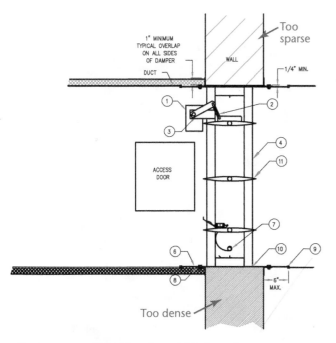

19 Incorrect Hatching in a CAD Drawing

Section-Lining in CAD

CAD programs usually include libraries that allow you to select from a variety of section lining patterns, making it easy to use different patterns, angles, and scales for the spacing of the pattern. When using CAD software to hatch an area in the drawing, be careful to specify a scale that relates to the printed drawing scale for that sheet. Otherwise the hatching may turn out so dense that the object appears to be filled in solidly, or so sparse that you do not see any hatching (Figure 19).

7 HALF SECTIONS

Objects that are symmetric can be shown effectively using a special type of section view called a **half section** (Figure 20). A half section exposes the interior for one half of the object and the exterior of the other half. This is done by removing one quarter of the object to produce a section view with one half in section and the other half as viewed from the outside. Half sections are not widely used to create detail drawings showing how to make a single part because it can be difficult to show all of the dimensions clearly when some internal features are only partly shown in the sectioned half (Figure 20b).

In general,

• Omit hidden lines from both halves of a half section, whenever possible.

• Use a centerline to divide the sectioned half and the unsectioned half, as shown in Figure 20b.

Half section drawings are most useful in showing an assembly where it is often necessary to show both internal and external construction in one drawing view and usually without dimensioning. A broken out section may be preferred in some cases.

Tear out Worksheet 2. Add the right-side view as a half section.

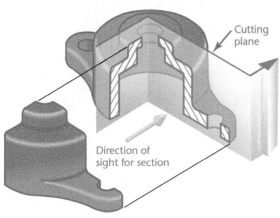

(a) Cutting plane

(b) Half section

20 Half Section

A 3D broken out section of a diesel engine by Caterpillar reveals its pistons.
Courtesy of Caterpillar, Inc.

8 BROKEN OUT SECTIONS

It often happens that only a partial section of a view is needed to expose interior shapes. Such a section, limited by a break line, is called a **broken out section.**

In Figure 21, a full or half section is not necessary, and a small broken out section is sufficient to explain the construction.

In Figure 22, a half section would have caused the removal of half the keyway. The keyway is preserved by breaking out around it. In this case, the section is limited partly by a break line and partly by a centerline in the drawing.

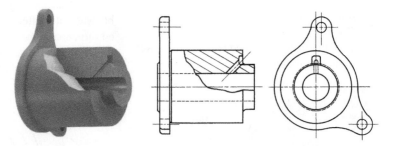

21   Broken Out Section

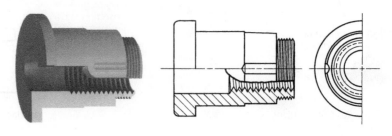

22   Break around Keyway

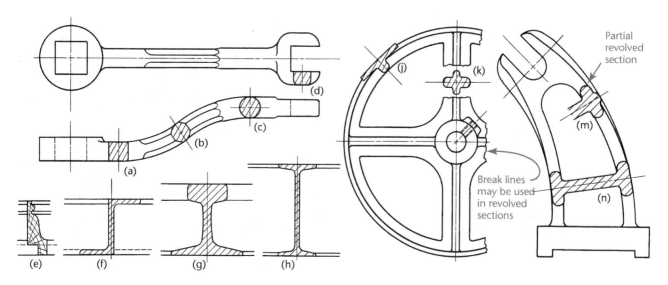

23   Revolved Sections

9 REVOLVED SECTIONS

You can show the shape of the cross section of a bar, arm, spoke, or other elongated object in the longitudinal view by using a **revolved section.** Figure 23 shows examples of how revolved sections look in a drawing.

To create a revolved section, first imagine a cutting plane perpendicular to the centerline or axis of the object, as shown in Figure 24a. Next, revolve the plane 90° about a center line at right angles to the axis as shown in Figures 24b and 24c.

The visible lines adjacent to a revolved section may be broken out if desired, as shown in Figure 25.

When you superimpose the revolved section over the top of the view, be sure that any original lines of the view that are covered by the revolved view are removed (Figure 26a).

Show the true shape of the revolved section, regardless of the direction of the lines in the view (Figure 26b).

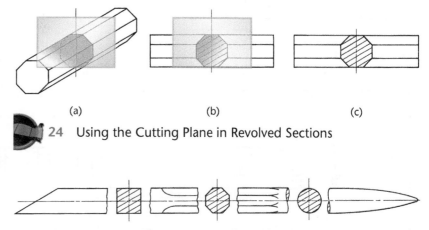

(a)   (b)   (c)

24   Using the Cutting Plane in Revolved Sections

25   Conventional Breaks Used with Revolved Sections

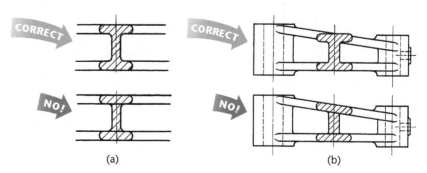

(a)   (b)

26   Common Errors in Drawing Revolved Sections

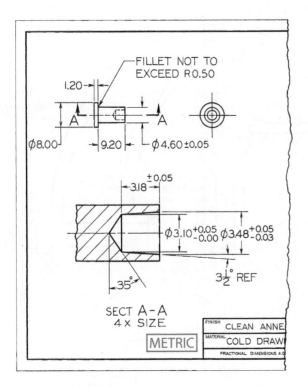

27 Removed Section

10 REMOVED SECTIONS

A **removed section** (Figure 27) is one that is not in direct projection from the view containing the cutting plane—that is, it is not positioned in agreement with the standard arrangement of views. Be sure to keep the section in its normal orientation and do not turn it a different direction on the sheet. If you must rotate the view, use a **rotation arrow** as shown in Figure 28 and note the angle the view was rotated.

Removed sections should be labeled, such as section A–A and section B–B, corresponding to the letters at the ends of the cutting-plane line (Figure 27). They should be arranged in alphabetical order from left to right on the sheet. Section letters should be used in alphabetical order, but letters I, O, and Q should not be used because they are easily confused with the numeral 1 or the zero. Figure 29 shows several removed sections.

28 Rotation Arrow Symbol. Use this to label a view that has been rotated. h = letter height in the drawing.

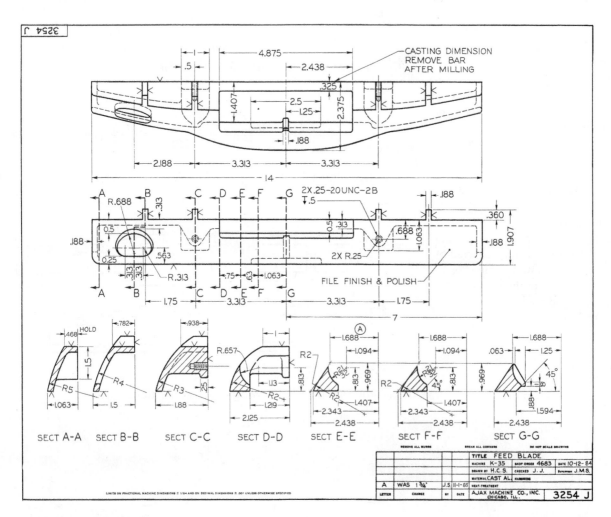

29 Removed Sections

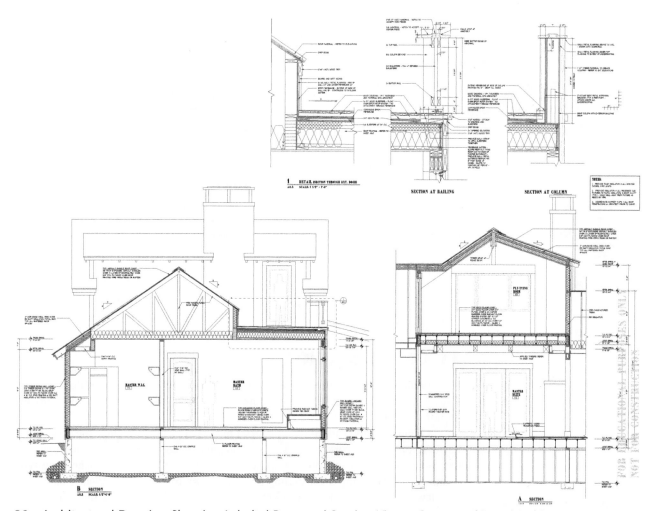

30 Architectural Drawing Showing Labeled Removed Section Views. *Courtesy of Locati Architects.*

A removed section is often a **partial section,** where only a portion of the section view is drawn. Removed sections are frequently drawn to an enlarged scale (Figure 29) to show detail and provide space for dimensions. When using an enlarged scale be sure to indicate the scale below the section view's title.

A removed section should be placed so that it no longer lines up in projection with any other view. It should be separated clearly from the standard arrangement of views (see Figure 30). Whenever possible, removed sections should be on the same sheet as the regular views. If a section must be placed on a different sheet, cross-references should be given on the related sheets. A note should be given below the section title, such as

SECTION B-B ON SHEET 4, ZONE A3

A similar note should be placed on the sheet on which the cutting-plane line is shown, with a leader pointing to the cutting-plane line and referring to the sheet on which the section will be found. Sometimes it is convenient to place removed sections on centerlines extended from the section cuts (Figure 31).

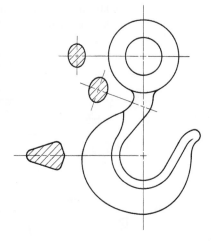

31 Removed Sections on Centerlines

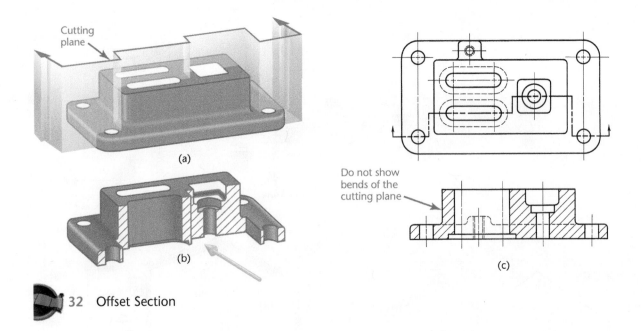

Cutting plane

(a)

(b)

Do not show bends of the cutting plane

(c)

32   Offset Section

11 OFFSET SECTIONS

In sectioning complex objects, it is often desirable to show features that do not lie in a straight line by "offsetting" or bending the cutting plane. These are called **offset sections.**

In Figure 32a the cutting plane is offset in several places to include the hole at the left end, one of the parallel slots, the rectangular recess, and one of the holes at the right end. The front portion of the object is then imagined to be removed (Figure 32b). The path of the cutting plane is shown by the cutting-plane line in the top view (Figure 32c), and the resulting offset section is shown in the front view.

- The offsets or bends in the cutting plane are all 90°.
- The bends in the cutting plane are never shown in the sectional view.

Figure 32 also illustrates how hidden lines in a section eliminate the need for an additional view. In this case, an extra view would be needed to show the small boss on the back if hidden lines were not shown.

Figure 33 shows an example of multiple offset sections. Notice that the visible background shapes appear in each sectional view without the use of hidden lines. It is also acceptable to show only the cut portion, but the views are easier to interpret when the lines that are visible behind the cutting plane are shown.

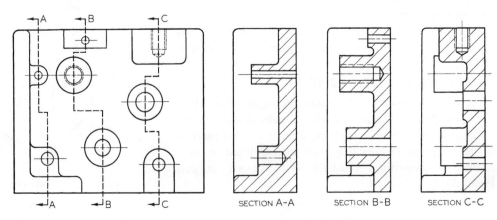

SECTION A-A   SECTION B-B   SECTION C-C

33   Three Offset Sections

12 RIBS IN SECTION

To avoid a false impression of thickness and solidity, ribs, webs, gear teeth, and other similar flat features are not hatched with section lining even though the cutting plane slices them. For example, in Figure 34, the cutting plane A–A slices through the center of the vertical web, or rib, and the web is not sectioned (Figure 34a). Do not hatch thin features even though the cutting plane passes lengthwise through them. The incorrect section is shown in Figure 34b. Note the false impression of thickness or solidity resulting from section lining the rib.

If the cutting plane passes crosswise through a rib or any thin member, as in section B–B, section line the feature in the usual manner, as in the top view of Figure 34c.

If a rib is not sectioned when the cutting plane passes through it flatwise, it is sometimes difficult to tell whether the rib is actually present, as, for example, ribs A in Figures 35a and 35b. It is difficult to distinguish spaces B as open spaces and spaces A as ribs. In such cases, double-spaced section lining of the ribs should be used (Figure 35c). This consists simply of continuing alternate section lines through the ribbed areas, as shown.

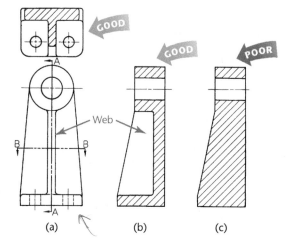

34 Web in Section

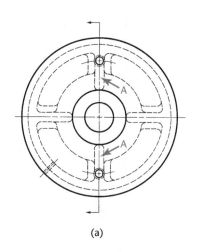

(a)

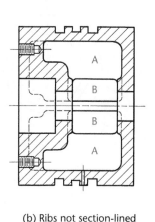

(b) Ribs not section-lined

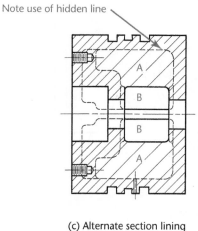

(c) Alternate section lining

35 Alternate Sectioning

13 ALIGNED SECTIONS

When sectioning parts with angled elements, the cutting plane may be bent to pass through those features. The plane and features are then imagined to be revolved into the original plane. For example, Figure 36 shows an **aligned section.** The cutting plane was bent to pass through the angled arm and then revolved to a vertical position (aligned), from where it was projected across to the sectional view.

The angle of revolution should always be less than 90° for an aligned section.

Do not revolve features when the clarity of your drawing is not improved. In the exercises later in the chapter, you will see examples showing when revolution should not be used.

Follow the direction on Worksheet 3 to practice drawing an aligned section.

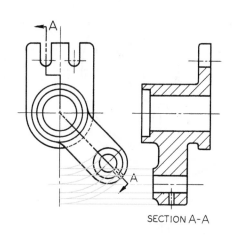

SECTION A-A

36 Aligned Section

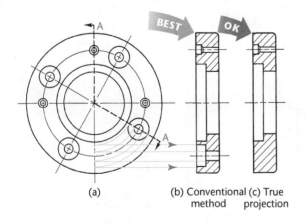

(a) (b) Conventional (c) True
method projection

37 Aligned Section

In Figure 37 the cutting plane is bent to include one of the drilled and counterbored holes in the sectional view. The correct section view in Figure 37b gives a clearer and more complete description than does the section in Figure 37c, which is shown without any bend in the cutting plane.

In Figure 38a, the projecting lugs are not sectioned for the same reason that the ribs are not sectioned. In Figure 38b, the projecting lugs are located so that the cutting plane passes through them crosswise; therefore, they are sectioned.

Another example involving rib sectioning and aligned sectioning is shown in Figure 39. In the circular view, the cutting plane is offset in circular-arc bends to include the upper hole and upper rib, the keyway and center hole, the lower rib, and one of the lower holes. These features are imagined to be revolved until they line up vertically and are then projected from that position to obtain the section shown in Figure 39b. Note that the ribs are not sectioned. If a regular full section of the object were drawn without using the conventions discussed here, the resulting section (Figure 39c) would be incomplete and confusing and would take more time to draw. Showing the

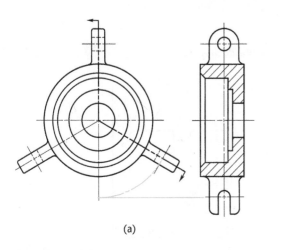

(a)

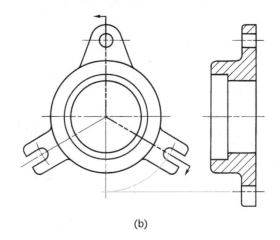

(b)

38 Aligned Section

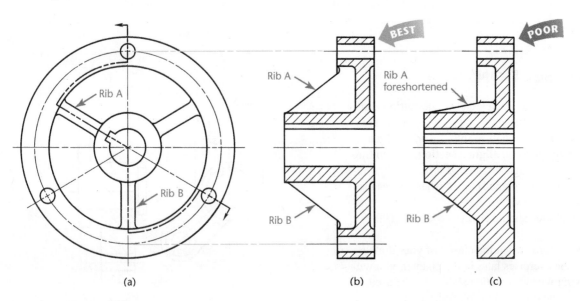

(a) (b) (c)

39 Symmetry of Ribs

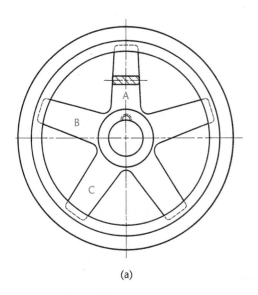

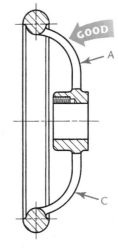

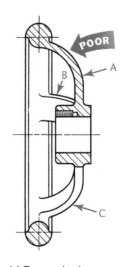

(a)   (b) Conventional method   (c) True projection

40   Spokes in Section

actual section is acceptable when it is generated from a 3D model. When doing so, take care to provide clear views that can be interpreted by the reader.

In sectioning a pulley or any spoked wheel (Figure 40a), it is standard practice to revolve the spokes if necessary (if there is an odd number) and not to section line the spokes (Figure 40b). If the spoke is sectioned, the section gives a false impression of continuous metal (Figure 40c). If the lower spoke is not revolved, it will be foreshortened in the sectional view, in which it presents an "amputated" and a misleading appearance.

Figure 40 also illustrates correct practice in omitting visible lines in a sectional view. Notice that spoke B is omitted in Figure 40b. If it is included, as shown in Figure 40c, the spoke is foreshortened, difficult and time-consuming to draw, and confusing to the reader of the drawing.

14 PARTIAL VIEWS

If space is limited on the paper or to save time, partial views may be used with sectioning (Figure 41). Half views are shown in Figures 41a and 41b in connection with a full section and a half section, respectively. In each case the back half of the object in the circular view is shown, to remove the front portion of the object and expose the back portion in the section.

Another method of drawing a partial view is to break out much of the circular view, retaining only those features that are needed for minimum representation (Figure 41c).

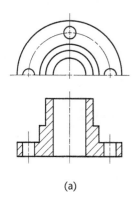

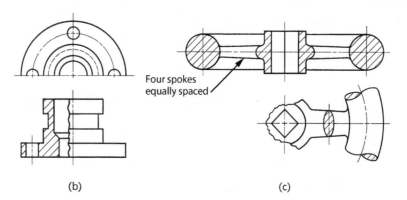

Four spokes equally spaced

(a)   (b)   (c)

41   Partial Views

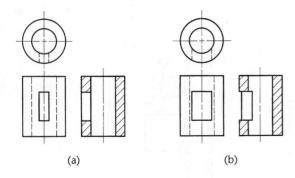

(a)   (b)

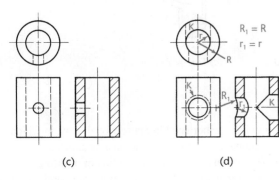

(c)   (d)

42   Intersections

15 INTERSECTIONS IN SECTIONS

Where an intersection is small or unimportant in a section, it is standard practice to disregard the true projection of the figure of intersection, as shown in Figures 42a and 42c. Larger intersections may be projected, as shown in Figure 42b, or approximated by circular arcs, as shown for the smaller hole in Figure 42d. Note that the larger hole K is the same diameter as the vertical hole. In such cases the curves of intersection (ellipses) appear as straight lines, as shown.

16 CONVENTIONAL BREAKS AND SECTIONS

Cross-hatching is often added when showing a conventional break. **Conventional breaks** are used to shorten the view of an object that is too long to show clearly at one scale on the drawing sheet. Figure 43 shows examples of hatching on conventional breaks. The parts to be broken must have the same section throughout, or if they are tapered they must have a uniform taper.

The breaks used on cylindrical shafts or tubes are often referred to as "S-breaks" and are usually drawn by eye, although S-break templates are available.

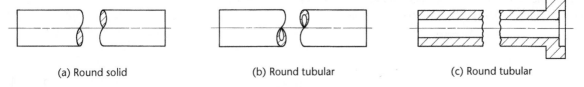

(a) Round solid   (b) Round tubular   (c) Round tubular

43   Conventional breaks often show crosshatching to show the cut material.

17 ASSEMBLY SECTIONS

Section views are often used to create assembly drawings. Figure 44 shows an orthographic drawing for an assembly. Notice that the hatching on different parts is shown using different hatch patterns or hatch at different angles. On the same part the hatching is always at the same angle to help you recognize the parts easily. Solid features that do not have interior structure are not hatched.

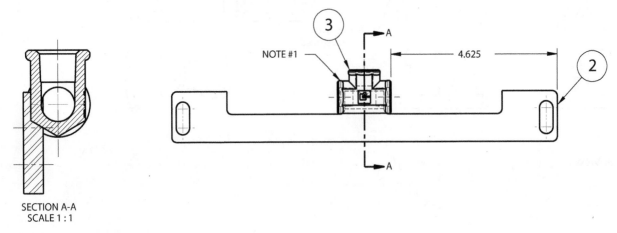

SECTION A-A
SCALE 1 : 1

44   Assembly Section. *Courtesy of Wood's Power-Grip Co., Inc.*

COMPUTER TECHNIQUES FOR SECTIONS

2D and 3D sectional views are created using CAD. Most CAD systems have a "hatch" command to generate the section lining and hatch patterns to fill an area automatically. A wide variety of hatch patterns are generally available to show materials such as steel, bronze, sand, concrete, and many more.

Creating a full-section view from a 3D model is generally very easy. You often only need to define the cutting plane, viewing direction, scale, and where to place the view on the sheet. Often the hatching for the cut surfaces is generated automatically. Sectioned views other than full sections can be more difficult to create. To create good sectional drawings using CAD, you should have a clear understanding of the standards for showing section views.

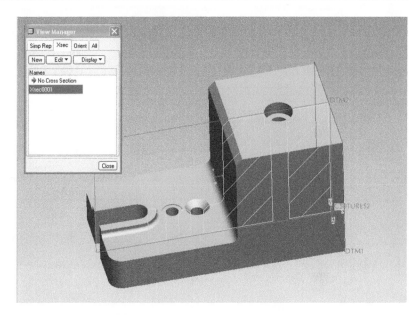

A Section Created in the 3D Model Using Pro/Engineer Wildfire Software's View Manager. *Courtesy of PTC.*

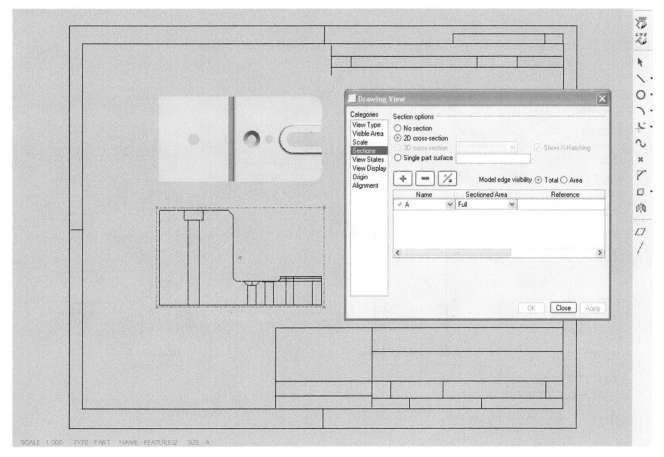

Sections can quickly be shown in orthographic drawings generated from a 3D model using CAD software such as Pro/Engineer. *Courtesy of PTC.*

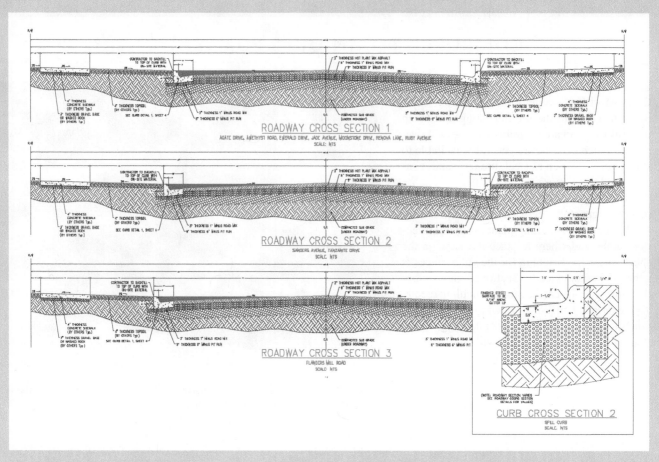

Roadway Sections. (Excerpted from a Larger Drawing). *Courtesy of Locati Architects.*

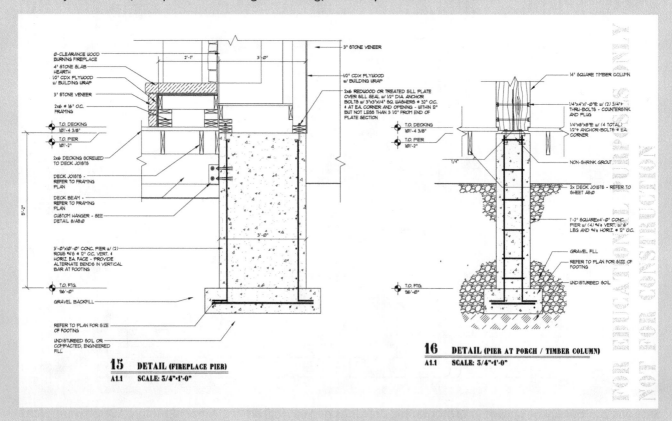

Section Detail. (Excerpted from a Larger Drawing). *Courtesy of Locati Architects.*

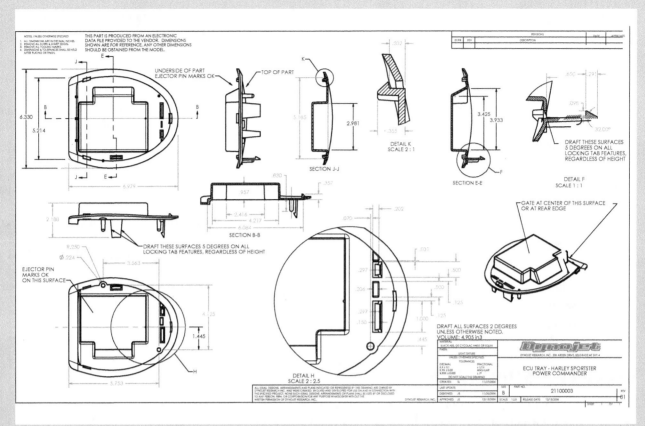

Detail Drawing for an Injection Molded Plastic Part with Removed Section Views. *Courtesy of Dynojet Research, Inc.*

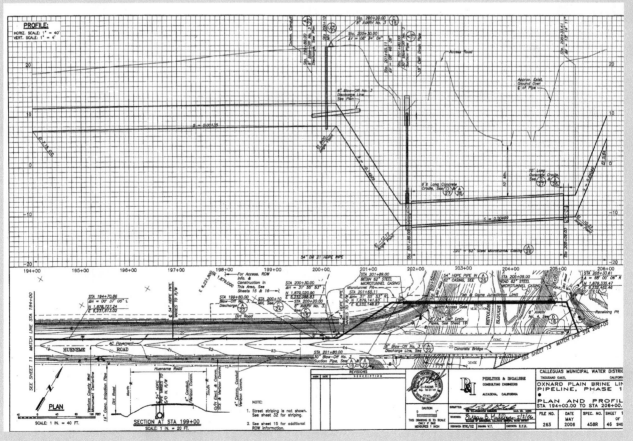

Plan and Profile Drawing with Sections. *Courtesy of Perliter & Ingalsbee Consulting Engineers.*

KEY WORDS

Section Views

Full Section

Cutting-Plane Line

Section Lining

Hatching

Section-Lining Symbols

Half Section

Broken Out Section

Revolved Section

Removed Section

Rotation Arrow

Partial Section

Offset Section

Aligned Section

Conventional Breaks

CHAPTER SUMMARY

Now that you have finished this chapter, you should be able to:

- Show internal details of objects without the need for hidden lines through the use of section views.
- Imagine a variety of objects cut apart along a cutting-plane line.
- Show section lining (hatching) to indicate the solid parts of the object which would be cut by the cutting plane.
- Check that you are not showing hidden lines where they would no longer be needed because the internal surfaces are exposed when the object is imagined cut.
- Use section-lining symbols to indicate the material of the object.
- Leave the section-lining off ribs, webs, and spokes that are sectioned lengthwise.
- Revolve symmetric features so the sectional view depicts the part's symmetry.
- Use conventional breaks on drawings to show object details when they would appear too small at a scale where the entire object would be shown on the sheet.
- Identify cross section assembly drawings.

REVIEW QUESTIONS

1. What does the cutting-plane line represent?
2. Sketch the section line symbols for 10 different materials.
3. List seven different types of sections and sketch an example of each.
4. Which sectional views are used to replace an existing primary view? Which sectional views are used in addition to the primary views?
5. How much of an object is imagined to be cut away in a half section?
6. What type of line is used to show the boundary of a broken out section?
7. Why are hidden lines generally omitted in a sectional view?
8. Why are some symmetrical features, like spokes and webs, revolved in the sectional view?
9. Why is a rib outlined with object lines and not filled with section lining?

SECTIONING EXERCISES

Any of the following exercises may be drawn freehand or with CAD. Study the chapter on dimensioning first if you are going to add dimensions to your drawings. Show cutting-plane lines for practice. Can you tell that in Exercises 4 number 2 and number 14 the cutting-plane lines should be shown to make the drawing easy to interpret?

Freehand Sectioning Problems

Exercises 1–4 are especially suited for sketching on 8.5" × 11" graph paper with appropriate grid squares. Sketch one or two problems per sheet, adding section views as indicated. To make your drawings fit on the paper easily, use each grid square as equal to either 6 mm or 1/4". An example is shown below.
Freehand Sectioning Exercise Example

Exercise 1 Freehand Sectioning Problems. Redraw the given views and add the front section view.

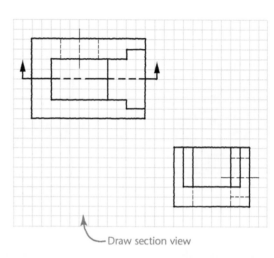

Draw section view

Exercise 2 Freehand Sectioning Problems. Redraw the top view, rotate the side view and move it into a position so that you can project the front view in section. Add the front section view. Each grid square equals 6 mm (¹/₄").

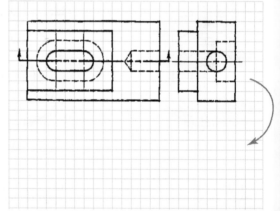

Rotate side view into position

Exercise 3 Freehand Sectioning Problems. Use the same directions for Exercise 2.

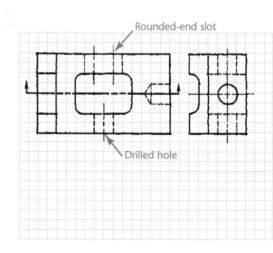

Rounded-end slot

Drilled hole

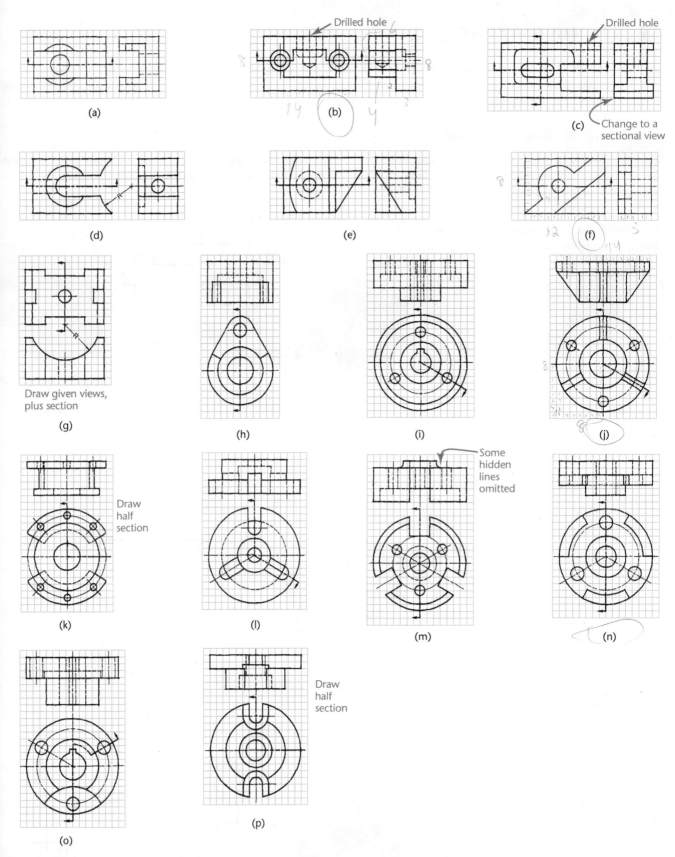

(a)

(b)

Drilled hole

14

4

3

(c)

Drilled hole

Change to a
sectional view

(d)

(e)

(f)

Draw given views,
plus section

(g)

(h)

(i)

(j)

Draw
half
section

(k)

(l)

Some
hidden
lines
omitted

(m)

(n)

(o)

Draw
half
section

(p)

Exercise 4 Freehand Sectioning Problems. Sketch views and add sections as indicated by the cutting-plane lines. Cutting-plane lines can be omitted except for parts B and C.

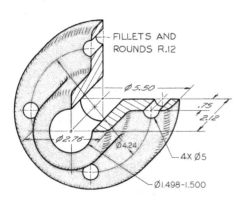

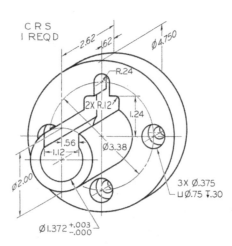

Exercise 5 Bearing. Draw necessary views, with full section.*

Exercise 8 Centering Bushing. Draw necessary views, with full section.*

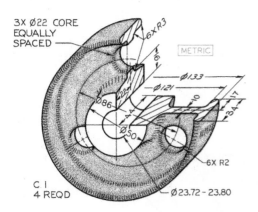

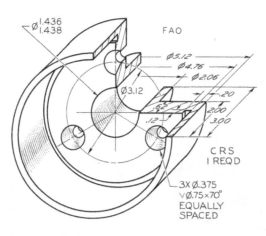

Exercise 6 Truck Wheel. Draw necessary views, with full section.*

Exercise 9 Special Bearing. Draw necessary views, with full section.*

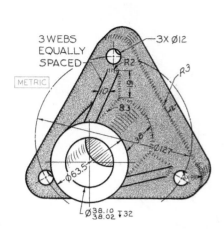

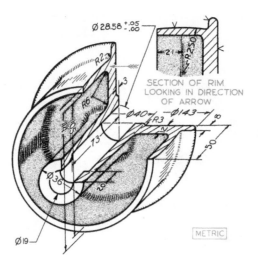

Exercise 7 Column Support. Draw necessary views, with broken out section.*

Exercise 10 Idler Pulley. Draw necessary views, with full section.*

*Leave out dimensions unless assigned by your instructor.

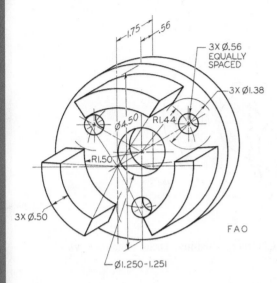

Exercise 11 Cup Washer. Draw necessary views, with full section.*

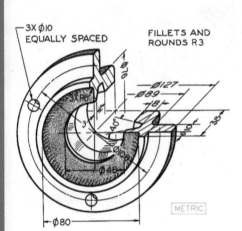

Exercise 12 Fixed Bearing Cup. Draw necessary views, with full section.*

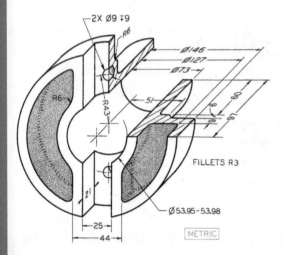

Exercise 13 Stock Guide. Draw necessary views, with half section.*

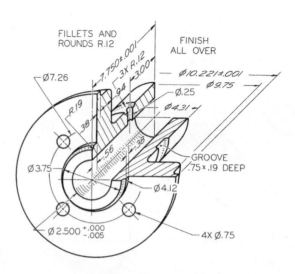

Exercise 14 Bearing. Draw necessary views, with half section. Scale: half size.*

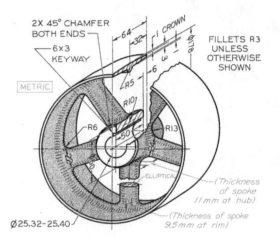

Exercise 15 Pulley. Draw necessary views, with full section, and revolved section of spoke.*

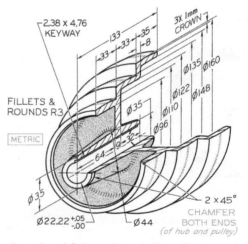

Exercise 16 Step-Cone Pulley. Draw necessary views, with full section.*

*Leave out dimensions unless assigned by your instructor.

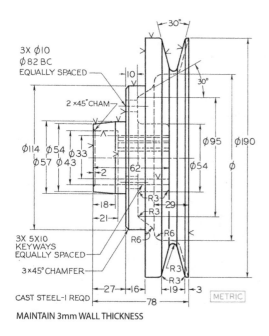

3X Ø10
Ø 82 BC
EQUALLY SPACED

2 ×45° CHAM

30°

30°

10

Ø95

Ø190

Ø114 Ø54 Ø33
Ø57 Ø43

Ø54

Ø

2

62

R3

29

R3

18

21

R6

R6

3X 5X10
KEYWAYS
EQUALLY SPACED

3×45° CHAMFER

R3

R3

CAST STEEL-I REQD

27   16   19   3

78

METRIC

MAINTAIN 3mm WALL THICKNESS

Exercise 17 Sheave. Draw two views, including half section.*

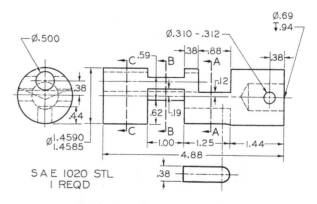

Ø.500

Ø.310 - .312

.38   .88

C   .59   B   A

Ø.69
.94

.38

.38

.12

.44

.62   .19

Ø1.4590
Ø1.4585

C   B   A

1.00   1.25   1.44

4.88

.38

S A E 1020 STL
I REQD

Exercise 18 Operating Valve. Given: Front, left-side, and partial bottom views. Required: Front, right-side, and full bottom views, plus indicated removed sections.*

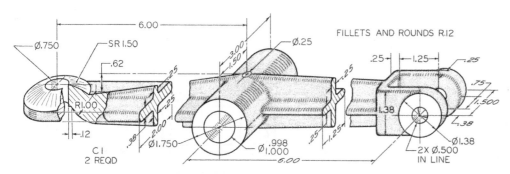

6.00

Ø.750

SR 1.50

.62

3.00

1.50

Ø.25

FILLETS AND ROUNDS R.12

.25

.25   1.25   .25

R1.00

.25

.75

1.500

.12

.38

2.00

.38

1.38

C I
2 REQD

Ø1.750

.998
1.000

.25   1.25

6.00

2X Ø.500
IN LINE

Ø1.38

Exercise 19 Rocker Arm. Draw necessary views, with revolved sections.*

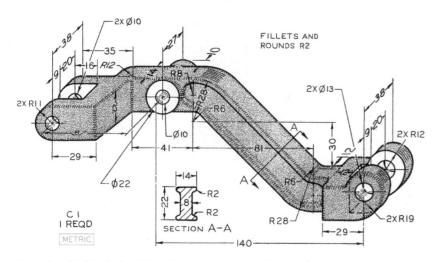

2X Ø10

.38

.27

10

FILLETS AND
ROUNDS R2

35

16   R12

R8

R28

2X Ø13

.38

9/20

R6

R6

2X R11

Ø10

A

30

9/20

2X R12

29

41

81

A

2X R19

Ø22

14

R2

22

8

R2

C I
I REQD

R28

R6

29

SECTION A-A

140

METRIC

Exercise 20 Dash Pot Lifter. Draw necessary views, using revolved section instead of removed section.*

*Leave out dimensions unless assigned by your instructor.

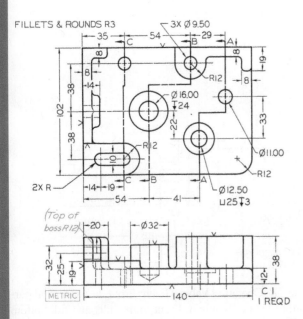

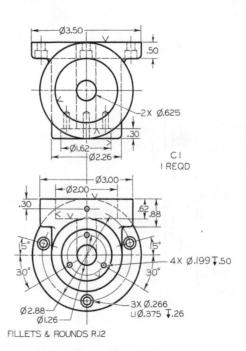

Exercise 21 Adjuster Base. Given: Front and top views. Required: Front and top views and sections A–A, B–B, and C–C. Show all visible lines.*

Exercise 23 Hydraulic Fitting. Given: Front and top views. Required: Front and top views and right-side view in full section.*

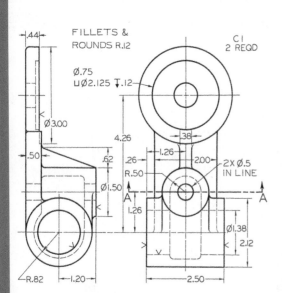

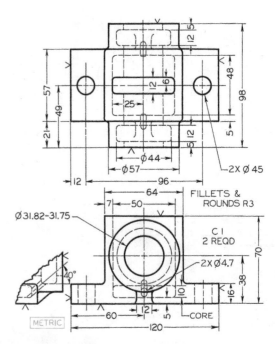

Exercise 22 Mobile Housing. Given: Front and left-side views. Required: Front view, right-side view in full section, and removed section A–A.*

Exercise 24 Auxiliary Shaft Bearing. Given: Front and top views. Required: Front and top views and right-side view in full section.*

*Leave out dimensions unless assigned by your instructor.

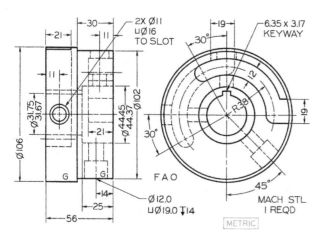

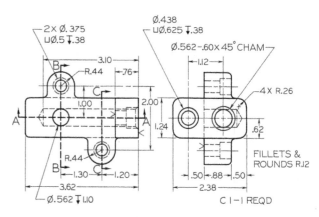

Exercise 25 Traverse Spider. Given: Front and left-side views. Required: Front and right-side views and top view in full section.*

Exercise 27 Bracket. Given: Front and right-side views. Required: Take front as new top; then add right-side view, front view in full section A–A, and sections B–B and C–C.*

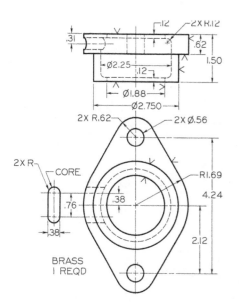

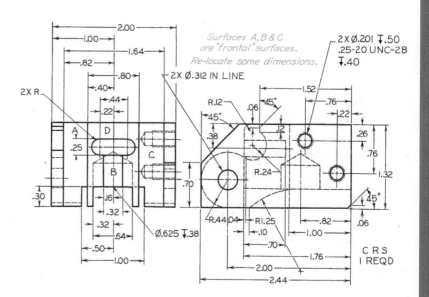

Exercise 26 Gland. Given: Front, top, and partial left-side views. Required: Front view and right-side view in full section.*

Exercise 28 Cocking Block. Given: Front and right-side views. Required: Take front as new top view; then add new front view, and right-side view in full section. Draw double size.*

*Leave out dimensions unless assigned by your instructor.

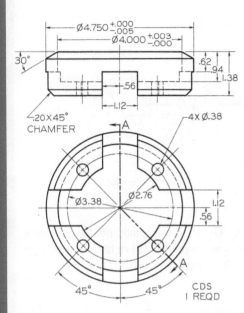

Exercise 29 Packing Ring. Given: Front and top views. Required: Front view and section A–A.*

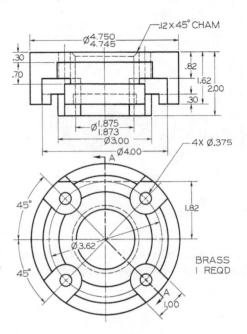

Exercise 31 Oil Retainer. Given: Front and top views. Required: Front view and section A–A.*

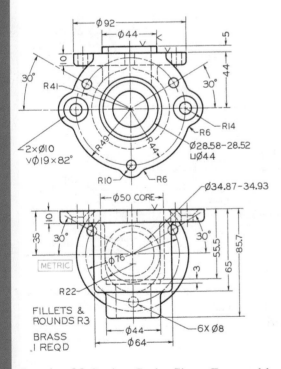

Exercise 30 Strainer Body. Given: Front and bottom views. Required: Front and top views and right-side view in full section.*

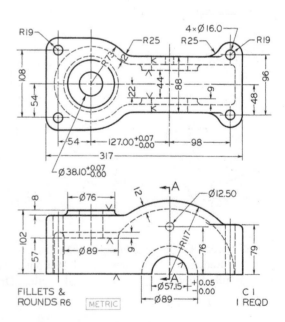

Exercise 32 Gear Box. Given: Front and top views. Required: Front in full section, bottom view, and right-side section A–A. Draw half size.*

*Leave out dimensions unless assigned by your instructor.

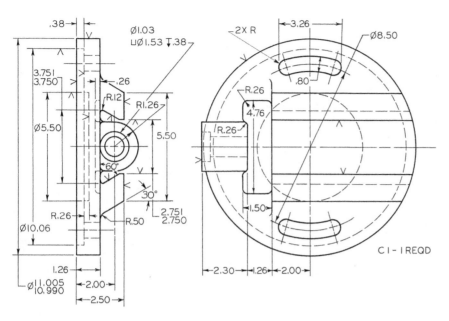

Exercise 33 Slotted Disk for Threading Machine. Given: Front and left-side views. Required: Front and right-side views and top full-section view. Draw half size.*

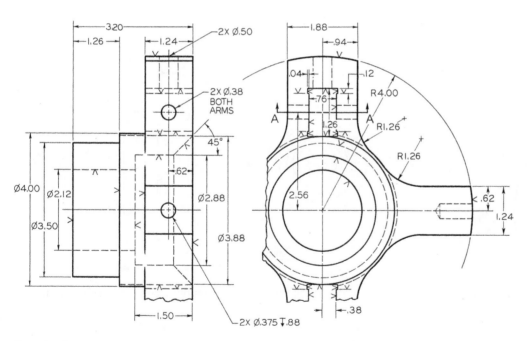

Exercise 34 Web for Lathe Clutch. Given: Partial front and left-side views. Required: Full front view, right-side view in full section, and removed section A–A.*

*Leave out dimensions unless assigned by your instructor.

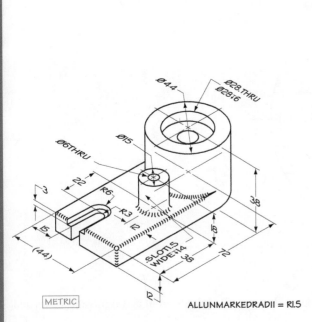

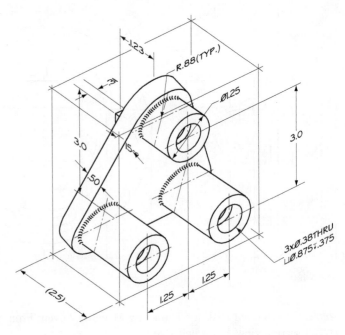

Exercise 35 Draw necessary views adding a section view.

Exercise 36 Bushing. Draw necessary views with a broken out section.*

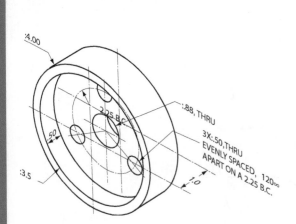

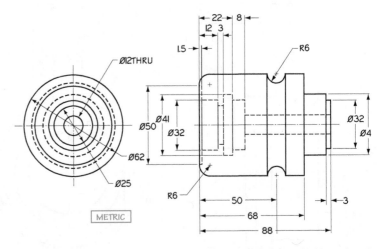

Exercise 37 Plastic Spacer. Draw all necessary views using an aligned section.*

Exercise 38 Motor. Draw all required views with one half section.*

*Leave out dimensions unless assigned by your instructor.

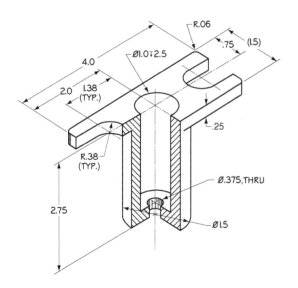

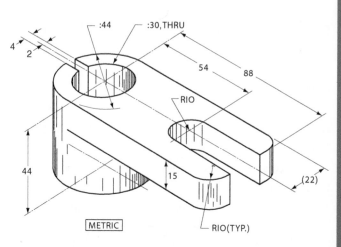

Exercise 39 Mounting Pin. Draw the necessary views showing the front view as a half section.*

Exercise 40 Clamp. Draw the necessary views showing the front view as a full section.*

*Leave out dimensions unless assigned by your instructor.

FIND THE ERRORS IN SECTION VIEWS

Directions:
Each of the drawings shown below represents a section view of the given top view. One is drawn correctly and the others are incorrect for various reasons. Match the description of what is wrong by writing its letter in the space provided. One has been done for you.

A. Missing lines of object that are visible behind cutting plane.

B. Correct.

C. Hatched areas are visible, never bounded by hidden lines.

D. Hidden lines are not usually shown.

E. Hatching always runs a single direction on a single part.

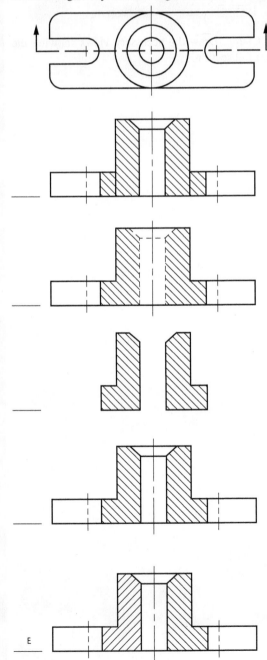

CUTTING-PLANE LINES AND SECTIONAL VIEWS

Directions:

Of the cutting-plane lines and corresponding sectional views shown below, two are incorrect and one is correct.

1. Use the pictorial views at right to help you determine which drawing shows the correct relationship between the cutting-plane line and the corresponding sectional view. Write "correct" on the line next to it.

2. Next to the drawings that show an incorrect relationship, write "incorrect." Sketch them correctly in the space provided.

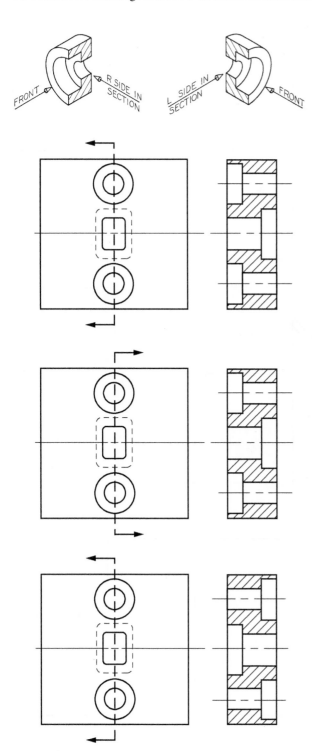

HATCHING

Directions:

What is wrong in each hatching sample below? Write answers in the spaces provided. The first one is done for you.

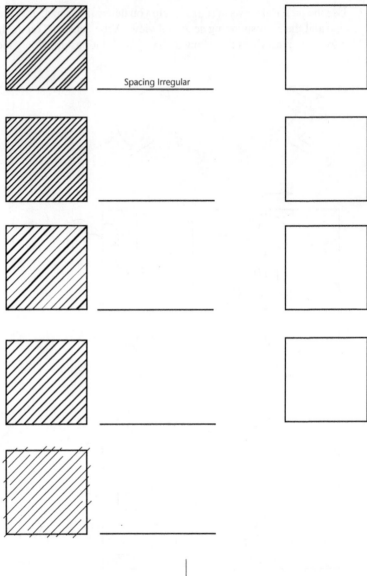

Spacing Irregular

Practice

Practice your hatching technique in the boxes below. Then add hatching to the drawing at right.

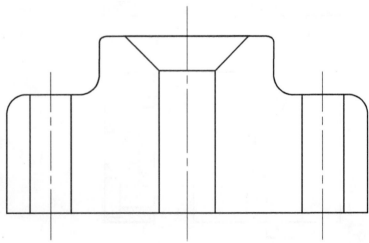

WORKSHEET 1   SKETCHING A FULL SECTION

Sketch the right-side view as a full section. The cutting plane has been shown, although in this case it is not necessary. Use the grid to help create thin hatch lines at an angle of 45° by drawing through the diagonals. Show hatching on the solid portions of the object cut through by the cutting plane. The left-side view is shown as your reference for the features you will sketch in the section.

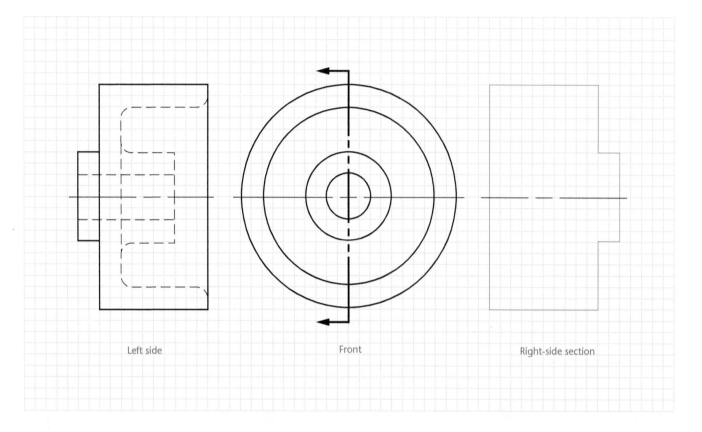

Left side   Front   Right-side section

Make copies of these pages to use for additional practice.

WORKSHEET 2   SKETCHING A HALF SECTION

Add the right-side view as a half section. Make sure to use a centerline to divide the sectioned and unsectioned halves. Notice the way the cutting plane is offset to pass through the hole. Keep in mind the practices for sectioning ribs and webs. The left-side view is shown as a reference.

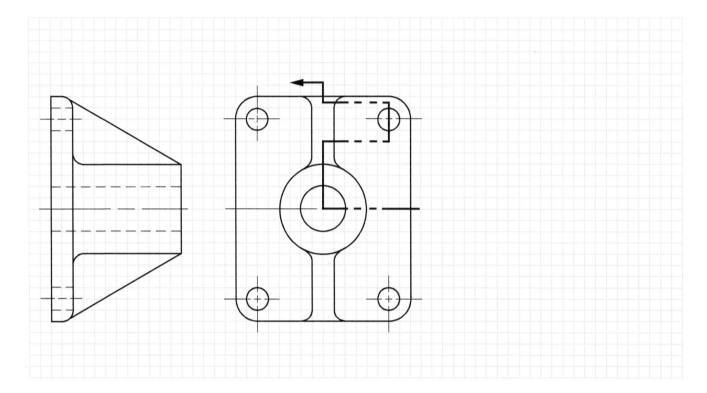

Make copies of these pages to use for additional practice.

WORKSHEET 3 | CREATING AN ALIGNED SECTION

Sketch an aligned section for the right-side view. Notice that in the left-side view the holes are shown revolved onto the vertical centerline. The left-side view is shown as a reference.

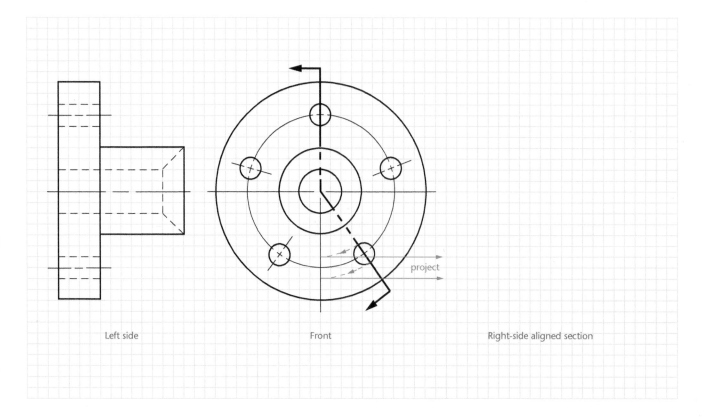

Left side   Front   Right-side aligned section

Make copies of these pages to use for additional practice.

AUXILIARY VIEWS

From Chapter 7 of *Modern Graphics Communication*, Fourth Edition, Frederick E. Giesecke, Alva Mitchell, Henry Cecil Spencer, Ivan Leroy Hill, John Thomas Dygdon, James E. Novak, Shawna Lockhart. Copyright © 2010 by Pearson Education, Inc. Published by Pearson Prentice Hall. All rights reserved.

AUXILIARY VIEWS

--- OBJECTIVES ---

After studying the material in this chapter, you should be able to:

1. Create an auxiliary view from orthographic views.

2. Draw folding lines or reference-plane lines between any two adjacent views.

3. Construct depth, height, or width auxiliary views.

4. Plot curves in auxiliary views.

5. Construct partial auxiliary views.

6. Create auxiliary section views.

7. Produce views to show the true length of a line, point view of a line, edge view of a surface, and true size view of a surface.

8. Show the true size of the angle between two planes (dihedral angle).

9. Construct the development of prisms, pyramids, cylinders, and cones.

10. Use triangulation to transfer surface shapes to a development.

11. Create the development of transition pieces.

12. Graphically solve for the intersection of solids.

13. Apply revolution to show true-length edges and true-size surfaces.

Refer to the following standard:
  • ANSI/ASME Y14.3—2003 Multiview and Sectional View Drawings

The companion website for this text is www.prenhall.com/chet_giesecke_modgraphic_4.

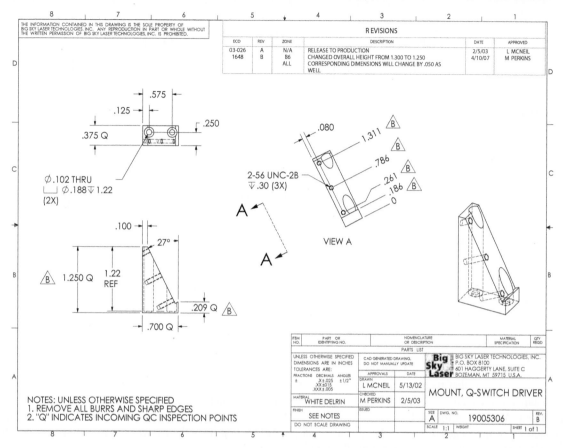

Auxiliary View Drawing. This switch mount uses an auxiliary view to show the true size of the inclined surface. *Courtesy of Big Sky Laser.*

OVERVIEW

Inclined planes and oblique lines do not appear true size or true length in any of the principal planes of projection. To show the true length of an oblique line or the true size of an inclined plane, an auxiliary view must be created. The principles for creating auxiliary views are the same whether you are using traditional drawing, sketching, or CAD: a line of sight and reference plane are defined. With traditional drawing, the view is manually created along line-of-sight projectors. With CAD drawing, the computer generates the view automatically if a 3D model of the object was originally created. Even if you are going to be using a CAD system to generate auxiliary views, it is important to understand the theory of developable surfaces. Some surfaces cannot be developed or "flattened out" to make an exact flat pattern for creating parts from sheet metal, cardboard packaging, or fabric. For example, a sphere can only be approximated. Understanding the development methods can aid you in using your CAD software to the fullest extent.

See the following Web sites:
- http://www.papertoys.com
- http://www.paperedcase.com

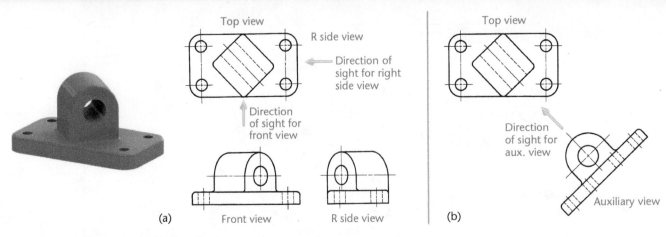

1 Regular Views and Auxiliary Views

UNDERSTANDING AUXILIARY VIEWS

Auxiliary views are useful for both design and documentation. Many objects are shaped so that their principal faces are not parallel to the standard planes of projection. For example, in Figure 1a the base of the design for the bearing is shown in its **true size** and shape, but the rounded upper portion is at an angle, so it does not appear true size and shape in any of the three regular views. When creating a drawing for documentation, you will often need to show the true size and shape of surfaces and angles. Likewise, you may need to create true size flat patterns for sheet metal, packaging, and other purposes.

To show the true circular shapes, use a direction of sight perpendicular to the plane of the curve, to produce a view as shown in Figure 1b. The result is an **auxiliary view:** an orthographic view that is not a standard projection. This view, together with the top view, completely describes the object. The front and right-side views are not necessary.

The Auxiliary Plane

The object shown in Figure 2a has an inclined surface (P) that does not appear in its true size and shape in any regular view. To show the inclined surface true size, the direction of sight must be perpendicular to the inclined plane. Or using the glass box model, the auxiliary plane is aligned parallel to the inclined surface P to give a true-size view of it. The **auxiliary plane** in this case is perpendicular to the frontal plane of projection and hinged to it. It is angled to the horizontal (top) and profile (side) viewing planes.

The horizontal and auxiliary planes are unfolded into the plane of the front view, as shown in Figure 2. Drawings do not show the planes of the glass box, but you can think of **folding lines** (H/F and F/T) representing the hinges that join the planes. The folding lines themselves are usually omitted in the actual drawing.

Inclined surface P is shown in its true size and shape in the auxiliary view. Note that both the top and auxiliary views show the depth of the object. One dimension of the surface is projected directly from the front view, and the depth is transferred from the top view.

The locations of the folding lines depend on the size of the glass box and the location of the object within it. If the object is further down in the box, distance Y is increased. If the object is moved back in the box, distances X increase but are still equal. If the object is moved to the left inside the glass box, distance Z is increased.

Tear out Worksheet 1 and use it to visualize the relationship for the auxiliary viewing plane.

Primary Auxiliary Views

Any view obtained by orthographic projection onto a plane other than the horizontal, frontal, and profile projection planes is an auxiliary view. A **primary auxiliary view** is projected onto a plane that is perpendicular to one of the principal planes of projection and is inclined to the other two. Figure 3 shows examples of primary auxiliary views.

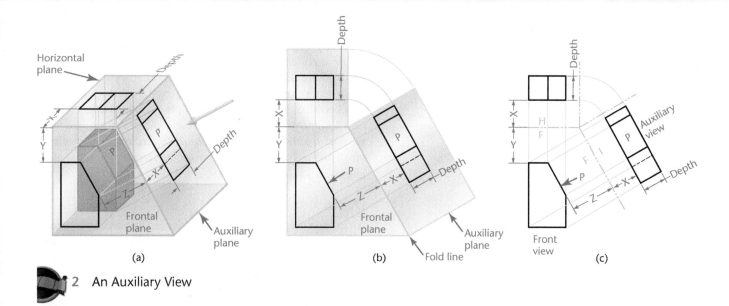

2 An Auxiliary View

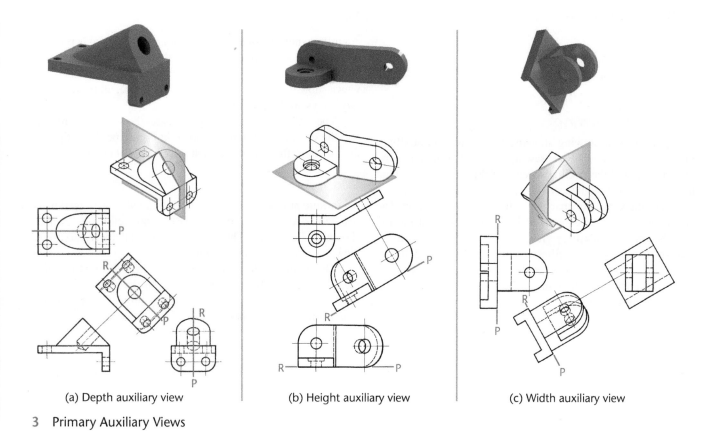

(a) Depth auxiliary view   (b) Height auxiliary view   (c) Width auxiliary view

3 Primary Auxiliary Views

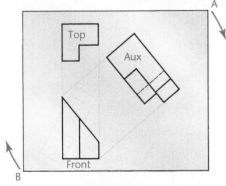

(a) Given drawing

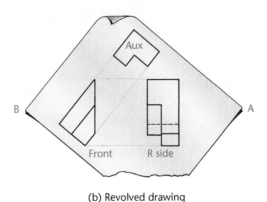

(b) Revolved drawing

4   Revolving a Drawing

Visualizing Auxiliary Views as a Revolved Drawing

In Figure 4a is a drawing showing top, front, and auxiliary views. Figure 4b shows the drawing revolved, as indicated by the arrows, until the auxiliary view and the front view line up horizontally. Although the views remain exactly the same, the names of the views are changed if drawn in this position. The auxiliary view now becomes a right-side view, and the top view becomes an auxiliary view. Sometimes it is easier to visualize and draw an auxiliary view when revolved to the position of a regular view in this manner. In any case, it should be understood that an auxiliary view basically is like any other view.

Classification of Auxiliary Views

Auxiliary views are named for the principal dimension shown in the auxiliary view. For example, the auxiliary views in Figure 5 are depth auxiliary views because they show the object's depth. Any auxiliary view projected from the front view, also known as a *front adjacent view,* is a depth auxiliary view.

Similarly, any auxiliary view projected from the top view, also known as a *top adjacent view,* is a height auxiliary view; and any auxiliary view projected from a side view, also known as a *side adjacent view,* is a width auxiliary view.

Depth Auxiliary Views

An infinite number of auxiliary planes can be hinged perpendicular to the frontal plane (F) of projection. Five such planes are shown in Figure 5a. The horizontal plane is included to show that it is similar to the others. All these views show the object's depth and therefore are all **depth auxiliary views.**

The unfolded auxiliary planes, shown in Figure 5b, show how depth dimensions are projected from the top view to all auxiliary views. The arrows indicate the directions of sight.

The complete drawing, with the outlines of the planes of projection omitted, is shown in Figure 5c. Note that the front view shows the height and the width of the object, but not the depth. The principal dimension shown in an auxiliary view is the one not shown in the adjacent view from which the auxiliary view was projected.

Height Auxiliary Views

An infinite number of auxiliary planes can be hinged perpendicular to the horizontal plane (H) of projection. Several are shown in Figure 6a. The front view and all these auxiliary views show the height of the object. Therefore, all these auxiliary views are **height auxiliary views.**

The unfolded projection planes are shown in Figure 6b, and the complete drawing is shown in Figure 6c. Note that in the top view, the only dimension not shown is height.

Width Auxiliary Views

An infinite number of auxiliary planes can also be hinged perpendicular to the profile plane (P) of projection. Some are shown in Figure 7a. The front view and all these auxiliary views are **width auxiliary views.**

The unfolded planes are shown in Figure 7b, and the complete drawing is shown in Figure 7c. In the right-side view, from which the auxiliary views are projected, the only dimension not shown is width.

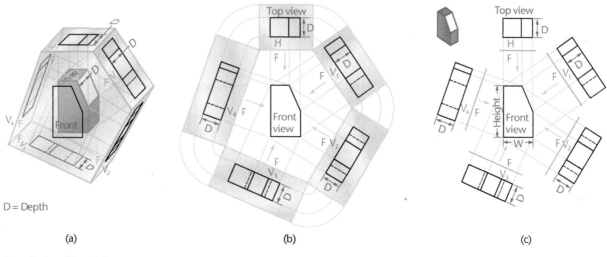

D = Depth

(a) (b) (c)

5   Depth Auxiliary Views

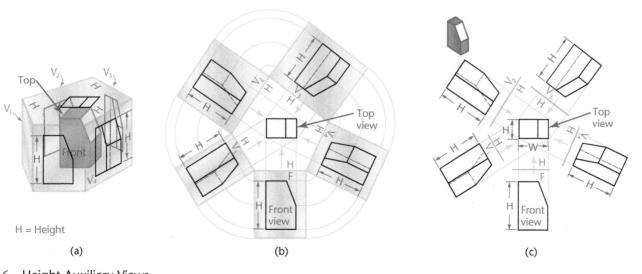

H = Height

(a) (b) (c)

6   Height Auxiliary Views

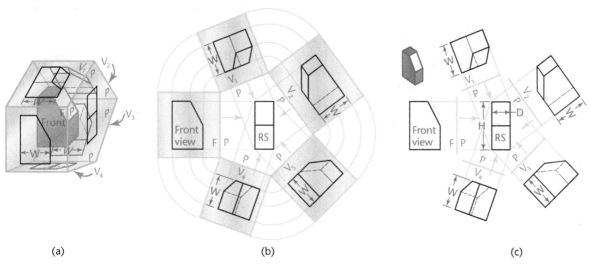

(a) (b) (c)

7   Width Auxiliary Views

Successive Auxiliary Views

Primary auxiliary views are projected from one of the principal views. In Figure 8, auxiliary view 1 is a primary auxiliary view projected from the top view.

From primary auxiliary view 1 a **secondary auxiliary view** 2 can be drawn; then from it a **third auxiliary view** 3, and so on. An infinite number of such successive auxiliary views may be drawn. However, secondary auxiliary view 2 is not the only one that can be projected from primary auxiliary view 1. As shown by the arrows around view 1, an infinite number of secondary auxiliary views, with different lines of sight, may be projected. Any auxiliary view projected from a primary auxiliary view is a secondary auxiliary view. Furthermore, any **succeeding auxiliary view** may be used to project an infinite series of views from it.

In this example, folding lines are more convenient than reference-plane lines. In auxiliary view 1, all numbered points of the object are the same distance from folding line H/1 as they are in the front view from folding line H/F. These distances, such as distance a, are transferred from the front view to the auxiliary view.

To draw the secondary auxiliary view 2, ignore the front view and focus on the sequence of three views: the top view, view 1, and view 2. Draw light projection lines parallel to the direction of sight desired for view 2. Draw folding line 1/2 perpendicular to the projection lines and at any convenient distance from view 1. Transfer the distances measured from folding line H/1 to locate all points in view 2. For example, transfer distance b to locate points 4 and 5 from folding line 1/2. Connect points to draw the object and determine visibility. The closest corner (11) in view 2 will be visible, and the one farthest away (1) will be hidden, as shown.

To draw views 3, 4, and so on, use a similar process. Remember to use the correct sequence of three views.

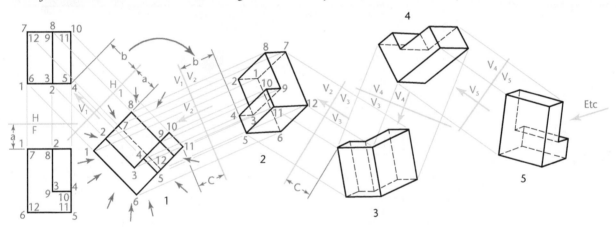

8   Successive Auxiliary Views

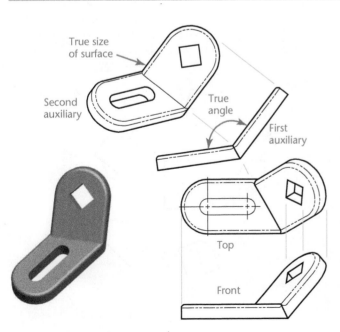

9   Second Auxiliary View, Showing the True Size of the Top Oblique Surface

Secondary Auxiliary Views

A secondary auxiliary view is projected from a primary auxiliary view onto a plane that is inclined to all three principal projection planes. As shown in Figure 9 a part that has an oblique surface often requires a second auxiliary view to show that surface's true size and shape. In this case, the primary auxiliary view shows the oblique plane on edge.

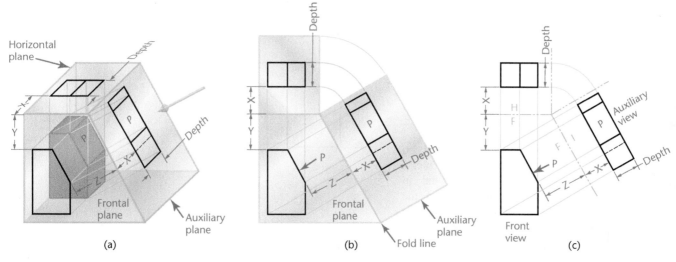

(a)   (b)   (c)

10   An Auxiliary View

Reference Planes

In the auxiliary view shown in Figure 10c, the folding line represents the edge view of the frontal plane of projection. In this case, the frontal plane is used for transferring distances—that is, depth measurements—from the top view to the auxiliary view.

Instead of using one of the planes of projection, you can use a **reference plane** parallel to the plane of projection and touching or cutting through the object. For example, in Figure 11a, a reference plane is aligned with the front surface of the object. This plane appears on edge, or as a line, in the top and auxiliary views. The two reference lines are used in the same manner as folding lines. Dimensions D in the top view and auxiliary views are equal. The advantage of the reference-plane method is that fewer measurements are required because some points of the object lie in the reference plane. Make the reference plane using light lines similar to construction lines.

You can use a reference plane that coincides with the front surface of the object, as shown in Figure 11a. When an object is symmetrical, it is useful to select the reference plane to cut through the object, as shown in Figure 11b. This way you have to make only half as many measurements to transfer

> **TIP**
>
> If you are using 2D CAD, you can draw half of the view and then mirror the object.

dimensions because they are the same on each side of the reference plane. You can also use the back surface of the object, as shown in Figure 11c, or any intermediate point that would be advantageous.

Position the reference plane so it is convenient for transferring distances. Remember the following:

1. Reference lines, like folding lines, are always at right angles to the projection lines between the views.
2. A reference plane appears as a line in two **alternate views,** never in **adjacent views.**
3. Measurements are always made at right angles to the reference lines or parallel to the projection lines.
4. In the auxiliary view, all points are at the same distances from the reference line as the corresponding points are from the reference line in the alternate view, or the second previous view.

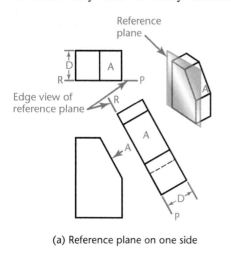

(a) Reference plane on one side

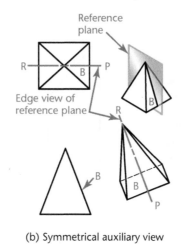

(b) Symmetrical auxiliary view

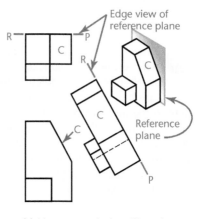

(c) Nonsymmetrical auxiliary view

11   Position of the Reference Plane

PROJECTING AN AUXILIARY VIEW

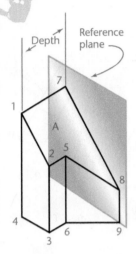

The object has been numbered in the pictorial view to aid in keeping track of the vertices. To create the auxiliary view:

1 Draw two views of the object and determine the direction of sight needed to produce a view that will show the true size of surface A.

Next, sketch projection lines parallel to the direction of sight.

Establish a reference plane. In this case the back surface of the object will work well. The reference lines in the top and auxiliary views are at right angles to the projection lines. These are the edge views of the reference plane.

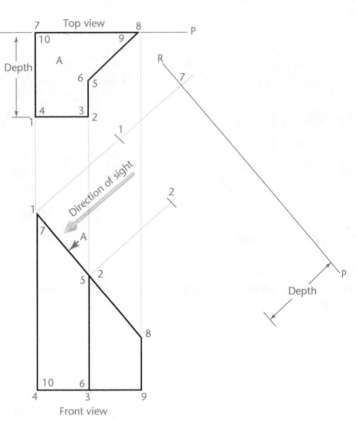

2 Draw the auxiliary view of surface A. It will be true size and shape because the direction of sight is perpendicular to that surface. Transfer depth measurements from the top view to the auxiliary view. Each point in the auxiliary view will be on its projection line from the front view and will be the same distance from the reference line as it is in the top view to the corresponding reference line. Finish projecting points 5 and 8.

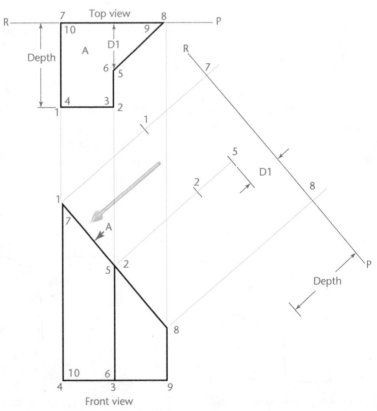

1 USING TRIANGLES TO SKETCH AUXILIARY VIEWS

You can use two triangles to quickly draw parallel and perpendicular lines for "accurate" sketches.

- Place two triangles together so that the 90° corners are on the outside, as shown in Figure 12.
- Slide them on your drawing until the outer edge of one triangle is along the line to which you want to sketch parallel.
- Hold down the triangle and slide the other along it.
- Draw parallel lines along one edge of the triangle. Draw perpendicular lines along the other edge.

This technique works well as an addition to freehand sketching when you want to show an auxiliary view.

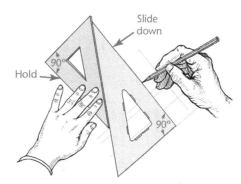

12 Triangles Can Be Used to Help Sketch Auxiliary Views

2 USING GRID PAPER TO SKETCH AUXILIARY VIEWS

You can use grid paper to help sketch auxiliary views by orienting the lines of the grid paper underneath your vellum or other semitransparent drawing sheet so that the grid is parallel to the inclined edge in the drawing, as shown in Figure 13. Use the grid to help sketch lines parallel and perpendicular to the edge in question.

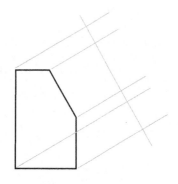

13 Sketching Auxiliary Views Using Grid Paper

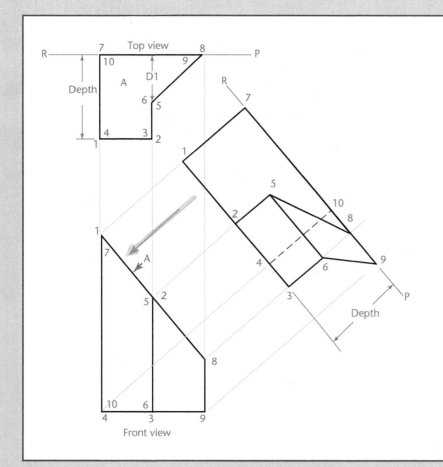

3 Draw surface A true size in the auxiliary view by connecting the vertices in the same order as they are shown connecting in the top view (1-7-8-5-2-1).

Complete the auxiliary view by adding other visible edges and surfaces of the object. Each numbered point in the auxiliary view lies on its projection line from the front view and is the same distance from the reference line as it is in the top view. Note that two surfaces of the object appear as lines in the auxiliary view.

STEP by STEP

SHOWING AN INCLINED ELLIPTICAL SURFACE TRUE SIZE

Given the front and side views shown, use these steps to project an auxiliary view showing true size of the elliptical surface.

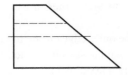

1 Since this is a symmetrical object, use a reference plane through the center of the object, as shown.

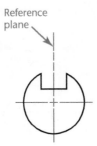

2 Select points on the circle in the side view.

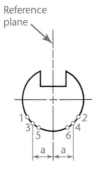

3 Locate the same points on the inclined surface and the left-end surface.

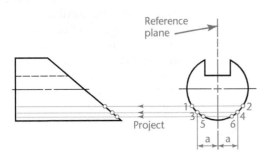

4 Project each point to the auxiliary view along its projection line.

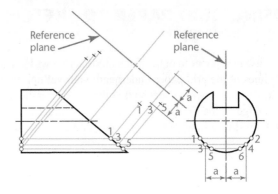

5 Transfer distances from the side view to the auxiliary view. Because the object is symmetrical, two points can be located with each measurement, as shown for points 1–2, 3–4, and 5–6. Project enough points to sketch the curves accurately.

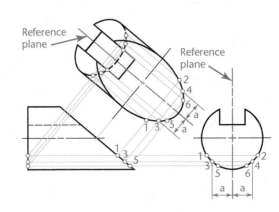

Since the major and minor axes are known, you can quickly create similar ellipses using CAD by locating the major and minor axes or the center and axes. For hand sketching you may want to use an ellipse template.

3 USING CAD TO CREATE AUXILIARY VIEWS

Most CAD systems allow you to rotate the grid or to create a new coordinate system (often called the *user coordinate system*) so that it aligns with the inclined surface. See Figure 14. If you are using 3D CAD, you can create true size auxiliary views by viewing the object perpendicular to the surface you want to show true size.

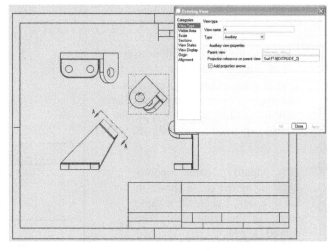

14 CAD software provides tools for generating auxiliary views. *Courtesy of Solidworks Corporation.*

4 CIRCLES AND ELLIPSES IN AUXILIARY VIEWS

Keep in mind that circular shapes appear as elliptical when viewed at an angle other than 90° (straight on to the circular shape). This is frequently the case when constructing auxiliary views (Figure 15).

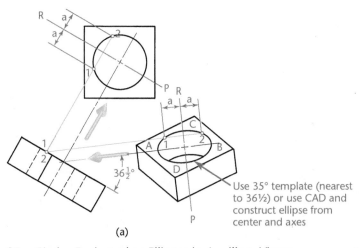

(a)

Use 35° template (nearest to 36½) or use CAD and construct ellipse from center and axes

(b)

15 Circles Projected as Ellipses in Auxiliary Views

5 HIDDEN LINES IN AUXILIARY VIEWS

Generally, hidden lines should be omitted in auxiliary views, unless they are needed to clearly communicate the drawing's intent. Note the use of hidden lines in Figure 16.

---- TIP ----

Your instructor may ask you to show all hidden lines for visualization practice, especially if the auxiliary view of the entire object is shown. Later, when you are familiar with drawing auxiliary views, omit hidden lines when they do not add needed information to the drawing.

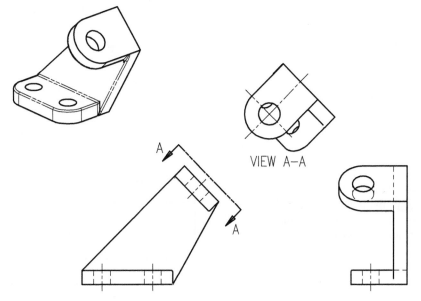

VIEW A–A

16 Omit hidden lines from auxiliary views when possible.

PLOTTING CURVES IN AN AUXILIARY VIEW

Use the following steps to create an auxiliary view that shows the true size and shape of the inclined cut through a piece of molding. The method of plotting points is similar to that explained for the ellipse.

1 Identify some points along the curve shown in the side view. Locate those same points in the front view. The curved shape is the inclined surface.

2 Locate the reference plane and project the points into the auxiliary view.

3 Finish projecting all of the points on the inclined surface and draw its true shape in the auxiliary view.

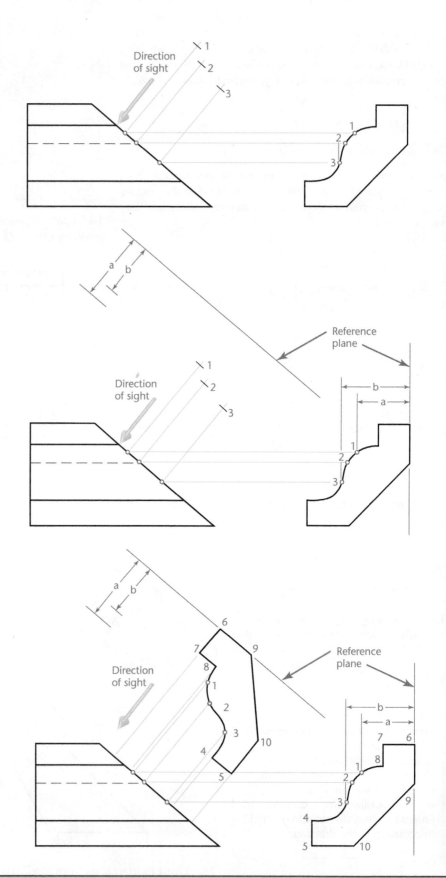

310

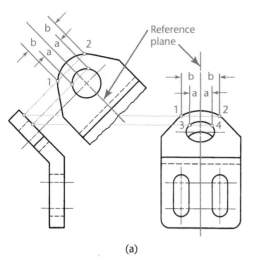

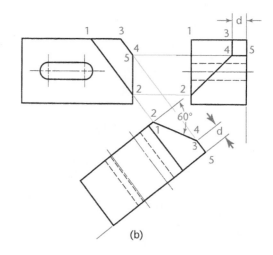

(a) (b)

17 Reverse Construction

6 REVERSE CONSTRUCTION

To complete the regular views, it is often necessary to first construct an auxiliary view where critical dimensions will be shown true size. For example, in Figure 17a, the upper part of the right-side view cannot be constructed until the auxiliary view is drawn. First, points are established on the curves and then projected back to the front view.

In Figure 17b, the 60° angle and the location of line 1–2 in the front view are given. To locate line 3–4 in the front view and lines 2–4, 3–4, and 4–5 in the side view, you must first construct the 60° angle in the auxiliary view and project it back to the front and side views, as shown.

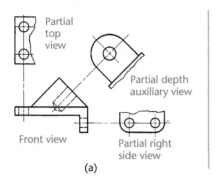

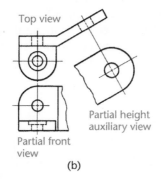

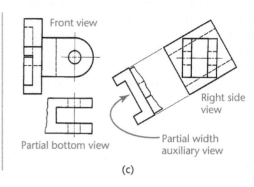

(a) (b) (c)

18 Partial Views

7 PARTIAL AUXILIARY VIEWS

Using an auxiliary view often makes it possible to omit one or more regular views, but auxiliary drawings are time consuming to create and may even be confusing because of the clutter of lines.

Partial views are often sufficient and easier to read. Figure 18 shows partial regular views and **partial auxiliary views**. Usually a break line is used to indicate the imaginary break in the views. Do not draw a break line coinciding with a visible line or hidden line.

So that partial auxiliary views (which are often small) do not appear "lost" and unrelated to any view, connect them to the views from which they project, either with a centerline or with one or two thin projection lines as shown in Figure 18.

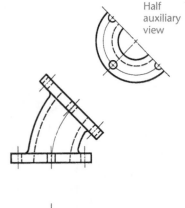

8 HALF AUXILIARY VIEWS

If an auxiliary view is symmetrical, and if it is necessary to save space on the drawing or to save time, a **half auxiliary view** may be drawn, as shown in Figure 19. In this case, half of a regular view is also shown since the bottom flange is also symmetrical. Note that in each case the near half is shown.

19 Half Views

311

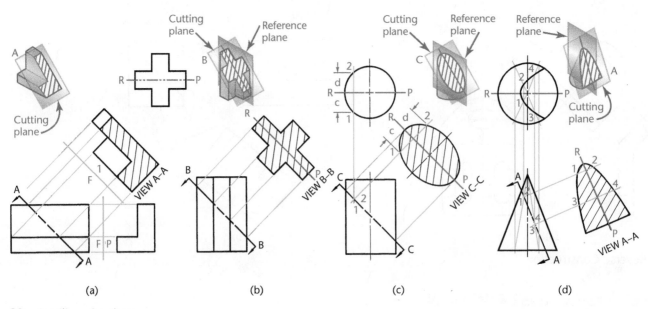

20   Auxiliary Sections

9 AUXILIARY SECTIONS

An **auxiliary section** is simply an auxiliary view in section. A typical auxiliary section is shown in Figure 20. In this example, there is not sufficient space for a revolved section, although a removed section could have been used instead of an auxiliary section. Note the cutting-plane line and the terminating arrows that indicate the direction of sight for the auxiliary section. In an auxiliary section drawing, the entire portion of the object behind the cutting plane may be shown, or the cut surface alone may be shown.

The cutting plane line indicates both the location of the cutting plane and the direction of sight for the auxiliary section. Figures 21 and 22 show examples of this. Notice that the auxiliary section is shown in alignment. Typically, a centerline is extended to locate the auxiliary sections or a few projection lines are shown in the drawing for this purpose.

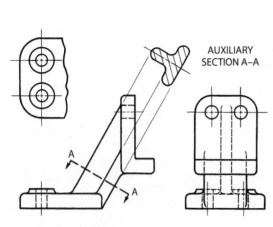

21   Auxiliary Section

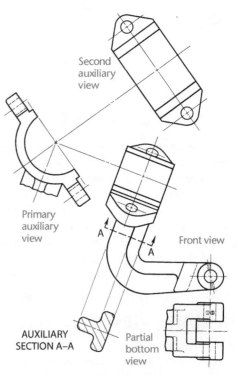

22   Secondary Auxiliary View—Partial Views

10 VIEWING-PLANE LINES AND ARROWS

When the drawing sheet is too crowded to show the auxiliary view in direction projection you can use a **viewing-plane line** or a **viewing direction arrow** to indicate the direction of sight for the auxiliary view.

A viewing-plane line and a cutting-plane line look essentially the same. The arrows on either end of the line point in the direction of sight for the removed view. The ends of the line are labeled with letters, starting with A, then B, and so on. The auxiliary view, when placed in a removed location, should still be shown in the same orientation it would have if it were aligned in projection. Figure 23a shows a removed auxiliary view and viewing-plane line.

A viewing direction arrow for a removed auxiliary view uses the same practices you learned earlier. Show an arrow pointing in the direction of sight for the removed auxiliary view. Label the removed view and place it in the same orientation it would have when projected, or if it is rotated, show a rotation arrow and specify the amount of rotation.

A centerline can be extended from a hole or other symmetric feature to indicate the alignment of the auxiliary view as shown in Figure 23b.

Viewing direction arrows are particularly useful when showing a second auxiliary view in a drawing that is created from a 3D CAD model. Often the primary auxiliary view is not necessary and can be left out if a viewing direction arrow is shown indicating the direction of sight for the second auxiliary view. An example of this use of a viewing direction arrow in a CAD drawing is shown in Figure 24.

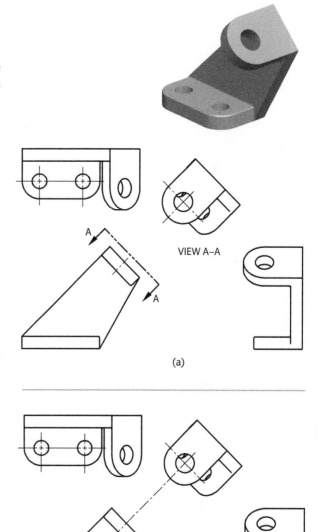

VIEW A–A

(a)

(b)

23 Using a Viewing Plane Line to Show the Direction of Sight for an Auxiliary View. Alternatively, a centerline can be extended to indicate the viewing direction.

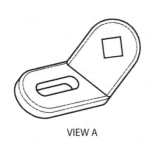

VIEW A

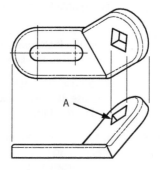

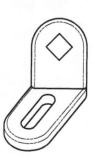

24 Arrow Showing the Direction of Sight for the View of an Oblique Surface

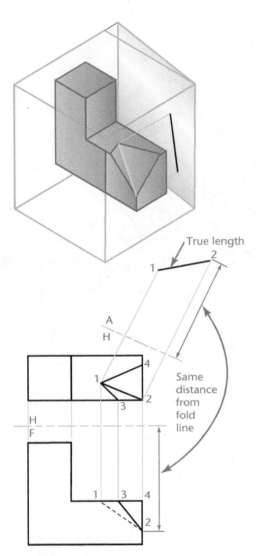

True length

Same distance from fold line

25   True Length of a Line

11 USES OF AUXILIARY VIEWS

Generally, auxiliary views are used to show the true shape or true angle of features that appear distorted in the regular views. Auxiliary views are often used to produce views that show the following:

1. True length of line
2. Point view of line
3. Edge view of plane
4. True size of plane

You can use the ability to generate views that show the specific things listed to solve a variety of engineering problems. **Descriptive geometry** is the term for using accurate drawings to solve engineering problems. An accurate CAD drawing database can be used to solve many engineering problems when you understand the four basic views from descriptive geometry. Using 3D CAD, you can often model objects accurately and query the database for lengths and angles. Even so, you will often need the techniques described below to produce views that will help you visualize, create, or display 3D drawing geometry.

12 TRUE LENGTH OF A LINE

As shown in Figure 25, a line will show true length in a plane of projection that is parallel to the line. In other words, a line will show true length in an auxiliary view where the direction of sight is perpendicular to the line. To show a line true length, make the fold line parallel to the line you want to show true length in the auxiliary view. Whenever a line is parallel to the fold line between two views, it will be true length in the adjacent view.

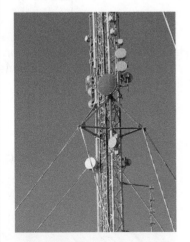

The slope of a guy wire can be determined when you see its true length. Foreshortened views do not show the actual angle

The Need to Show the True Length of a Line in CAD

Whether you are using 2D or 3D CAD or creating a sketch or drawing by hand, it is often necessary to understand how to create a view that shows a certain line true length. For example, a line must appear true length if you want to find its slope.

When you are working in a 3D CAD program, it is generally easy to list the true length of a line or an edge; but knowing the dimension is not the same as being able to show it on a drawing so that others can correctly interpret it.

In order to annotate the dimension on a drawing view where the line in question is shown true length you must understand how to create a view that is parallel to the line.

If you use 2D CAD you will use the same methods explained in this chapter. If you use 3D CAD, reading about how to show a line at true length will help you understand how to create a plane parallel to that line in 3D CAD.

Understanding when a line is true length and when it is foreshortened in a view is also helpful in developing your ability to accurately visualize a 3D object from a 2D drawing.

SHOWING THE TRUE LENGTH OF A HIP RAFTER

The top and front views of the hip rafter (line 1–2) are shown. Use an auxiliary view to show the line true length.

1 Choose the direction of sight to be perpendicular to line 1–2 (front view).

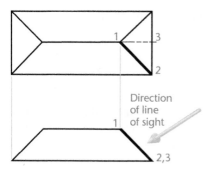

2 Draw the H/F folding line between the top and front view, as shown.

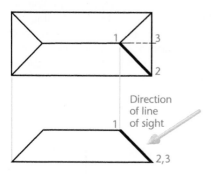

3 Draw the F/1 folding line parallel to line 1–2 and any convenient distance from line 1–2 (front view).

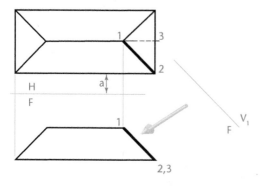

4 Draw projection lines from points 1, 2, and 3 to begin creating the auxiliary view.

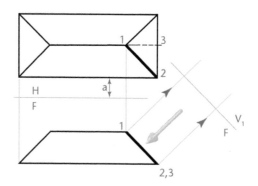

5 Transfer points 1 and 2 to the auxiliary view at the same distance from the folding line as they are in the top view, and along their respective projection lines. The hip rafter (line 1–2) is shown true length in the auxiliary view. Also, triangle 1–2–3 in the auxiliary view shows the true size and shape as that portion of the roof because the direction of sight for the auxiliary view is perpendicular to triangle 1–2–3.

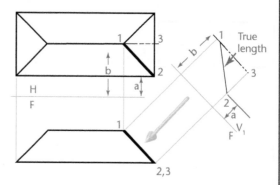

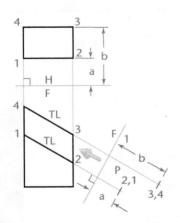

26 Point View of a Line

13 POINT VIEW OF A LINE

As shown in Figure 26, a line will show as a point view when projected to a plane perpendicular it. To show the point view of a line, choose the direction of sight parallel to the line where it is true length.

Showing the Point View of a Line

Refer to Figure 27 for the following steps:

1. Choose the direction of sight to be parallel to line 1–2.
2. Draw folding line H/F between the top and front view, as shown.
3. Draw folding line F/1 perpendicular to line 1–2 where it is true length, and any convenient distance from line 1–2 (front view).
4. Draw projection lines from points 1 and 2 to begin creating the auxiliary view.
5. Transfer points 1 and 2 to the auxiliary view at the same distance from the folding line as they are in the top view and along their respective projection lines. They will line up exactly with each other to form a point view of the line.

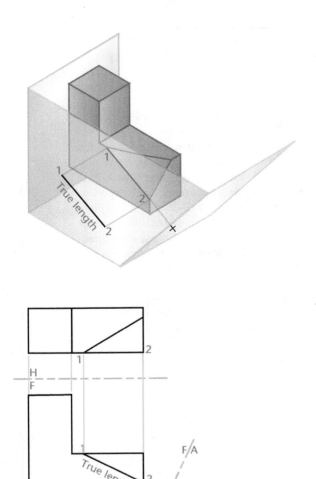

27 Point View of a Line

TIP

Viewing a Line as a Point

Draw a line in a plane—for example, a straight line on a sheet of paper. Then tilt the paper to view the line as a point. You will see that when the line appears as a point, the plane containing it appears as a line. (Since your paper will end up being viewed on edge, it may be a little hard to see the line when it is oriented correctly.)

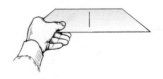

14 EDGE VIEW OF A PLANE

As shown in Figure 28, a plane will show on edge in a plane of projection that shows a point view of any line that lies entirely within the plane. To get the point view of a line, the direction of sight must be parallel to the line where it is true length. To show the edge view of a plane, choose the direction of sight parallel to a true length line lying in the plane.

Finding the edge view of a plane is a useful tool for the following types of problems:

- Finding the shortest line from a point to a plane. The shortest line will be perpendicular from the point to the plane. This is easiest to show in a view showing the plane on edge.

- Finding the slope of a plane. When you are working in a 3D CAD program, it is easy to create a view from any direction. Understanding how to choose a direction that will produce the most useful view for your purposes is easier yet when you understand these basic principles. Even though you can use CAD inquiry tools to quickly determine the angle between planes, often you may need to document the angle of a plane in a view showing the plane on edge.

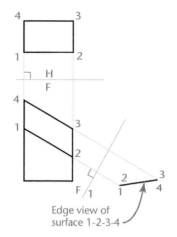

28   Edge View of a Surface

Showing the Edge View of a Plane

Refer to Figure 29 for the following steps:

1. Choose the direction of sight to be parallel to line 1–2 in the front view where it is already shown true length.
2. Draw folding line H/F between the top and front view, as shown.
3. Draw folding line F/1 perpendicular to true-length line 1–2 and any convenient distance.
4. Draw projection lines from points 1, 2, 3, and 4 to begin creating the auxiliary view.
5. Transfer points 1, 2, 3, and 4 to the auxiliary view at the same distance from the folding line as they are in the top view and along their respective projection lines. Plane 1–2–3–4 will appear on edge in the finished drawing.

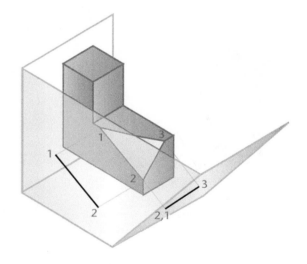

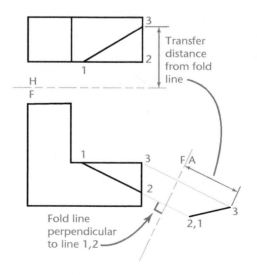

29   Edge View of a Plane

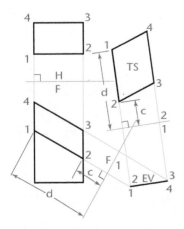

30   True Size of an Oblique Surface

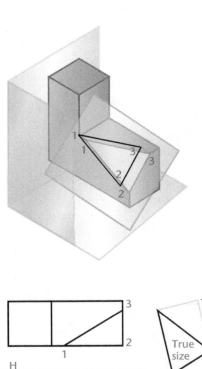

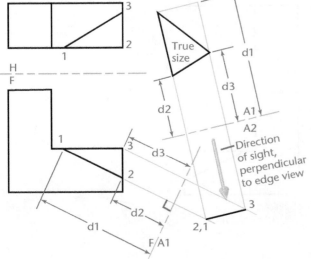

31   True-Size View of an Oblique Surface

15 TRUE SIZE OF AN OBLIQUE SURFACE

As shown in Figure 30, a plane will show true size when the plane of projection is parallel to it.

To show the true size view of a plane, choose the direction of sight perpendicular to the edge view of the plane.

Showing the true size of a surface continues from the method presented for showing inclined surfaces true size, where the edge view is already given. But to show an oblique surface true size, you need to first show the oblique surface on edge and then construct a second auxiliary view to show it true size.

Showing the True Size and Shape of an Oblique Surface

To show the true size and shape of an oblique surface, such as surface 1–2–3–4 in Figure 31, create a second auxiliary view. In this example folding lines are used, but you can achieve the same results for all of the preceding examples using reference lines.

1. Draw the auxiliary view showing surface 1–2–3–4 on edge, as explained previously.
2. Create a second auxiliary view with the line of sight perpendicular to the edge view of plane 1–2–3–4 in the primary auxiliary view. Project lines parallel to the arrow. Draw folding line 1/2 perpendicular to these projection lines at a convenient distance from the primary auxiliary view.
3. Draw the secondary auxiliary view. Transfer the distance to each point from folding line F/1 to the second auxiliary view—for example, dimensions c and d. The true size TS of the surface 1–2–3–4 is shown in the secondary auxiliary view since the direction of sight is perpendicular to it.

Figure 32 shows an example of the steps to find the true size of an oblique surface. The first step, illustrated in Figure 32a, shows the oblique surface on edge. Figure 32b establishes the direction of sight perpendicular to the edge view. The final true size view of the surface is projected in Figure 32c.

Figure 33 shows a similar example using the reference plane method.

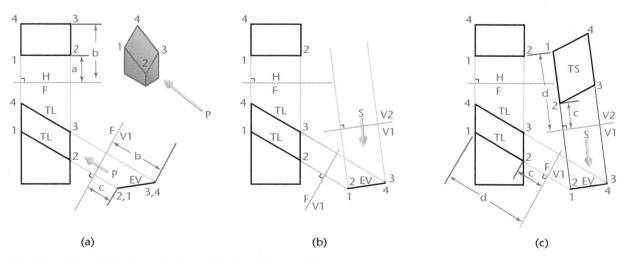

32 True Size of Oblique Surface—Folding Line Method

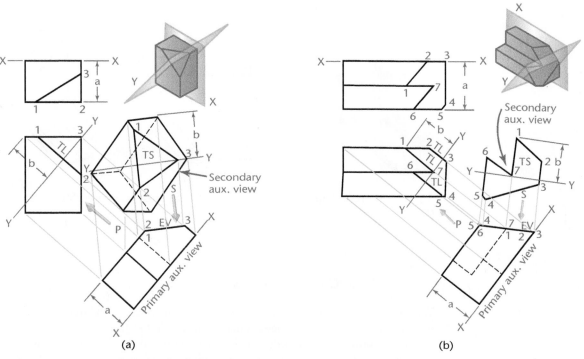

33 True Size of an Oblique Surface—Reference-Plane Method

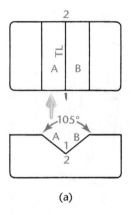

(a)   (b)   (c)

34 Dihedral Angles

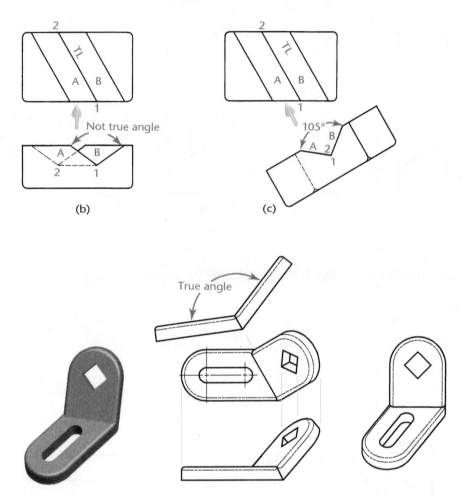

35 Using an Auxiliary View to Show the True Angle between Surfaces (Dihedral Angle)

16 DIHEDRAL ANGLES

The angle between two planes is called a **dihedral angle.** Auxiliary views often need to be drawn to show dihedral angles true size, mainly for dimensioning purposes. In Figure 34a, a block with a V-groove is shown where the dihedral angle between inclined surfaces A and B is shown true size in the front view.

In Figure 34b, the V-groove on the block is at an angle to the front surface so that the true dihedral angle is not shown. Assume that the actual angle is the same as in Figure 34a. Does the angle show larger or smaller than in Figure 34a? To show the true dihedral angle, the line of intersection (in this case 1–2) must appear as a point. Since the line of intersection for the dihedral angle is in both planes, showing it as a point will produce a view which shows both planes on edge.

This will give you the true-size view of the dihedral angle.

In Figure 34a, line 1–2 is the line of intersection of planes A and B. Now, line 1–2 lies in both planes at the same time; therefore, a point view of this line will show both planes as lines, and the angle between them is the dihedral angle between the planes. To get the true angle between two planes, find the point view of the line intersection of the planes.

In Figure 34c, the direction of sight is parallel to line 1–2 so that line 1–2 appears as a point, planes A and B appear as lines, and the true dihedral angle is shown in the auxiliary view. Figure 35 shows a drawing using an auxiliary view to show the true angle between surfaces.

UNDERSTANDING DEVELOPMENTS AND INTERSECTIONS

A **development** is a flat representation or pattern that when folded together creates a 3D object (Figure 36). An **intersection** is the result of two objects that intersect each other (Figure 37). Sheet metal construction is the most common application for developments and intersections. The development of surfaces, such as those found in sheet metal fabrication, is a flat pattern that represents the unfolded or unrolled surface of the form. The resulting flat pattern gives the true size of each connected area of the form so that the part or structure can be fabricated. Auxiliary views are a primary tool used in creating developments. Many specialized software packages are available to automate creating developments and intersections. You can also apply what you have learned about auxiliary views to create developments and intersections using your CAD system.

Surface Terminology

The following terminology describes objects and concepts used in developments and intersections:

A *ruled surface* is one that may be generated by sweeping a straight line, called the **generatrix,** along a path, which may be straight or curved (Figure 38). Any position of the generatrix is an **element** of the surface. A ruled surface may be a plane, a single-curved surface, or a warped surface.

A *plane* is a ruled surface that is generated by a line, one point of which moves along a straight path while the generatrix remains parallel to its original position. Many geometric solids are bounded by plane surfaces (Figure 39).

A *single-curved surface* is a developable ruled surface; that is, it can be unrolled to coincide with a plane. Any two adjacent positions of the generatrix lie in the same plane. Examples are the cylinder (Figure 40) and the cone.

A *double-curved surface* is generated by a curved line and has no straight-line elements (Figure 41). A surface generated by revolving a curved line about a straight line in the plane of the curve is called a **double-curved surface of revolution.** Common examples are the **sphere, torus, ellipsoid,** and **hyperboloid.**

A *warped surface* is a ruled surface that is not developable. Some examples are shown in Figure 42. No two adjacent positions of the generatrix lie in a flat plane. Warped surfaces cannot be unrolled or unfolded to lie flat. Many exterior surfaces on an airplane or automobile are warped surfaces.

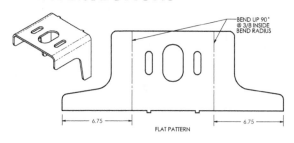

36 A Flat Pattern. *Courtesy of Dynojet Research, Inc.*

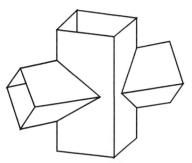

37 Intersecting Prisms

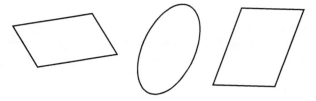

38 Ruled Surface

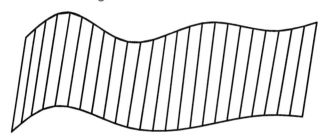

39 Plane Surfaces

40 Single-Curved Surface

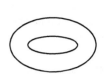

41 Double-Curved Surface

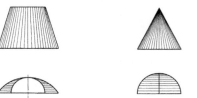

(a) Cylindroid   (b) Conoid   (c) Helicoid   (d) Hyperboloid   (e) Hyperbolic paraboloid

42 Warped Surfaces

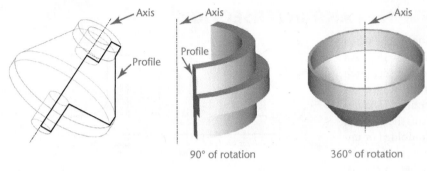

43 Solids Formed by Revolution

Axis

Profile

Axis

Profile

90° of rotation

Axis

360° of rotation

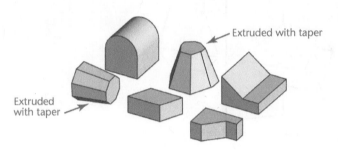

Extruded with taper

Extruded with taper

44 Solids Formed by Extrusion

Revolved and Extruded Solids

A solid generated by revolving a plane figure about an axis in the plane of the figure is a **revolved solid** (Figure 43). Revolved solids that are created from plane figures composed of straight lines are capable of being flattened to create a pattern. Revolving a curved figure creates a double-curved surface, which can have an approximated flat pattern.

An **extruded solid** is one formed by "sweeping" a shape along a linear path as shown in Figure 44. Many CAD software platforms also allow you to specify a taper for the surfaces. Extruded solids can have flat patterns formed for them.

Solids bounded by warped surfaces have no group name. The most common example of such solids is the screw thread.

Developable Surfaces

A **developable surface** may be unfolded or unrolled to lie flat. Surfaces composed of single-curved surfaces, of planes, or of combinations of these types are developable.

Warped surfaces and double-curved surfaces are not directly developable. They may be developed by approximating their shape using developable surfaces. If the material used in the actual manufacturing is sufficiently pliable, the flat sheets may be stretched, pressed, stamped, spun, or otherwise forced to assume the desired shape. Nondevelopable surfaces are often produced by a combination of developable surfaces that are then formed slightly to produce the required shape. Figure 45 shows examples of developable surfaces.

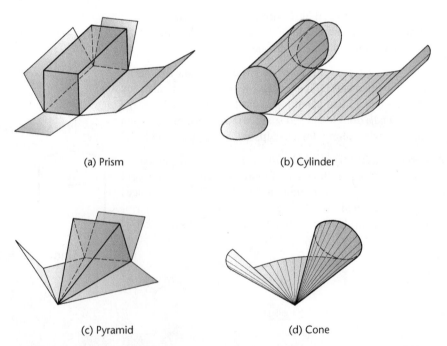

(a) Prism

(b) Cylinder

(c) Pyramid

(d) Cone

45 Development of Surfaces

Principles of Intersections

Typical examples of the need for accurate drawings showing the intersections of planes and solids include openings in roof surfaces for flues and stacks; openings in wall surfaces for pipes, chutes, and so on; and the building of sheet metal structures such as tanks and boilers. In such cases, you generally need to determine the true size and shape of the intersection of a plane and one of the more common geometric solids. Figure 46 shows an example where you would need to determine the intersection of a solid and a plane to create the correctly shaped opening in the vertical prism—the main flue—where the horizontal prism joins it.

For solids bounded by plane surfaces, you need only find the points of intersection of the edges of the solid with the plane and to join these points, in consecutive order, with straight lines.

For solids bounded by curved surfaces, it is necessary to find the points of intersection of several elements of the solid with the plane and to trace a smooth curve through these points. The intersection of a plane and a circular cone is called a **conic section.** Some typical conic sections are shown in Figure 47.

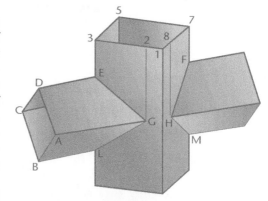

46   Intersecting Prisms

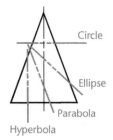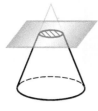

Circle

Ellipse

Parabola

Hyperbola

47   Conic Sections

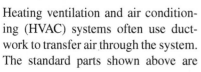

Heating ventilation and air conditioning (HVAC) systems often use ductwork to transfer air through the system. The standard parts shown above are made of 26 gauge galvanized steel and can be purchased "off the self". When ducts must connect at odd angles to fit into existing spaces custom designed developments and intersections are required.

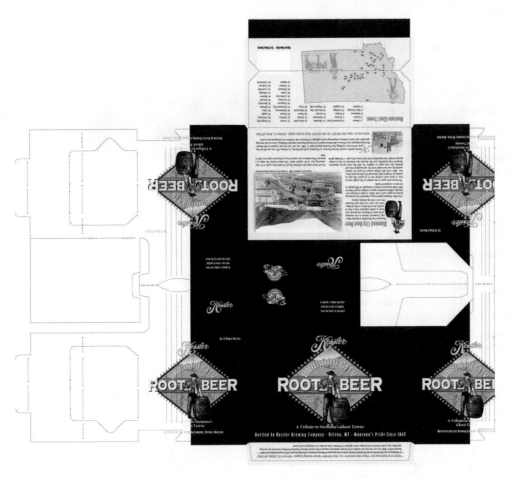

48 Flat Pattern for a Root Beer Package. *Courtesy of Kessler Brewing Co.*

17 DEVELOPMENTS

The **development of a surface** is that surface laid out on a plane. Practical applications of developments occur in sheet metal work, stone cutting, pattern making, packaging, and package design. See Figure 48.

Single-curved surfaces and the surfaces of polyhedra can be developed. Developments for warped surfaces and double-curved surfaces can only be approximated.

In sheet metal layout, extra material must be provided for laps and seams. If the material is heavy, the thickness may be a factor, and the crowding of metal in bends must be considered. You must also take stock sizes into account and make layouts to economize on material and labor. In preparing developments, it is best to put the seam at the shortest edge and to attach the bases at edges where they match; this will minimize processing such as soldering, welding, and riveting.

It is common to draw development layouts with the inside surfaces up. This way, all fold lines and other markings are related directly to inside measurements, which are the important dimensions in all ducts, pipes, tanks, and vessels. In this position they are also convenient for use in the fabricating shop.

Finding the Intersection of a Plane and a Prism and Developing the Prism

In order to create flat patterns for sheet metal, packaging, and other purposes, you must first determine the true size of the surface. The true size and shape of the intersection of a plane and a prism is shown in the auxiliary view in Figure 49. The length AB is the same as AB in the front view, and the width AD is the same as AD in the top view.

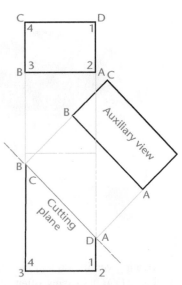

49 Auxiliary View Showing True Size and Shape of the Intersection of a Plane and a Prism

DEVELOPING A PRISM

These are the steps to create the development for the prism shown here on this page.

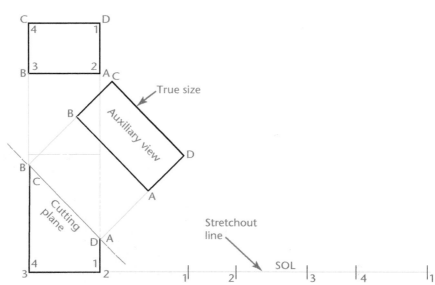

1 Draw the stretchout line, which represents the axis along which the part is unfolded or unrolled. On the stretchout line, transfer the true sizes of the faces 1–2 and 2–3, which are shown true length in the top view. Remember that a line appears true length when the view is perpendicular to the line. In other words, when a line is parallel to the fold line between views, the line is true length in the adjacent view.

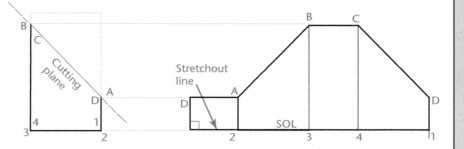

2 Where two surfaces join, draw perpendiculars to the stretchout line and transfer the true height of each respective edge. The front view shows the true heights in this case. Project the heights from the front view, as shown. Complete the development of these surfaces using straight lines to join the points you have plotted. Identify other surfaces that are connected to these and attach their true sizes to the development of the lower base and the upper base. Use an auxiliary view to find the true size of the surface and then draw it in place.

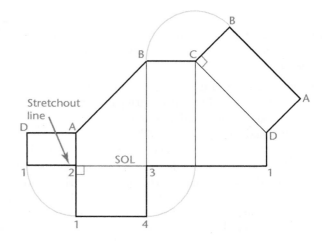

3 When you finish, you will have drawn the development of the entire prism, as shown. If needed, add tabs so that there is material to connect the surfaces when folded up.

Cut out and fold up Worksheet 2 and check that it forms the flat pattern for the object shown. Add gluing tabs to some of the edges if necessary.

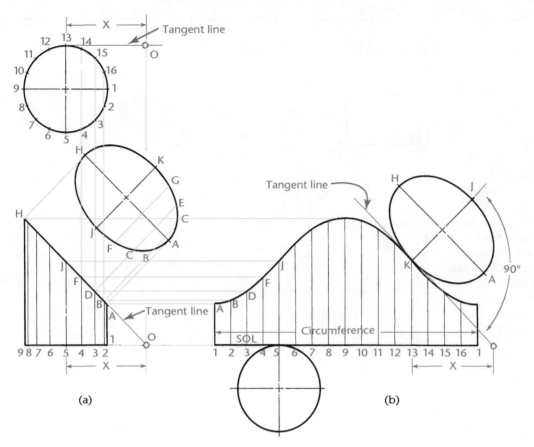

(a)

(b)

50 Plane and Cylinder

Finding the Intersection of a Plane and a Cylinder and Developing the Cylinder

The intersection of a plane and a cylinder is an ellipse whose true size is shown in the auxiliary view of Figure 50. The steps for developing a cylinder are as follows:

- Draw elements of the cylinder. It is usually best to divide the base of the cylinder into equal parts, shown in the top view and then projected into the front view.
- In the auxiliary view, the widths BC, DE, and so on are transferred from the top view at 2–16, 3–15, respectively, and the ellipse is drawn through these points, as you practiced earlier in this chapter. The major axis AH shows true length in the front view, and the minor axis JK shows true length in the top view. You can use this information to quickly draw the ellipse using CAD.

- Draw the stretchout line for the cylinder. It will be equal to the circumference of the base, whose length is determined by the formula πd.
- Divide the stretchout line into the same number of equal parts as the circumference of the base and draw an element through each division perpendicular to the line.
- Transfer the true height by projecting it from the front view, as shown in Figure 50b.
- Draw a smooth curve through the points A, B, D, and so on.
- Draw the tangent lines and attach the bases as shown in Figure 50b.

See Worksheet 3.

326

18 HEMS AND JOINTS FOR SHEET METAL AND OTHER MATERIALS

Figure 51 shows a wide variety of hems and joints used in fabricating sheet metal parts and other items. Hems are used to eliminate the raw edge as well as to stiffen the material. Joints and seams may be made for sheet metal by bending, welding, riveting, and soldering and for package materials by gluing and stapling.

You must add material for hems and joints to the layout or development. The amount you add depends on the thickness of the material and the production equipment. A good place to

find more information is from manufacturers. They can be extremely helpful in identifying specifications related to the exact process you will use in designing a part.

A good way to locate manufacturers and products is through the online Thomas Register: http://www.thomasregister.com/index.html

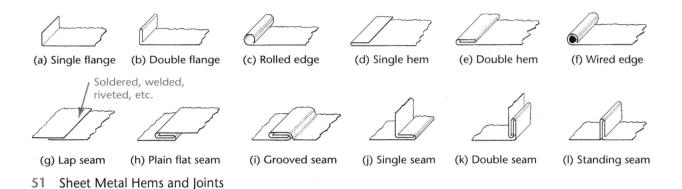

(a) Single flange   (b) Double flange   (c) Rolled edge   (d) Single hem   (e) Double hem   (f) Wired edge

Soldered, welded, riveted, etc.

(g) Lap seam   (h) Plain flat seam   (i) Grooved seam   (j) Single seam   (k) Double seam   (l) Standing seam

51   Sheet Metal Hems and Joints

19 MORE EXAMPLES OF DEVELOPMENTS AND INTERSECTIONS

Developing a Plane and an Oblique Prism

The intersection of a plane and an oblique prism is shown in Figure 52a. Where the plane is normal to the prism formed by plane WX (called a right section) it appears as a regular hexagon as shown in the auxiliary view labeled Right section. The oblique section cut by horizontal plane YZ is shown true size in the top view.

The development for this oblique prism is shown in Figure 52b. Use the right section to create stretchout line WX. On the stretchout line, set off the true widths of the faces 1–2, 2–3, and so on, which are shown true size in the auxiliary view. Draw perpendiculars through each division. Transfer the true heights of the respective edges, which are shown true size in the front view. Join the points A, B, C, and so on with straight lines. Finally attach the bases, which are shown in their true sizes in the top view, along an edge.

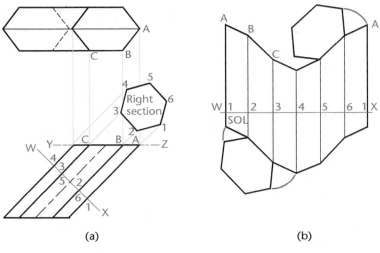

(a)   (b)

52   Plane and Oblique Prism

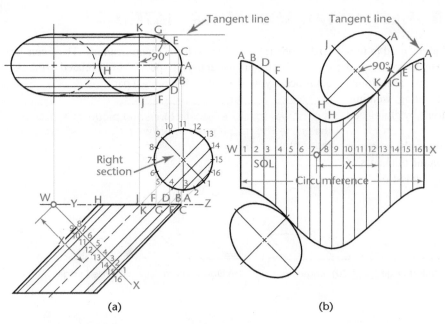

53 Plane and Oblique Circular Cylinder

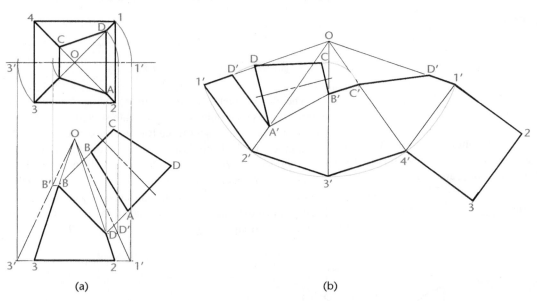

54 Plane and Pyramid

Developing a Plane and an Oblique Cylinder

The development of the intersection of a plane and an oblique cylinder is similar to that for a plane and an oblique prism, as shown in Figure 53.

Developing a Plane and a Pyramid

The intersection of a plane and a pyramid is a trapezoid, as shown in Figure 54.

Developing a Plane and a Cone

The intersection of a plane and a cone is an ellipse, as shown in Figure 55. If a series of horizontal cutting planes are passed perpendicular to the axis, each plane will cut a circle from the cone that will show as true size and shape in the top view. Points in which these circles intersect the original cutting plane are points on the ellipse. Since the cutting plane is shown on edge in the front view (Figure 54a), all of these piercing points can be projected from there to the others, as shown in Figure 54b.

To develop the lateral surface of a cone, think of the cone as a pyramid having an infinite number of edges. The development is similar to that for a pyramid.

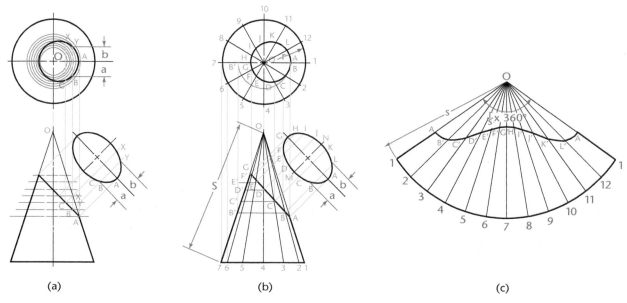

(a) (b) (c)

55 Plane and Cone

Developing a Hood and Flue

The development of a hood and flue is shown in Figure 56. Since the hood is a conical surface, it may be developed as shown in Figure 55. The two end sections of the elbow are cylindrical surfaces. The two middle sections of the elbow are cylindrical surfaces, but their bases are not perpendicular to the axes, so they will not develop into straight lines.

Develop them similar to an oblique cylinder. Make auxiliary planes AB and DC perpendicular to the axes so they cut right sections from the cylinders, which will develop into the straight lines AB and CD in the developments. By arranging the developments as shown, the elbow can be constructed from a rectangular sheet of metal without wasting material. The patterns are shown in the right top portion of Figure 56 as they will be separated after cutting.

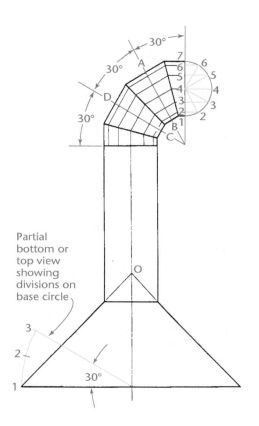

Partial bottom or top view showing divisions on base circle

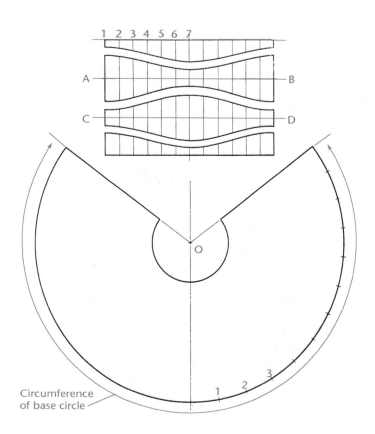

Circumference of base circle

56 A Hood and Flue

(a)   (b)   (c)   (d)   (e)

57   Transition Pieces

20 TRANSITION PIECES

A **transition piece** is one that connects two differently shaped, differently sized, or skewed position openings. In most cases, transition pieces are composed of plane surfaces and conical surfaces, as shown in Figure 57. You will learn about developing conical surfaces by triangulation next. Triangula-

tion can also be used to develop, approximately, certain warped surfaces. Transition pieces are used extensively in air conditioning, heating, ventilating, and similar construction.

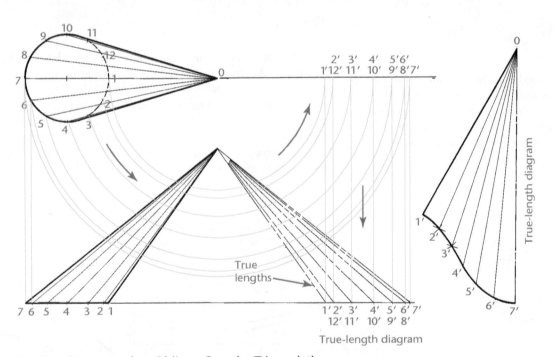

58   Development of an Oblique Cone by Triangulation

21 TRIANGULATION

Triangulation is simply a method of dividing a surface into a number of triangles and transferring them to the development. To find the development of an oblique cone by triangulation, divide the base of the cone in the top view into any number of equal parts and draw an element at each division point, as shown in Figure 58. Find the true length of each element. If the divisions of the base are comparatively small, the lengths of the chords may be used in the development to represent the lengths of the respective arcs. Since the development is symmetrical, it is necessary to lay out only half the development, as shown at the right side of Figure 58.

22 DEVELOPING A TRANSITION PIECE CONNECTING RECTANGULAR PIPES ON THE SAME AXIS

The transition piece can be a frustum of a pyramid that connects rectangular pipes on the same axis, as shown in Figure 59. As a check on the development, lines parallel on the surface must also be parallel on the development.

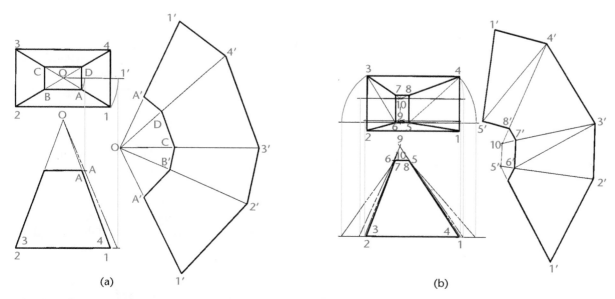

59 Development of a Transition Piece—Connecting Rectangular Pipes on the Same Axis

23 DEVELOPING A PLANE AND A SPHERE

The intersection of a plane and a sphere is a circle. The diameter of the circle depends on where the plane is located. Any circle cut by a plane through the center of the sphere is called a **great circle.** If a plane passes through the center and is perpendicular to the axis, the resulting great circle is called the **equator.** If a plane contains the axis, it will cut a great circle called a **meridian.**

The surface of a sphere is double curved and is not developable, but it may be developed approximately by dividing it into a series of zones and substituting a portion of a right-circular cone for each zone. If the conical surfaces are inscribed within the sphere, the development will be smaller than the spherical surface, but if they are circumscribed about the sphere, the development will be larger. If the conical surfaces are partly

inside and partly outside the sphere, the resulting development is closely approximate to the spherical surface. This method of developing a spherical surface, the **polyconic** method, is shown in Figure 60a. It is used on government maps of the United States.

Another method of making an approximate development of the double-curved surface of a sphere is to divide the surface into equal sections with meridian planes and substitute cylindrical surfaces for the spherical sections. The cylindrical surfaces may be inscribed within the sphere, circumscribed about it, or located partly inside and partially outside. This method, the **polycylindric** method (sometimes called the *gore* method) is shown in Figure 60b.

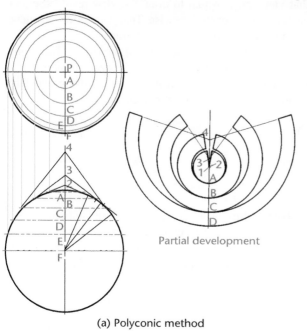

Partial development

(a) Polyconic method

Quarter development

(b) Polycylindric method

60 Approximate Development of a Sphere

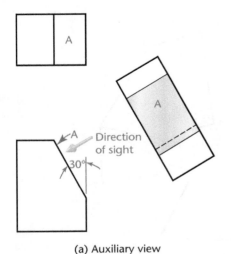

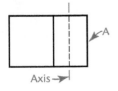

(a) Auxiliary view

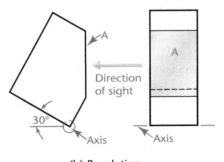

(b) Revolution

61   Auxiliary View and Revolution Compared

24 REVOLUTION

Revolution, like auxiliary view projection, is a method of determining the true length and true size of inclined and oblique lines and planes. To create the auxiliary view imagine that the object remains stationary and a new viewing plane is added as shown by the arrow in Figure 61a. Surface A shows true size and shape in the auxiliary view.

The same view of the object can be obtained by moving the object with respect to the viewing planes, as shown in Figure 61b. Here the object is revolved until surface A appears in its true size and shape in the right-side view. Revolution determines true length and true size without creating another view. Instead, revolution positions an object in space to create standard views that show the true size and shape of the inclined or oblique surface.

25 AXIS OF REVOLUTION

Imagine the axis of revolution to be perpendicular to the front plane of projection in Figure 61b. The **axis of revolution** appears as a point in this view. The object revolves but does not change shape in this view. In the adjacent views in which the axis of revolution, if it were drawn, would show as a line in true length, the dimensions of the object that are parallel to the axis of revolution do not change. Other dimensions may appear foreshortened.

Creating a Revolved Drawing

To make a drawing using revolution to show the true size of a surface,

1. Select the view that has the inclined surface showing as an edge, or other feature, that you want to revolve to produce a true-size feature in the adjacent view.
2. Select any point at any convenient position on or outside that view about which to draw the view revolved either clockwise or counterclockwise. That point is the end view, or point view, of the axis of revolution.
3. Draw this first view on the plane of projection. This is the only view that remains unchanged in size and shape.
4. Project the other views from this view using standard orthographic projection techniques.

26 PRIMARY AND SUCCESSIVE REVOLUTIONS

The axis of revolution is usually perpendicular to one of the three principal planes of projection. A **primary revolution** is one where the object is revolved about an axis perpendicular to the horizontal, frontal, or profile planes of projection.

Successive revolutions are drawings that use multiple revolutions of the same object to produce a final revolved drawing with the desired result. Figure 62 shows an example. As you can imagine, this is accomplished in one step using CAD.

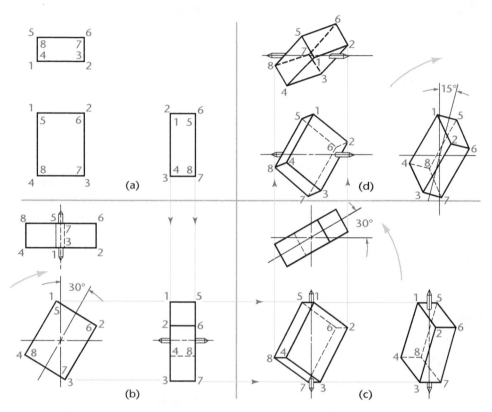

62 Successive Revolutions of a Prism

27 TRUE LENGTH OF A LINE: REVOLUTION METHOD

A line (edge) appears true length when it is parallel to one of the planes of projection. In Figure 63a, line AB (an element of the cone) is oblique to the planes of projection. Line AB appears foreshortened, not true length. If AB is revolved about the axis of the cone until it coincides with either of the contour elements (for example, ABR), it will be shown in its true length in the front view because it will then be parallel to the front plane of projection.

In Figure 63b, to show the edge of the pyramid CD true length, revolve it about the axis of the pyramid until it is

parallel to the frontal plane of projection and therefore shows true length in the front view. In Figure 63c, line EF is shown true length in the front view because it has been revolved about a vertical axis until it is parallel to the front plane of projection.

The true length of a line may also be found by constructing a right triangle or a true length diagram (Figure 63d) whose base is equal to the top view of the line and whose altitude is the difference in elevation of the ends. The hypotenuse of the triangle is equal to the true length of the line.

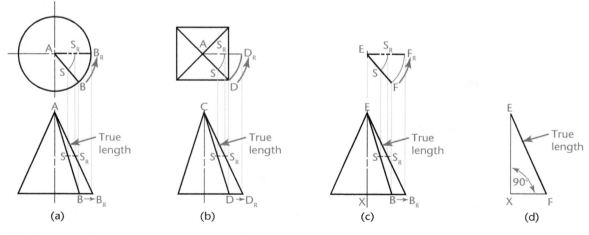

63 True Length of a Line—Revolution Method

CREATING AUXILIARY VIEWS USING 3D CAD

Using 3D CAD, any view can be generated in one or two steps, eliminating the need to project auxiliary views and revolve views manually. It is still very important to have a clear understanding of which line of sight will produce a true size view or a view that shows a true dihedral angle. When measuring or dimensioning a view from a CAD screen, if the surface or angle is not true size, the automatic dimension from the CAD system may be that of the apparent, or projected, distance. Incorrectly dimensioned dihedral angles can be an error in CAD drawings created by inexperienced

operators. Drawings should show angles true size where they are dimensioned or note it clearly if this is not the case.

Solid modeling techniques can be used to create accurate intersections between various solids. Some CAD programs have commands that will create transition pieces that blend solids of two differing shapes, for example, a sweep/join operation. Not all CAD software is capable of producing developments (flat patterns) of surfaces. Some surfaces, such as spheres or tori, can only be approximated by a flattened shape.

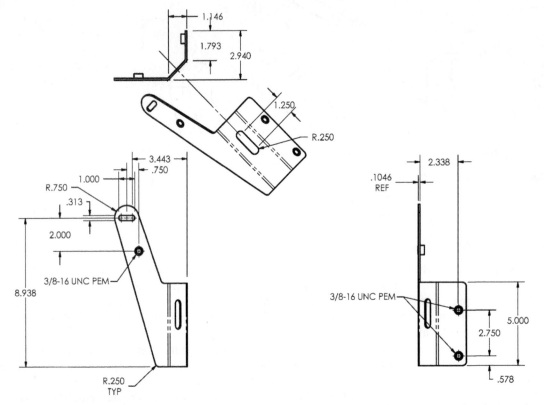

An auxiliary view is used on the drawing for this sheet metal part so that dimensions can be shown where feature to show true size. *Courtesy of Dynojet Research, Inc.*

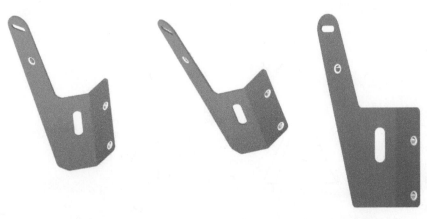

Views of the Solid Model from Which the Detail Drawings Above Were Created. *Courtesy of Dynojet Research, Inc.*

KEY WORDS

True Size
Auxiliary View
Auxiliary Plane
Folding Lines
Primary Auxiliary View
Depth Auxiliary Views
Height Auxiliary Views
Width Auxiliary Views
Secondary Auxiliary View
Third Auxiliary View
Succeeding Auxiliary View
Reference Plane
Alternate View
Adjacent View
Partial Auxiliary Views
Half Auxiliary View
Auxiliary Section
Viewing-Plane Line
Viewing Direction Arrow
Descriptive Geometry
Dihedral Angle
Development
Intersection
Ruled Surface
Generatrix
Element
Plane
Single-Curved Surface
Double-Curved Surface
Double-Curved Surface of Revolution
Sphere
Torus
Ellipsoid
Hyperboloid
Warped Surface
Revolved Solid
Extruded Solid
Developable Surface
Conic Section
Development of a Surface
Transition Piece
Triangulation
Great Circle
Equator
Meridian
Polyconic
Polycylindric
Revolution
Axis of Revolution
Primary Revolution
Successive Revolutions

CHAPTER SUMMARY

- An auxiliary view can be used to create a projection that shows the true length of a line or true size of a plane.
- An auxiliary view can be directly produced using CAD if the original object was drawn as a 3D model.
- Folding lines or reference lines represent the edge views of projection planes.
- Points are projected between views parallel to the line of sight and perpendicular to the reference lines or folding lines.
- A common use of auxiliary views is to show dihedral angles in true size.
- Curves are projected to auxiliary views by plotting them as points.
- A secondary auxiliary view can be constructed from a previously drawn (primary) auxiliary view.
- The technique for creating the development of solids is determined by the basic geometric shape. Prisms, pyramids, cylinders, and cones each have a particular development technique.
- The intersection of two solids is determined by plotting the intersection of each surface and transferring the intersection points to each development.
- Cones and pyramids use radial development. Prisms and cylinders use parallel development.
- Truncated solids, cones, and pyramids are created by developing the whole solid and then plotting the truncated endpoints on each radial element.
- Transition pieces are developed by creating triangular surfaces that approximate the transition from rectangular to circular. The smaller the triangular surfaces, the more accurate the development.
- Revolution moves an object in space, to reveal what would normally be an auxiliary view of the object in a primary view (top, front, right side).
- The main purpose of revolution is to reveal the true length and true size of inclined and oblique lines and planes in a primary view.

REVIEW QUESTIONS

1. What is meant by true length? By true size?
2. Why is a true-length line always parallel to an adjacent reference line?
3. If an auxiliary view is drawn from the front view, what other views would show the same depth dimensions?
4. Describe one method for transferring depth between views.
5. What is the difference between a complete auxiliary view and a partial auxiliary view?
6. How many auxiliary views are necessary to draw the true size of an inclined plane? Of an oblique plane?
7. What is the angle between the reference plane line (or folding line) and the direction-of-sight lines?
8. How is the development of a pyramid similar to the development of a cone?
9. When developing a truncated cone or pyramid, why is the complete solid developed first?
10. What descriptive geometry techniques are used to determine the intersection points between two solids?
11. What is a transition piece?
12. What is a stretchout line?
13. Which parts of a development are true size and true shape?
14. What building trades use developments and intersections?
15. What is the purpose of revolution?
16. What is the axis of revolution? What determines where the axis is drawn?
17. What are successive revolutions?

EXERCISES

Auxiliary View Projects

The projects in Exercises 2–43 are to be drawn with CAD or freehand. If partial auxiliary views are not assigned, the auxiliary views are to be complete views of the entire object, including all necessary hidden lines.

It is often difficult to space the views of an auxiliary view sketch. Make sure to provide enough space for the auxiliary view by lightly blocking in the overall dimensions first and by blocking in the overall dimensions of the auxiliary view. Add more detail after you have established the basic layout of the sketch.

A wide selection of intersection and development projects is provided in Figures 44–50. These projects are designed to fit A, B size, or A3 sheets. Because developments are used to create patterns, they should be drawn accurately or dimensioned. They can also be solved on most CAD systems, using either 2D or solid modeling.

Design Project

Exercise 1 Breakfast cereal has traditionally been sold in a rectangular box. The packaging also must keep the product fresh, be reasonably durable, look attractive on the shelf, and be useful for dispensing the product. Create an innovative new packaging for breakfast cereal that meets these requirements. Make your design a sensible candidate for mass production, striving for a low consumer price and the conservation of raw materials. Consider whether to make your packaging disposable, reusable, or refillable. Use the graphic communication skills you have learned so far to represent your design clearly.

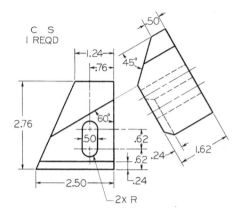

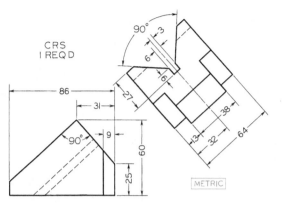

Exercise 2 RH Finger. Given: Front and auxiliary views. Required: Complete front, auxiliary, left-side, and top views.

Exercise 3 V-Block, Given: Front and auxiliary views. Required: Complete front, top, and auxiliary views.

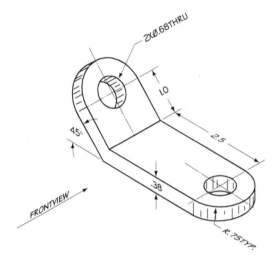

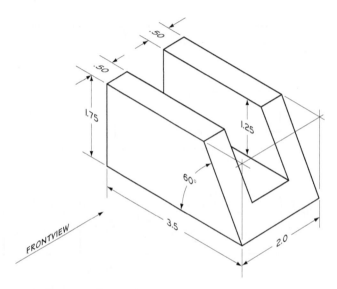

Exercise 4 Clamp.

Exercise 5 Plastic Slide.

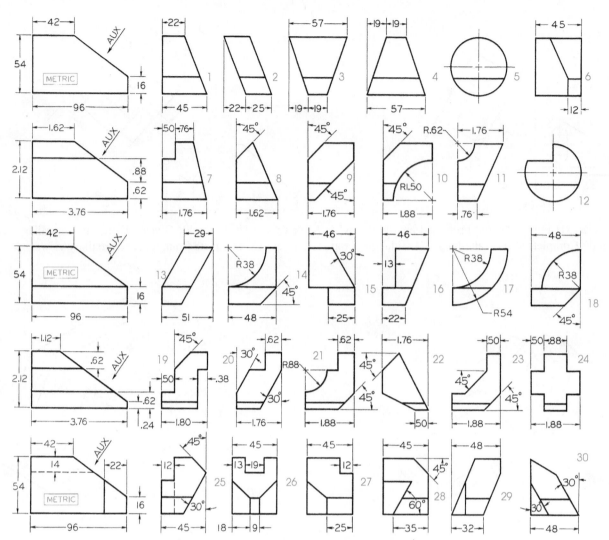

Exercise 6 Auxiliary View Problems. Make freehand sketch or instrument drawing of selected problem as assigned. Draw given front and right-side views, and add incomplete auxiliary view, including all hidden lines. If assigned, design your own right-side view consistent with given front view; and then add complete auxiliary view.

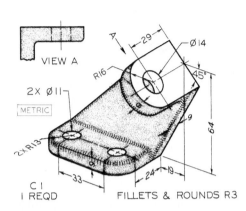

VIEW A

2X Ø11

METRIC

2X R13

C1
1 REQD

A

29

Ø14

R16

45°

9

64

33

24   19

FILLETS & ROUNDS R3

Exercise 7 Anchor Bracket. Draw necessary views or partial views.*

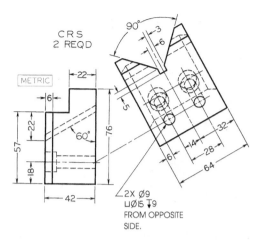

CRS
2 REQD

METRIC

22

6

22

57

18

42

60°

90°   3

6

5

76

14   32

28

6

64

2X Ø9
⊔Ø15 ⊤9
FROM OPPOSITE
SIDE.

Exercise 10 Guide Block. Given: Right-side and auxiliary views. Required: Right-side, auxiliary, plus front and top views—complete.*

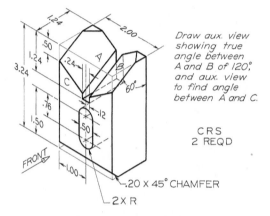

1.24

2.00

.50

1.24

3.24

.24   A

C   B

60°

.76   .12

1.50

.50

1.00

FRONT

.20 X 45° CHAMFER

2X R

Draw aux. view
showing true
angle between
A and B of 120°,
and aux. view
to find angle
between A and C.

CRS
2 REQD

Exercise 8 Centering Block. Draw complete front, top, and right-side views, plus indicated auxiliary views.*

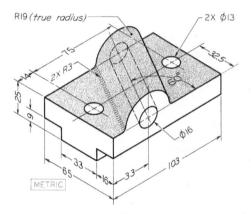

R19 (true radius)

2X Ø13

75

2X R3

14

2X R3

25

9

60°

Ø16

33

65   16   3.3

103

METRIC

32.5

Exercise 11 Angle Bearing. Draw necessary views, including complete auxiliary view.*

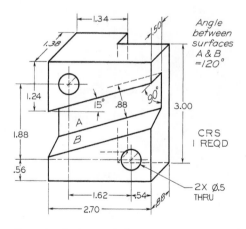

1.34

.50

1.38

1.24

15°   .88

A

1.88

B

.56

1.62   .54

.88

2.70

90°

3.00

Angle
between
surfaces
A & B
=120°

CRS
1 REQD

2X Ø.5
THRU

Exercise 9 Clamp Slide. Draw necessary views completely.*

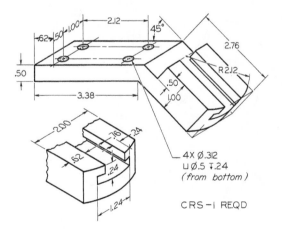

.62   .50   1.00

2.12

45°

2.76

.50

3.38

.50

1.00

R 2.12

2.00

.76   .24

.62   .24

1.24

4X Ø.312
⊔Ø.5 ⊤.24
(from bottom)

CRS −1 REQD

Exercise 12 Guide Bracket. Draw necessary views or partial views.*

*Use metric or decimal-inch dimensions as assigned.

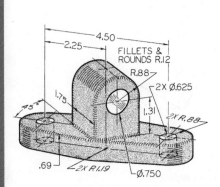

Exercise 13 Rod Guide. Draw necessary views, including complete auxiliary view showing true shape of upper rounded portion.*

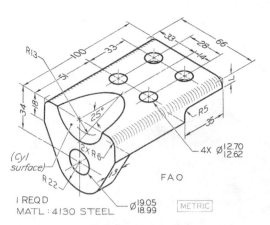

Exercise 16 Angle Guide. Draw necessary views, including a partial auxiliary view of cylindrical recess.*

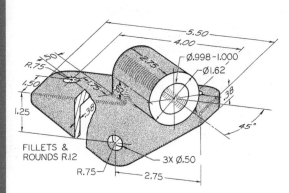

Exercise 14 Brace Anchor. Draw necessary views, including partial auxiliary view showing true shape of cylindrical portion (Layout B-4 or A3–4 adjusted.)*

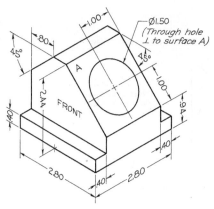

Exercise 17 Holder Block. Draw front and right-side views (2.80″ apart) and complete auxiliary view of entire object showing true shape of surface A and all hidden lines.*

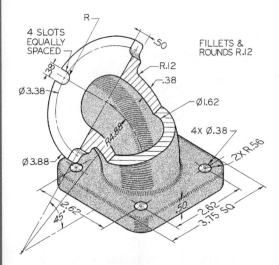

Exercise 15 45° Elbow. Draw necessary views, including a broken section and two half views of flanges.*

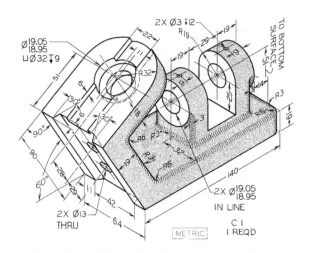

Exercise 18 Control Bracket. Draw necessary views, including partial auxiliary views and regular views.*

*Use metric or decimal-inch dimensions as assigned.

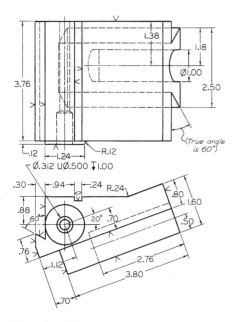

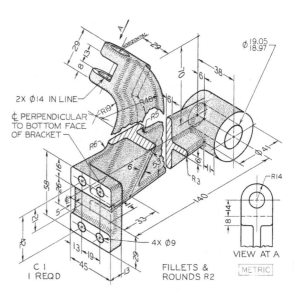

Exercise 19 Tool Holder Slide. Draw given views, and add complete auxiliary view showing true curvature of slot on bottom.*

Exercise 21 Guide Bearing. Draw necessary views and partial views, including two partial auxiliary views.*

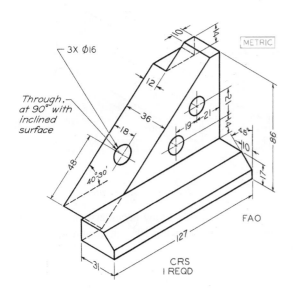

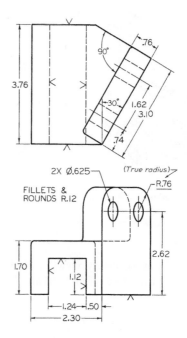

Exercise 20 Adjuster Block. Draw necessary views, including complete auxiliary view showing true shape of inclined surface.*

Exercise 22 Drill Press Bracket. Draw given views and add complete auxiliary views showing true shape of inclined face.*

*Use metric or decimal-inch dimensions as assigned.

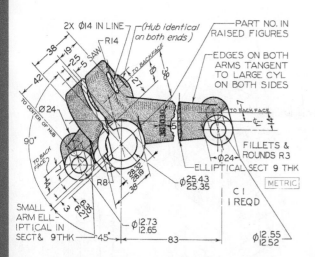

Exercise 23 Brake Control Lever. Draw necessary views and partial views.*

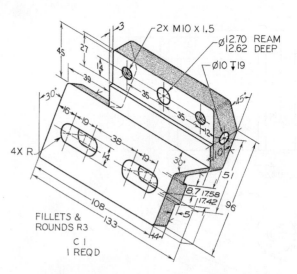

Exercise 25 Cam Bracket. Draw necessary views or partial views as needed.*

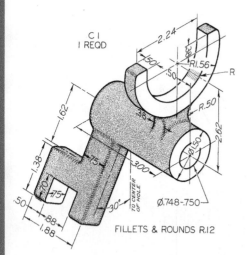

Exercise 24 Shifter Fork. Draw necessary views, including partial auxiliary view showing true shape of inclined arm.*

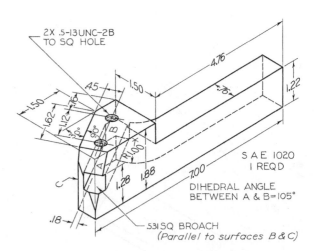

Exercise 26 RH Tool Holder. Draw necessary views, including partial auxiliary views showing 105° angle and square hole true size.*

*Use metric or decimal-inch dimensions as assigned.

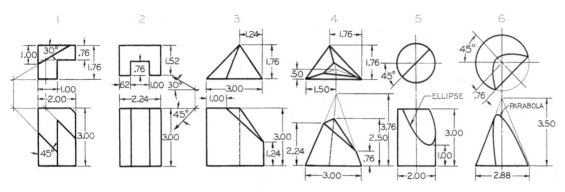

Exercise 27 Draw complete secondary auxiliary views, showing the true sizes of the inclined surfaces (except for Problem 2). In Problem 2 draw secondary auxiliary view as seen in the direction of the arrow given in the problem.*

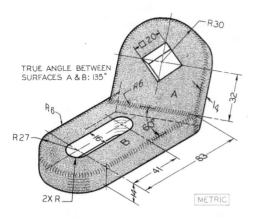

Exercise 28 Control Bracket. Draw necessary views including primary and secondary auxiliary views so that the latter shows true shape of oblique surface A.*

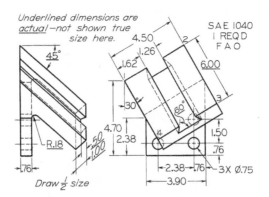

Exercise 30 Dovetail Slide. Draw complete given views and auxiliary views, including view showing true size of surface 1–2–3–4.*

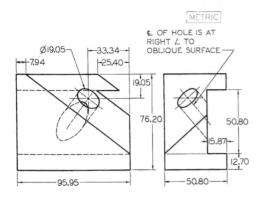

Exercise 29 Holder Block. Draw given views and primary and secondary auxiliary views so that the latter shows true shape of oblique surface.*

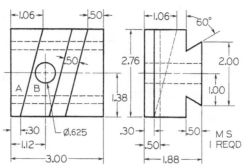

Draw primary aux. view showing angle between planes A and B; then secondary auxiliary view showing true size of surface A.

Exercise 31 Dovetail Guide. Draw given views plus complete auxiliary views as indicated.*

*Use metric or decimal-inch dimensions as assigned.

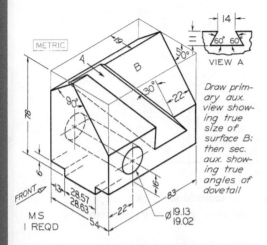

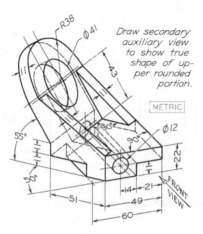

Exercise 32 Adjustable Stop. Draw complete front and auxiliary views plus partial right-side view. Show all hidden lines.*

Exercise 33 Tool Holder. Draw complete front view, and primary and secondary auxiliary views as indicated.*

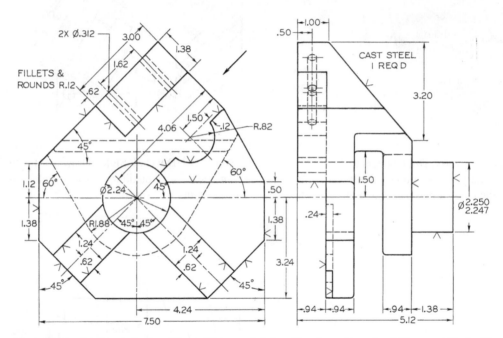

Exercise 34 Box Tool Holder for Turret Lathe. Given: Front and right-side views. Required: Front and left-side views, and complete auxiliary view as indicated by arrow.*

*Use metric or decimal-inch dimensions as assigned.

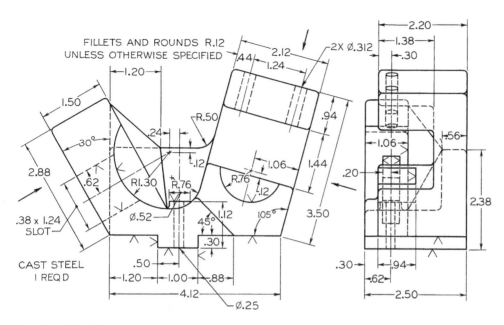

Exercise 35 Pointing Tool Holder for Automatic Screw Machine. Given: Front and right-side views. Required: Front view and three partial auxiliary views.[*]

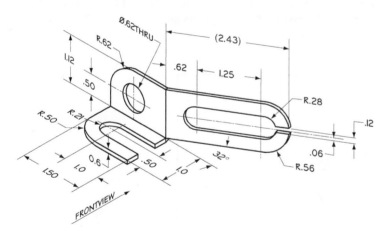

Exercise 36 Mounting Clip. Draw all required views. Include at least one auxiliary view.[*]

[*]Use metric or decimal-inch dimensions as assigned.

REVOLUTION PROBLEMS

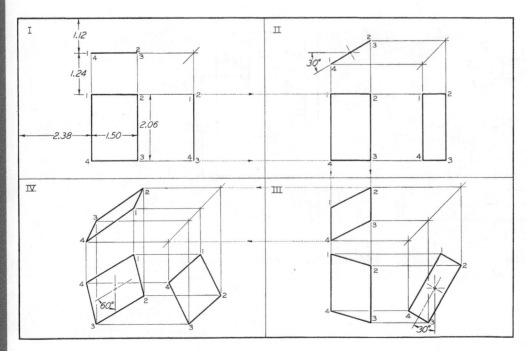

Exercise 37 Divide working area into four equal parts, as shown. Draw given views of the rectangle, and then the primary revolution in space II, followed by successive revolutions in spaces III and IV. Number points as shown. Omit dimensions. Use Form 3 title box.

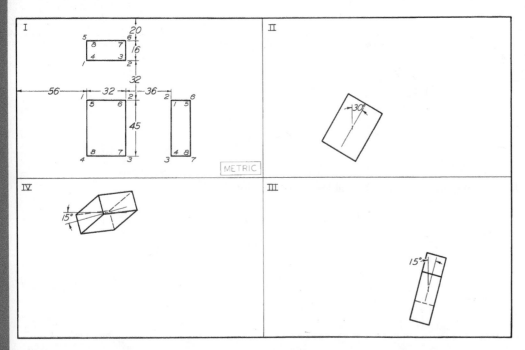

Exercise 38 Divide working area into four equal parts, as shown. Draw given views of prism as shown in space I; then draw three views of the revolved prism in each succeeding space, as indicated. Number all corners. Omit dimensions. Use Form 3 title box.

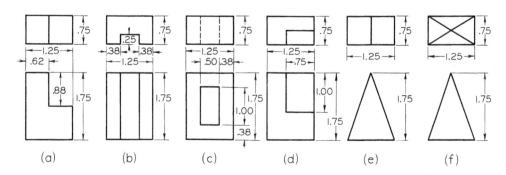

(a)   (b)   (c)   (d)   (e)   (f)

Exercise 39 Divide your sheet into four equal parts as in Exercise 37. In the upper left space draw the original drawing as in Figure 62a, in the upper right draw a simple revolution as in Figure 62b and in the lower two spaces, draw successive revolutions as in Figure 62c and 62d, but for each problem use a block assigned from Exercise 39. Alternative assignment: Divide into two equal spaces. In the left space draw the original views. In the right space draw a simple revolution as in Figure 62b, but use an object assigned from Exercise 39.

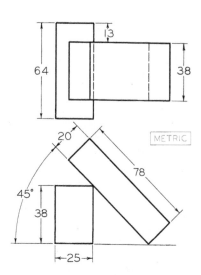

Exercise 40 Draw three views of the blocks but revolved 30° clockwise about an axis perpendicular to the top plane of projection. Do not change the relative positions of the blocks.

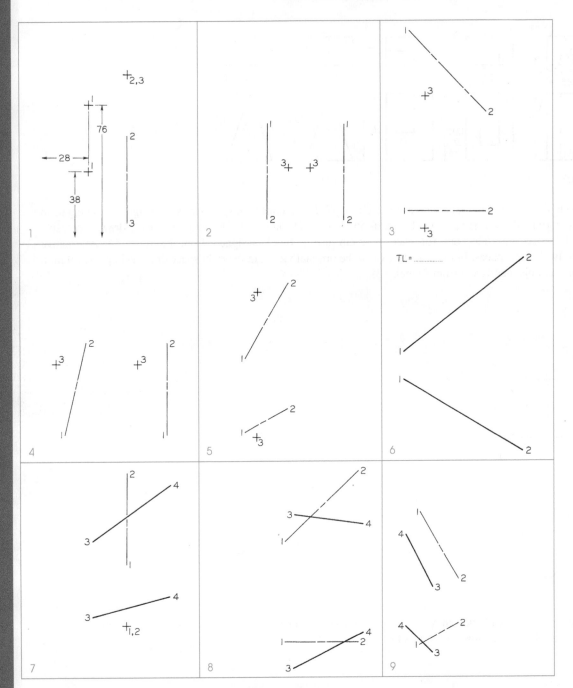

Exercise 41 Divide the working area into four equal areas for four problems per sheet to be assigned by the instructor. Data for the layout of each problem are given by a coordinate system in metric dimensions. For example, in Exercise 38 no. 1, is located by the scale coordinates (28 mm, 38 mm, 76 mm). The first coordinate locates the front view of the point from the left edge of the problem area. The second one locates the front view of the point from the bottom edge of the problem area. The third one locates either the top view of the point from the bottom edge of the problem area or the side view of the point from the left edge of the problem area. Inspection of the given problem layout will determine which application to use.

1. Revolve clockwise point 1(28, 38, 76) through 210° about the axis 2(51, 58, 94)–3(51, 8, 94).
2. Revolve point 3(41, 38, 53) about the axis 1(28, 64, 74)–2(28, 8, 74) until point 3 is at the farthest distance behind the axis.
3. Revolve point 3(20, 8, 84) about the axis 1(10, 18, 122)–2(56, 18, 76) through 210° and to the rear of line 1–2.
4. Revolve point 3(5, 53, 53) about the axis 1(10, 13, 71)–2(23, 66, 71) to its extreme position to the left in the front view.
5. Revolve point 3(15, 8, 99) about the axis 1(8, 10, 61)–2(33, 25, 104) through 180°.
6. By revolution find the true length of line 1(8, 48, 64)–2(79, 8, 119). Scale: 1:100.
7. Revolve line 3(30, 38, 81)–4(76, 51, 114) about axis 1(51, 33, 69)–2(51, 33, 122) until line 3–4 is shown true length and below the axis 1–2.
8. Revolve line 3(53, 8, 97)–4(94, 28, 91) about the axis 1(48, 23, 81)–2(91, 23, 122) until line 3–4 is in true length and above the axis.
9. Revolve line 3(28, 15, 99)–4(13, 30, 84) about the axis 1(20, 20, 97)–2(43, 33, 58) until line 3–4 is level above the axis.

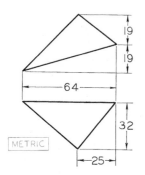

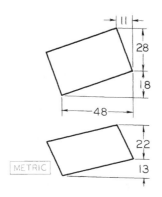

Exercise 42 Draw three views of a right prism 38 mm high that has as its lower base the triangle shown above. See Figure 63.

Exercise 43 Draw three views of a right pyramid 51 mm high, having as its lower base the parallelogram shown above. See Figure 63.

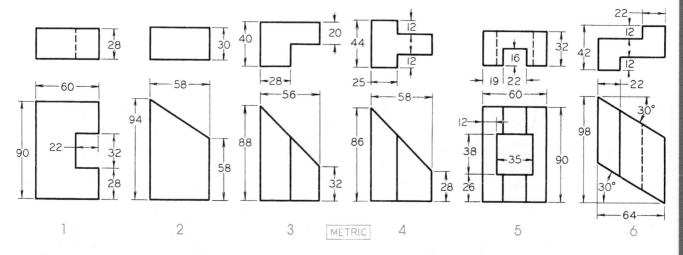

Exercise 44 Draw given views and develop the lateral surface.

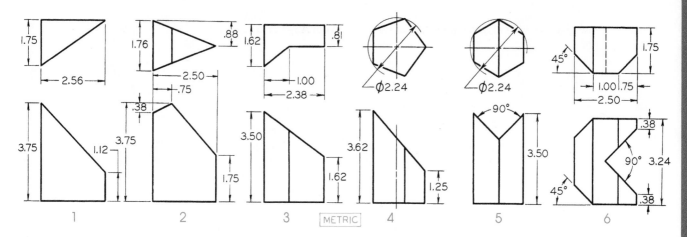

Exercise 45 Draw given views and develop the lateral surface.

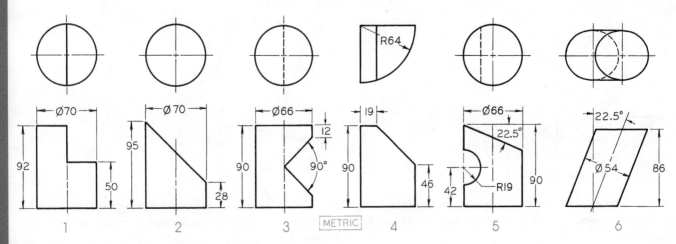

Exercise 46 Draw given views and develop the lateral surface.

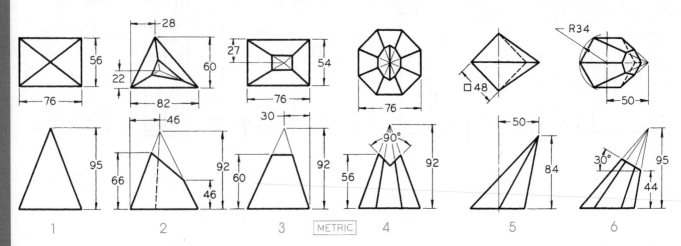

Exercise 47 Draw given views and develop the lateral surface (Layout A3–3 or B–3).

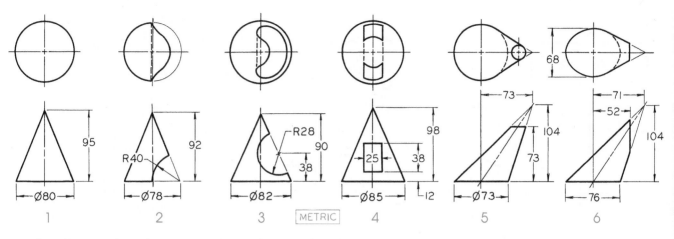

Exercise 48 Draw given views and develop the lateral surface (Layout A3–3 or B–3).

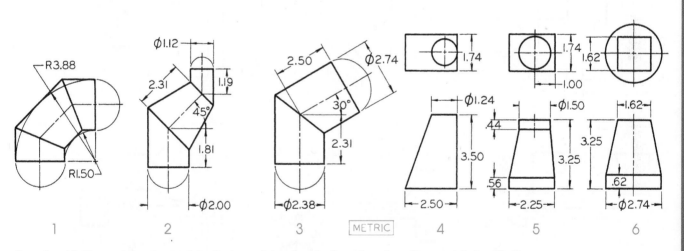

Exercise 49 Draw given views of the forms and develop the lateral surface (Layout A3–3 or B–3).

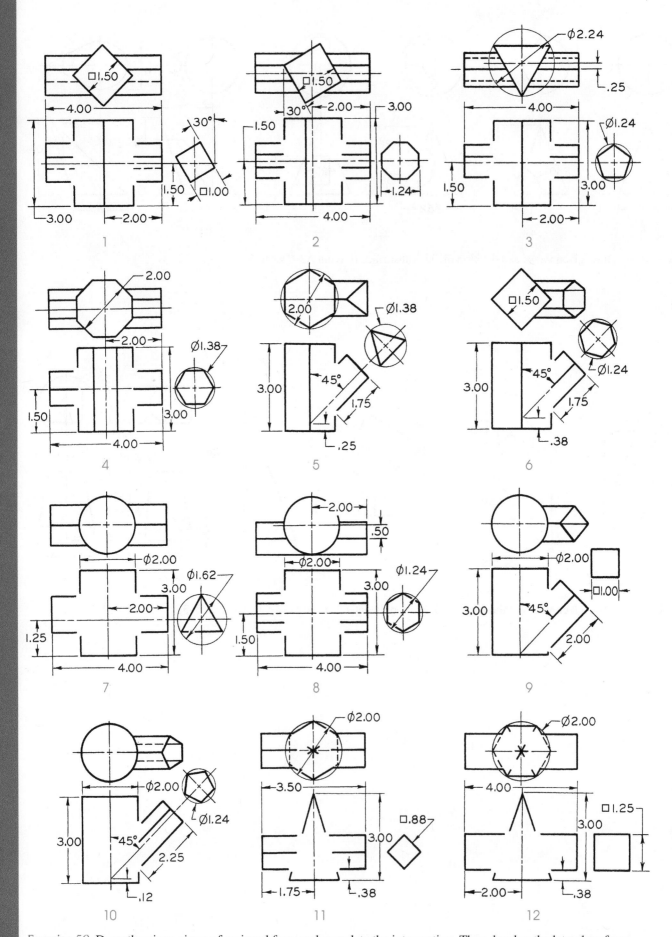

Exercise 50 Draw the given views of assigned form and complete the intersection. Then develop the lateral surfaces.

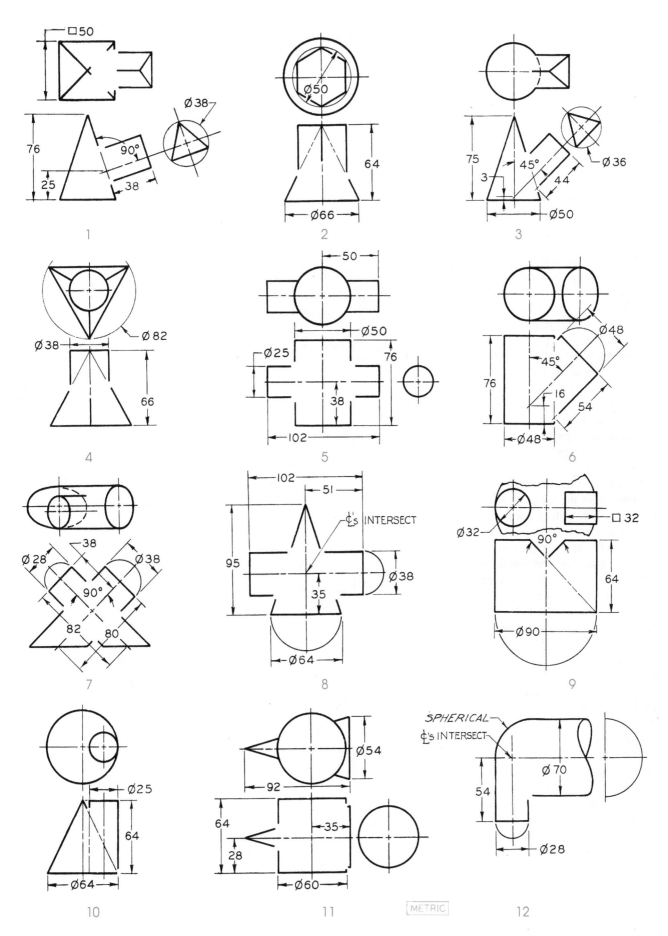

Exercise 51 Draw the given views of assigned form and complete the intersection. Then develop the lateral surfaces.

PROJECTING AUXILIARY VIEWS USING A REFERENCE PLANE

The object has been numbered for you in the pictorial view at right. To create the auxiliary view:

1. Draw two views of the object and determine the direction of sight needed to produce a view that will show the true size of surface A. This step has been completed for you.

2. Next, sketch projection lines parallel to the direction of sight. Some of them have been drawn in for you. Complete all the projection lines.

3. Establish a reference plane. The reference lines in the top and auxiliary views are at right angles to the projection lines and have been drawn for you. These are the edge views of the reference plane.

4. Draw auxiliary view of surface A. It will be true size and shape because the direction of sight is perpendicular to that surface. Transfer depth measurements from the top view to the auxiliary view with dividers or a scale. Each point in the auxiliary view will be on its projection line from the front view and will be the same distance from the reference line as it is in the top view to the corresponding reference line. Points 1, 2, 7, and 8 have been projected for you. Finish projecting the points on surface A. Draw surface A true size in the auxiliary view by connecting the vertices in the same order as they are shown connecting in the top view (1-7-14-12-10-8-5-2-1).

5. Complete the auxiliary view by adding other visible edges and surfaces of the object. Each numbered point in the auxiliary view lies on its projection line from the front view and is the same distance from the reference line as it is in the top view. Note that some surfaces of the object appear as lines in the auxiliary view.

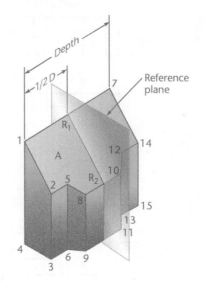

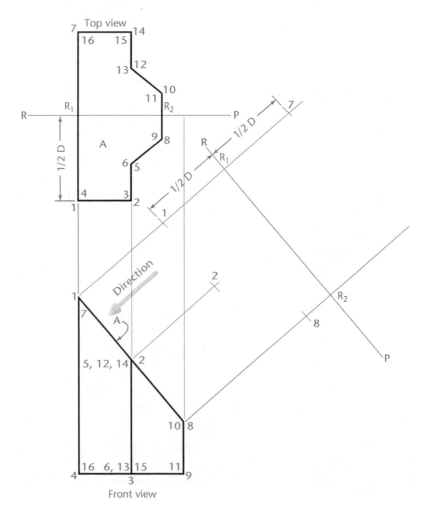

PLOTTING CURVES

The auxiliary view shows the true size and shape of the inclined cut through a piece of molding.

1. Identify some points along the curve shown in the side view. This step has been completed for you.
2. Locate those same points in the front view. The curved shape is the inclined surface. Some of these have been located for you.
3. Project the points into the auxiliary view. The reference plane has been located for you and a few points projected.
4. Finish projecting all of the points on the inclined surface and draw its true shape in the auxiliary view.

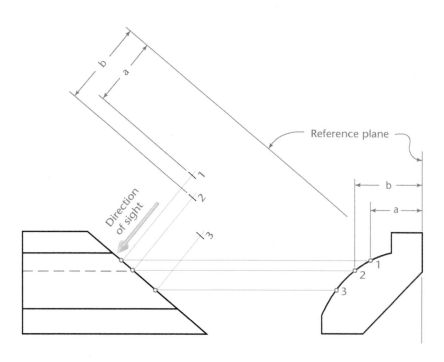

DIRECTIONS

Cut out the paper representation of a glass box with an auxiliary viewing plane shown below.

Neatly letter the names "horizontal plane," "frontal plane," and "auxiliary plane" on the appropriate planes. Label the viewing planes with the principal dimensions that will show in each view. (For example, the front view will show the height and width of an object placed inside the box.)

Project an auxiliary view of the object shown pictorially at the upper right from the two views shown.

Fold on the folding lines and use a small piece of tape to join the top and auxiliary viewing planes. Then use the box to help you answer the questions below.

1. Why must the depth dimension be the same in the top view as in the auxiliary view?

2. Why can you draw projection lines between the front view and the auxiliary view?

3. Could this box have been cut and folded in a different way so that you could project from the top view?

4. How many other auxiliary viewing planes could you construct that would show the depth dimension?

5. Would this particular box show a true-size auxiliary view for all objects?

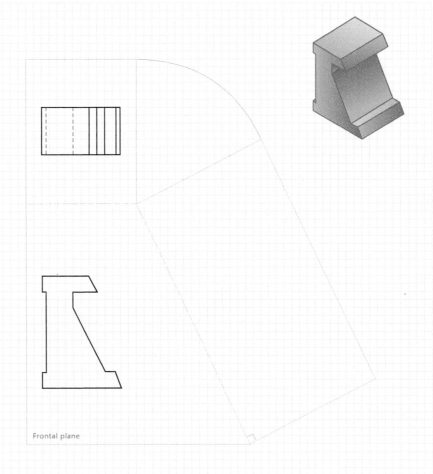

Frontal plane

Make copies of these pages to use for additional practice.

WORKSHEET 2 DEVELOPING A PRISM

The development of a prism is shown below. Cut on the solid lines and fold on the fold lines to create the prism. Tabs are provided to help you glue or tape the development together.

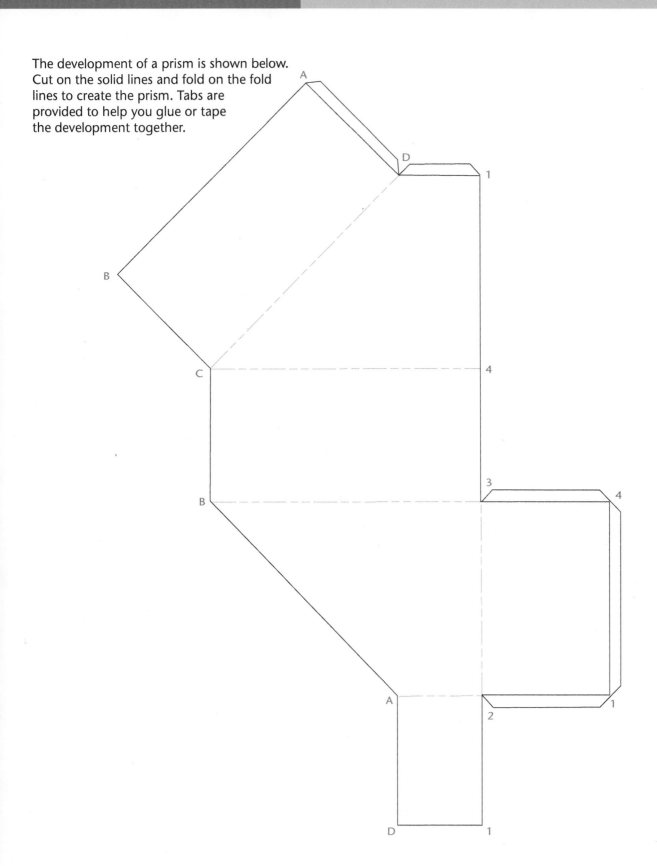

Make copies of these pages to use for additional practice.

The development of a cylinder is shown below. Cut on the solid lines and fold on the fold lines to create the cylinder. Tabs are provided to help you glue or tape the development together.

Cut out the development on Worksheet 3. Assemble it and use it to visualize the development of a cylinder.

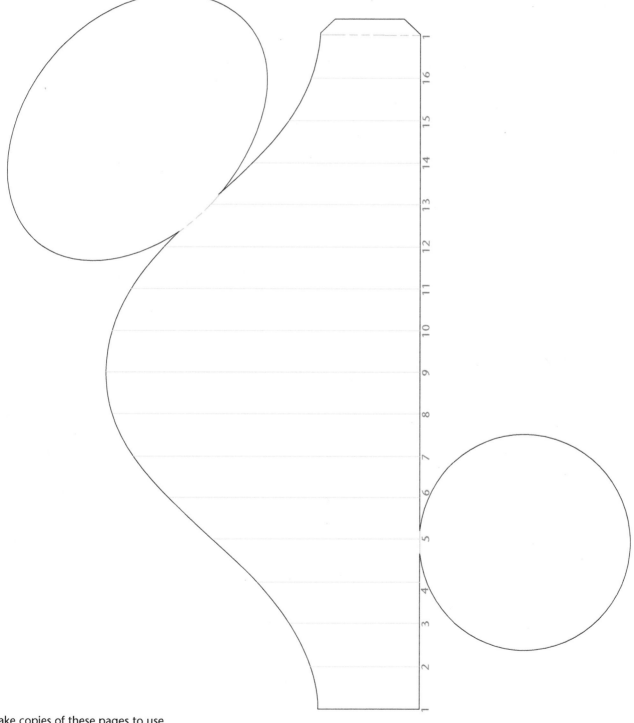

Make copies of these pages to use
for additional practice.

DIMENSIONING

From Chapter 9 of *Modern Graphics Communication*, Fourth Edition, Frederick E. Giesecke, Alva Mitchell, Henry Cecil Spencer, Ivan Leroy Hill, John Thomas Dygdon, James E. Novak, Shawna Lockhart. Copyright © 2010 by Pearson Education, Inc. Published by Pearson Prentice Hall. All rights reserved.

DIMENSIONING

OBJECTIVES

After studying the material in this chapter, you should be able to:

1. Use conventional dimensioning techniques to describe size and shape accurately on an engineering drawing.

2. Create and read a drawing at a specified scale.

3. Correctly place dimension lines, extension lines, angles, and notes.

4. Dimension circles, arcs, and inclined surfaces.

5. Apply finish symbols and notes to a drawing.

6. Dimension contours.

7. Use standard practices for dimensioning prisms, cylinders, holes, and curves.

8. List practices for dimensioning a solid model as documentation.

9. Identify guidelines for the do's and don'ts of dimensioning.

Refer to the following standards:
- ANSI/ASME Y14.5M-1994 Dimensioning and Tolerancing
- ASME Y14.41-2003 Digital Product Definition Data Practices

The companion website for this text is www.prenhall.com/chet_giesecke_modgraphic_4.

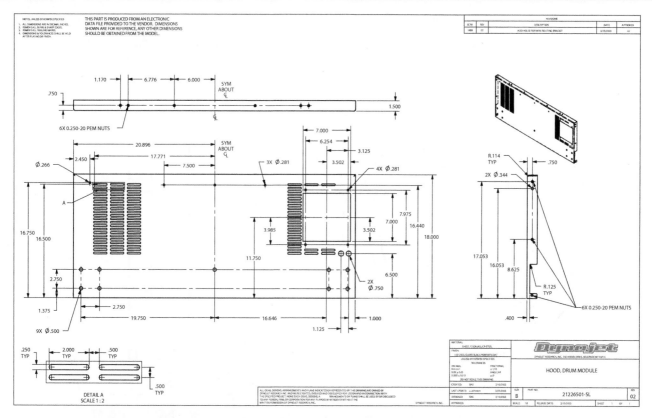

Dimensioned Drawing from Solid Model. This dimensioned drawing for the sheet metal drum module hood was created from a 3D model using Solidworks. *Courtesy of Dynojet Research, Inc.*

OVERVIEW

It is essential to describe not only the shape of the features you design, but also their sizes and locations. Dimensions and notes define the size, finish, and other requirements to fully define what you want manufactured.

Standards organizations prescribe how dimensions should appear and the general rules for their selection and placement in the drawing and in digital models, but it takes skill and practice to dimension drawings so that their interpretation is clear and unambiguous.

Whether you are creating 2D drawings or 3D models, CAD systems are great for producing dimensions that follow standards for the appearance of the dimensions themselves. However, the job of selecting which dimension to show or where to place it in a drawing takes a level of intelligence that is not part of most CAD systems. Those important decisions are still up to the CAD user—or in other words, *you.*

Learning good practices for dimensioning and tolerancing to define part geometry can also help you to create better 3D solid models. If you have a good understanding of how the sizes and locations of model features will be defined, you can plan ahead to show this information clearly in the model.

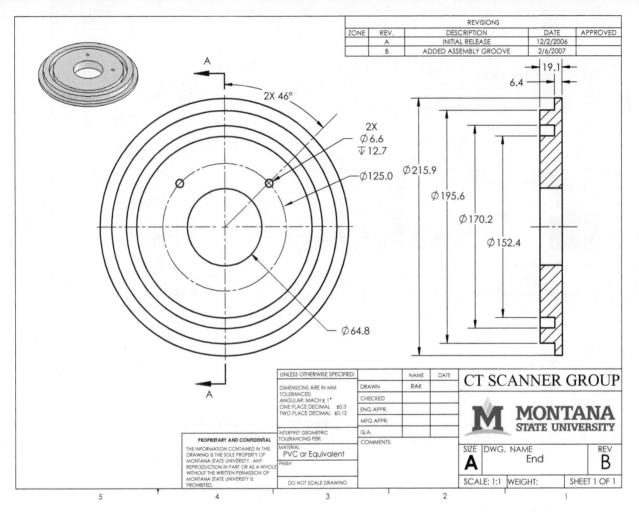

REVISIONS				
ZONE	REV.	DESCRIPTION	DATE	APPROVED
	A	INITIAL RELEASE	12/2/2006	
	B	ADDED ASSEMBLY GROOVE	2/6/2007	

2X 46°

2X
∅6.6
▽12.7

∅125.0

∅215.9

∅195.6

∅170.2

∅152.4

∅64.8

19.1

6.4

A

A

UNLESS OTHERWISE SPECIFIED:		NAME	DATE	CT SCANNER GROUP		
DIMENSIONS ARE IN MM TOLERANCES: ANGULAR: MACH± 1° ONE PLACE DECIMAL ±0.3 TWO PLACE DECIMAL ±0.12	DRAWN	RAK				
	CHECKED					
	ENG APPR.			**MONTANA** STATE UNIVERSITY		
	MFG APPR.					
INTERPRET GEOMETRIC TOLERANCING PER:	Q.A.					
PROPRIETARY AND CONFIDENTIAL THE INFORMATION CONTAINED IN THIS DRAWING IS THE SOLE PROPERTY OF MONTANA STATE UNIVERSITY. ANY REPRODUCTION IN PART OR AS A WHOLE WITHOUT THE WRITTEN PERMISSION OF MONTANA STATE UNIVERSITY IS PROHIBITED.	COMMENTS:					
	MATERIAL PVC or Equivalent			SIZE **A**	DWG. NAME End	REV **B**
	FINISH					
	DO NOT SCALE DRAWING			SCALE: 1:1	WEIGHT:	SHEET 1 OF 1

1 Automatically Generated Dimensions. Views and dimensions can be generated automatically from a solid model. *Courtesy of Robert Kincaid.*

UNDERSTANDING DIMENSIONING

You have been learning to completely describe an object's shape using different types of drawing views. By providing dimensions, you describe the sizes and locations of design features.

The need for interchangeability of parts is the basis for modern part dimensioning. Drawings for products must be dimensioned so that production personnel all over the world can make mating parts that will fit properly when assembled or when used to replace parts.

The increasing need for precision manufacturing and interchangeability has shifted responsibility for size control to the design engineer or detail drafter. The production worker must properly interpret the instructions given on the drawings to produce the required part or construct the building or system. You should be familiar with materials and methods of construction and with production requirements in order to create drawings that define exactly what you want to have manufactured.

Practices for dimensioning architectural and structural drawings are similar in many ways to those for dimensioning manufactured parts, but some practices differ. The portfolio section throughout this text shows a variety of drawings that you can use to familiarize yourself with practices from other disciplines.

Figure 1 shows a dimensioned CAD drawing created from a solid model. Although CAD can be a great help for proper dimensioning technique, you must provide the intelligence to choose and place the dimensions in order to create a drawing that conveys the design clearly. Even if you are going to transmit 3D CAD files as the product definition, you still need to consider how accurately the parts that you will eventually receive back must match the model definition. Directly specifying tolerances in the model is one way to do this.

Three Aspects of Good Dimensioning

Dimensions are given in the form of distances, angles, and notes regardless of the dimensioning units being used. For both CAD and hand drawing, the ability to create good dimensioned drawings requires:

Technique of dimensioning The standard for appearance of lines, the spacing of dimensions, the size of arrowheads, and so on, allows others to read your drawing. A typical dimensioned drawing is shown in Figure 2. Note the strong contrast between the visible lines of the object and the thin lines used for the dimensions. The dimensions are easily legible because they follow the standards for dimensioning technique.

Placement of dimensions Use logical placement for dimensions according to standard practices so that they are legible, easy to find, and easy for the reader to interpret. Notice that when dimensions are placed in between two views, it is easier to see how the dimension relates to the feature as shown in each view.

Choice of dimensions The dimensions you show affect how your design is manufactured. Dimension first for function and then review the dimensioning to see if you can make improvements for ease of manufacturing without adversely affecting the final result. 3D CAD models can be transmitted as all or part of a digital product definition but this still requires a thorough understanding of the sizes and relationships between the part features.

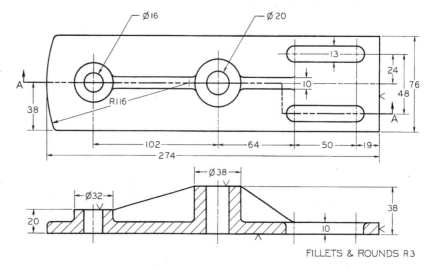

2   A Drawing Dimensioned in Millimeters

A drawing released for production should show the object in its completed state, and should contain all necessary information specifying the final part. As you select which dimensions to show, provide functional dimensions that can be interpreted to manufacture the part as you want it built. Keep in mind:

• The finished piece.
• The function of the part in the total assembly.
• How you will inspect the final part to determine its acceptability.
• Production processes.

Also, remember the following points:

• Give dimensions that are necessary and convenient for producing the part.
• Give sufficient dimensions so that none must be assumed.
• Avoid dimensioning to points or surfaces inaccessible to the worker.
• Do not provide unnecessary or duplicate dimensions.

Tolerance

When a finished part is measured, it will vary slightly from the exact dimension specified. **Tolerance** is the total amount that the feature on the actual part is allowed to vary from what is specified by the drawing or model dimension.

A good understanding of tolerance is important to understanding dimensioning, especially when choosing which dimensions to show. For now, keep in mind that tolerance can be specified generally by giving a note on the drawing such as:

ALL TOLERANCES ±.02 INCH
UNLESS OTHERWISE NOTED.

Another method of specifying tolerance is illustrated in the title block shown in Figure 3.

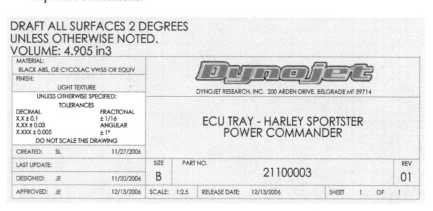

3   A Title Block Specifying Tolerances. *Courtesy of Dynojet Research, Inc.*

Geometric Breakdown

Engineering structures are composed largely of simple geometric shapes, such as the prism, cylinder, pyramid, cone, and sphere. They may be exterior (positive) or interior (negative) forms. For example, a steel shaft is a positive cylinder, and a round hole is a negative cylinder.

These shapes result directly from design necessity—keeping forms as simple as possible—and from the requirements of the fundamental manufacturing operations. Forms having plane surfaces are produced by planing, shaping, milling, and so forth, while forms having cylindrical, conical, or spherical surfaces are produced by turning, drilling, reaming, boring, countersinking, and other rotary operations. One way to consider dimensioning of engineering structures involves two basic steps:

1. Give the dimensions showing the sizes of the simple geometric shapes, called **size dimensions**.
2. Give the dimensions locating these elements with respect to each other, called **location dimensions**. Note that a location dimension locates a 3D geometric element and not just a surface; otherwise, all dimensions would have to be classified as location dimensions.

This process of geometric analysis helps you determine the features of the object and the features' relationships to one another, but it is not enough just to dimension geometry. You must also consider the function of the part in the assembly and the manufacturing requirements. This process is similar to that used when modeling designs in 3D CAD.

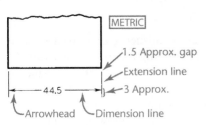

4   Dimension Line

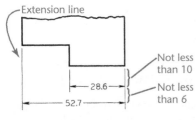

5   Extension Lines

1 LINES USED IN DIMENSIONING

A **dimension line** is a thin, dark, solid line terminated by an arrowhead, indicating the direction and extent of a dimension (Figure 4). In a machine drawing, the dimension line is usually broken near the middle to place the dimension value in the line. In structural and architectural drawing, the dimension figure is placed above an unbroken dimension line.

As shown in Figure 5, the dimension line nearest the object outline should be spaced at least 10 mm (3/8 in.) away. All other parallel dimension lines should be at least 6 mm (1/4 in.) apart, and more if space is available. The spacing of dimension lines should be uniform throughout the drawing.

An **extension line** is a thin, dark, solid line that extends from a point on the drawing to which a dimension refers (Figure 5). The dimension line meets the extension lines at right angles, except in special cases. A gap of about 1.5 mm (1/16 in.) should be left where the extension line would join the object outline. The extension line should extend about 3 mm (1/8 in.) beyond the outermost arrowhead.

A **centerline** is a thin, dark line alternating long and short dashes. Centerlines are commonly used as extension lines in locating holes and other symmetrical features (Figure 6). When extended for dimensioning, centerlines cross over other lines of the drawing without gaps. Always end centerlines using a long dash. Refer to Figures 4–6 for examples of lines used in dimensioning.

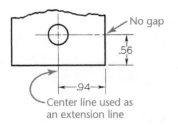

6   Centerlines

DIMENSIONING BY GEOMETRIC BREAKDOWN

To dimension the object shown in isometric at right, use the geometric breakdown as follows:

1 Consider the geometric features of the part.

In this case the features to be dimensioned include:

- two positive prisms
- one positive cylinder
- one negative cone
- six negative cylinders

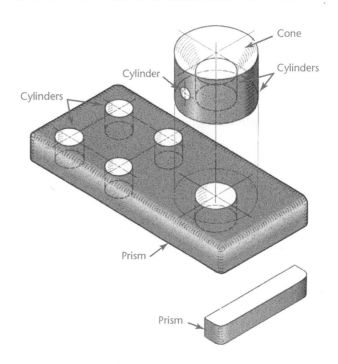

2 Specify the size dimensions for each feature by lettering the dimension values as indicated. (In this illustration, the word "size" indicates the various dimension values.) Note that the four cylinders of the same size can be specified with one dimension. (You will learn more about how to combine information and use symbols to indicate the countersink later in this chapter.)

3 Finally, locate the geometric features with respect to each other. (Actual values would replace the words "size" and "location" in this illustration.) Always check to see that the object is fully dimensioned.

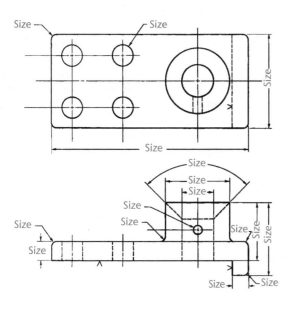

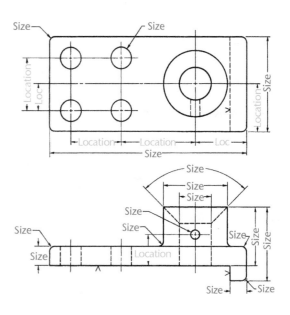

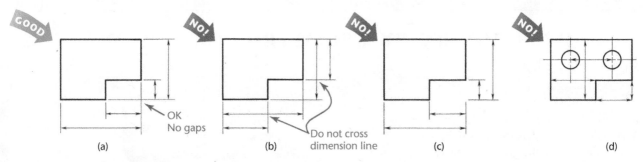

7   Dimension and Extension Lines

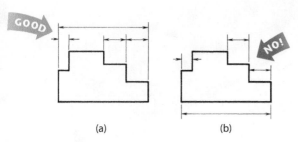

8   Grouped Dimensions

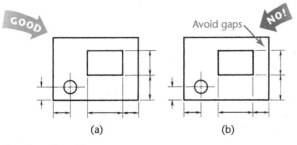

9   Crossing Lines

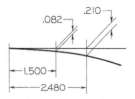

10   Oblique Extension

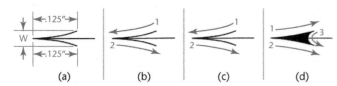

11   Arrowheads

2 USING DIMENSION AND EXTENSION LINES

Dimension lines and extension lines should follow the guidelines shown in Figure 7a. The shorter dimensions are nearest to the object outline. Dimension lines should not cross extension lines, as in Figure 7b, which results from placing the shorter dimensions outside. Note that it is perfectly satisfactory to cross extension lines (Figure 7a), but they should not be shortened (Figure 7c). A dimension line should never coincide with or extend from any line of the drawing (Figure 7d). Avoid crossing dimension lines wherever possible.

Dimensions should be lined up and grouped together as much as possible, as in Figure 8a, and not as in Figure 8b.

In many cases, extension lines and centerlines must cross visible lines of the object (Figure 9a). When this occurs, gaps should not be left in the lines (Figure 9b).

Dimension lines are normally drawn at right angles to extension lines, but an exception may be made in the interest of clarity, as in Figure 10.

3 ARROWHEADS

Arrowheads, shown in Figure 11, indicate the extent of dimensions. They should be uniform in size and style throughout the drawing, not varied according to the size of the drawing or the length of dimensions. Sketch arrowheads freehand so that the length and width have a ratio of 3:1. The arrowhead's length should be equal to the height of the dimension values (about 3 mm or 1/8 in. long). For best appearance, fill in the arrowhead, as in Figure 11d. Figure 12 shows the preferred arrowhead styles for mechanical drawings. Most CAD systems allow you to select from a variety of styles.

> — TIP —
> When you are drawing by hand and using the arrowhead method in which both strokes are directed toward the point, it is easier to make the strokes toward yourself.

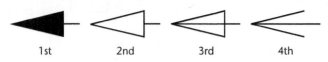

12   Order of Preference for Arrow Styles on Mechanical Drawings

4 LEADERS

A **leader** is a thin, solid line directing attention to a note or dimension and starting with an arrowhead or dot.

A leader should be an inclined straight line drawn at a large angle, except for the short horizontal shoulder (about 3–6 mm or 1/8–1/4 in.) extending from the center of the first or last line of lettering for the note. A leader to a circle should be a radial line, which is a line that would pass through the center of the circle if extended. Figures 13a through 13d show examples of leader lines. More examples of radial lines are shown in Section 22.

Use an arrowhead to start the leader when you can point to a particular line in the drawing, such as the edge of a hole. Use a dot to start the leader when locating something within the

outline of the object, such as an entire surface (see Figures 13e and 13f).

For the Best Appearance, Make Leaders

- near each other and parallel
- across as few lines as possible

Don't Make Leaders

- parallel to nearby lines of the drawing
- through a corner of the view
- across each other
- longer than needed
- horizontal or vertical

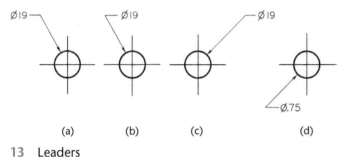
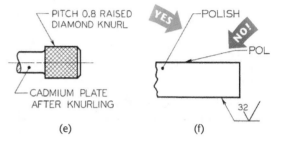

13 Leaders

---

5 DRAWING SCALE AND DIMENSIONING

Drawing scale is indicated in the title block. The scale is intended to help you visualize the object by giving an approximate idea of its size, but is not intended to communicate dimensions. Never scale measurements from drawings to find an unknown dimension. Many standard title blocks include a note such as DO NOT SCALE DRAWING FOR DIMENSIONS, as shown in Figure 14.

Draw a heavy straight line under any single dimension value that is not to scale (Figure 15). Before CAD was widely used, if a change made in a drawing was not important enough to justify correcting the drawing, the practice was simply to change the dimension value. If a dimension does not match the appearance in the drawing, the part is made as dimensioned, not as pictured. If there seems to be an error, many manufacturers check to confirm that the drawing is correct; however, it is your responsibility to specify exactly what you want built. If the entire drawing is not prepared to a standard scale, note NONE in the scale area of the title block. You may see the abbreviation NTS on older drawings, meaning not to scale.

When you create a drawing using CAD, make sure to define dimensions according to the proper standards. Since it is easy to edit CAD drawings, you should generally fix the drawing geometry when making changes, and not merely change dimension values. If you are using a digital model as the sole definition for the part, the model dimensions must be represented accurately.

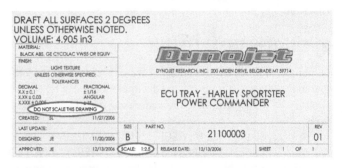

14 Drawing scale is noted in the title block. The drawing should not be scaled for dimensions. *Courtesy of Dynojet Research, Inc.*

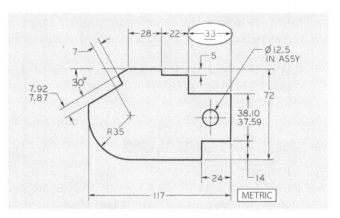

15 Draw a heavy line under any dimension value that is not to scale.

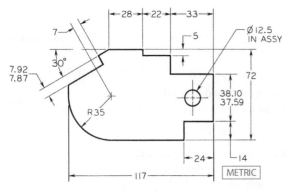

16   Unidirectional Dimension Figures

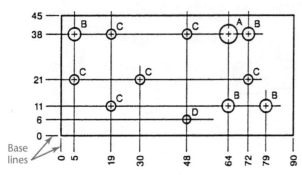

17   Rectangular coordinate dimensioning may show values reading from the right. *Reprinted from Y14.5M-1994, by permission of The American Society of Mechanical Engineers. All rights reserved.*

Keeping Dimensions and Lettering Legible at Smaller Scales

The sizes for lettering height, dimension line spacing, and so on, are to be shown that size on the plotted sheet, otherwise the lettering and dimensioning are often illegible. If you are going to use reduced size working prints, increase the lettering, dimension arrows, and other sizes by approximately 50% (depending upon the amount of reduction) to maintain legibility on the smaller print.

6 DIRECTION OF DIMENSION VALUES AND NOTES

All dimension values and notes are lettered horizontally to be read from the bottom of the sheet, as oriented by the title block. Figure 16 shows the direction for reading dimension values.

The exception is when dimensioning from a baseline as in coordinate dimensioning. Then dimension figures may be aligned with the dimension lines so that they may be read from the bottom or right side of the sheet as shown in Figure 17. In both systems, general notes on the sheet and dimensions and notes shown with leaders are always aligned horizontally to read from the bottom of the drawing.

7 DIMENSION UNITS

Dimension values are shown using the metric system or decimal inch values. Millimeters and decimal inches can be added, subtracted, multiplied, and divided easily compared to fractions.

A note, stating ALL MEASUREMENTS IN MILLIMETERS or ALL MEASUREMENTS IN INCHES UNLESS OTHERWISE NOTED is used in the title block to indicate the measurement units, as was shown in Figure 14. No units are needed with the dimension values in this case. When indicating dimensions:

* Millimeters are indicated by the lowercase letters mm placed to the right of the numeral, as in 12.5 mm.
* Meters are indicated by the lowercase m, as in 50.6 m.
* Inches are indicated by the symbol ″ placed slightly above and to the right of the numeral.
* Feet are indicated by the symbol ′ similarly placed. It is customary in such expressions to omit the inch mark.

It is standard practice to omit millimeter designations and inch marks on drawings and note the units in the title block except when there is a possibility of misunderstanding. For example, 1 VALVE should be 1″ VALVE.

Either meters or feet and inches and fractional inches are used in architectural and structural work where precision in the thousandths of an inch is not necessary and the steel tape or framing square is used to make measurements. Commodities such as pipe and lumber are identified by standard nominal sizes that are close to the actual dimensions.

In some industries, all dimensions, regardless of size, are given in inches; in others, dimensions up to and including 72 inches are given in inches, and dimensions greater than 72 inches are given in feet and inches. In U.S. structural and architectural drafting, all dimensions of 1 foot or more are usually expressed in feet and inches.

8 MILLIMETER VALUES

The millimeter is the commonly used unit for most metric engineering drawings. One-place millimeter decimals are used when tolerance limits permit. Two (or more)–place millimeter decimals are used when higher tolerances are required. One drawing can combine dimensions shown with more and fewer decimal places depending on the necessary tolerance. Keep in mind that 0.1 mm is approximately equal to .004 in. If you are used to working in U.S. customary units, don't provide an unrealistic precision when specifying millimeter values.

Figure 18 shows an example drawing dimensioned in millimeters. Figure 19 shows various ways that millimeter values can be shown for dimensioning.

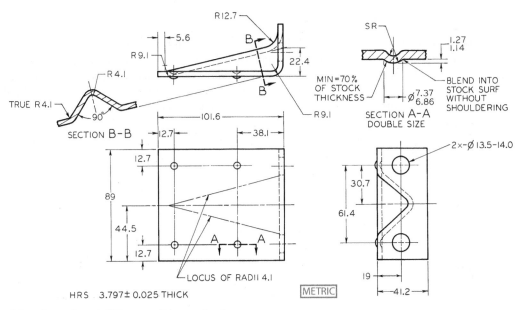

18 Complete Millimeter Dimensioning

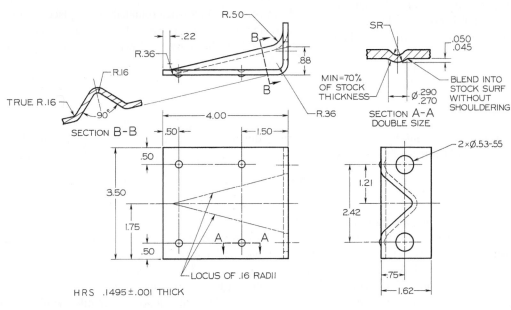

19 Millimeter Dimension Values

9 DECIMAL INCH VALUES

Two-place inch decimals are typical when tolerance limits permit. Three or more decimal places are used for tolerance limits in the thousandths of an inch. In two-place decimals, the second place preferably should be an even digit (for example, .02, .04, and .06 are preferred to .01, .03, or .05) so that when the dimension is divided by 2 (for example, when determining the radius from a diameter), the result will still be a two-place decimal. However, odd two-place decimals are used when required for design purposes, such as in dimensioning points on a smooth curve or when strength or clearance is a factor. A typical example of the use of the complete decimal inch system is shown in Figure 20.

20 Complete Decimal Dimensioning

10 RULES FOR DIMENSION VALUES

Good hand-lettering is important for dimension values on sketches. The shop produces according to the directions on the drawing, and to save time and prevent costly mistakes, make all lettering perfectly legible.

Make all decimal points bold, allowing ample space. Where the metric dimension is a whole number, do not show either a decimal point or a zero. Where the metric dimension is less than 1 mm, a zero precedes the decimal point.

Where the decimal-inch dimension is used on drawings, a zero is not used before the decimal point of values less than 1 in. Typical values are shown to two decimal places even when they represent a whole number (e.g., use 2.00 instead of 2). Correct decimal dimension values are shown in Figures 21a–e.

.125″   .125″   .063″   .125″ high

1.800 +.000   .375   .186   .998   .250
       −.002   .373   .184   .995

.063″

(a)   (b)   (c)   (d)   (e)

21   Decimal Inch Dimension Values

11 RULES FOR ROUNDING DECIMAL DIMENSION VALUES

It is difficult to maintain tolerances smaller than a few thousandths of an inch in manufacturing. In order to provide reasonable tolerances that can be achieved in manufacturing, calculated dimension values for drawings sometimes need to be rounded. Unlike rounding rules used for statistical values, it is preferred to round drawing values to an even number.

When rounding a decimal value to fewer places, regardless of whether the dimension is expressed in inches or metric units, follow these rules:

- If the number following the rounding position is less than 5, make no change.
- If the number following the rounding position is more than 5, round up.
- If the number following the rounding position is a 5, round to an even number. (To do this, note whether the number in the rounding position is even or odd. If the 5 follows an odd number in the rounding position, round up

to an even number. If the 5 follows an even number in the rounding position, make no change.)

Examples of Rounded Decimal Values

- 3.4632 becomes 3.463 when rounded to three places. (Make no change, because the 2 following the rounding position is less than 5.)
- 3.4637 becomes 3.464 when rounded to three places. (Round up, because the 7 following the rounding position is more than 5.)
- 8.37652 becomes 8.376 when rounded to three places. (Make no change, because the 6 in the rounding position is even and the number following the rounding position is a 5.)
- 4.375 becomes 4.38 when rounded to two places. (Round up to an even number, because the 7 in the rounding position is odd and the number following the rounding position is a 5.)

12 DUAL DIMENSIONING

Dual dimensioning is used to show metric and decimal-inch dimensions on the same drawing. Two methods of displaying the dual dimensions are described below.

Position Method

In the **position method** of dual dimensioning, the millimeter dimension is placed above the inch dimension, and the two are separated by a dimension line, or by an added line when the **unidirectional** system of dimensioning is used. An alternative arrangement is the millimeter dimension to the left of the inch dimension, with the two separated by a slash line, or virgule. Placement of the inch dimension above or to the left of the

millimeter dimension is also acceptable. Each drawing should illustrate the dimension identification as $\frac{\text{MILLIMETER}}{\text{INCH}}$ or MILLIMETER/INCH.

Bracket Method

In the **bracket method** of dual dimensioning, the millimeter dimension is enclosed in parentheses. The location of this dimension is optional but should be uniform on any drawing—that is, above or below or to the left or the right of the inch dimension. Each drawing should include a note to identify the dimension values, such as DIMENSIONS IN () ARE MILLIMETERS.

13 COMBINATION UNITS

At times when more than one measurement system is used on the same drawing, the main units are indicated through a note in or near the title block. The alternative units are indicated with an abbreviation after the dimension value. Use mm after the dimension value if millimeters, or IN if inches, only when combining two measurement systems on one drawing. In the U.S. to facilitate the changeover to metric dimensions, some drawings are dual-dimensioned in millimeters and decimal inches as shown in Figure 22. The second set of units shown in parentheses are for reference only.

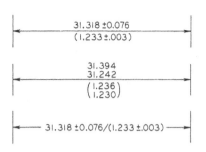

22   Dual-Dimensioned Drawing in Millimeters. On drawing (*Inch values are given for reference only.*)

14 DIMENSION SYMBOLS

A variety of dimensioning symbols shown in Figure 23 are used to replace traditional terms or abbreviations. The symbols are preferred because (1) they take less space in the drawing and (2) they are internationally recognized and therefore do not have translation issues if the part is manufactured in a country where a different language is spoken.

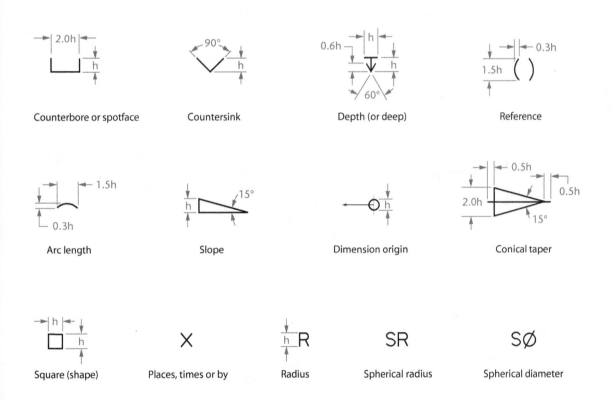

h = Letter height

23   Form and Proportion of Dimensioning Symbols. *Reprinted from Y14.5M-1994, by permission of The American Society of Mechanical Engineers. All rights reserved.*

15 PLACING AND SHOWING DIMENSIONS LEGIBLY

Rules for the placement of dimensions help you to dimension your drawings so that they are clear and readable. They also help locate dimensions in standard places so that someone manufacturing the part doesn't have to search a complicated drawing to find a dimension. You cannot always follow every placement rule to the letter, so keep in mind that the ultimate goal is to dimension the drawing clearly so that the parts are built to your specifications.

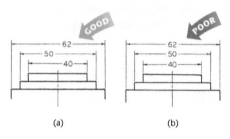

24   Staggered Numerals, Metric

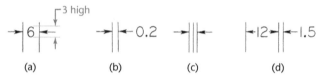

25   Fitting Dimension Values in Limited Spaces (Metric Dimensions)

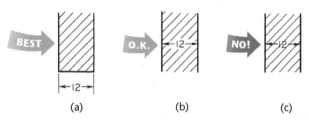

26   Dimensions and Section Lines

Rules for Placing Dimensions Properly

- Never letter a dimension value over any line on the drawing; if necessary, break the line.
- In a group of parallel dimension lines, the dimension values should be staggered, as in Figure 24a, and not stacked up one above the other, as in Figure 24b.
- Do not crowd dimension figures into limited spaces, making them illegible. There are techniques for showing dimension values outside extension lines or in combination with leaders (Figure 25). If necessary, add a removed partial view or detail to an enlarged scale to provide the space needed for clear dimensioning.
- Place dimensions between views when possible, but attached to only a single view. This way it is clear that the dimension relates to the feature, which can be seen in more than one view.
- When a dimension must be placed in a hatched area or on the view, leave an opening in the hatching or a break in the lines for the dimension values, as shown in Figure 26b and 26c.
- Dimensions should not be placed on a view unless it promotes the clarity of the drawing, as shown in Figure 27. In complicated drawings such as Figure 27c, it is often necessary to place dimensions on a view.
- Avoid dimensioning to hidden lines. (See Figure 28.)
- Do not attach dimensions to visible lines where the meaning is not clear, such as the dimension 20 in the top view shown in Figure 29b.
- Notes for holes are usually placed where you see the circular shape of the hole, as in Figure 29a, but give the diameter of an external cylindrical shape where it appears rectangular. This way it is near the dimension for the length of the cylinder.
- Give dimensions where the shapes are shown—where the contours of the object are defined—as is shown in Figure 29.
- Locate holes in the view that shows the shape of the hole clearly.

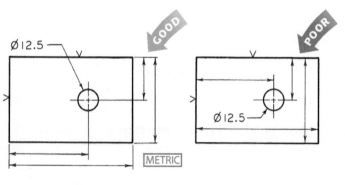

(a) Preferrred dimension placement is off the view.

(b) Do not place dimensions on the view except to enhance clarity.

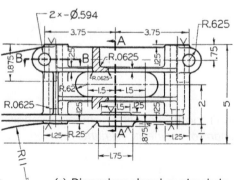

(c) Dimensions placed on view help clarity on a complex drawing.

27   Place dimensions on view only when clarity is enhanced.

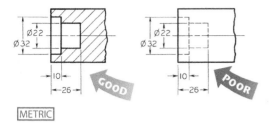

28 Placement of Dimensions

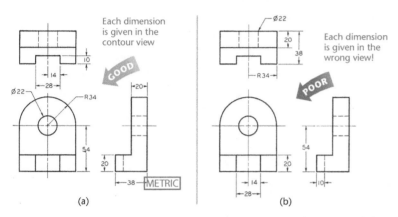

(a)   (b)

29 Place dimensions where the contours of the object are defined.

TIP

Thinking of Dimensioning in Terms of Material Removal

There are many ways to dimension a drawing. If you are having trouble getting started, it may help to consider the overall block of material and what features are to be removed from it, similar to the way you visualize for a sketch. This is especially true when the part is to be manufactured using a process that removes material, such as milling.

Look for the largest portions to be removed and give dimensions for their sizes and locations first. Next add dimensions for the smaller features.

Since the overall dimensions will be the largest, they will be placed furthest from the view. If you are using CAD, it is easy to move dimensions later if you need more space. When you are sketching, block the overall dimension in lightly and leave substantial space between it and the drawing view for placement of shorter dimensions.

Use the rules that you have learned to place dimensions on the view that best shows the shape, and close to where the feature is shown. This makes the drawing easier to read.

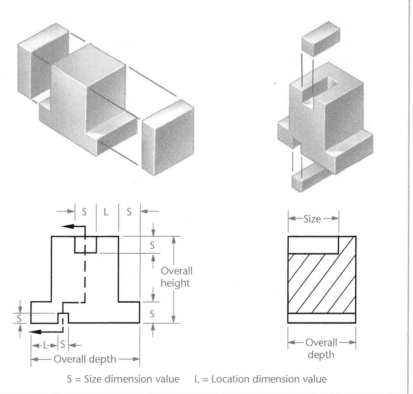

S = Size dimension value   L = Location dimension value

16 SUPERFLUOUS DIMENSIONS

All necessary dimensions must be shown, but do not give unnecessary or **superfluous** dimensions. Figure 30a–l shows examples of how to omit unnecessary dimensions. Do not repeat dimensions on the same view or on different views, or give the same information in two different ways.

As Figure 29b shows, it can be impossible to determine how the designer intended to apply the tolerance when a dimension is given two different ways. When chaining dimensions, one dimension of the chain should be left out if the overall dimension is given, so that the machinist works from one surface only. This is particularly important where an accumulation of tolerances can cause problems with how parts fit or function.

Do not omit dimensions, thinking, for example, that a hole is symmetrical and will be understood to be centered. Note in Figure 30b that one of the two location dimensions should be given for the hole at the right side of the part, even though it is centered. As the creator of the drawing, you should specify exactly how the part is to be built and inspected.

As shown in Figure 30e, when one dimension clearly applies to several identical features, or a uniform thickness, it need not be repeated, but the number of places should be indicated. Dimensions for fillets and rounds and other noncritical features need not be repeated, nor need the number of places be specified. For example, the radii of the rounded ends in Figure 30e need not be repeated.

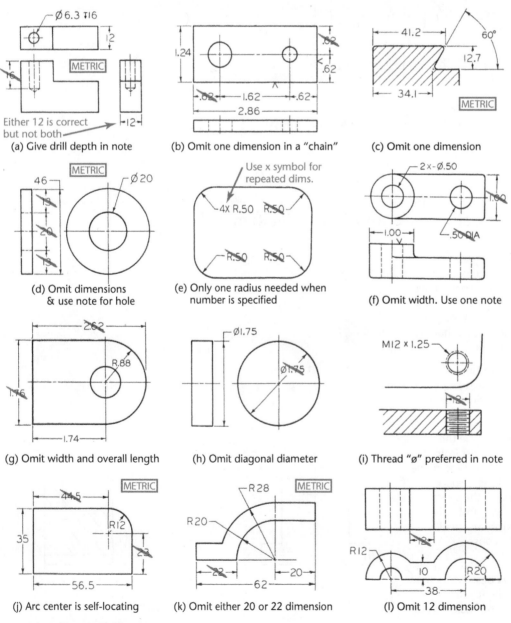

(a) Give drill depth in note
(b) Omit one dimension in a "chain"
(c) Omit one dimension
(d) Omit dimensions & use note for hole
(e) Only one radius needed when number is specified
(f) Omit width. Use one note
(g) Omit width and overall length
(h) Omit diagonal diameter
(i) Thread "ø" preferred in note
(j) Arc center is self-locating
(k) Omit either 20 or 22 dimension
(l) Omit 12 dimension

30 Superfluous Dimensions

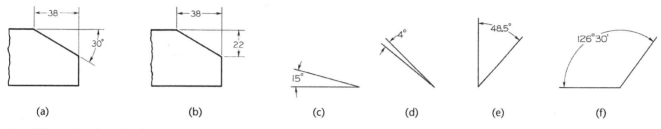

31   Dimensioning Angles

17 DIMENSIONING ANGLES

Dimension angles by specifying the angle in degrees and a linear dimension as shown in Figure 31a. You can also give coordinate dimensions for two legs of a right triangle, as shown in Figure 31b. The coordinate method is better when a high degree of accuracy is required. Variations in degrees of angle are hard to control because the amount of variation increases with the distance from the vertex of the angle. Methods of indicating angles are shown in Figure 31.

In civil engineering drawings, **slope** represents the angle with the horizontal, whereas **batter** is the angle referred to the vertical. Both are expressed by making one member of the ratio equal to 1, as shown in Figure 32. **Grade,** as of a highway, is similar to slope but is expressed in percentage of rise per 100 feet of run. Thus a 20-foot rise in a 100-foot run is a grade of 20%. In structural drawings, angular measurements are made by giving the ratio of run to rise, with the larger size being 12 in. These right triangles are referred to as *bevels.*

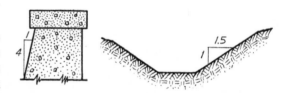

32   Angles in Civil Engineering Projects

18 DIMENSIONING ARCS

A circular arc is dimensioned in the view where you see its true shape by giving the value for its radius preceded by the abbreviation R (Figure 33). Mark the centers with small crosses to clarify the drawing, but not for small or unimportant radii or undimensioned arcs. When there is room enough, both the radius value and the arrowhead are placed inside the arc. If not, the arrowhead is left inside but the value is moved outside, or both the arrowhead and value are moved outside. When section lines or other lines are in the way, you can use a leader and place the value and leader outside of the sectioned or crowded area. For a long radius, when the center falls outside the available space, the dimension line is drawn toward the actual center; but a false center may be indicated and the dimension line "jogged" to it (Figue 33f).

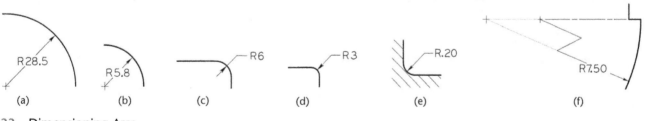

33   Dimensioning Arcs

19 FILLETS AND ROUNDS

Individual fillets and rounds are dimensioned like other arcs. If there are only a few and they are obviously the same size, giving one typical radius is preferred. However, fillets and rounds are often numerous on a drawing, and they usually are some standard size, such as metric R3 and R6, or R.125 and R.250 when using decimal-inch. In this case, give a general note in the lower portion of the drawing, such as:

FILLETS R6 AND ROUNDS R3 UNLESS OTHERWISE SPECIFIED

or

ALL CASTING RADII R6 UNLESS NOTED

or simply

ALL FILLETS AND ROUNDS R6.

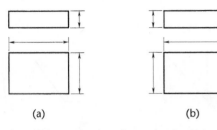
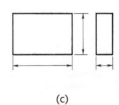

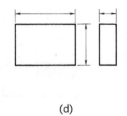

(a)   (b)   (c)   (d)

34 Dimensioning Rectangular Prisms

20 SIZE DIMENSIONS: PRISMS

The right rectangular prism is probably the most common geometric shape. Front and top views are dimensioned as shown in Figures 34a and 34b. The height and width are usually given in the front view, and the depth in the top view. The vertical dimensions can be placed on the left or right, usually in-line. Place the

horizontal dimension between views as shown and not above the top or below the front view. Front and side views should be dimensioned as in Figures 34c and 34d. An example of size dimensions for a machine part made entirely of rectangular prisms is shown in Figure 35.

Tear out Worksheet 1. Practice the technique, choice, and placement of dimensions by adding dimensions for the prismatic shapes.

Tear out Worksheet 2. Consider the best way to dimension the angled feature.

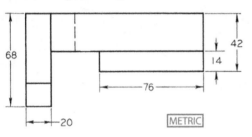

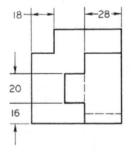

Cutter block for milling fixture

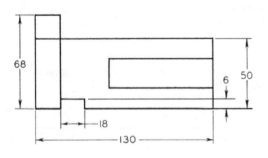

35 Dimensioning a Machine Part Composed of Prismatic Shapes

21 SIZE DIMENSIONS: CYLINDERS

The right circular cylinder is the next most common geometric shape and is commonly seen as a shaft or a hole. Cylinders are usually dimensioned by giving the diameter and length where the cylinder appears as a rectangle. If the cylinder is drawn vertically, give the length at the right or left, as in Figure 36. If the cylinder is drawn horizontally, give the length above or below the rectangular view, as in Figure 36.

Do not use a diagonal diameter inside the circular view, except when clarity is improved. Using several diagonal diameters on the same center becomes very confusing.

The radius of a cylinder should never be given because measuring tools, such as the micrometer caliper, are designed to check diameters. Holes are usually dimensioned by means of notes specifying the diameter and the depth, as

shown in Figure 37, with or without manufacturing operations.

Give the diameter symbol Ø before all diameter dimensions, as in Figure 38a (ANSI/ASME Y14.5M-1994). In some cases, the symbol Ø may be used to eliminate the circular view, as shown in Figure 38b. The abbreviation DIA following the numerical value was used on older decimal inch drawings.

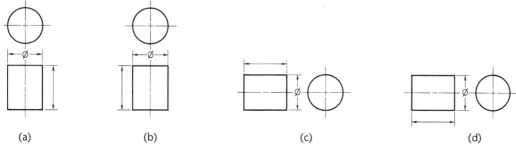

36   Dimensioning Cylinders

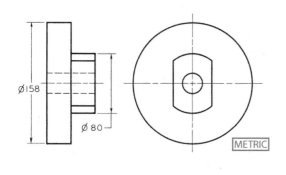

Use ìØ" to i ndicate circular shape

(a)

Use "Ø" to indicate circular view

(b)

37   Use of Ø in Dimensioning Cylinders

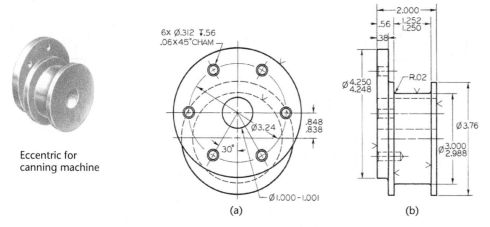

Eccentric for
canning machine

(a)

(b)

38   Dimensioning a Machine Part Composed of Cylindrical Shapes

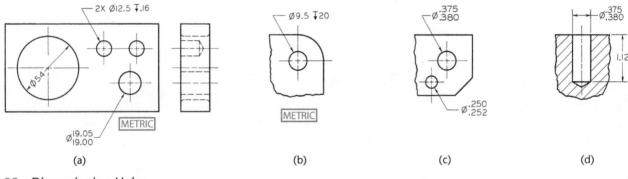

(a)   (b)   (c)   (d)

39   Dimensioning Holes

22 SIZE DIMENSIONING HOLES

Figure 39 shows standard symbols used in dimensioning holes. Figure 40 shows radial leader lines. Countersunk, counterbored, and tapped holes are usually specified by standard symbols or abbreviations, as shown in Figure 41. The order of items in a note corresponds to the order of procedure in the shop in producing the hole. The leader of a note should point to the circular view of the hole, if possible.

When the circular view of the hole has two or more concentric circles, as for counterbored, countersunk, or tapped holes, the arrowhead should touch the outer circle. Draw a **radial leader line,** that is, one that would pass through the center of the circle if it were extended. Figure 40 shows good and bad examples of leader lines.

Two or more holes can be dimensioned by a single note and by specifying the number of holes, as shown at the top of Figure 41. It is widely acceptable to use decimal fractions for both metric or inch drill sizes, as shown in Figure 41b. For numbered or letter-size drills, specify the decimal size or give

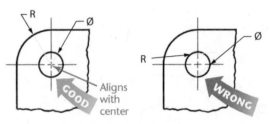

40   Good and Bad Examples of Radial Leader Lines

the number or letter designation followed by the decimal size in parentheses—for example #28 (.1405) or "P" (.3230). Metric drills are all in decimal sizes and are not designated by number or letter.

Specify only the dimensions of the holes, without a note listing whether the holes are to be drilled, reamed, or punched, as shown in Figures 41c and 41d. The manufacturing technician or engineer is usually better suited to determine the least expensive process to use that will achieve the tolerance required.

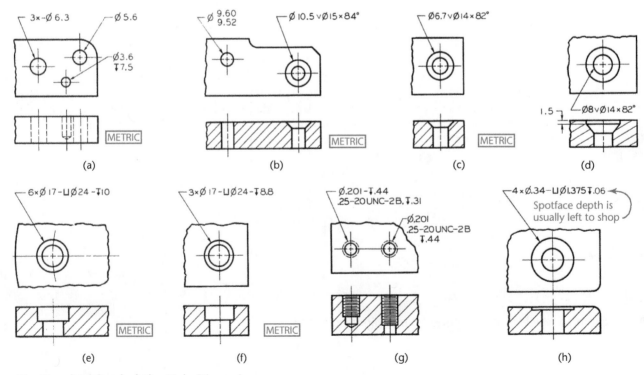

(a)   (b)   (c)   (d)

(e)   (f)   (g)   (h)

41   Standard Symbols for Hole Dimensions

23 APPLYING STANDARD DIMENSIONING SYMBOLS

Use standard dimensioning symbols when possible to save space and communicate dimensions clearly. (Refer back to Figure 23 for details on how to draw the symbols.) Most CAD software contains a palette of standard symbols. Figure 42 shows the application of a variety of standard symbols. Note that Figure 42a shows the *basic dimension* symbol used in geometric dimensioning and tolerancing (GD&T). In this case, "basic" does not mean "ordinary."

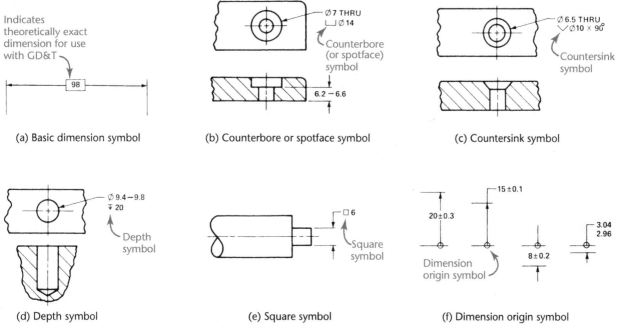

(a) Basic dimension symbol

(b) Counterbore or spotface symbol

(c) Countersink symbol

(d) Depth symbol

(e) Square symbol

(f) Dimension origin symbol

42   Use of Dimensioning Symbols. *Reprinted from Y14.5M-1994, by permission of The American Society of Mechanical Engineers. All rights reserved.*

24 DIMENSIONING TRIANGULAR PRISMS, PYRAMIDS, AND CONES

To dimension a triangular prism, give the height, width, and displacement of the top edge in the front view, and the depth in the top view, as is shown in Figure 43a.

For a rectangular pyramid, give the heights in the front view and the dimensions of the base and the centering of the vertex in the top view, as in Figure 43b. If the base is square, you need only give dimensions for one side of the base, preceded by the square symbol, as in Figure 43c (or on older drawings you may see it labeled SQ).

For cones, give the altitude and the diameter of the base in the triangular view (Figure 43d). For a frustum of a cone, give the vertical angle and the diameter of one of the bases (Figure 43e). Another method is to give the length and the diameters of both ends in the front view. Still another is to give the diameter at one end and the amount of taper per foot in a note.

Figure 43f shows a two-view drawing of a plastic knob. Overall, it is spherical and is dimensioned by giving its diameter preceded by the abbreviation and symbol for spherical diameter, SØ (in older notations it may be followed by the abbreviation SPHER). The torus-shaped bead around the knob is dimensioned by giving the thickness of the ring and the outside diameter.

Figure 43g shows a spherical end dimensioned by a radius preceded by the abbreviation SR. Internal shapes corresponding to the external shapes in Figure 43 would be dimensioned similarly.

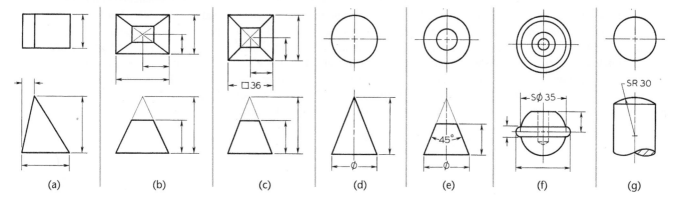

(a)   (b)   (c)   (d)   (e)   (f)   (g)

43   Dimensioning Various Shapes

25 DIMENSIONING CURVES

One way to dimension curves is to give a group of radii, as shown in Figure 44a. Note that in dimensioning the R126 arc, whose center is inaccessible, the center may be moved inward along a centerline and a jog made in the dimension line. Another method is to dimension the outline envelope of a curved shape so that the various radii are self-locating from "floating centers," as shown in Figure 44b. Both circular and noncircular curves may be dimensioned by using coordinate dimensions, or datums, as in Figure 44c.

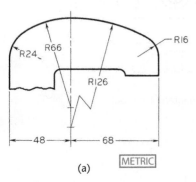

(a)

METRIC

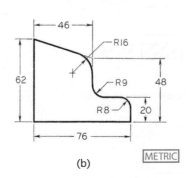

(b)

METRIC

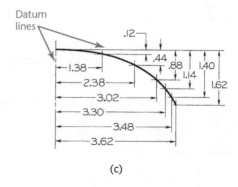

(c)

44   Dimensioning Curves

26 DIMENSIONING CURVED SURFACES

When angular measurements are unsatisfactory, you may give **chordal dimensions,** as shown in Figure 45a, or linear dimensions on the curved surfaces, as shown in Figure 45b.

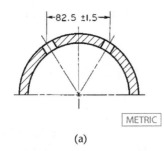

(a)

METRIC

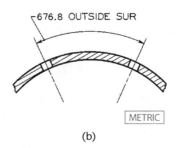

(b)

METRIC

45   Dimensioning Along Curved Surfaces

27 DIMENSIONING ROUNDED-END SHAPES

The method for dimensioning rounded-end shapes depends on the degree of accuracy required. If precision is not necessary, use methods convenient for manufacturing, as in Figures 46a–c. Figures 46d–g show methods used when accuracy is required.

The link to be cast (or cut from sheet metal or plate) in Figure 46a is dimensioned as it would be laid out for manufacture, giving the center-to-center distance and the radii of the ends. Note that only one radius dimension is necessary, and the number of places is included with the size dimension.

In Figure 46b, the pad on a casting with a milled slot is dimensioned from center to center to help the pattern maker and machinist in layout. This also gives the total travel of the milling cutter. The width dimension indicates the diameter of the milling cutter, so give the diameter of a machined slot. A cored slot, however, would be dimensioned by radius to conform with the pattern making procedure.

The semicircular pad in Figure 46c is laid out like the pad in Figure 46b, except that angular dimensions are used. Angular tolerances can be used if necessary.

Tear out Worksheet 3. Practice dimensioning rounded shapes. Consider size and location.

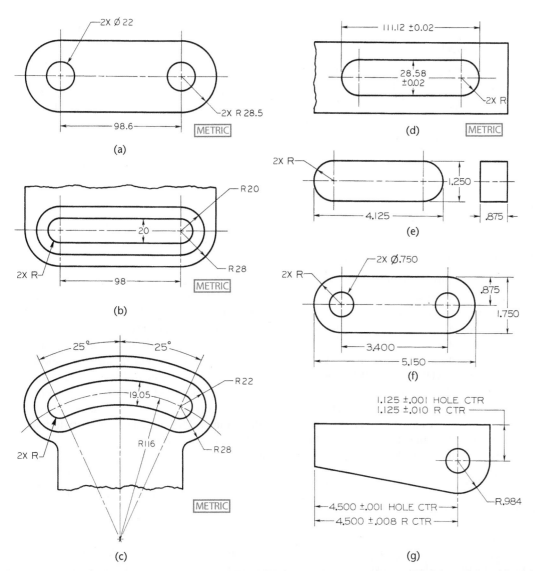

46 Dimensioning Rounded-End Shapes. For accuracy, in Figure 46d–g, overall lengths of rounded-end shapes are given, and radii are indicated, but without specific values. The center-to-center distance may be required for accurate location of some holes. In Figure 46g, the hole location is more critical than the location of the radius, so the two are located.

28 DIMENSIONING THREADS

Local notes are used to specify dimensions of threads. For tapped holes, the notes should, if possible, be attached to the circular views of the holes, as shown in Figure 47. For external threads, the notes are usually placed in the longitudinal views, where the threads are more easily recognized, as in Figures 47b and 47c.

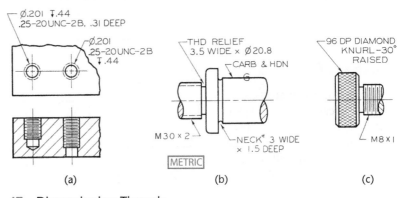

47 Dimensioning Threads

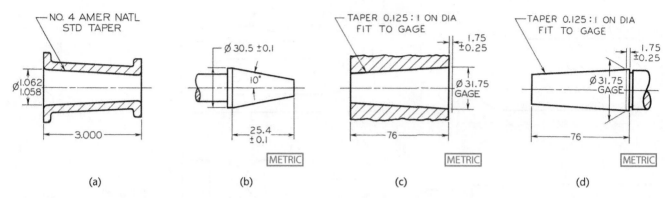

48 Dimensioning Tapers

29 DIMENSIONING TAPERS

A taper is a conical surface on a shaft or in a hole. The usual method of dimensioning a taper is to give the amount of taper in a note, such as TAPER 0.167 ON DIA (with TO GAGE often added), and then give the diameter at one end with the length or give the diameter at both ends and omit the length. Taper on diameter means the difference in diameter per unit of length.

Standard machine tapers are used on machine spindles, shanks of tools, or pins, and are described in "Machine Tapers" in ANSI/ASME B5.10-1994. Such standard tapers are dimensioned on a drawing by giving the diameter (usually at the large end), the length, and a note, such as NO. 4 AMERICAN NATIONAL STANDARD TAPER as shown in Figure 48a.

For not-too-critical requirements, a taper may be dimensioned by giving the diameter at the large end, the length, and the included angle, all with proper tolerances, as shown in Figure 48b. Alternately, the diameters of both ends, plus the length, may be given with necessary tolerances.

For close-fitting tapers, the amount of taper per unit on diameter is indicated as shown in Figure 48c and 48d. A gage line is selected and located by a comparatively generous tolerance, while other dimensions are given appropriate tolerances as required.

30 DIMENSIONING CHAMFERS

A chamfer is a beveled or sloping edge. It is dimensioned by giving the length of the offset and the angle, as in Figure 49a. A 45° chamfer also may be dimensioned in a manner similar to that shown in Figure 49a, but usually it is dimensioned by note, as in Figure 49b.

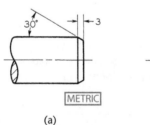
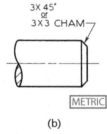

49 Dimensioning Chamfers

31 SHAFT CENTERS

Shaft centers are required on shafts, spindles, and other conical or cylindrical parts for turning, grinding, and other operations. Such a center may be dimensioned, as shown in Figure 50. Normally the centers are produced by a combined drill and countersink.

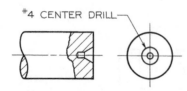

50 Shaft Center

386

32 DIMENSIONING KEYWAYS

The methods of dimensioning keyways for Woodruff keys and stock keys are shown in Figure 51. Note, in both cases, the use of a dimension to center the keyway in the shaft or collar. The preferred method of dimensioning the depth of a keyway is to give the dimension from the bottom of the keyway to the opposite side of the shaft or hole, as shown. The method of computing such a dimension is shown in Figure 51d. Values for A may be found in machinists' handbooks.

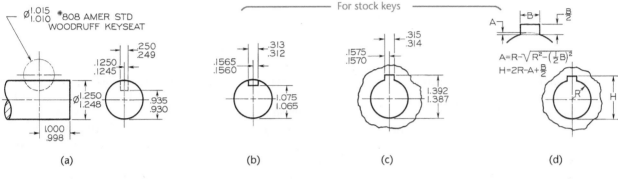

51   Dimensioning Keyways

33 DIMENSIONING KNURLS

A knurl is a roughened surface to provide a better handgrip or to be used for a press fit between two parts. For handgrip purposes, it is necessary only to give the pitch of the knurl, the type of knurling, and the length of the knurled area, as shown in Figure 52a and 52b. To dimension a knurl for a press fit, the toleranced diameter before knurling should be given, as shown in Figure 52c. A note should be added that gives the pitch and type of knurl and the minimum diameter after knurling (see ANSI/ASME B94.6-1984 (R1995)).

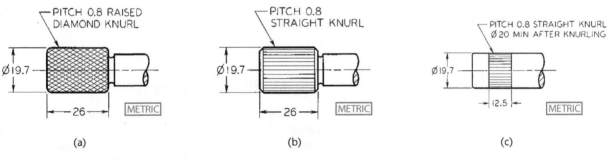

52   Dimensioning Knurls

387

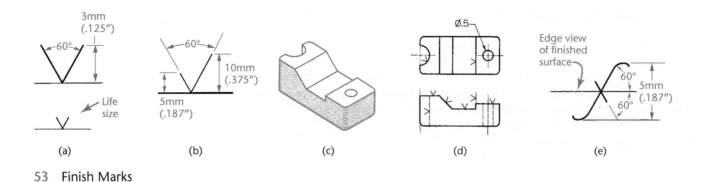

53   Finish Marks

34 FINISH MARKS

A **finish mark** is used to indicate that a surface is to be machined, or finished, as on a rough casting or forging. To the patternmaker or diemaker, a finish mark means that allowance of extra metal in the rough workpiece must be provided for the machining.

On drawings of parts to be machined from rolled stock, finish marks are generally unnecessary, because it is obvious that the surfaces are finished. Similarly, it is not necessary to show finish marks when the dimension implies a finished surface, such as Ø6.22–6.35 (metric) or Ø2.45–2.50 (decimal-inch).

As shown in Figure 53, three styles of finish marks, the general symbol ∨, the new basic symbol √, and the old symbol ✗, are used to indicate an ordinary smooth machined surface. The symbol is like a capital V, made about 3 mm high in conformity with the height of dimensioning lettering. The extended symbol, preferred by ANSI, is like a larger capital with the right leg extended. The short leg is made about 5 mm high and the height of the long leg is about 10 mm. The basic symbol may be altered for more elaborate surface texture specifications.

Figure 53c shows a simple casting having several finished surfaces. In Figure 53d, two views of the same casting show how the finish marks are indicated on a drawing. The finish mark is shown only on the edge view of a finished surface and is repeated in any other view in which the surface appears as a line, even if the line is a hidden line.

If a part is to be finished all over, finish marks should be omitted, and a general note, such as FINISH ALL OVER or FAO, should be lettered on the lower portion of the sheet.

The several kinds of finishes are detailed in machine shop practice manuals. The following terms are among the most commonly used: finish all over, rough finish, file finish, sand blast, pickle, scrape, lap, hone, grind, polish, burnish, buff, chip, spotface, countersink, counterbore, core, drill, ream, bore, tap, broach, and knurl. When it is necessary to control the surface texture of finished surfaces beyond that of an ordinary machine finish, the symbol √ is used as a base for the more elaborate surface quality symbols.

Finished surfaces can be measured more accurately, so provide dimensions from these when possible, as in Figure 54.

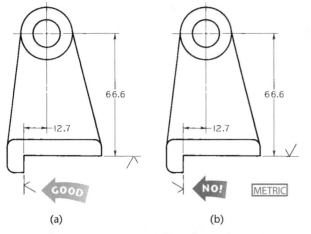

(a)   (b)

54   Correct and Incorrect Marks Showing Dimensions to Finished Surfaces. The point of the symbol should be directed inward toward the body of metal similar to a tool bit, not upside down, as is shown in Figure 54b.

35 SURFACE ROUGHNESS

The demands of automobiles, airplanes, and other machines that can stand heavy loads and high speeds with less friction and wear have increased the need for accurate control of surface quality by the designer, regardless of the size of the feature. Simple finish marks are not adequate to specify surface finish on such parts.

Surface finish is intimately related to the functioning of a surface, and proper specification of finish of surfaces such as bearings and seals is necessary. Surface quality specifications should be used only where needed, since the cost of producing a finished surface becomes greater as the quality of the surface called for is increased. Generally, the ideal surface finish is the roughest that will do the job satisfactorily.

The system of surface texture symbols recommended by ANSI/ASME (Y14.36M-1996) for use on drawings, regardless of the system of measurement used, is now broadly accepted by American industry. These symbols are used to define surface

	Symbol	Symbol
(a)	$\sqrt{}$	Basic texture surface symbol. Surface may be produced by any method except when the bar or circle, (b) or (d), is specified.
(b)	$\overline{\sqrt{}}$	Material removal by machining is required. The horizontal bar indicates that material removal by machining is required to reproduce the surface and that material must be provided for that purpose.
(c)	3.5 $\overline{\sqrt{}}$	Material removal allowance. The number indicates the amount of stock to be removed by machining in millimeters (or inches). Tolerances may be added to the basic value shown or in a general note.
(d)	$\varnothing$	Material removal prohibited. The circle in the vee indicates that the surface must be produced by processes such as casting, forging, hot finishing, cold finishing, die casting, powder metallurgy, or injection molding without subsequent removal.
(e)	$\sqrt{}$	Surface texture symbol. To be used when any surface characteristics are specified above the horizontal line or to the right of the symbol. Surface may be produced by any method except when the bar or circle, (b) or (d), is specified.

55 Surface Texture Symbols and Construction. *Reprinted from Y14.36M-1996, by permission of The American Society of Mechanical Engineers. All rights reserved.*

texture, roughness, and lay. See Figure 55 for the meaning and construction of these symbols. The basic surface texture symbol in Figure 55a indicates a finished or machined surface by any method, just as does the general V symbol. Modifications to the basic surface texture symbol, shown in Figures 55b–d, define restrictions on material removal for the finished surface. Where surface texture values other than roughness average are specified, the symbol must be drawn with the horizontal extension, as shown in Figure 55e. Construction details for the symbols are given in Figure 55f.

Applications of Surface Roughness Symbols

Applications of the **surface texture symbols** are given in Figure 56a. Note that the symbols read from the bottom and/or the right side of the drawing and that they are not drawn at any angle or upside down. Measurements for roughness and waviness, unless otherwise specified, apply in the direction that gives the maximum reading, usually across the lay, as shown in Figure 56b.

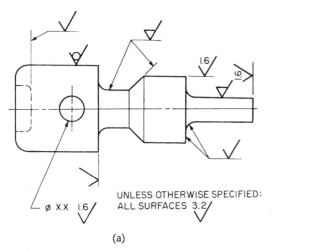

(a)

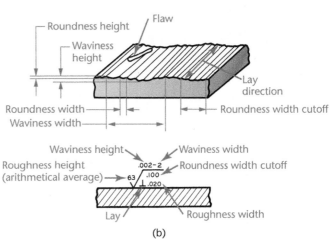

(b)

56 Application of Surface Texture Symbols and Surface Characteristics. *Reprinted from Y14.36M-1996, by permission of The American Society of Mechanical Engineers. All rights reserved.*

Recommended Roughness and Waviness Values

Recommended roughness height values are given in Table 1. When it is necessary to indicate the roughness-width cutoff values, the standard values used are listed in Table 2. If no value is specified, the 0.80 value is assumed.

When maximum waviness height values are required, the recommended values to be used are as given in Table 3.

Table 1 Preferred Series Roughness Average Values.* *Reprinted from Y14.36M-1996, by permission of The American Society of Mechanical Engineers. All rights reserved.*

Micrometers	Micro-inches
0.012	0.5
0.025	1
0.050	2
0.075	3
0.10	4
0.125	5
0.15	6
0.20	8
0.25	10
0.32	13
0.40	16
0.50	20
0.63	25
0.80	32
1.00	40
1.25	50
1.60	63
2.0	80
2.5	100
3.2	125
4.0	180
5.0	200
6.3	250
8.0	320
10.0	400
12.5	500
15	600
20	800
25	1000

Table 2 Standard Roughness Sampling Length (Cutoff) Values. *Reprinted from Y14.36M-1996, by permission of The American Society of Mechanical Engineers. All rights reserved.*

Millimeters (mm)	Inches (in.)
0.08	.003
0.25	.010
0.80	.030
2.5	.1
8.0	.3
25.0	1.0
8.0	320
10.0	400
12.5	500
15	600
20	800
25	1000

Table 3 Preferred Series Maximum Waviness Height Values. *Reprinted from Y14.36M-1996, by permission of The American Society of Mechanical Engineers. All rights reserved.*

Millimeters (mm)	Inches (in.)
0.0005	.00002
0.0008	.00003
0.0012	.00005
0.0020	.00008
0.0025	.0001
0.005	.0002
0.008	.0003
0.012	.0005
0.020	.0008

* Micrometers are the same as thousandths of a millimeter.

Lay Symbols and Surface Texture Symbols

When you need to indicate lay, the lay symbols in Figure 57 are added to the surface texture symbols as shown in the given examples. Selected applications of the surface texture values to the symbols are given and explained in Figure 58.

Symbol	Designation	Example	Symbol	Designation	Example
=	Lay parallel to the line representing the surface to which the symbol is applied	Direction of tool marks	X	Lay angular in both directions to the line representing the surface to which the symbol is applied	Direction of tool marks
⊥	Lay perpendicular to the line representing the surface to which the symbol is applied	Direction of tool marks	M	Lay multidirectional	
C	Lay approximately circular to the line representing the surface to which the symbol is applied		R	Lay approximately radial to the line representing the surface to which the symbol is applied	

57 Lay Symbols. *Reprinted from Y14.36M-1996, by permission of The American Society of Mechanical Engineers. All rights reserved.*

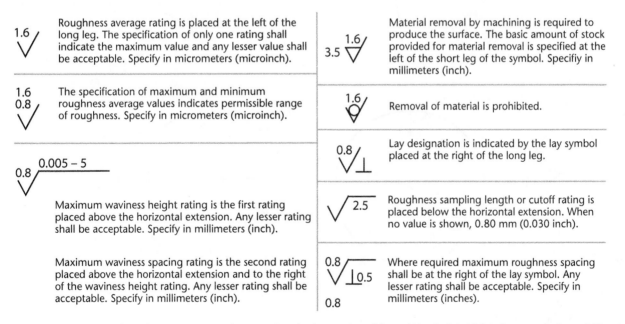

1.6	Roughness average rating is placed at the left of the long leg. The specification of only one rating shall indicate the maximum value and any lesser value shall be acceptable. Specify in micrometers (microinch).
1.6 / 0.8	The specification of maximum and minimum roughness average values indicates permissible range of roughness. Specify in micrometers (microinch).
0.8 / 0.005 – 5	Maximum waviness height rating is the first rating placed above the horizontal extension. Any lesser rating shall be acceptable. Specify in millimeters (inch). Maximum waviness spacing rating is the second rating placed above the horizontal extension and to the right of the waviness height rating. Any lesser rating shall be acceptable. Specify in millimeters (inch).
1.6 / 3.5	Material removal by machining is required to produce the surface. The basic amount of stock provided for material removal is specified at the left of the short leg of the symbol. Specifiy in millimeters (inch).
1.6	Removal of material is prohibited.
0.8 ⊥	Lay designation is indicated by the lay symbol placed at the right of the long leg.
2.5	Roughness sampling length or cutoff rating is placed below the horizontal extension. When no value is shown, 0.80 mm (0.030 inch).
0.8 / 0.5 / 0.8	Where required maximum roughness spacing shall be at the right of the lay symbol. Any lesser rating shall be acceptable. Specify in millimeters (inches).

58 Application of Surface Texture Values to Symbol. *Reprinted from Y14.36M-1996, by permission of The American Society of Mechanical Engineers. All rights reserved.*

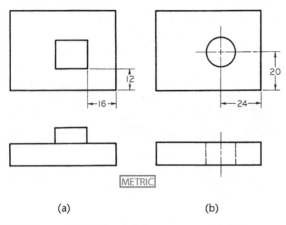

59 Location Dimensions

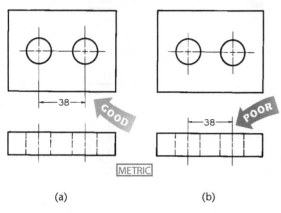

60 Locating Holes

36 LOCATION DIMENSIONS

After you have specified the sizes of the geometric shapes composing the structure, give **location dimensions** to show the relative positions of these geometric shapes. Figure 59a shows rectangular shapes located by their faces. In Figure 59b, cylindrical or conical holes or bosses, or other symmetrical shapes, are located by their centerlines. Location dimensions for holes are preferably given where the holes appear circular, as shown in Figure 60 and Figure 61.

In general, location dimensions should be built from a finished surface or from an important center or centerline. Location dimensions should lead to finished surfaces wherever possible because rough castings and forgings vary in size, and unfinished surfaces cannot be relied on for accurate measurements. The starting dimension, used in locating the first machined surface on a rough casting or forging, must necessarily lead from a rough surface or from a center or a centerline of the rough piece.

When several cylindrical surfaces have the same centerline (as in Figure 62b) you do not need location dimensions to show they are concentric; the centerline is enough. Holes equally spaced about a common center may be dimensioned by giving the diameter of the circle of centers, or bolt circle. Use a note such as 3X to indicate repetitive features or dimensions, where the X means *times* and the 3 indicates the number of repeated features. Put a space between the letter X and the dimension as shown in Figure 61. Unequally spaced holes are located by means of the bolt circle diameter plus angular measurements with reference to only one of the centerlines. Examples are shown in Figure 61.

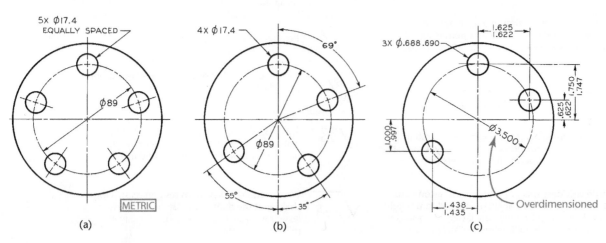

61 Locating Holes about a Center

Where greater accuracy is required, **coordinate dimensions** should be given, as shown in Figure 61c. In this case, the diameter of the bolt circle is enclosed in parentheses to indicate that it is to be used only as a reference dimension. Reference dimensions are given for information only. They are not intended to be measured and do not govern the manufacturing operations. They represent calculated dimensions and are often useful in showing the intended design sizes.

When several nonprecision holes are located on a common arc, they are dimensioned by giving the radius and the angular measurements from a **baseline,** as shown in Figure 62a. In this case, the baseline is the horizontal centerline.

In Figure 62b, the three holes are on a common centerline. One dimension locates one small hole from the center; the other gives the distances between the small holes. Note the dimension at X is left off. This method is used when the distance between the small holes is the important consideration. If the relation between the center hole and each of the small holes is more important, then include the distance at X and make the overall dimension a reference dimension.

Figure 62c shows another example of coordinate dimensioning. The three small holes are on a bolt circle whose diameter is given for reference purposes only. From the main center, the small holes are located in two mutually perpendicular directions.

Another example of locating holes by means of linear measurements is shown in Figure 62d. In this case, one measurement is made at an angle to the coordinate dimensions because of the direct functional relationship of the two holes.

In Figure 62e, the holes are located from two baselines, or datums. When all holes are located from a common datum, the sequence of measuring and machining operations is controlled, overall tolerance accumulations are avoided, and proper functioning of the finished part is assured. The datum surfaces selected must be more accurate than any measurement made from them, must be accessible during manufacture, and must be arranged to facilitate tool and fixture design. It may be necessary to specify accuracy of the datum surfaces in terms of straightness, roundness, flatness, and so on.

Figure 62f shows a method of giving, in a single line, all the dimensions from a common datum. Each dimension except the first has a single arrowhead and is accumulative in value. The overall dimension is separate.

These methods of locating holes are applicable to locating pins or other symmetrical features.

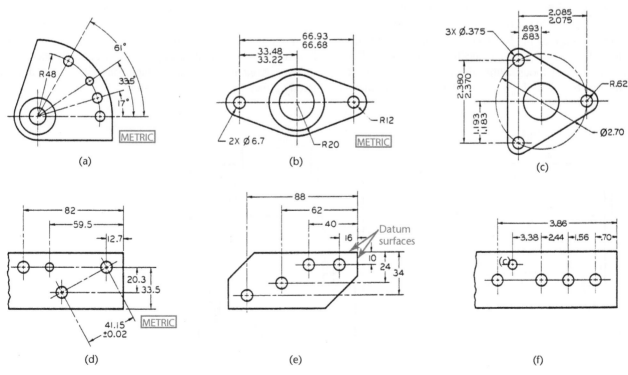

(a) (b) (c)

(d) (e) (f)

62 Locating Holes

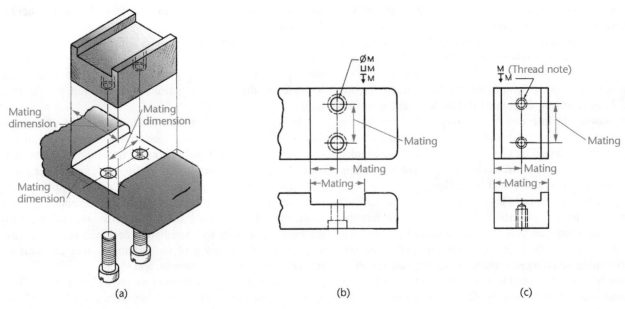

63   Mating Dimensions

37 MATING DIMENSIONS

In dimensioning a single part, its relation to mating parts must be taken into consideration. For example, in Figure 63a a guide block fits into a slot in a base. Those dimensions common to both parts are mating dimensions, as indicated.

These **mating dimensions** should be given on the multiview drawings in the corresponding locations, as shown in Figure 63b and 63c. Other dimensions are not mating dimensions since they do not control the accurate fitting together of two parts. The actual values of two corresponding mating dimensions may not be exactly the same. For example, the width of the slot in Figure 63b may be dimensioned 1/32 in. (0.8 mm) or several thousandths of an inch larger than the width of the block in Figure 63c, but these are mating

dimensions figured from a single basic width. Mating dimensions need to be specified in the corresponding locations on the two parts and toleranced to ensure proper fitting of the parts.

In Figure 64a, the dimension A is a necessary mating dimension and should appear on both the drawings of the bracket and of the frame. In Figure 64b, which shows a redesign of the bracket into two parts, dimension A is not used on either part because it is not necessary to closely control the distance between the cap screws. But dimensions F are now essential mating dimensions and should appear on the drawings of both parts. The remaining dimensions, E, D, B, and C, are not considered to be mating dimensions since they do not directly affect the mating of the parts.

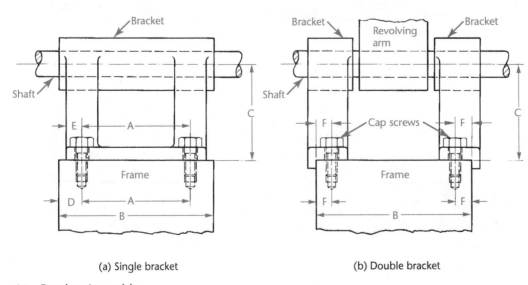

(a) Single bracket   (b) Double bracket

64   Bracket Assembly

38 TABULAR DIMENSIONS

A series of objects having like features but varying in dimensions may be represented by one drawing, as shown in Figure 65. Letters are substituted for dimension figures on the drawing, and the varying dimensions are given in tabular form. The dimensions of many standard parts are given in this manner in catalogs and handbooks. Another way to dimension is shown in Figure 66.

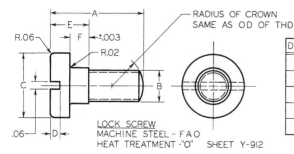

DETAIL	A	B	C	D	E	F	UNC THD	STOCK	LBS
1	.62	.38	.62	.06	.25	.135	.312-18	Ø.75	.09
2	.88	.38	.62	.09	.38	.197	.312-18	Ø.75	.12
3	1.00	.44	.75	.12	.38	.197	.375-16	Ø.875	.19
4	1.25	.50	.88	.12	.50	.260	.437-14	Ø.1	.30
5	1.50	.56	1.00	.16	.62	.323	.5-13	Ø1.125	.46

65   Tabular Dimensioning

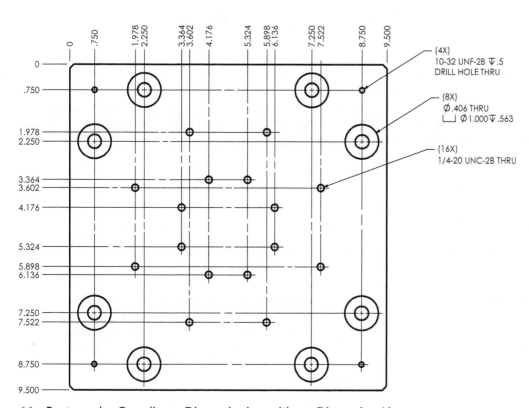

66   Rectangular Coordinate Dimensioning without Dimension Lines

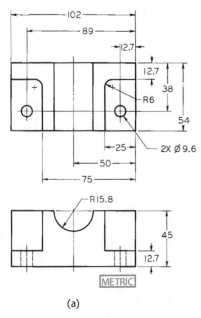

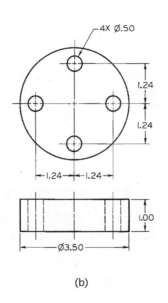

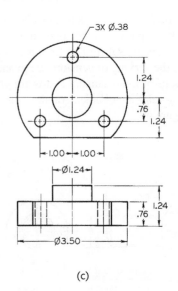

(a)   (b)   (c)

67 Coordinate Dimensioning

39 COORDINATE DIMENSIONING

Basic coordinate dimensioning practices are generally compatible with the data requirements for tape- or computer-controlled automatic production machines.

However, to design for automated production, you should consult the manufacturing machine manuals before making production drawings. What follows are the basic guidelines for coordinate dimensioning.

A set of three mutually perpendicular datum or reference planes is usually required for coordinate dimensioning. These planes either must be obvious as shown in Figure 67 or must be clearly identified.

The designer selects as origins for dimensions those surfaces or features most important to the functioning of the part. Enough of these features are selected to position the part in

relation to the set of mutually perpendicular planes. All related dimensions are then made from these planes. Rectangular coordinate dimensioning without dimension lines is shown in Figure 68.

- All dimensions should be in decimals.
- Angles should be given, where possible, in degrees and decimal parts of degrees.
- Tools such as drills, reamers, and taps should be left up to the manufacturer unless a certain process is specifically required.
- All tolerances should be determined by the design requirements of the part, not by the capability of the manufacturing machine.

40 MACHINE, PATTERN, AND FORGING DIMENSIONS

The pattern maker is interested in the dimensions required to make the pattern, and the machinist is concerned only with the dimensions needed to machine the part. Frequently, a dimension that is convenient for the machinist is not convenient for the pattern maker, or vice versa. Since the pattern maker uses the drawing only once, while making the pattern, and the machinist refers to it continuously, the dimensions should be given primarily for the convenience of the machinist.

If the part is large and complicated, two separate drawings are sometimes made—one showing the pattern dimensions and

the other the machine dimensions. The usual practice, however, is to prepare one drawing for both the pattern maker and the machinist.

For forgings, it is common practice to make separate forging drawings and machining drawings. A forging drawing of a connecting rod, showing only the dimensions needed in the forge shop, is shown in Figure 69. A machining drawing of the same part would contain only the dimensions needed in the machine shop.

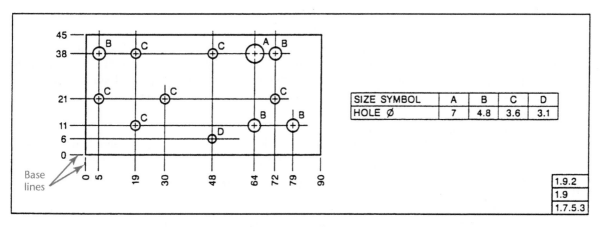

68 A hole table is often used to dimension complicated patterns of holes. *Reprinted from Y14.5M-1994, by permission of The American Society of Mechanical Engineers. All rights reserved.*

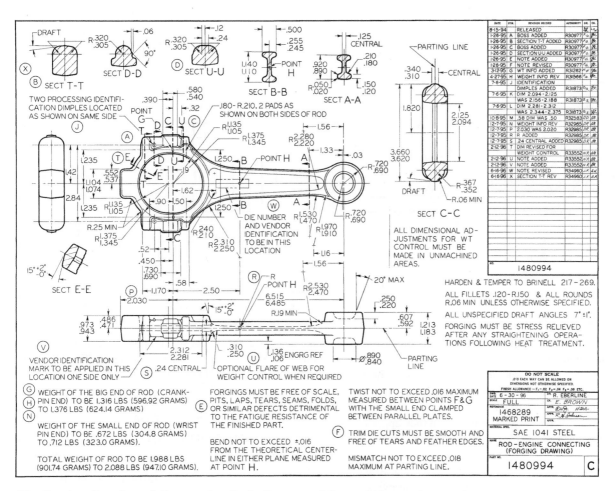

69 Forging Drawing of Connecting Rod. *Courtesy of General Motors Corporation.*

41 SHEET METAL BENDS

In sheet metal dimensioning, allowance must be made for bends. The intersection of the plane surfaces adjacent to a bend is called the *mold line,* and this line, rather than the center of the arc, is used to determine dimensions, as shown in Figure 70. The following procedure for calculating bends is typical. If the two inner plane surfaces of an angle are extended, their line of intersection is called the *inside mold line* or IML, as shown in Figure 71a–c. Similarly, if the two outer plane surfaces are extended, they produce the *outside mold line* or OML. The centerline of bend (⊄ B) refers primarily to the machine on which the bend is made and is at the center of the bend radius.

The length, or *stretchout,* of the pattern equals the sum of the flat sides of the angle plus the distance around the bend measured along the neutral axis. The distance around the bend is called the *bend allowance.* When metal bends, it compresses on the inside and stretches on the outside. At a certain zone in between, the metal is neither compressed nor stretched, and this is called the *neutral axis,* as shown in Figure 71d. The neutral axis is usually assumed to be 0.44 of the thickness from the inside surface of the metal.

The developed length of material, or bend allowance (BA), to make the bend is computed from the empirical formula

$$BA = (0.017453R + 0.0078T)N$$

where R = radius of bend, T = metal thickness, and N = number of degrees of bend as in Figure 71c.

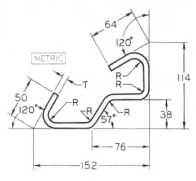

70　Profile Dimensioning

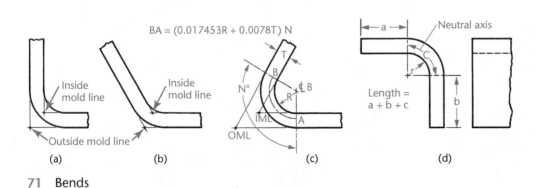

71　Bends

---

42 NOTES

It is usually necessary to supplement the direct dimensions with notes. Notes should be brief and carefully worded to allow only one interpretation. Notes should always be lettered horizontally on the sheet and arranged systematically. They should not be crowded and should not be placed between views, if possible. Notes are classified as general notes when they apply to an entire drawing and as local notes when they apply to specific items.

　General Notes General notes should be lettered in the lower right-hand corner of the first sheet of a set of drawings, above or to the left of the title block or in a central position below the view to which they apply. If notes are continued onto a second sheet, that sheet number should be given in a note on the first sheet of the drawing set. For example: NOTES CONTINUED ON PAGE 4.

Examples

FINISH ALL OVER (FAO)

BREAK SHARP EDGES TO R0.8

G33106 ALLOY STEEL-BRINELL 340–380

ALL DRAFT ANGLES 3° UNLESS OTHERWISE SPECIFIED

DIMENSIONS APPLY AFTER PLATING

In machine drawings, the title strip or title block will carry many general notes, including those for materials, general tolerances, heat treatments, and patterns.

Local Notes **Local notes** apply to specific operations only and are connected by a leader to the point at which such operations are performed, as shown in Figure 72. The leader should be attached at the front of the first word of a note, or just after the last word, and not at any intermediate place.

Use common abbreviations in notes (such as THD, DIA, MAX) only when they cannot be misunderstood. Avoid less common abbreviations. "When in doubt, spell it out" is a rule of thumb to avoid problems with misunderstood notes.

If a common symbol is available, it is preferred to the abbreviation because symbols are internationally recognized

and not language dependent. All abbreviations should conform to ANSI Y14.39-1999.

In general, leaders and notes should not be placed on the drawing until the dimensioning is substantially completed. Notes and lettering should not touch lines of the drawing or title block. If notes are lettered first, they may be in the way of necessary dimensions and will have to be moved.

When using CAD to add text for drawing notes, keep in mind the final scale to which the drawing will be plotted. You may need to enlarge the text in order for it to be legible when plotted to a smaller scale.

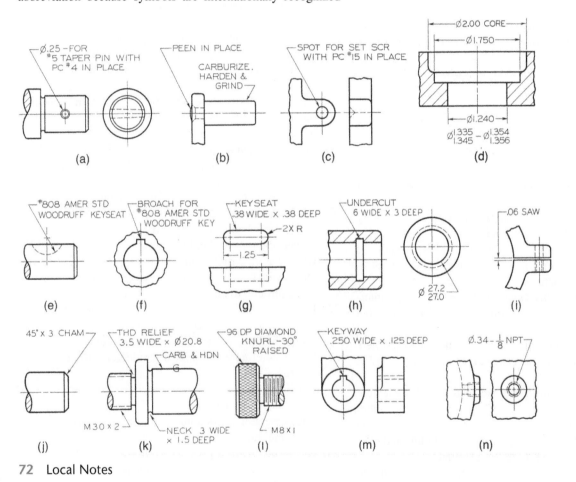

72 Local Notes

---

43 STANDARDS

Dimensions should be given, wherever possible, to make use of readily available materials, tools, parts, and gages. The dimensions for many commonly used machine elements—such as bolts, screws, nails, keys, tapers, wire, pipes, sheet metal, chains, belts, ropes, pins, and rolled metal shapes—have been standardized, and the drafter must obtain these sizes from company standards manuals, from published handbooks, from ANSI standards, or from manufacturers' catalogs.

Such standard parts are not delineated on detail drawings unless they are to be altered for use; they are conventionally drawn on assembly drawings and are listed in parts lists. Common fractions are often used to indicate the nominal sizes of standard parts or tools. If the complete decimal inch system is used, all such sizes are ordinarily expressed by decimals—for example, .250 DRILL instead of 1/4 DRILL. If the all-metric system of dimensioning is used, then the preferred metric drill of the approximate same size (.2480″) will be indicated as 6.30 DRILL.

44 DO'S AND DON'TS OF DIMENSIONING

The following checklist summarizes briefly most of the situations in which a beginning designer is likely to make a mistake in dimensioning. Students should check the drawing by this list before submitting it to the instructor.

1. Each dimension should be given clearly so that it can be interpreted in only one way.
2. Dimensions should not be duplicated, nor should the same information be given in two different ways—except for dual dimensioning—and no dimensions should be given except those needed to produce or inspect the part.
3. Dimensions should be given between points or surfaces that have a functional relation to each other or that control the location of mating parts.
4. Dimensions should be given to finished surfaces or important centerlines, in preference to rough surfaces, wherever possible.
5. Dimensions should be given so that it will not be necessary for the machinist to calculate, scale, or assume any dimension.
6. Dimension features should be attached to the view where the feature's shape is best shown.
7. Dimensions should be placed in the views where the features dimensioned are shown true shape.
8. Dimensioning to hidden lines should be avoided wherever possible.
9. Dimensions should not be placed on a view unless clarity is promoted and long extension lines are avoided.
10. Dimensions applying to two adjacent views should be placed between views, unless clarity is promoted by placing some of them outside.
11. The longer dimensions should be placed outside all intermediate dimensions so that dimension lines will not cross extension lines.
12. In machine drawing, all unit marks should be omitted, except when necessary for clarity; for example, 1″ VALVE or 1 mm DRILL.
13. Don't expect production personnel to assume that a feature is centered (as a hole on a plate), but give a location dimension from one side. However, if a hole is to be centered on a symmetrical rough casting, mark the centerline and omit the locating dimension from the centerline.
14. A dimension should be attached to only one view, not to extension lines connecting two views.
15. Detail dimensions should line up in chain fashion.
16. A complete chain of detail dimensions should be avoided; it is better to omit one. Otherwise add a reference to the overall dimension by enclosing it within parentheses.
17. A dimension line should never be drawn through a dimension figure. A figure should never be lettered over any line of the drawing. The line can be broken if necessary.

18. Dimension lines should be spaced uniformly throughout the drawing. They should be at least 10 mm (.38 in.) from the object outline and 6 mm (.25 in.) apart.
19. No line of the drawing should be used as a dimension line or coincide with a dimension line.
20. A dimension line should never be joined end to end with any line of the drawing.
21. Dimension lines should not cross, if avoidable.
22. Dimension lines and extension lines should not cross, if avoidable. (Extension lines may cross each other.)
23. When extension lines cross extension lines or visible lines, no break in either line should be made.
24. A centerline may be extended and used as an extension line, in which case it is still drawn like a centerline.
25. Centerlines should not extend from view to view.
26. Leaders for notes should be straight, not curved, and point to the center of circular views of holes wherever possible.
27. Leaders should slope at 45°, 30°, or 60° with horizontal, but may be made at any convenient angle except vertical or horizontal.
28. Leaders should extend from the beginning or the end of a note, with the horizontal "shoulder" extending from mid-height of the lettering.
29. Dimension figures should be approximately centered between the arrowheads, except in a stack of dimensions, where they should be staggered.
30. Dimension figures should be about 3 mm (.13 in.) high for whole numbers and 6 mm (.25 in.) high for fractions.
31. Dimension figures should never be crowded or in any way made difficult to read.
32. Dimension figures should not be lettered over lines or sectioned areas unless necessary, in which case a clear space should be reserved for the dimension figures.
33. Dimension figures for angles should generally be lettered horizontally.
34. Fraction bars should never be inclined except in confined areas, such as in tables.
35. The numerator and denominator of a fraction should never touch the fraction bar.
36. Notes should always be lettered horizontally on the sheet.
37. Notes should be brief and clear, and the wording should be standard in form.
38. Finish marks should be placed on the edge views of all finished surfaces, including hidden edges and the contour and circular views of cylindrical surfaces.
39. Finish marks should be omitted on holes or other features where a note specifies a machining operation.
40. Finish marks should be omitted on parts made from rolled stock.

41. If a part is finished all over, all finish marks should be omitted and the general note FINISH ALL OVER or FAO should be used.

42. A cylinder is dimensioned by giving both its diameter and length in the rectangular view, except when notes are used for holes. A diagonal diameter in the circular view may be used in cases where it increases clarity.

43. Manufacturing processes are generally determined by the tolerances specified, rather than specifically noted in the drawing. When the manufacturing process must be noted for some reason—such as for dimension holes to be bored, drilled, and reamed—use leaders that preferably point toward the center of the circular views of the holes. Give the manufacturing processes in the order they would be performed.

44. Drill sizes should be expressed in decimals, giving the diameter. For drills designated by number or letter, the decimal size must also be given.

45. In general, a circle is dimensioned by its diameter, an arc by its radius.

46. Diagonal diameters should be avoided, except for very large holes and for circles of centers. They may be used on positive cylinders for clarity.

47. A diameter dimension value should always be preceded by the symbol $\emptyset$.

48. A radius dimension should always be preceded by the letter R. The radial dimension line should have only one arrowhead, and it should pass through or point through the arc center and touch the arc.

49. Cylinders should be located by their centerlines.

50. Cylinders should be located in the circular views, if possible.

51. Cylinders should be located by coordinate dimensions in preference to angular dimensions where accuracy is important.

52. When there are several rough, noncritical features obviously the same size (fillets, rounds, ribs, etc.), it is necessary to give only typical (abbreviation TYP) dimensions or to use a note.

53. When a dimension is not to scale, it should be underscored with a heavy straight line or marked NTS or NOT TO SCALE.

54. Mating dimensions should be given correspondingly on both drawings of mating parts.

55. Pattern dimensions should be given in two-place decimals or in common whole numbers and fractions to the nearest 1/16 in.

56. Decimal dimensions should be used for all machining dimensions.

57. Cumulative tolerances should be avoided where they affect the fit of mating parts.

THE CAD DATABASE AS DESIGN DOCUMENTATION

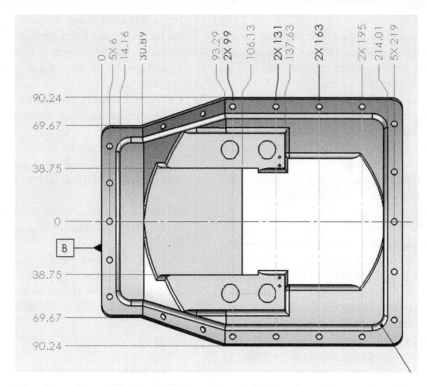

Edrawing software allows you to view 3D and 2D drawings. Many companies transmit and store edrawings as their design record. *Courtesy of Zolo Technologies Inc.*

It is an important advantage of producing an accurate CAD database that you can use the model as a basis for manufacturing. Today's CAD packages offer tools for incorporating tolerances and manufacturing notes into the 3D CAD database itself that improve its ability to document the design. A good understanding of the type of information available in your CAD database combined with the knowledge of how to show critical dimensions and tolerances clearly are important in achieving the most benefit from 3D CAD software.

To use the CAD database as design documentation, companies must consider the legal requirements for maintaining a permanent record of the design. For some industries, a permanent record (or snapshot) of the design used for production must be maintained. A changeable record on the computer may not be considered a legally acceptable practice, or it may be acceptable only if a standard of model/drawing control is met.

ASME Y14.41-2003, Digital Product Definition Data Practices, describes the standard for using a digital product definition to document designs. Some companies use the 3D model with electronic annotations stored in the file or a related database as the final documentation for the product. Other companies produce 2D original drawings from the 3D model to communicate the design for manufacturing and to provide design documentation for the project. For those companies the 3D model may be stored, but the design record is the fully dimensioned 2D drawings.

Other companies use a combination of the computer files and 2D drawings to document the design. The 2D drawings are used to communicate information about critical tolerances and other information that may not be easily visible in the 3D file. The CAD file serves as the interface to automated manufacturing processes, but the drawing allows the company to call attention to those elements of the design that are critical to its function. Because the manufacturer may not have the same software that was used to create the CAD model, the documentation needs to use a format that can be interpreted by the manufacturer, mold maker, or others who will create or inspect the parts. This is frequently a combination of electronic files in a common 3D format (such as IGES) for the model, and 2D CAD documentation drawings (either printed or in a common 2D file format such as DXF) showing critical dimensions.

Whether the 2D drawings are printed on paper or stored electronically, correctly shown orthographic views still provide much of the basis for communicating and documenting the design. Correctly shown drawing views are also used to communicate information for user manuals and repair manuals, as well as for manufacture and inspection.

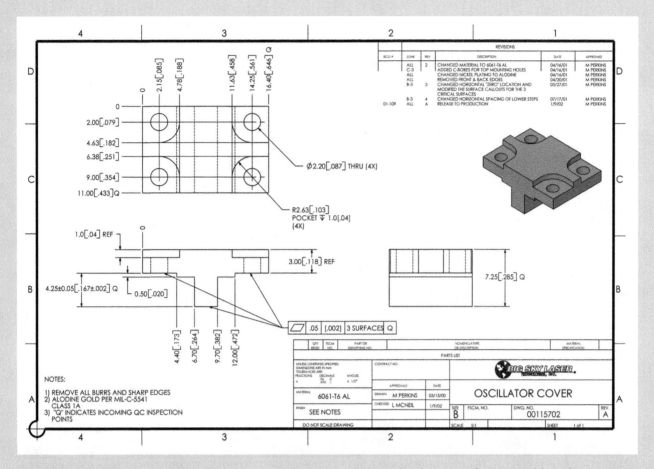

This drawing for a small part shows dimensions in millimeters with the inch values given [in brackets] for reference. *Courtesy of Big Sky Laser.*

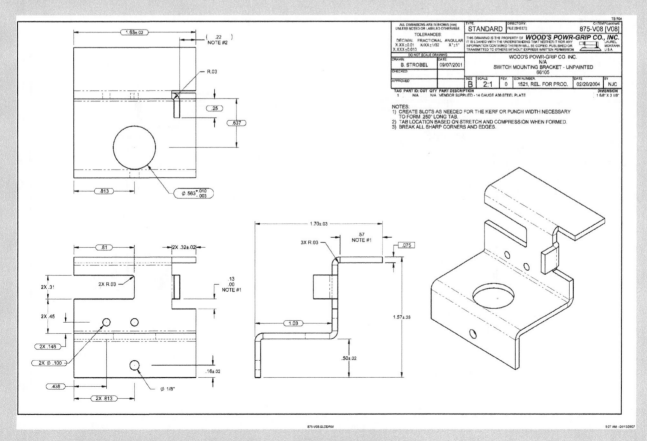

Dimensioned Drawing for a Sheet Metal Part. *Courtesy of Wood's Power-Grip Co., Inc.*

P O R T F O L I O

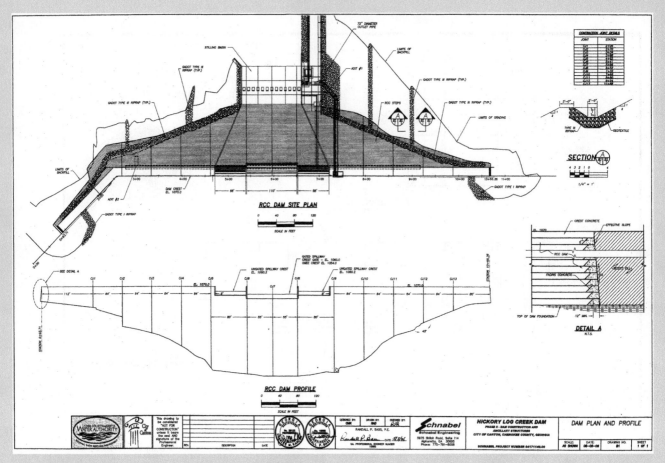

Plan and Profile for Dam Site. *Courtesy of Schnabel Engineering.*

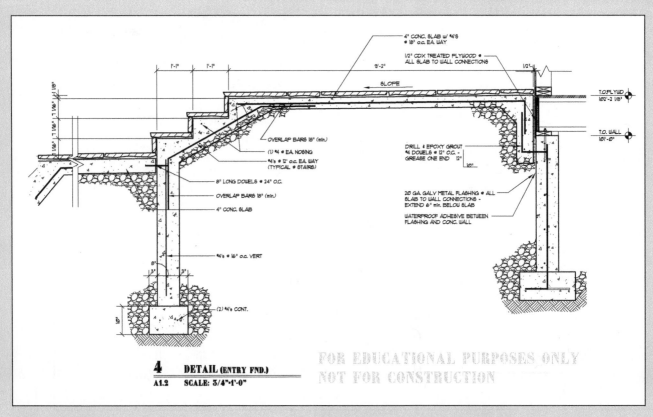

Portion of a Drawing Showing Dimensioned Architectural Details. *Courtesy of Locati Architects.*

KEY WORDS

Dimensions

Tolerance

Size Dimensions

Location Dimensions

Dimension Line

Extension Line

Centerline

Arrowheads

Leader

Dual Dimensioning

Position Method

Unidirectional

Bracket Method

Superfluous

Slope

Batter

Grade

Radial Leader Line

Chordal Dimensions

Finish Mark

Surface Texture Symbols

Location Dimensions

Coordinate Dimensions

Baseline

Mating Dimensions

Local Notes

CHAPTER SUMMARY

- To increase clarity, dimensions and notes are added to a drawing to precisely describe size, location, and manufacturing process.
- Drawings are scaled to fit on a standard sheet of paper. Drawings created by hand are drawn to scale. CAD drawings are drawn full size and scaled when they are printed.
- Dimensions and notes are placed on drawings according to prescribed standards.
- Use good placement practices to make your drawings easy to read.
- Special dimensioning techniques are used for surfaces that have been machined by one of the manufacturing processes.

REVIEW QUESTIONS

1. What are the different units used when a drawing is created using a metric scale? Using an architects' scale?
2. Explain the concept of contour dimensioning.
3. Which type of line is never crossed by any other line when dimensioning an object?
4. How is geometric analysis used in dimensioning?
5. What is the difference between a size dimension and a location dimension?
6. Which dimension system allows dimensions to be read from the bottom and from the right? When can a dimension be read from the left?
7. Draw an example of dimensioning an angle.
8. When are finish marks used? Draw two types.
9. How are negative and positive cylinders dimensioned? Draw examples.
10. How are holes and arcs dimensioned? Draw examples.
11. What are notes and leaders used for?
12. Why is it important to avoid superfluous dimensions?

DIMENSIONING EXERCISES

Most of your practice in dimensioning will be in connection with working drawings. However, some dimensioning problems are available here. The problems are designed for 8.5″ × 11″ size sheets and are to be drawn and dimensioned to a full-size scale. Size 297 mm × 420 mm sheets may be used with appropriate adjustments in the title strip layout.

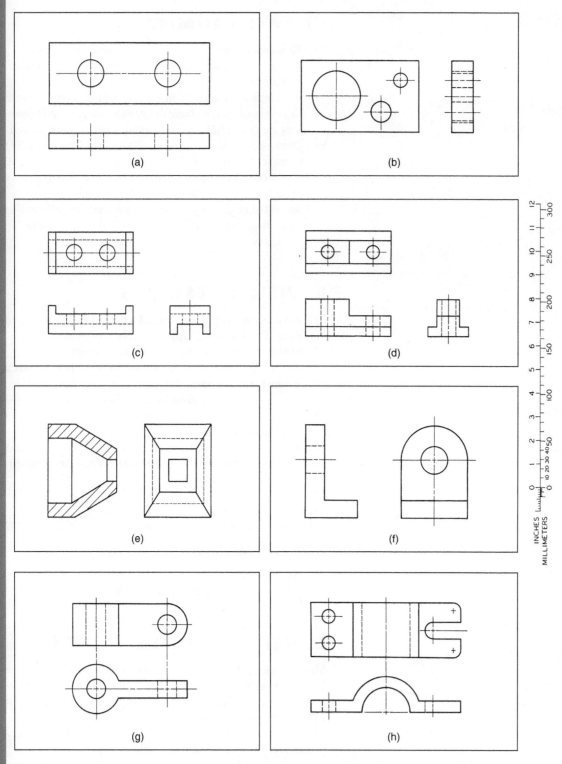

Exercise 1 To obtain sizes, use the views on this page and transfer to scale at the side to obtain values completely. Dimension drawing completely in one-place millimeters or two-place inches as assigned, full size.

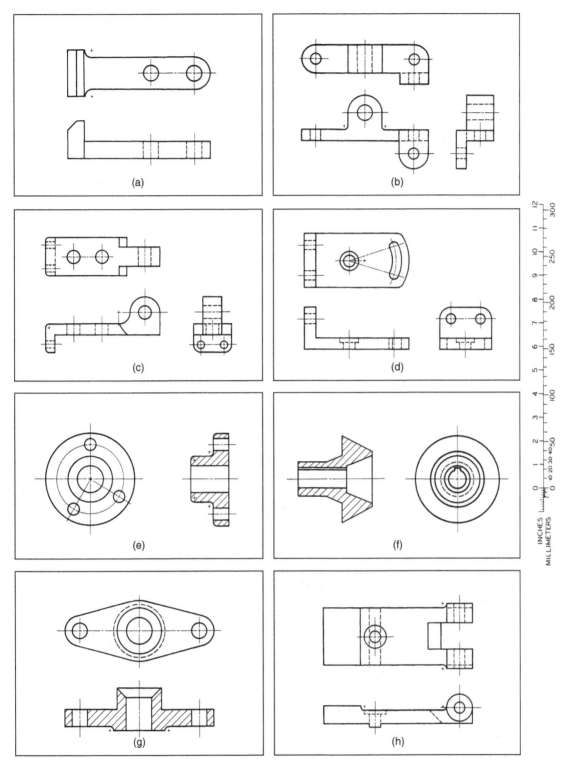

Exercise 2 To obtain sizes, use the views on this page and transfer to scale at the side to obtain values completely. Dimension drawing completely in one-place millimeters or two-place inches as assigned, full size.

DIMENSIONING TECHNIQUE

Sketch lines, arrowheads, leaders, dimension values, and gaps and sizes similar to the examples shown at left.

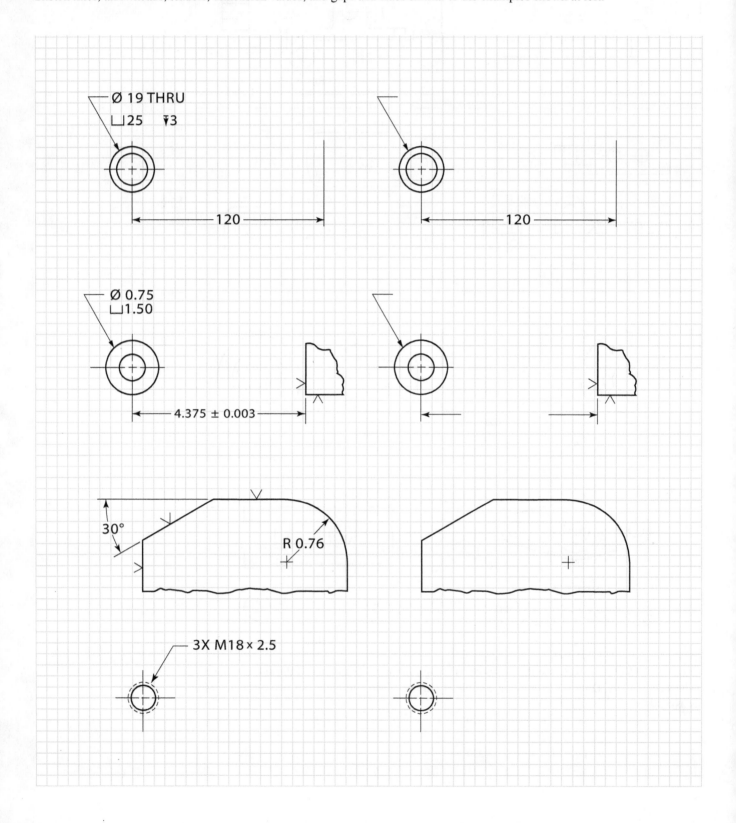

WORKSHEET 1   DIMENSIONING

Add dimensions to the drawing views shown below using good technique, choice, and placement of dimension. Use the grid to help size the dimension features. Determine the dimension values by measuring the views or from the 1/8″ grid spacing. The drawing is full scale. Use two-place decimal inch measurements.

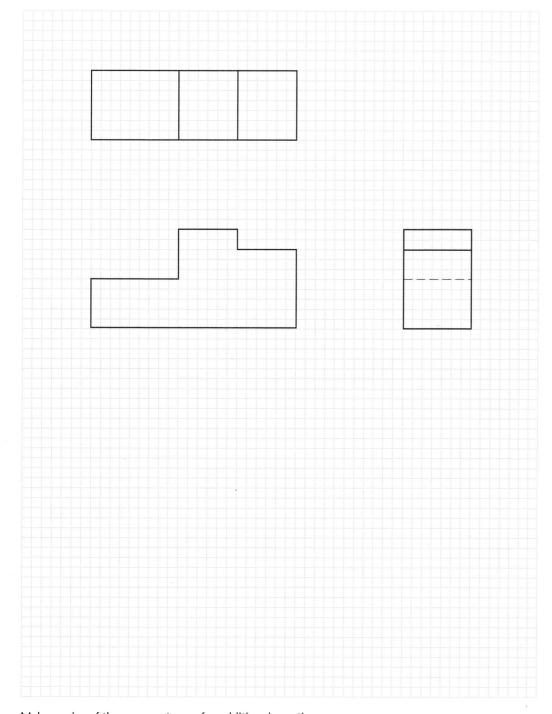

Make copies of these pages to use for additional practice.

WORKSHEET 2 DIMENSIONING

Some lines are missing. Add the missing lines, then measure the object and dimension using two-place decimal inches. It is shown full size.

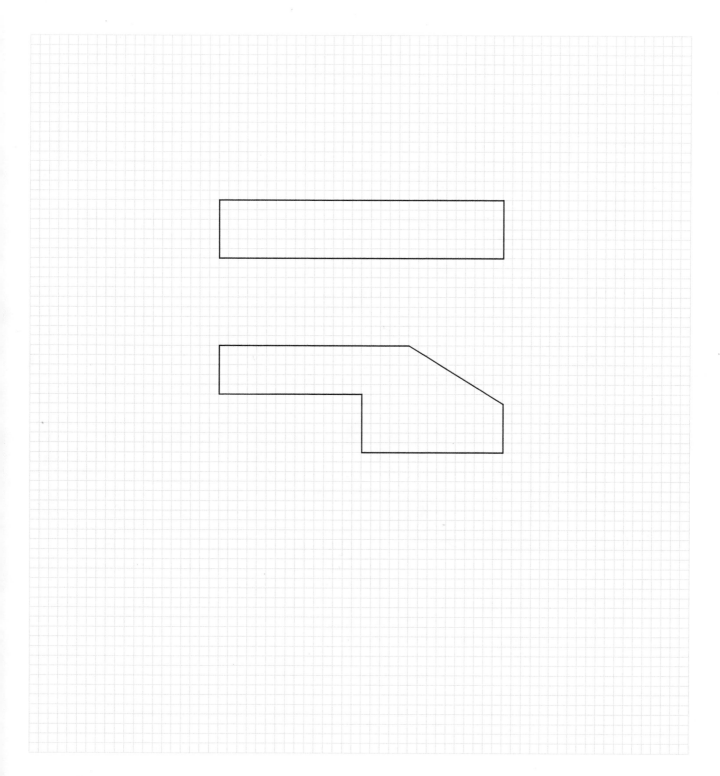

Make copies of these pages to use for additional practice.

WORKSHEET 3   DIMENSIONING

Measure the object in millimeters and dimension to the nearest whole millimeter. It is shown on a 5-mm grid.

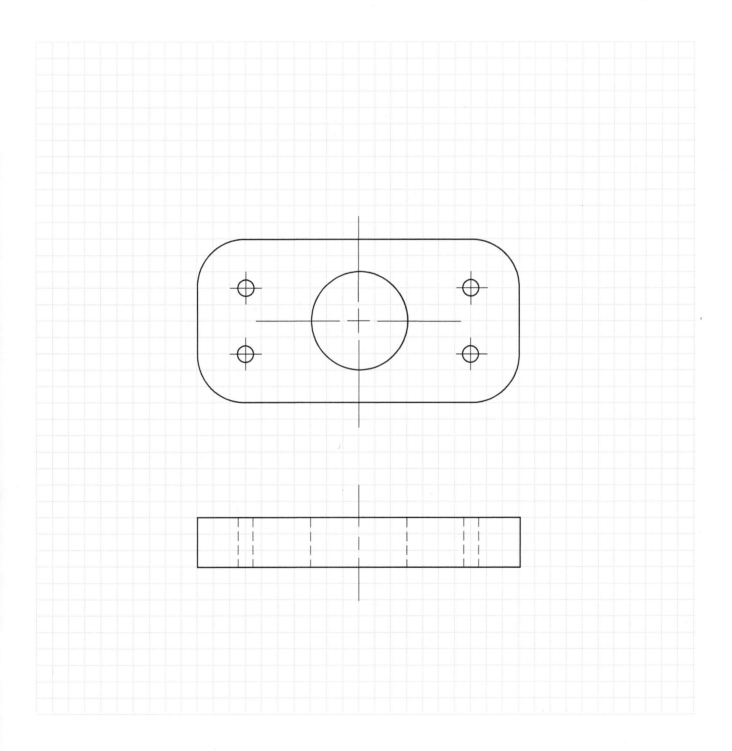

Make copies of these pages to use for additional practice.

THREADS, FASTENERS, AND SPRINGS

From Chapter 11 of *Modern Graphics Communication*, Fourth Edition, Frederick E. Giesecke, Alva Mitchell, Henry Cecil Spencer, Ivan Leroy Hill, John Thomas Dygdon, James E. Novak, Shawna Lockhart. Copyright © 2010 by Pearson Education, Inc. Published by Pearson Prentice Hall. All rights reserved.

THREADS, FASTENERS, AND SPRINGS

OBJECTIVES

After studying the material in this chapter, you should be able to:

1. Define and label the parts of a screw thread.

2. Identify various screw thread forms.

3. Draw detailed, schematic, and simplified threads.

4. Define typical thread specifications.

5. Identify various fasteners and describe their use.

6. Draw various screw head types.

7. Draw springs.

Refer to the following standards:
- ANSI/ASME B1.1
- ANSI/ASME B1.7M
- ANSI/ASME B1.13M
- ANSI/ASME Y14.6
- ANSI/ASME Y14.6aM

The companion website for this text is www.prenhall.com/chet_giesecke_modgraphic_4.

Fasteners. *Courtesy of TwinNut Corp., Germany.*

OVERVIEW

Threaded fasteners are the principal devices used for assembling components. To speed production time and reduce costs, many new types of fasteners are created every year. Existing fasteners are also modified to improve their insertion in mass production. Many companies provide CAD drawings of their fasteners on the Web. When you are using standard fasteners in your designs, save time by downloading drawings or models.

Thread is usually dimensioned by giving a thread note in the drawing. This allows you to combine more information in a compact space.

The information in this chapter will prepare you to specify various types of thread and fasteners and use the standard methods of representing them in your drawings.

Web sites related to this chapter
- http://www.mcmaster.com/ A great site for standard parts including fasteners
- http://www.pemnet.com/fastening_products PEM fasteners
- https://sdp-si.com/eStore/ More standard parts with downloadable CAD files

1 Thread Used for Attachment.
Courtesy of Arthur S. Aubry/Getty Images, Inc.-Photodisc.

UNDERSTANDING THREADS AND FASTENERS

Screw threads are vital to industry. They are designed for hundreds of different purposes. The three basic applications are as follows:

1. To hold parts together (Figure 1).
2. To provide for adjustment between parts (Figure 2).
3. To transmit power (Figure 3).

The shape of the helical (spiral shaped) thread is called the **thread form.** The metric thread form is the international standard, although the unified thread form is common in the United States. Other thread forms are used in specific applications.

CAD drawing programs are often used to automatically depict threads. The thread specification is a special leader note that defines the type of thread or fastener. This is an instruction for the shop technician so the correct type of thread is created during the manufacturing process.

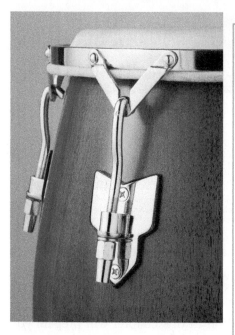

2 Thread Used for Adjustment

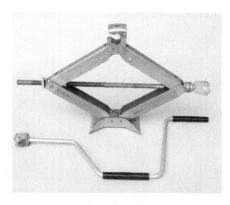

3 Thread Used to Transmit Power

THE STANDARDIZATION OF SCREW THREADS

At one time, there was no such thing as standardization. Nuts made by one manufacturer would not fit the bolts of another. In 1841 Sir Joseph Whitworth started crusading for a standard screw thread, and soon the Whitworth thread was accepted throughout England.

In 1864 the United States adopted a thread proposed by William Sellers of Philadelphia, but the Sellers nuts would not screw onto a Whitworth bolt or vice versa. In 1935 the American standard thread, with the same 60° V form of the old Sellers thread, was adopted in the United States.

Still there was no standardization among countries. In peacetime it was a nuisance; in World War I it was a serious inconvenience; and in World War II the obstacle was so great that the Allies decided to do something about it. Talks began among the Americans, British, and Canadians, and in 1948 an agreement was reached on the unification of American and British screw threads. The new thread was called the Unified screw thread, and it represented a compromise between the American standard and Whitworth systems, allowing complete interchangeability of threads in three countries.

Sir Joseph Whitworth. *Courtesy of National Park Service.*

In 1946 a committee called the International Organization for Standardization (ISO) was formed to establish a single international system of metric screw threads. Consequently, through the cooperative efforts of the Industrial Fasteners Institute (IFI), several committees of the American National Standards Institute, and the ISO representatives, a metric fastener standard was prepared.

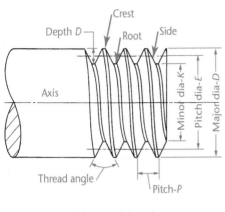

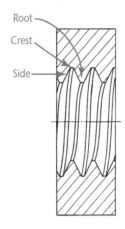

(a) External thread

(b) Internal thread

4   Screw Thread Nomenclature

Screw Thread Terms

The following definitions apply to screw threads in general and are shown on the illustration Figure 4. For additional information regarding specific Unified and metric screw thread terms and definitions, refer to the appropriate standards.

Screw Thread: A ridge of uniform cross section in the form of a helix on the external or internal surface of a cylinder.

External Thread: A thread on the outside of a member, as on a shaft.

Internal Thread: A thread on the inside of a member, as in a hole.

Major Diameter: The largest diameter of a screw thread (for both internal and external threads).

Minor Diameter: The smallest diameter of a screw thread (for both internal and external threads).

Pitch: The distance from a point on a screw thread to a corresponding point on the next thread measured parallel to the axis. In the U.S., the pitch is equal to 1 divided by the number of threads per inch.

Pitch Diameter: The diameter of an imaginary cylinder passing through the threads where the widths of the threads and the widths of the spaces would be equal.

Lead: The distance a screw thread advances axially in one turn.

Angle of Thread: The angle between the sides of the thread measured in a plane through the axis of the screw.

Crest: The top surface joining the two sides of a thread.

Root: The bottom surface joining the sides of two adjacent threads.

Side: The surface of the thread that connects the crest with the root.

Axis of Screw: The longitudinal centerline through the screw.

Depth of Thread: The distance between the crest and the root of the thread measured normal to the axis.

Form of Thread: The cross section of thread cut by a plane containing the axis.

Series of Thread: The standard number of threads per inch for various diameters.

Electron Microscope View of a Thread Surface. *Courtesy of David Gnizak/Phototake NYC.*

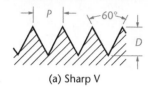

(a) Sharp V

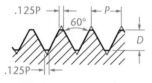

(b) American national

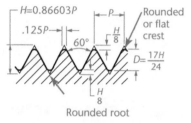

(c) Unified (external)

5   Sharp, American National and Unified Screw Thread Forms

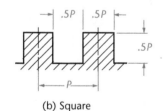

(a) Metric

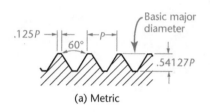

(b) Square

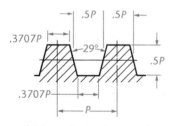

(c) Acme (general purpose)

6   Metric, Square, and Acme Screw Thread Forms

Screw Thread Forms

The thread form is the cross sectional shape of the thread. Various forms of threads are used for different purposes. The main uses for threads are to hold parts together, to adjust parts with reference to each other, and to transmit power. Figures 5–7 show some of the typical thread forms.

Sharp-V thread (60°) useful for certain adjustments because of the increased friction resulting from the full thread face. It is also used on brass pipe work (Figure 5a).

American national thread, with flattened roots and crests, is a stronger thread. This form replaced the sharp- V thread for general use. (Figure 5b)

Unified thread is the standard thread agreed upon by the United States, Canada, and Great Britain in 1948. It has replaced the American national form. The crest of the external thread may be flat or rounded, and the root is rounded; otherwise, the thread form is essentially the same as the American national. Some earlier American national threads are still included in the new standard, which lists 11 different numbers of threads per inch for the various standard diameters, together with selected combinations of special diameters and pitches. The 11 series includes: the coarse thread series (UNC or NC), recommended for general use; the fine thread series (UNF or NF), for general use in automotive and aircraft work and in applications where a finer thread is required; the extra fine series (UNF or NF), which is the same as the SAE extra fine series, used particularly in aircraft and aeronautical equipment and generally for threads in thin walls; and the eight series of 4, 6, 8, 12, 16, 20, 28, and 32 threads with constant pitch. The 8UN or 8N, 12UN or 12N, and 16UN or 16N series are recommended for the uses corresponding to the old 8-, 12-, and 16-pitch American national threads. In addition, there are three special thread series—UNS, NS, and UN—that involve special combinations of diameter, pitch, and legth of engagement (Figure 5c).

Unified extra fine thread series (UNEF) has many more threads per inch for given diameters than any series of the American national or unified. The form of thread is the same as the American national. These small threads are used in thin metal where the length of thread engagement is small, in cases where close adjustment is required, and where vibration is great.

Metric thread is the standard screw thread agreed upon for international screw thread fasteners. The crest and root are flat, but the external thread is often rounded if formed by a rolling process. The form is similar to the American national and unified threads but with less depth of thread. The preferred metric thread for commercial purposes conforms to the ISO basic profile M for metric threads. This M profile design is comparable to the unified inch profile, but the two are not interchangeable. For commercial purposes, two series of metric threads are preferred—coarse (general purpose) and fine—much fewer than previously used (Figure 6a).

Square thread is theoretically the ideal thread for power transmission, since its face is nearly at right angles to the axis, but due to the difficulty of cutting it with dies and because of other inherent disadvantages (such as the fact that split nuts will not readily disengage), square thread has been displaced to a large extent by the acme thread. Square thread is not standardized (Figure 6b).

Acme thread is a modification of the square thread and has largely replaced it. It is stronger than the square thread, is easier to cut, and has the advantage of easy disengagement from a split nut, as on the lead screw of a lathe (Figure 6c).

Standard worm thread (not shown) is similar to the acme thread but is deeper. It is used on shafts to carry power to worm wheels.

Whitworth thread was the British standard and has been replaced by the unified thread. The uses of Whitworth thread correspond to those of the American national thread (Figure 7a).

Knuckle thread is often used on electric bulbs. *Stephen Oliver © DORLING KINDERSLEY.*

Knuckle thread is usually rolled from sheet metal but is sometimes cast. In modified forms knuckle thread is used in electric bulbs and sockets, bottle tops, etc. (Figure 7b).

Buttress thread is designed to transmit power in one direction only. It is commonly used in large guns, in jacks, and in other mechanisms that have high strength requirements (Figure 7c).

A number of different thread forms are defined in various ASME standards which specify requirements for the design and selection of screw threads. For example, the old N thread series has been superseded by the UN series.

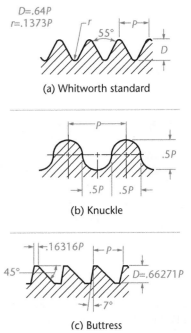

7 Whitworth Standard, Knuckle, and Buttress Screw Thread Forms

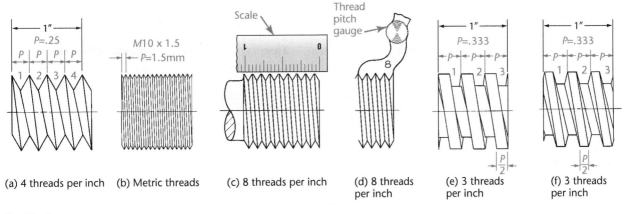

(a) 4 threads per inch   (b) Metric threads   (c) 8 threads per inch   (d) 8 threads per inch   (e) 3 threads per inch   (f) 3 threads per inch

8 Pitch

Thread Pitch

The pitch of any thread form is the distance parallel to the axis between corresponding points on adjacent threads, as shown in Figure 8.

For metric threads, this distance is specified in millimeters. The pitch for a metric thread that is included with the major diameter in the thread designation determines the size of the thread—for example, as shown in Figure 8b.

For threads dimensioned in inches, the pitch is equal to 1 divided by the number of threads per inch. Thread tables giving more information on standard numbers of threads per inch for various thread series and diameters. For example, a unified coarse thread of 1" diameter has eight threads per inch, and the pitch P equals 1/8" (.125").

If a thread has only four threads per inch, the pitch and the threads themselves are quite large, as shown in Figure 8a. If there are 16 threads per inch, the pitch is only 1/16" (.063"), and the threads are relatively small, similar to those in Figure 8b.

The pitch or the number of threads per inch can be measured with a scale or with a **thread pitch gage.**

421

An Archimedean Screw.
© 2007 Jupiterimages
Corporation.

The concept of the screw thread seems to have occurred first to Archimedes, the third-century-B.C. mathematician who wrote briefly on spirals and designed several simple devices applying the screw principle. By the first century B.C., the screw was a familiar element but was crudely cut from wood or filed by hand on a metal shaft. Not much was heard of the screw thread until the 15th century.

Leonardo da Vinci understood the screw principle, and created sketches showing how to cut screw threads by machine. In the 16th century, screws appeared in German watches and were used to fasten suits of armor. In 1669, the Frenchman Besson invented the screw-cutting lathe, but this method of production did not take hold for another century and a half; nuts and bolts continued to be made largely by hand. Screw manufacturing began in 18th century England, during the Industrial Revolution.

Thread Series

ASME/ANSI Y14.6-2001, Screw Thread Representation, is a standard for drawing, specifying, and dimensioning threads on drawings.

The thread series is the detail of the shape and number of threads per inch composing different groups of fasteners. Table 1 shows the thread series for UN thread.

Five series of threads were used in the old ANSI standards:

Coarse thread— A general-purpose thread used for holding. It is designated NC (national coarse).

Fine thread— A greater number of threads per inch it is used extensively in automotive and aircraft construction. It is designated NF (national fine).

8-pitch thread—All diameters have eight threads per inch. It is used on bolts for high-pressure pipe flanges, cylinder-head studs, and similar fasteners. It is designated 8N (national form, 8 threads per inch).

12-pitch thread—All diameters have 12 threads per inch. It is used in boiler work and for thin nuts on shafts and sleeves in machine construction. It is designated 12N (national form, 12 threads per inch).

16-pitch thread— All diameters have 16 threads per inch. It is used where necessary to have a fine thread regardless of diameter, as on adjusting collars and bearing retaining nuts. It is designated 16N (national form, 16 threads per inch).

Table 1 Thread Series of UN Thread.

Basic Thread Series	Constant Pitch	Coarse	Fine	Extra Fine	Special Diameter
UN	UN	UNC	UNF	UNEF	UNS
UNJ	UNJ	UNJC	UNJF	UNJEF	UNJS
N	N	NC	NF	NEF	NS
UNR	UNR	UNRC	UNRF	UNREF	UNRS

This series is superseded by the UN series.

Right-Hand and Left-Hand Threads

A right-hand thread is one that advances into a nut when turned clockwise, and a left-hand thread is one that advances into a nut when turned counterclockwise, as shown in Figure 9. A thread is always considered to be right-handed (RH) unless otherwise specified. A left-hand thread is always labeled LH on a drawing.

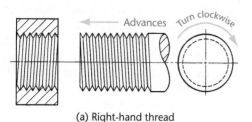

(a) Right-hand thread

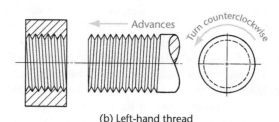

(b) Left-hand thread

9 Right-Hand
and Left-Hand
Threads

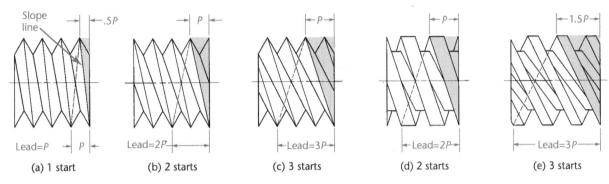

| (a) 1 start | (b) 2 starts | (c) 3 starts | (d) 2 starts | (e) 3 starts |

10   Multiple Threads

Single and Multiple Threads

A **single thread,** as the name implies, is composed of one ridge, and the lead is therefore equal to the pitch. Multiple threads are composed of two or more ridges running side by side. As shown in Figures 10a–c, the slope line is the hypotenuse of a right triangle whose short side equals .5P for single threads, P for double threads, 1.5P for triple threads, and so on. This applies to all forms of threads. In double threads, the lead is twice the pitch; in triple threads, the lead is three times the pitch, and so on. On a drawing of a single or triple thread, a root is opposite a crest; in the case of a double or quadruple thread, a root is drawn opposite a root. Therefore,

in one turn, a double thread advances twice as far as a single thread, and a triple thread advances three times as far. RH double square and RH triple acme threads are shown in Figures 10d and 10e, respectively.

Multiple threads are used wherever quick motion, but not great power, is desired, as on ballpoint pens, toothpaste caps, valve stems, and so on. The threads on a valve stem are frequently multiple threads to impart quick action in opening and closing the valve. Multiple threads on a shaft can be recognized and counted by observing the number of thread starts on the end of the screw.

American National Thread Fits

For general use, three classes of screw thread fits between mating threads (as between bolt and nut) have been established by ANSI.

These fits are produced by the application of tolerances listed in the standard and are as follows:

Class 1 fit—Recommended only for screw thread work where clearance between mating parts is essential for rapid assembly and where shake or play is not objectionable.

Class 2 fit—Represents a high quality of commercial thread product and is recommended for the great bulk of interchangeable screw thread work.

Class 3 fit—Represents an exceptionally high quality of commercially threaded product and is recommended only in

cases where the high cost of precision tools and continual checking are warranted.

The standard for unified screw threads specifies tolerances and allowances defining the several classes of fit (degree of looseness or tightness) between mating threads. In the symbols for fit, the letter A refers to the external threads and B to internal threads. There are three classes of fit each for external threads (1A, 2A, 3A) and internal threads (1B, 2B, 3B). Classes 1A and 1B have generous tolerances, facilitating rapid assembly and disassembly. Classes 2A and 2B are used in the normal production of screws, bolts, and nuts, as well as in a variety of general applications. Classes 3A and 3B provide for applications needing highly accurate and close-fitting threads.

Metric and Unified Thread Fits

Some specialized metric thread applications are specified by tolerance grade, tolerance position, class, and length of engagement. There are two general classes of metric thread fits. The first is for general-purpose applications and has a tolerance class of 6H for internal threads and a class of 6g for external threads. The second is used where closer fits are necessary and has a tolerance class of 6H for internal threads and a class of 5g6g for external threads. Metric thread tolerance classes of 6H/6g are generally assumed if not otherwise designated

and are used in applications comparable to the 2A/2B inch classes of fits.

The single-tolerance designation of 6H refers to both the tolerance grade and position for the pitch diameter and the minor diameter for an internal thread. The single-tolerance designation of 6g refers to both the tolerance grade and position for the pitch diameter and the major diameter of the external thread. A double designation of 5g6g indicates separate tolerance grades for the pitch diameter and for the major diameter of the external thread.

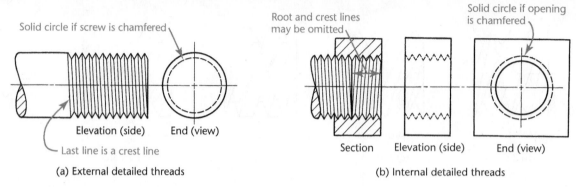

Solid circle if screw is chamfered

Root and crest lines may be omitted

Solid circle if opening is chamfered

Elevation (side)　　　End (view)

Last line is a crest line

Section　　Elevation (side)　　End (view)

(a) External detailed threads

(b) Internal detailed threads

11 Detailed Metric, American National, and Unified Threads

Three Methods for Drawing Thread

There are three methods of representing screw threads on drawings—the schematic, simplified, and detailed methods. Schematic, simplified, and detailed thread symbols may be combined on a single drawing.

Schematic and the more common simplified representations are used to show threads. The symbols are the same for all forms of threads, such as metric, unified, square, and acme, but the thread specification identifies which is to be used.

Detailed representation is a closer approximation of the exact appearance of a screw thread, where the true profiles of the thread's form are drawn; but the helical curves are replaced by straight lines. The true projection of the helical curves of a screw thread takes too much time to draw, so it is rarely used in practice.

Do not use detailed representation unless the diameter of the thread on the drawing is more than 1" or 25 mm and then only to call attention to the thread when necessary. Schematic representation is much simpler to draw and still presents the appearance of thread. Detailed representation is shown in Figure 11. Whether the crests or roots are flat or rounded, they are represented by single lines and not double lines. American national and unified threads are drawn the same way. Figure 12 shows schematic thread symbols, and Figure 13 shows simplified thread symbols.

Figure 14 shows detailed directions for drawing schematic and simplified thread.

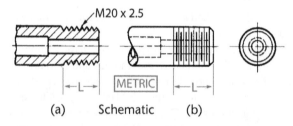

M20 x 2.5

METRIC

(a)　　Schematic　　(b)

12 Schematic Thread Symbols

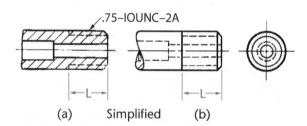

.75–IOUNC–2A

(a)　　Simplified　　(b)

13 Simplified Thread Symbols

SHOWING DETAILED THREAD

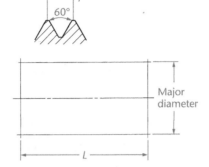

1 Make centerline and lay out length and major diameter as shown at right.

Major diameter

L

2 Find the number of threads per inch for American National and Unified threads. This number depends on the major diameter of the thread and whether the thread is internal or external.

Find *P* (pitch) by dividing 1 by the number of threads per inch. The pitch for metric threads is given directly in the thread designation. For example, the thread has a pitch of 2 mm.

Establish the slope of the thread by offsetting the slope line .5*P* for single threads, *P* for double threads, 1.5*P* for triple threads, and so on. For right-hand external threads, the slope line slopes upward to the left; for left-hand external threads, the slope line slopes upward to the right.

By eye, mark off even spacing for the pitch. If using CAD, make a single thread and array the lines using the pitch as the spacing.

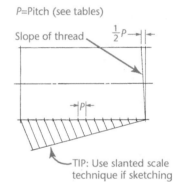

P=Pitch (see tables)

Slope of thread $\frac{1}{2}P$

P

TIP: Use slanted scale technique if sketching

3 From the pitch points, make crest lines parallel to the slope line. These should be dark, thin lines. Make two V's to establish the depth of thread, and sketch light guidelines for the root of thread, as shown.

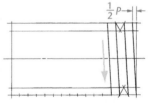

$\frac{1}{2}P$

Single, RH external thread

4 Finish the final 60° V's. The V's should be vertical; they should not lean with the thread.

Make root lines. Root lines will not be parallel to crest lines, but should appear parallel to each other.

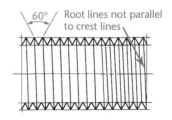

60°   Root lines not parallel to crest lines

5 When the end is chamfered (usually 45° with end of shaft, sometimes 30°), the chamfer extends to the thread depth. The chamfer creates a new crest line, which you make between the two new crest points. It is not parallel to the other crest lines. When finished, all thread root and crest lines should be shown thin, but dark.

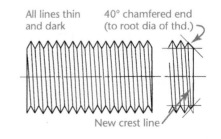

All lines thin and dark   40° chamfered end (to root dia of thd.)

New crest line

TIP

The thread depth table within Figure 14 gives approximate thread depths for a variety of common diameters.

MAJOR DIAMETER	#5 (.125) TO #12 (.216)	.25	.3125	.375	.4375	.5	.5625	.625	.6875	.75	.8125	.875	.9375	1.
DEPTH, D	.03125	.03125	.03125	.0468	.0468	.0625	.0625	.0625	.0625	.0781	.0937	.0937	.0937	.0937
PITCH, P	.0468	.0625	.0625	.0625	.0625	.0937	.0937	.0937	.0937	.125	.125	.125	.125	.125

Approximate thread depth table   (For metric values: 1″ = 25.4mm or see inside front cover)

--- Steps for drawing simplified external threads ---

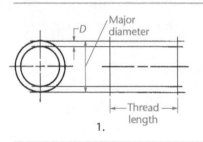
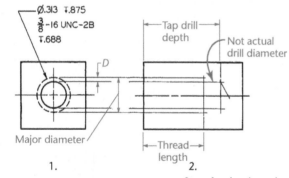
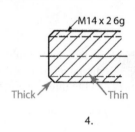

1.   2.   3.   4.

--- Steps for drawing simplified internal threads ---

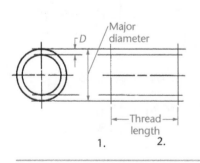
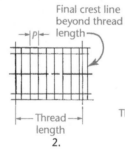
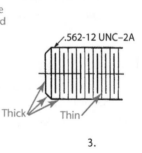
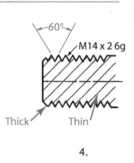

1.   2.   3.   4.

--- Steps for drawing schematic external threads ---

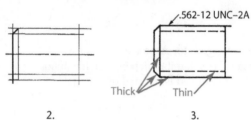
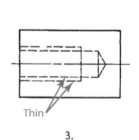
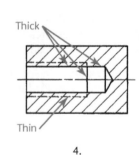

1.   2.   2.   3.   4.

--- Steps for drawing schematic internal threads ---

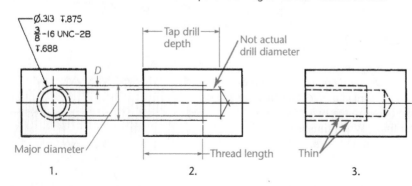
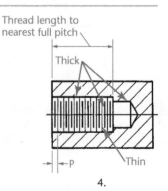

1.   2.   3.   4.

426   **14   Steps to Draw Thread Symbols—Simplified and Schematic**

1 THREAD NOTES

ASME/ANSI Y14.6-2001, Screw Thread Representation, is a standard for representing, specifying, and dimensioning screw threads on drawings. Thread notes for metric, unified, and American national screw threads are shown in Figures 15 and 16. These same notes or symbols are used in correspondence, on shop and storeroom records, and in specifications for parts, taps, dies, tools, and gages.

Metric screw threads are designated basically by the letter M for metric thread symbol followed by the thread form and nominal size (basic major diameter) in millimeters and separated by the symbol × followed by the pitch, also in millimeters. For example, the basic thread note M10 × 1.5 is adequate for most commercial purposes, as shown in Figure 15. If needed, the class of fit and LH for left-hand designation is added to the note. (The absence of LH indicates a RH thread.)

If necessary, the length of the thread engagement is added to the thread note. The letter S stands for short, N means normal, and L means long. For example, the single note M10 × 1.5-6H/6g-N-LH combines the specifications for internal and external mating of left-hand metric threads of 10 mm diameter and 1.5 mm pitch with general-purpose tolerances and normal length of engagement.

If the thread is a multiple thread, the word STARTS, with the number of thread starts all contained in parentheses, should precede the thread form; otherwise, the thread is understood to be single. For example:

(2 STARTS) UNC

would indicate that this is double thread.

A thread note for a blind tapped hole is shown in Figure 15b. A tap drill is sized to form a hole that will leave enough material for thread to be cut using a tap in order to form a threaded hole. In practice the tap drill size and depth are omitted and left up to the shop. At times it is desirable to state a tolerance range for the size of the hole prior to threading. This can be stated as follows:

Ø.656–.658 BEFORE THD .75–20–NEF–2B

Thread notes for holes are preferably attached to the circular views of the holes. Thread notes for external threads are preferably given where the threaded shaft appears rectangular, as shown in Figures 15c–g. A sample special thread designation is 1.50-7N-LH.

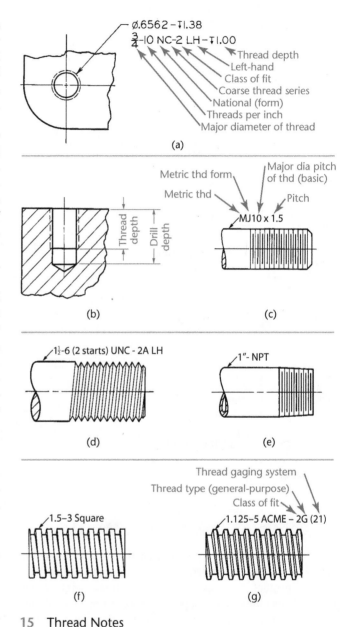

15   Thread Notes

General-purpose acme threads are indicated by the letter G, and centralizing acme threads by the letter C. Typical thread notes are 1-4 ACME-2G or 1-6 ACME-4C.

Thread notes for unified threads are shown in Figures 15d and e. The letters A and B designate external or internal, respectively, after the numeral designating the class of fit. If the letters LH are omitted, the thread is understood to be right hand. Some typical thread notes are:

.25 -20 (3 STARTS) UNC-2A
9/16 -18 UNF-2B
1.75 -16 UN-2A

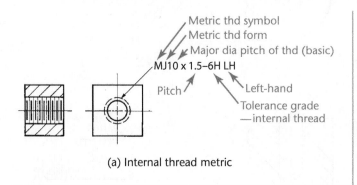

(a) Internal thread metric

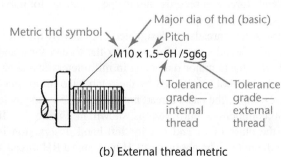

(b) External thread metric

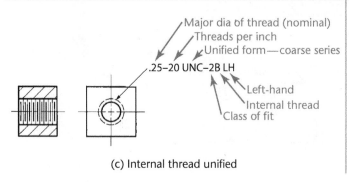

(c) Internal thread unified

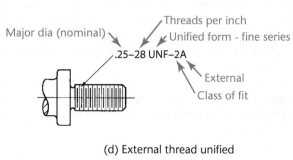

(d) External thread unified

16   Thread Notes

2 EXTERNAL THREAD SYMBOLS

Simplified representations for external threads are shown in Figures 17a and b. The threaded portions are indicated by hidden lines parallel to the axis at the approximate depth of the thread, whether the cylinder appears rectangular or circular. The depth shown is not always the actual thread depth, just a representation of it. Use the table in Figure 14 for the general appearance of these lines.

When the schematic form is shown in section, as in Figure 18a, show the V's of the thread to make the thread obvious. It is not necessary to show the V's to scale or to the actual slope of the crest lines. To draw the V's, use the schematic thread depth, as shown in Figure 15, and determine the pitch by drawing 60° V's.

Schematic threads are indicated by alternate long and short lines, as shown in Figure 18b. The short lines representing the root lines are thicker than the long crest lines. Theoretically, the crest lines should be spaced according to actual pitch, but this would make them crowded and tedious to draw, defeating the purpose, which is to save time in sketching them. Space the crest lines carefully by eye, then add the heavy root lines halfway between the crest lines. Generally, lines closer together than about 1/16" are hard to distinguish. The spacing should be proportionate for all diameters. You do not need to use these actual measurements in sketching schematic threads, just use them to get a feel for how far apart to make the lines.

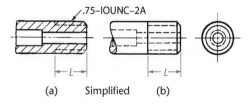

(a)   Simplified   (b)

17   External Thread Symbols for Simplified Thread

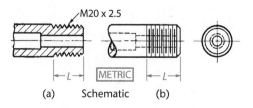

(a)   Schematic   (b)

18   External Thread Symbols for Schematic Thread

3 INTERNAL THREAD SYMBOLS

Internal thread symbols are shown in Figure 19. Note that the only differences between the schematic and simplified internal thread symbols occur in the sectional views. The representation of the schematic thread in section in Figures 19k, 19m, and 19n is exactly the same as the external representation shown in Figure 18b. Hidden threads, by either method, are represented by pairs of hidden lines. The hidden dashes should be staggered, as shown.

In the case of blind tapped holes, the drill depth normally is drawn at least three schematic pitches beyond the thread length, as shown in Figures 19d, 19e, 19l, and 19m. The symbols in Figures 19f and 19n represent the use of a bottoming tap, when the length of thread is the same as the depth of drill. The thread length you sketch may be slightly longer than the actual given thread length. If the tap drill depth is known or given, draw the drill to that depth. If the thread note omits this information, as is often done in practice, sketch the hole three schematic thread pitches beyond the thread length. The tap drill diameter is represented approximately, not to actual size.

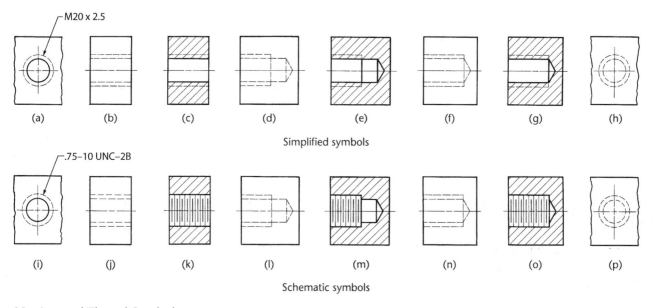

Simplified symbols

Schematic symbols

19 Internal Thread Symbols

---

4 DETAILED REPRESENTATION: METRIC, UNIFIED, AND AMERICAN NATIONAL THREADS

The detailed representation for metric, unified, and American national threads is the same, since the flats are disregarded.

Internal detailed threads in section are drawn as shown in Figure 20. Notice that for left-hand threads the lines slope upward to the left (Figures 20a to 20c), while for right-hand threads the lines slope upward to the right (Figures 20d to 20f).

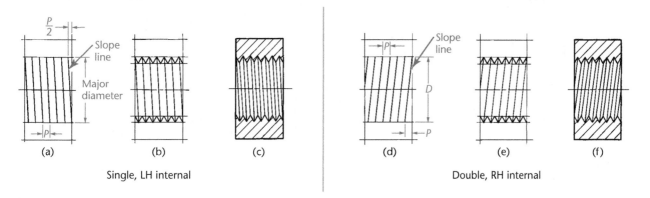

Single, LH internal

Double, RH internal

20 Detailed Representation—Internal Metric, Unified, and American

Detailed External Square Thread

Figure 21 is an assembly drawing showing an external square thread partly screwed into a nut. When the external and internal threads are assembled, the thread in the nut overlaps and covers up half of the V, as shown at B.

Sometimes in assemblies the root and crest lines may be omitted from the *nut only* portion of the drawing so that it is easier to identify the inserted screw.

Detailed Internal Square Thread

The internal thread construction is the same as in Figure 22. Note that the thread lines representing the back half of the internal threads (since the thread is in section) slope in the opposite direction from those on the front side of the screw.

Steps in drawing a single internal square thread in section are shown in Figure 22. Note in Figure 22b that a crest is drawn opposite a root. This is the case for both single and triple threads. For double or quadruple threads, a crest is opposite a crest. Thus, the construction in Figures 22a and b is the same for any multiple of thread. The differences appear in Figure 22c, where the threads and spaces are distinguished and outlined.

The same internal thread is shown in Figure 22e from an external view. The profiles of the threads are drawn in their normal position, but with hidden lines, and the sloping lines are omitted for simplicity. The end view of the same internal thread is shown in Figure 22f. Note that the hidden and solid circles are opposite those for the end view of the shaft.

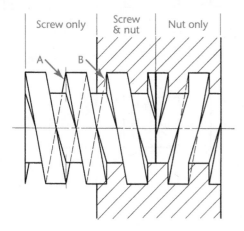

21   Square Threads in Assembly

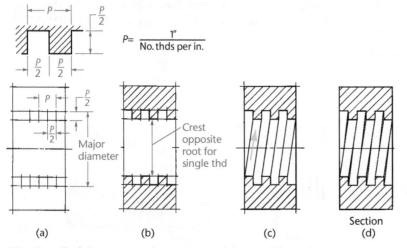

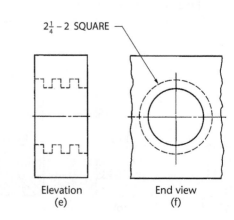

$$P = \frac{1''}{\text{No. thds per in.}}$$

Crest opposite root for single thd

Major diameter

$2\frac{1}{4} - 2$ SQUARE

| (a) | (b) | (c) | Section (d) | Elevation (e) | End view (f) |

22   Detailed Representation—Internal Square Threads

DETAILED REPRESENTATION OF SQUARE THREADS

Detailed representation of external square threads is used only when the major diameter is over about 1" or 25 mm, and it is important to show the detail of the thread on the finished sketch or plotted drawing. The steps to create detailed square thread are as follows.

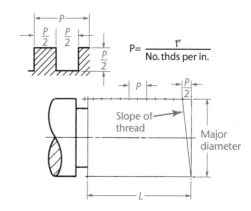

$$P = \frac{1''}{\text{No. thds per in.}}$$

1 Make a centerline and lay out the length and major diameter of the thread. For U.S. drawings, determine the pitch (P) by dividing 1 by the number of threads per inch. For a single right-hand thread, the lines slope upward to the left, and the slope line is offset as for all single threads of any form. On the upper line, use spacing equal to $P/2$, as shown.

2 From the points on the upper line, draw guidelines for root of thread, making the depth as shown.

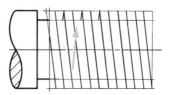

Single, R H external thread

3 Make parallel visible back edges of threads.

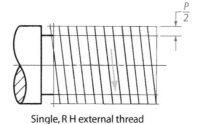

4 Make parallel visible root lines.

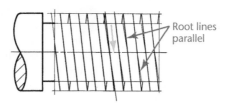

Root lines parallel

5 All lines should be thin and dark.

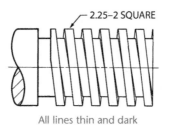

2.25–2 SQUARE

All lines thin and dark

TIP

End view of a shaft

The end view of the shaft illustrated in this Step by Step feature is shown below. Note that the root circle is hidden. When sketching, no attempt is made to show the true projection of any but the major diameter.

If the end of a shaft is chamfered, a solid circle is drawn instead of the hidden circle.

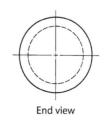

End view

DETAILED REPRESENTATION OF ACME THREADS

Detailed representation of acme threads is used only to call attention when details of the thread are important and the major diameter is larger than 1" or 25 mm on the drawing. The steps are as follows.

1 Make a centerline and lay out the length and major diameter of the thread, as shown. For U.S. drawings, determine the pitch by dividing 1 by the number of threads per inch. Make construction lines for the root diameter, making the thread depth $P/2$. Make construction lines halfway between crest and root guidelines.

Single R H external thread

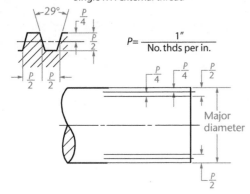

$$P = \frac{1''}{\text{No. thds per in.}}$$

2 Mark off spaces on the intermediate construction lines.

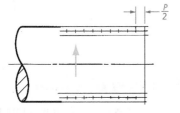

3 Through alternate points, make construction lines for the sides of the threads at 15° (instead of 14 1/2°).

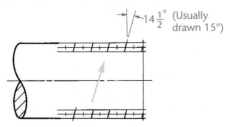

$14\frac{1}{2}°$ (Usually drawn 15°)

4 Make construction lines for the other sides of the threads, as shown. For single and triple threads, a crest is opposite a root, while for double and quadruple threads, a crest is opposite a crest. Finish tops and bottoms of threads.

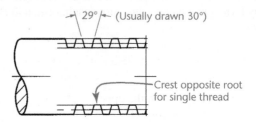

29° (Usually drawn 30°)

Crest opposite root for single thread

5 Make parallel crest lines.

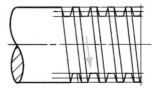

6 Make parallel root lines, and finish the thread profiles. All lines should be thin and dark. The internal threads in the back of the nut and the external threads on the front side of the screw will slope in opposite directions.

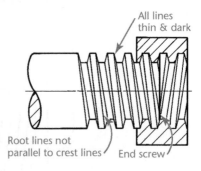

All lines thin & dark

Root lines not parallel to crest lines

End screw

End views of acme threaded shafts and holes are drawn exactly like those for the square thread.

THREADS, FASTENERS, AND SPRINGS

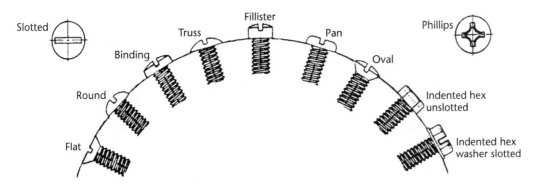

29   Types of Screw Heads

one end, it is force fitted into place. As a rule, a stud is passed through a clearance hole in one member, is screwed into another member, and uses a nut on the free end, as shown in Figure 28c.

A machine screw is similar to a slotted head cap screw but usually smaller. It may be used with or without a nut. Figure 29 shows different screw head types.

A set screw is a screw, with or without a head, that is screwed through one member and whose special point is forced against another member to prevent motion between the two parts.

Do not section bolts, nuts, screws, and similar parts when drawn in assembly because they do not have interior detail that needs to be shown.

9   TAPPED HOLES

The bottom of a drilled hole, formed by the point of a twist drill, is cone-shaped, as shown in Figures 30a and 30b. When an ordinary drill is used to make holes that will be tapped, it is referred to as a tap drill. When drawing the drill point, use an angle of 30° to approximate the actual 31° slope of the drill bit.

The thread length is the length of full or perfect threads. The tap drill depth does not include the cone point of the drill. In Figure 30c and 30d, the drill depth shown beyond the threads (labeled A) includes several imperfect threads produced by the chamfered end of the tap. This distance varies according to drill size and whether a plug tap or a bottoming tap is used to finish the hole.

A drawing of a tapped hole finished with a bottoming tap is shown in Figure 30e. Blind bottom-tapped holes are hard to form and should be avoided when possible. Instead, a relief with its diameter slightly greater than the major diameter of the thread is used, as shown in Figure 30f. Tap drill sizes and lengths may be given in the thread note, but are generally left to the manufacturer to determine. Since the tapped thread length contains only full threads, it is necessary to make this length only one or two pitches beyond the end of the engaging screw. In simplified or schematic representation, don't show threads in the bottoms of tapped holes. This way the ends of the screw show clearly.

The thread length in a tapped hole depends on the major diameter and the material being tapped. The minimum engagement length (X), when both parts are steel, is equal to the diameter (D) of the thread. Table 2 shows different engagement lengths for different materials.

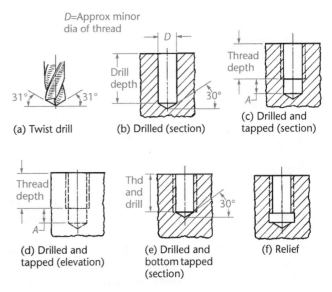

30   Drilled and Tapped Holes

Table 2 Thread Engagement Lengths for Different Materials.

Screw Material	Material of Parts	Thread Engagement*
Steel	Steel	D
Steel	Cast iron	$1 1/2 D$
Steel	Aluminum	$2D$

*Requirements for thread engagement vary based on the specific materials. Use these rules of thumb only as guidelines.

435

─── **TIP** ───────────────────────────────

Prevent tap breakage: A chief cause of tap breakage is insufficient tap drill depth. When the depth is too short, the tap is forced against a bed of chips in the bottom of the hole. Don't specify a blind hole when a through hole of not much greater length can be used. When a blind hole is necessary, the tap drill depth should be generous.

Clearance holes: When a bolt or a screw passes through a **clearance hole**, the hole is often drilled 0.8 mm larger than the screw for screws of 3/8" (10 mm) diameter and 1.5 mm larger for larger diameters. For more precise work, the

clearance hole may be only 1/64" (0.4 mm) larger than the screw for diameters up to 10 mm and 0.8 mm larger for larger diameters.

Closer fits may be specified for special conditions. The clearance spaces on each side of a screw or bolt need not be shown on a drawing unless it is necessary to show clearly that there is no thread engagement. When it is necessary to show that there is no thread engagement, the clearance spaces should be drawn about 3/64" (1.2 mm) wide.

10 STANDARD BOLTS AND NUTS

American National Standard hexagon bolts and nuts are made in both metric and inch sizes. Square bolts and nuts, shown in Figure 31, are produced only in inch sizes. Metric bolts, cap screws, and nuts also come in hexagon form. Square heads and nuts are chamfered at 30°, and hexagon heads and nuts are chamfered at 15–30°. Both are drawn at 30° for simplicity.

Bolt Types Bolts are grouped into **bolt types** according to use: regular bolts for general use and heavy bolts for heavier use or easier wrenching. Square bolts come only in the regular type; hexagon bolts, screws, nuts, and square nuts are available in both regular and heavy.

Metric hexagon bolts are grouped according to use: regular and heavy bolts and nuts for general service and high-strength bolts and nuts for structural bolting.

Finish Square bolts and nuts, hexagon bolts, and hexagon flat nuts are unfinished. Unfinished bolts and nuts are not machined on any surface except for the threads. Hexagon cap screws, heavy hexagon screws, and all hexagon nuts, except hexagon flat nuts, are considered finished to some degree and have a "washer face" machined or otherwise formed on the bearing surface. The washer face is 1/64" thick (drawn 1/32" so that it will be visible on the plotted drawing), and its diameter is 1.5 times the body diameter for the inch series.

For nuts, the bearing surface may also be a circular surface produced by chamfering. Hexagon screws and hexagon nuts have closer tolerances and a more finished appearance but are not completely machined. There is no difference in the drawing for the degree of finish on finished screws and nuts.

Proportions Proportions for both inch and metric are based on the diameter (*D*) of the bolt body. These are shown in Figure 32.

For regular hexagon and square bolts and nuts, proportions are:

$$W = 1\tfrac{1}{2}D \qquad H = \tfrac{2}{3}D \qquad T = \tfrac{7}{8}D$$

where W = width across flats, H = head height, and T = nut height.

For heavy hexagon bolts and nuts and square nuts, the proportions are:

$$W = 1\tfrac{1}{2}D + \tfrac{1}{8}\text{" (or + 3 mm)}$$
$$H = \tfrac{2}{3}D \qquad T = D$$

© Dorling Kindersley.

The washer face is always included in the head or nut height for finished hexagon screw heads and nuts.

Threads Square and hex bolts, hex cap screws, and finished nuts in the inch series are usually Class 2 and may have coarse, fine, or 8-pitch threads. Unfinished nuts have coarse threads and are Class 2B.

Thread lengths For bolts or screws up to 6" (150 mm) long,

$$\text{Thread length} = 2D + \tfrac{1}{4}\text{" (or + 6 mm)}$$

For bolts or screws over in length,

$$\text{Thread length} = 2D + \tfrac{1}{2}\text{" (or + 12 mm)}$$

Fasteners too short for these formulas are threaded as close to the head as practical. For drawing purposes, use approximately three pitches. The threaded end may be rounded or chamfered, but it is usually drawn with a 45° chamfer from the thread depth, as shown in Figure 32.

Bolt Lengths Have not been standardized because of the endless variety required by industry. Short bolts are typically available in standard length increments of 1/4" (6 mm), while long bolts come in increments of 1/2" to 1 inch (12 to 25 mm).

31 Standard Bolt and Nut

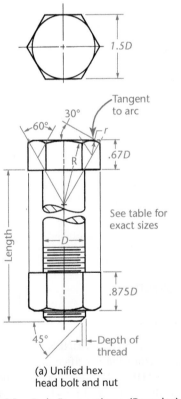

(a) Unified hex
head bolt and nut

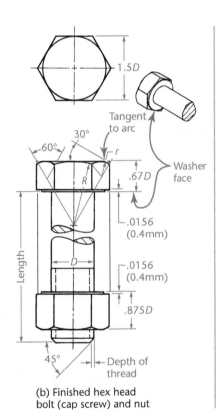

(b) Finished hex head
bolt (cap screw) and nut

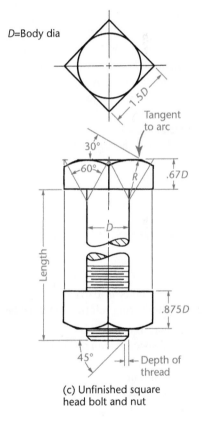

(c) Unfinished square
head bolt and nut

32 Bolt Proportions (Regular)

11 DRAWING STANDARD BOLTS

Detail drawings show all of the necessary information defining the shape, size, material, and finish of a part. Standard bolts and nuts do not usually require detail drawings unless they are to be altered (for example, by having a slot added through the end of a bolt), because they are usually stock parts that can easily be purchased. But you often need to show them on assembly drawings.

Templates are available to help you add bolts quickly to sketches, or you can use the dimensions if accuracy is important, as in figuring clearances. In most cases, a quick representation, where proportions are based on the body diameter, is sufficient. Three typical bolts illustrating the use of these proportions are shown in Figure 32.

Many CAD systems have fastener libraries that you can use to add a wide variety of nuts and bolts to your drawings. Often these symbols are based on a diameter of 1 unit so that you can quickly figure a scale at which to insert them. Other systems prompt for the diameter and lengths and create a symbol to your specifications. In 3D models, when nuts and bolts are represented, the thread is rarely shown because it adds to the complexity and size of the drawing and is difficult to model. The thread specification is annotated in the drawing.

Generally, bolt heads and nuts should be drawn "across corners" in all views, regardless of projection. This conventional violation of projection is used to prevent confusion between the square and hexagon heads and nuts and to show actual clearances. Only when there is a special reason should bolt heads and nuts be drawn across flats, as shown in Figure 33.

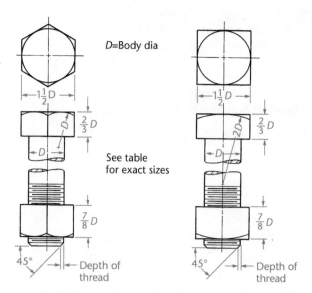

33 Bolts "Across Flats"

12 SPECIFICATIONS FOR BOLTS AND NUTS

In specifying bolts in parts lists, in correspondence, or elsewhere, the following information must be covered in order:

1. Nominal size of bolt body
2. Thread specification or thread note
3. Length of bolt
4. Finish of bolt
5. Style of head
6. Name

Example (complete decimal inch)

.75-10 UNC- HEXAGON CAP SCREW

Example (abbreviated decimal inch)

HEXCAP SCR

Example (metric)

HEXCAP SCR

Nuts may be specified as follows:

Example (complete)

$\frac{5}{8}$–11 UNC–2B SQUARE NUT

Example (abbreviated)

$\frac{5}{8}$ SQ NUT

Example (metric)

HEX NUT

For either bolts or nuts, REGULAR or GENERAL PURPOSE are assumed if omitted from the specification. If the heavy series is intended, the word HEAVY should appear as the first word in the name of the fastener. Likewise, HIGH STRENGTH STRUCTURAL should be indicated for such metric fasteners. However, the number of the specific ISO standard is often included in the metric specifications—for example, HEXAGON NUT ISO. Finish need not be mentioned if the fastener or nut is correctly named.

SKETCHING HEXAGONAL BOLTS, CAP SCREWS, AND NUTS

1 Determine the diameter of the bolt, the length (from the underside of the bearing surface to the tip), the style of head (square or hexagon), the type (regular or heavy), and the finish before starting to draw.

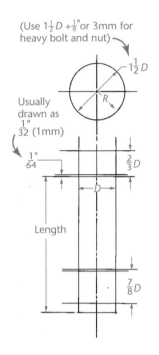

(Use $1\frac{1}{2}D + \frac{1}{8}$" or 3mm for heavy bolt and nut)

$1\frac{1}{2}D$

R

Usually drawn as $\frac{1}{32}$" (1mm)

$\frac{1}{64}$"

$\frac{2}{3}D$

D

Length

$\frac{7}{8}D$

2 Lightly sketch the top view as shown, where D is the diameter of the bolt. Project the corners of the hexagon or square to the front view. Sketch the head and nut heights. Add the 1/64" (0.4 mm) washer face if needed. Its diameter is equal to the distance across flats of the bolt head or nut. Only the metric and finished hexagon screws or nuts have a washer face. The washer face is 1/64" thick, but is shown at about 1/32" (1 mm) for clarity. The head or nut height includes the washer face.

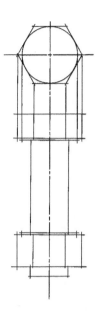

STEP by STEP

3 Represent the curves produced by the chamfer on the bolt heads and nuts as circular arcs, although they are actually hyperbolas. On drawings of small bolts or nuts under approximately 1/2" (12 mm) in diameter, where the chamfer is hardly noticeable, omit the chamfer in the rectangular view.

4 Chamfer the threaded end of the screw at 45° from the schematic thread depth.

5 Show threads in simplified or schematic form for diameters of 1" (25 mm) or less on the drawing. Detailed representation is rarely used because it clutters the drawing and takes too much time.

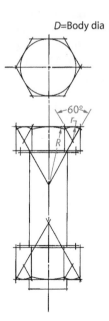

D=Body dia

60°

r

R

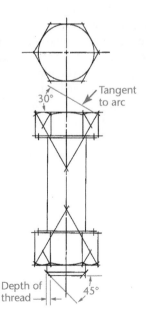

30°

Tangent to arc

Depth of thread

45°

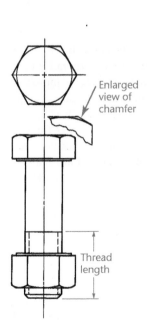

Enlarged view of chamfer

Thread length

439

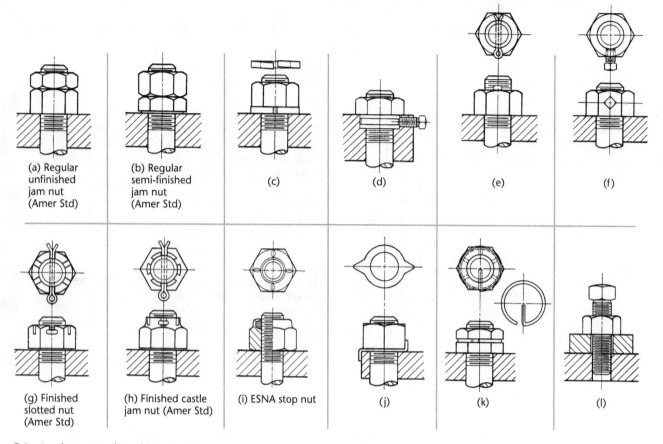

(a) Regular unfinished jam nut (Amer Std)

(b) Regular semi-finished jam nut (Amer Std)

(c)

(d)

(e)

(f)

(g) Finished slotted nut (Amer Std)

(h) Finished castle jam nut (Amer Std)

(i) ESNA stop nut

(j)

(k)

(l)

34 Locknuts and Locking Devices

13 LOCKNUTS AND LOCKING DEVICES

Many types of special nuts and devices to prevent nuts from unscrewing are available, and some of the most common are shown in Figure 34. The American National Standard jam nuts, as shown in Figures 34a and 34b, are the same as the hexagon or hexagon flat nuts, except that they are thinner. The application shown in Figure 34b, where the larger nut is on top and is screwed on more tightly, is recommended. They are the same distance across flats as the corresponding hexagon nuts (1-1/2D or 1"). They are slightly over 1/2D in thickness but are drawn 1/2D for simplicity. They are available with or without the washer face in the regular and heavy types. The tops of all are flat and chamfered at 30°, and the finished forms have either a washer face or a chamfered bearing surface.

The lock washer, shown in Figure 34c, and the cotter pin, shown in Figure 34e, are very common. The set screw, shown in Figure 34f, is often made to press against a plug of softer material, such as brass, which in turn presses against the threads without deforming them. For use with cotter pins, it is recommended to use a hex slotted nut (Figure 34g), a hex castle nut (Figure 34h), or a hex thick slotted nut or a heavy hex thick slotted nut.

Similar metric locknuts and locking devices are available. See fastener catalogs for details.

Reid Tool is one company that has a free download of its catalog available as CAD files at
• http://www.reidtool.com/download.htm.

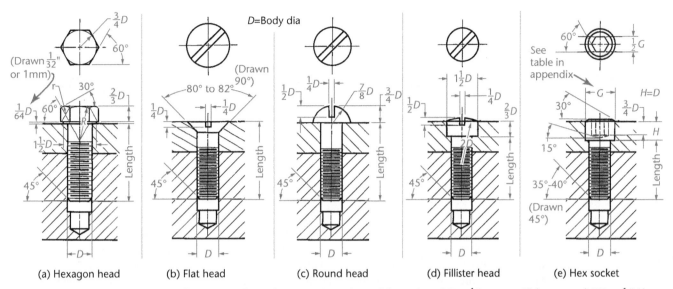

| (a) Hexagon head | (b) Flat head | (c) Round head | (d) Fillister head | (e) Hex socket |

Hexagon Head Screws Coarse, fine, or 8-thread series, 2A. Thread length = $2D + \frac{1}{4}$" up to 6" long and $2D + \frac{1}{2}$" if over 6" long. For screws too short for formula, threads extend to within $2\frac{1}{2}$ threads of the head for diameters up to 1". Screw lengths not standardized.

Slotted Head Screws Coarse, fine, or 8-thread series, 2A. Thread length = $2D + \frac{1}{4}$". Screw lengths not standardized. For screws too short for formula, threads extend to within $2\frac{1}{2}$ threads of the head.

Hexagon Socket Screws coarse or fine threads, 3A. Coarse thread length = $2D + \frac{1}{2}$" where this would be over $\frac{1}{2}L$; otherwise thread length = $\frac{1}{2}L$. Fine thread length = $1\frac{1}{2}D + \frac{1}{2}$" where this would be over $\frac{3}{8}L$; otherwise thread length = $\frac{3}{8}L$. Increments in screw lengths = $\frac{1}{8}$" for screws $\frac{1}{4}$" to 1" long, $\frac{1}{4}$" for screws 1" to 3" long, and $\frac{1}{2}$" for screws $3\frac{1}{2}$" to 6" long.

35   Standard Cap Screws

14 STANDARD CAP SCREWS

Five types of American National Standard cap screws are shown in Figure 35. The first four of these have standard heads, while the socket head cap screws, as shown in Figure 35e, have several different shapes of round heads and sockets. Cap screws are normally finished and are used on machine tools and other machines when accuracy and appearance are important. The hexagon head cap screw and hex socket head cap screw are also available in metric.

Cap screws ordinarily pass through a clearance hole in one member and screw into another. The clearance hole need not be shown on the drawing when the presence of the unthreaded clearance hole is obvious.

Cap screws are inferior to studs when frequent removal is necessary. They are used on machines requiring few adjustments. The slotted or socket-type heads are used for crowded conditions.

Actual dimensions may be used in drawing cap screws when exact sizes are necessary. Figure 35 shows the proportions in terms of body diameter (*D*) that are usually used. Hexagonal head cap screws are drawn similar to hex head bolts. The points are chamfered at 45° from the schematic thread depth.

Note that screwdriver slots are drawn at 45° in the circular views of the heads, without regard to true projection, and that threads in the bottom of the tapped holes are omitted so that the ends of the screws may be clearly seen. A typical cap screw note is:

Example (complete)

.375-16 UNC-2A × 2.5 HEXAGON HEAD CAP SCREW

Example (abbreviated)

.375 × 2.5 HEXHD CAP SCR

Example (metric)

M20 × 2.5 × 80 HEXHD CAP SCR

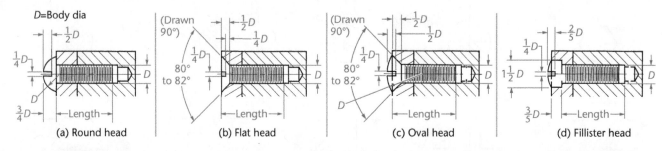

(a) Round head   (b) Flat head   (c) Oval head   (d) Fillister head

36   Standard Machine Screws

15 STANDARD MACHINE SCREWS

Machine screws are similar to cap screws but are usually smaller (.060" to .750" diameter) and the threads generally go all the way to the head. There are eight ANSI-approved forms of heads. The hexagonal head may be slotted if desired. All others are available in either slotted- or recessed-head forms. Standard machine screws are produced with a naturally bright finish, not heat treated, and have plain-sheared ends, not chamfered.

Machine screws are used for screwing into thin materials, and the smaller-numbered screws are threaded nearly to the head. They are used extensively in firearms, jigs, fixtures, and dies. Machine screw nuts are used mainly on the round head, pan head, and flat head types and are usually hexagonal.

Exact dimensions of machine screws are seldom needed for drawing purposes. The four most common types of machine screws are shown in Figure 36, with proportions based on the diameter (D). Clearance holes and counterbores should be made slightly larger than the screws.

Typical machine screw notes are:
Example (complete)
NO. 10 (.1900) -32 NF-3 $\times \frac{5}{8}$
FILLISTER HEAD MACHINE SCREW
Example (abbreviated)
NO. 10 (.1900) $\times \frac{5}{8}$ FILH MSCR
Example (metric)
M8 $\times$ 1.25 $\times$ 30 SLOTTED PAN
HEAD MACHINE SCREW

16 STANDARD SET SCREWS

Set screws, shown in Figure 37, are used to prevent motion, usually rotary, between two parts, such as the movement of the hub of a pulley on a shaft. A set screw is screwed into one part so that its point bears firmly against another part. If the point of the set screw is cupped, or if a flat is milled on the shaft, the screw will hold much more firmly. Obviously, set screws are not efficient when the load is heavy or when it is suddenly applied. Usually they are manufactured of steel and case hardened.

Headless set screws have come into greater use because the projecting head of headed set screws has caused many industrial casualties; this has resulted in legislation prohibiting their use in many states.

Metric hexagon socket headless set screws with the full range of points are available. Nominal diameters of metric hex socket set screws are 1.6, 2, 2.5, 3, 4, 5, 6, 8, 10, 12, 16, 20, and 24 mm.

Square head set screws have coarse, fine, or 8-pitch threads and are Class 2A, but are usually furnished with coarse threads since the square head set screw is generally used on the rougher grades of work. Slotted headless and socket set screws have coarse or fine threads and are Class 3A.

Nominal diameters of set screws range from number 0 up through 2"

set-screw lengths are standardized in increments of 1/32" to 1" depending on the overall length of the set screw.

Metric set screw length increments range from 0.5 to 4 mm, again depending on overall screw length.

Set screws are specified as follows:
Example (complete)
  .375- 16UNC-2A $\times$ .75 SQUARE
    HEAD FLAT POINT SET SCREW
Example (abbreviated)
  .375- $\times$ 1.25 SQH FP SSCR
  .438 $\times$ .750 HEXSOC CUP PT SSCR
  $\frac{1}{4}$ -20 UNC 2A $\times \frac{1}{2}$ SLTD HDLS
    CONE PT SSCR
Example (metric)
  M10 $\times$ 1.5 12 HEX SOCKET HEAD
    SET SCREW

37   Set Screws. *Courtesy of Penninsula Components Inc.*

17 AMERICAN NATIONAL STANDARD WOOD SCREWS

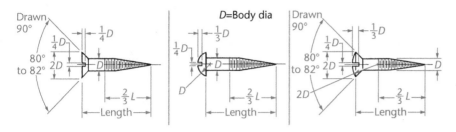

38   American National Standard Wood Screws

Wood screws with three types of heads—flat, round, and oval—have been standardized. The approximate dimensions sufficient for drawing purposes are shown in Figure 38.

The Phillips style recessed head is also available on several types of

fasteners, as well as on wood screws. Three styles of cross recesses have been standardized by ANSI. A special screwdriver is used, as shown in Figure 39q, and this results in rapid assembly without damage to the head.

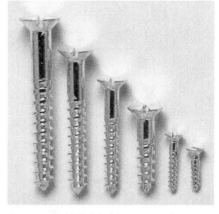

*Courtesy of Michael Newman/
PhotoEdit Inc.*

18 MISCELLANEOUS FASTENERS

Many other types of fasteners have been devised for specialized uses. Some of the more common types are shown in Figure 39. A number of these are American National Standard round head bolts,

including carriage, button head, step, and countersunk bolts.

Helical-coil-threaded inserts, as shown in Figure 39p, are shaped like a spring except that the cross section of the

wire conforms to threads on the screw and in the hole. These are made of phosphor bronze or stainless steel, and they provide a hard, smooth protective lining for tapped threads in soft metals and plastics.

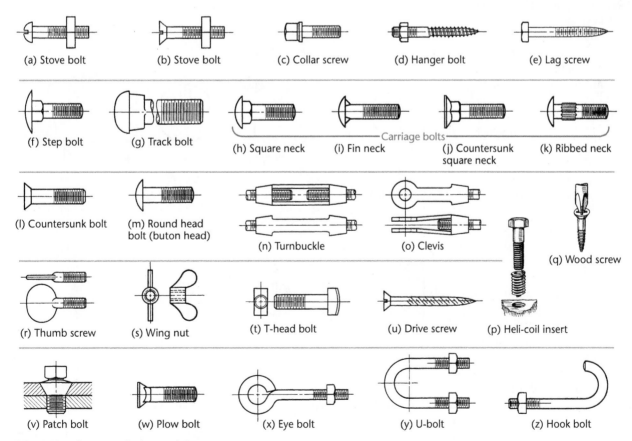

39   Miscellaneous Bolts and Screws

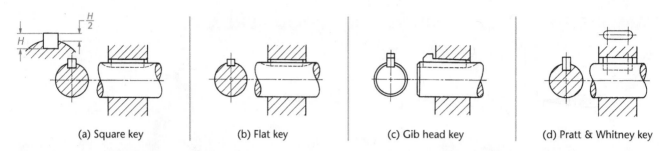

(a) Square key   (b) Flat key   (c) Gib head key   (d) Pratt & Whitney key

40   Square and Flat Keys

19 KEYS

Keys are used to prevent movement between shafts and wheels, couplings, cranks, and similar machine parts attached to or supported by shafts, as shown in Figure 40. A keyseat is in a shaft; a keyway is in the hub or surrounding part.

For heavy-duty functions, rectangular keys (flat or square) are used, and sometimes two rectangular keys are necessary for one connection. For even stronger connections, interlocking splines may be machined on the shaft and in the hole.

A *square key* is shown in Figure 40a.

A *flat key* is shown in Figure 40b. The widths of keys are generally about one fourth the shaft diameter. In either case, one half the key is sunk into the shaft. The depth of the keyway or the keyseat is measured on the side—not the center—as shown in Figure 40a. Square and flat keys may have the top surface tapered 1/8″ per foot, in which case they become square taper or flat taper keys.

A *feather key* is rectangular to prevent rotary motion, but permits relative longitudinal motion. Usually feather keys have gib heads, or are fastened so they cannot slip out of the keyway.

A *gib head key* (Figure 40c) is the same as a square taper or flat taper key except that a gib head allows its easy removal. Square and flat keys are made from cold-finished stock and are not machined.

A *Pratt & Whitney key* (P&W key) is shown in Figure 40d. It is rectangular, with semicylindrical ends. Two-thirds of its height is sunk into the shaft keyseat.

Woodruff keys are semicircular, as shown in Figure 41. This key fits into a semicircular key slot cut with a Woodruff cutter, as shown, and the top of the key fits into a plain rectangular keyway. Sizes of keys for given shaft diameters are not standardized. For average conditions, select a key whose diameter is approximately equal to the shaft diameter. See manufacturers' catalogs for specifications for metric counterparts.

Typical specifications for keys are:

.25 × 1.50 SQ KEY
No. 204 WOODRUFF KEY
1/4 × 1/6 × 1-FLAT KEY
No. 10 P&W KEY

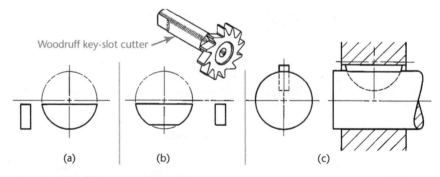

Woodruff key-slot cutter

(a)   (b)   (c)

41   Woodruff Keys and Key-Slot Cutter

20 MACHINE PINS

Machine pins include taper pins, straight pins, dowel pins, clevis pins, and cotter pins. For light work, taper pins can be used to fasten hubs or collars to shafts. Figure 42 shows the use of a taper pin where the hole through the collar and shaft is drilled and reamed when the parts are assembled. For slightly heavier duty, a taper pin may be used parallel to the shaft as for square keys.

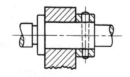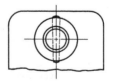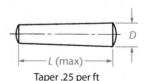

L (max)

Taper .25 per ft

42   Taper Pin

Dowel pins are cylindrical or conical and usually used to keep two parts in a fixed position or to preserve alignment. They are usually used where accurate alignment is essential. Dowel pins are generally made of steel and are hardened and ground in a centerless grinder.

Clevis pins are used in a clevis and held in place by cotter pins.

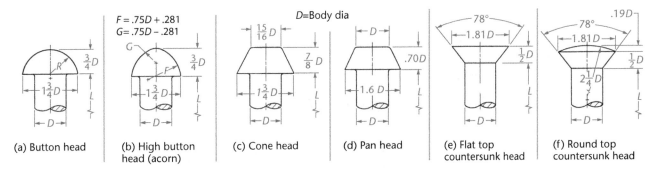

(a) Button head

(b) High button head (acorn)

(c) Cone head

(d) Pan head

(e) Flat top countersunk head

(f) Round top countersunk head

43   Standard Large Rivets

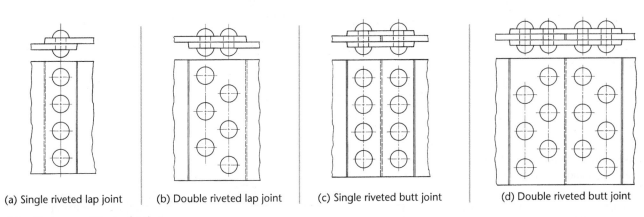

(a) Single riveted lap joint

(b) Double riveted lap joint

(c) Single riveted butt joint

(d) Double riveted butt joint

44   Common Riveted Joints

21 RIVETS

Rivets are regarded as permanent fastenings, unlike removable fastenings, such as bolts and screws. Rivets are generally used to hold sheet metal or rolled steel together and are made of wrought iron, carbon steel, copper, or occasionally other metals.

To fasten two pieces of metal together, holes are punched, drilled, or punched and then reamed, all slightly larger in diameter than the shank of the rivet. Rivet diameters are made from $d = 1.2\sqrt{t}$ to $d = 1.4\sqrt{t}$, where d is the rivet diameter and t is the metal thickness. The larger rivet diameter size is used for steel and single-riveted joints, and the smaller may be used for multiple-riveted joints. In structural work it is common to make the hole 1.6 mm (1/16") larger than the rivet.

When the red-hot rivet is inserted, a "dolly bar" with a depression the shape of the driven head is held against the head. A riveting machine is used to drive the rivet and forms the head on the plain end. This causes the rivet to swell and fill the hole tightly.

Large rivets or heavy hex structural bolts are often used in structural work of bridges and buildings and in ship and boiler construction. They are shown in their exact formula proportions in Figure 43. Button heads (Figure 43a), and countersunk heads (Figure 43e), are the rivets most commonly used in structural work. The button head and cone head are commonly used in tank and boiler construction.

Riveted Joints

Typical riveted joints are shown in Figure 44. Note that the rectangular view of each rivet shows the shank of the rivet with both heads made with circular arcs, and the circular view of each rivet is represented by only the outside circle of the head.

Rivet Symbols

Since many engineering structures are too large to be built in the shop, they are built in the largest units possible and then are transported to the desired location. Trusses are common examples of this. The rivets driven in the shop are called shop rivets, and those driven on the job are called field rivets. However, heavy steel bolts are commonly used on the job for structural work. Solid black circles are used to represent field rivets, and other standard symbols are used to show other features, as shown in Figure 45.

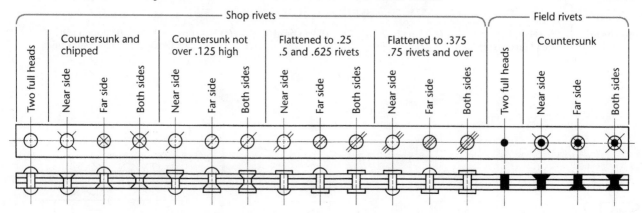

45 Conventional Rivet Symbols

Small Rivets

Small rivets are used for light work. American National Standard small solid rivets are illustrated with dimensions that show their standard proportions in Figure 46, ANSI/ASME B18.1.1–1972 (R1995). Included in the same standard are tinners', coppers', and belt rivets. Metric rivets are also available. Dimensions for large rivets are in ANSI/ASME B18.1.2-1972 (R1995). See manufacturers' catalogs for additional details.

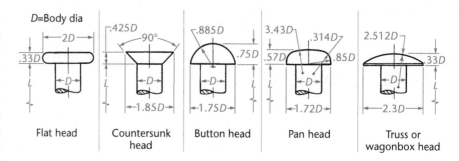

46 American National Standard Small Solid Rivet Proportions

Blind Rivets

Blind rivets, commonly known as pop rivets (Figure 47), are often used for fastening together thin sheet-metal assemblies. Blind rivets are hollow and are installed with manual or power-operated rivet guns which grip a center pin or mandrel, pulling the head into the body and expanding the rivet against the sheet metal. They are available in aluminum, steel, stainless steel, and plastic. As with any fastener, the designer should be careful to choose an appropriate material to avoid corrosive action between dissimilar metals.

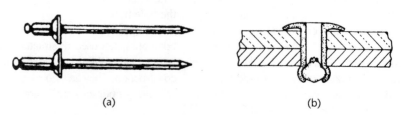

47 Blind Rivets (a) Before Installation, and (b) Installed

446

22 SPRINGS

A spring is a mechanical device designed to store energy when deflected and to return the equivalent amount of energy when released, ANSI Y14.13M-1981 (R1992). Springs are commonly made of spring steel, which may be music wire, hard-drawn wire, or oil-tempered wire. Other materials used for compression springs include stainless steel, beryllium copper, and phosphor bronze. Urethane plastic is used in applications where conventional springs would be affected by corrosion, vibration, or acoustic or magnetic forces.

Springs are classified as *helical springs* (Figure 48), or *flat springs*.

Helical Springs

Helical springs are usually cylindrical but may also be conical. There are three types of helical springs.

- **Compression springs** offer resistance to a compressive force.
- **Extension springs** offer resistance to a pulling force.
- **Torsion springs** offer resistance to a torque or twisting force.

Springs. *Reprinted by permission of Pearson Education, Inc., Upper Saddle River, NJ.*

On working drawings, true projections of helical springs are not drawn because of the labor involved. Like screw threads, they are drawn in detailed and schematic methods, using straight lines to replace helical curves, as shown in Figure 48.

A square wire spring is similar to the square thread with the core of the shaft removed, as in Figure 48b. Use standard cross-hatching if the areas in section are large, as in Figures 48a and b. Small sectioned areas may be made solid black, as in Figure 48c.

In cases where a complete picture of the spring is not necessary, use phantom lines to save time in drawing the coils, as in Figure 48d. If the drawing of the spring is too small to be represented by the outlines of the wire, use schematic representation, shown in Figures 48e and f.

Compression springs have plain ends, as in Figure 49a, or squared (closed) ends, as in Figure 49b. The ends may be ground, as shown in Figure 49c, or both squared and ground, as in Figure 49d. Required dimensions are indicated in the figure. When required, RH or LH is specified for right-hand or left-hand coil direction.

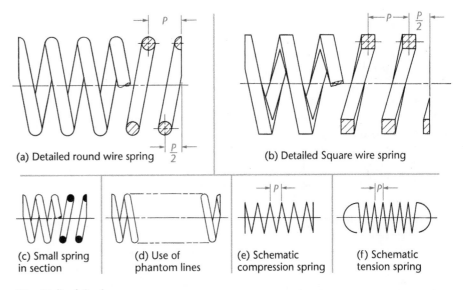

(a) Detailed round wire spring

(b) Detailed Square wire spring

(c) Small spring in section

(d) Use of phantom lines

(e) Schematic compression spring

(f) Schematic tension spring

48   Helical Springs

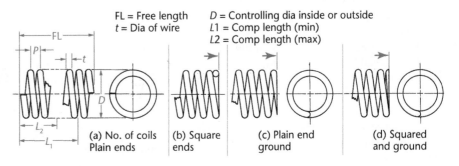

FL = Free length
t = Dia of wire
D = Controlling dia inside or outside
L1 = Comp length (min)
L2 = Comp length (max)

(a) No. of coils Plain ends

(b) Square ends

(c) Plain end ground

(d) Squared and ground

49   Compression Springs

Extension springs may have many types of ends, so it is necessary to draw the spring or at least the ends and a few adjacent coils, as shown in Figure 50.

A typical torsion spring drawing is shown in Figure 51. A typical flat spring drawing is shown in Figure 52. Other types of flat springs are power springs (or flat coil springs), Belleville springs (like spring washers), and leaf springs (commonly used in automobiles).

Many companies use a printed specification form to provide the necessary spring information, including data such as load at a specified deflected length, load rate, finish, and type of service.

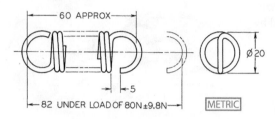

MATERIAL: 2.00 OIL TEMPERED SPRING STEEL WIRE
14.5 COILS RIGHT HAND
MACHINE LOOP AND HOOK IN LINE
SPRING MUST EXTEND TO 110 WITHOUT SET
FINISH: BLACK JAPAN

50 Extension Spring Drawing

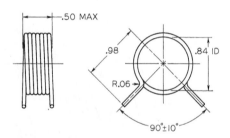

MATERIAL : .059 MUSIC WIRE
6.75 COILS RIGHT HAND NO INITIAL TENSION
TORQUE : 2.50 INCH LB AT 155° DEFLECTION SPRING MUST
DEFLECT 180° WITHOUT PERMANENT SET AND
MUST OPERATE FREELY ON .75 DIAMETER SHAFT
FINISH : CADMIUM OR ZINC PLATE

51 Torsion Spring Drawing

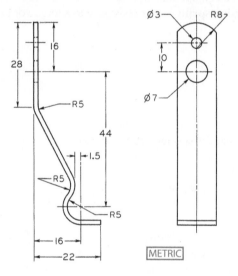

MATERIAL : 1.20 X 14.0 SPRING STEEL
HEAT TREAT : 44-48C ROCKWELL
FINISH : BLACK OXIDE AND OIL

52 Flat Spring

23 DRAWING HELICAL SPRINGS

The construction for a schematic elevation view of a compression spring with six total coils is shown in Figure 53a. Since the ends are closed, or squared, two of the six coils are "dead" coils, leaving only four full pitches to be set off along the top of the spring.

If there are six total coils, as shown in Figure 53, the spacings will be on opposite sides of the spring. The construction of an extension spring with six active coils and loop ends is shown in Figure 53c.

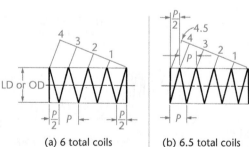

(a) 6 total coils compression spring

(b) 6.5 total coils compression spring

(c) 6.5 total coils extension spring

53 Schematic Spring Representation.

Figure 54 shows the steps in drawing a detailed section and elevation view of a compression spring. The spring is shown pictorially in Figure 54a. Figure 54b shows the cutting plane through the centerline of the spring. Figure 54c

shows the section with the cutting plane removed. Steps to construct the sectional view are shown in Figures 54d–f. Figure 54g shows the corresponding elevation view.

If there are a fractional number of coils, such as the five coils in Figure 54h, the half-rounds of sectional wire are placed on opposite sides of the spring.

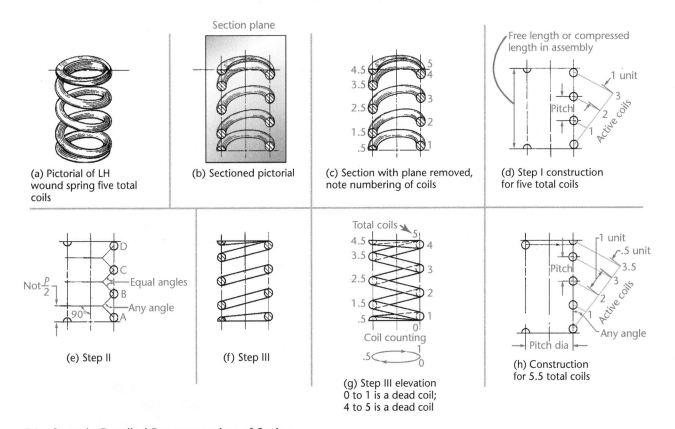

(a) Pictorial of LH wound spring five total coils

(b) Sectioned pictorial

(c) Section with plane removed, note numbering of coils

(d) Step I construction for five total coils

(e) Step II

(f) Step III

(g) Step III elevation
0 to 1 is a dead coil;
4 to 5 is a dead coil

(h) Construction for 5.5 total coils

54   Steps in Detailed Representation of Spring

24 COMPUTER GRAPHICS

Standard representations of threaded fasteners and springs, in both detailed and schematic forms, are available in CAD symbol libraries. Use of computer graphics frees the drafter from the need to draw time-consuming repetitive features by hand and also makes it easy to modify drawings if required.

In 3D modeling, thread is not usually represented because it can be

difficult to create and computer intensive to view and edit. Instead, the nominal diameter of a threaded shaft or hole is usually created along with notation calling out the thread. Sometimes the depth of the thread is shown in the 3D drawing to call attention to the thread and to help in determining fits and clearances.

DOWNLOADING STANDARD FASTENERS

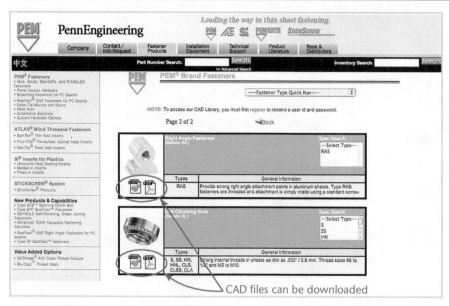

(a) PEM brand fasteners, available from Penn Engineering are an example of the many stock fasteners that you can download in CAD file formats for easy insertion into drawings. *Courtesy of PennEngineering.*

Many stock fasteners in standard CAD formats are available to download, ready to use in CAD drawings and models. One example of such a site is http://www.pemnet.com/fastening_products, from the Penn Engineering company. Their PEM brand fasteners are often used to fasten sheet metal parts, such as the part shown in Figure B.

The CAD files that you download can be inserted into your drawings to save drawing time. The stock fastener type is specified in a drawing note as shown in Figure B.

Data sheets in PDF format are also available from the Pemnet site. Figure C shows the cover of a 12-page PDF booklet that lists material, thread size, performance data, and other key data for unified and metric self-clinching nuts that the company carries.

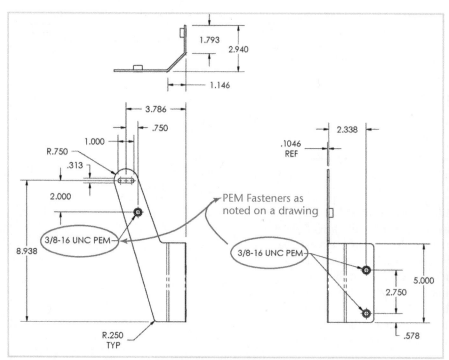

(b) PEM stock fasteners shown on a drawing. *Courtesy of Dynojet Research, Inc.*

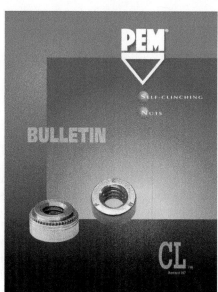

(c) Data sheets are often available in PDF format, as in this example from PEM. *Courtesy of PennEngineering.*

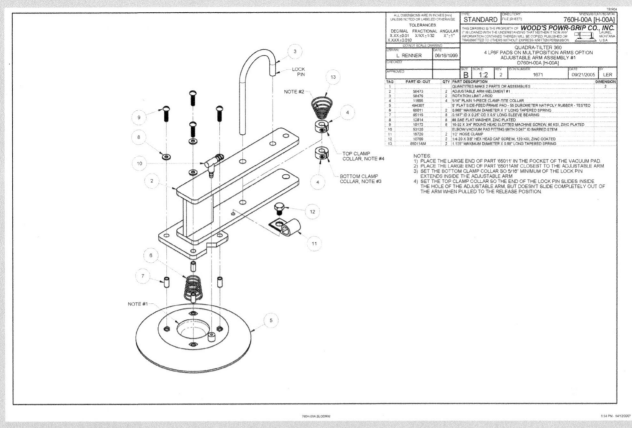

Assembly drawing showing fasteners and springs. *Courtesy of Wood's Power-Grip Co. Inc.*

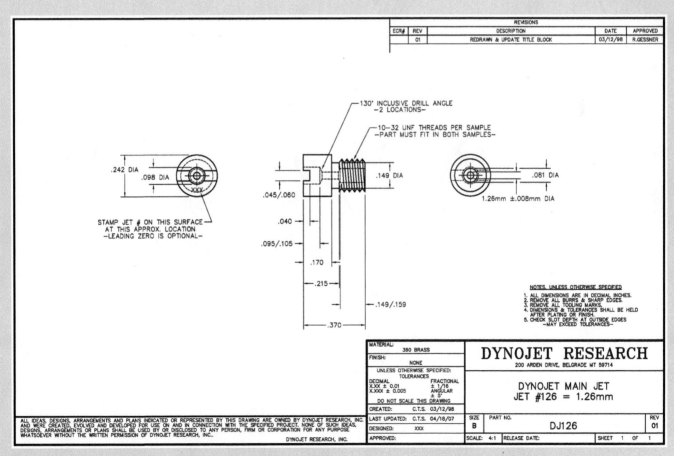

Part drawing for a special-purpose threaded part (scale 4:1). *Courtesy of Dynojet Research, Inc.*

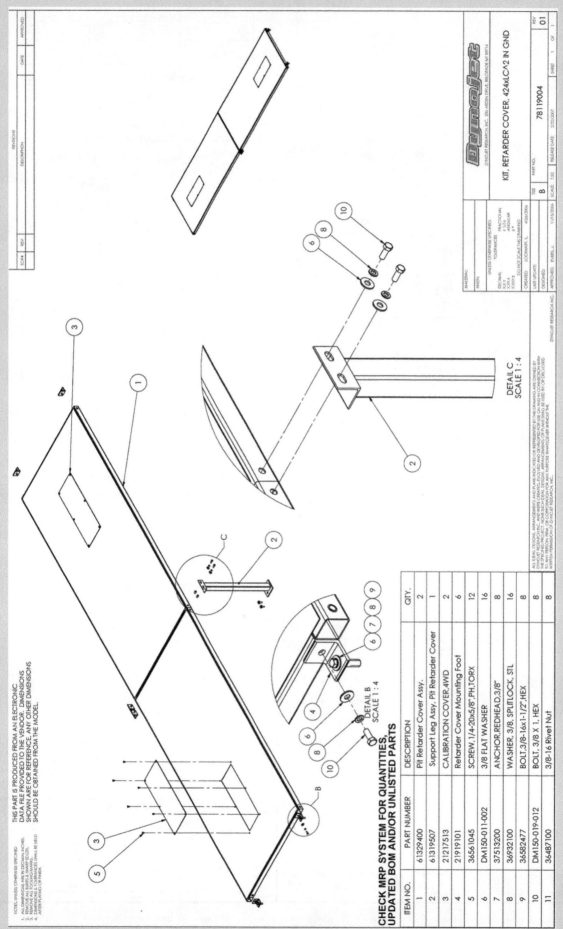

CHECK MRP SYSTEM FOR QUANTITIES, UPDATED BOM AND/OR UNLISTED PARTS

ITEM NO.	PART NUMBER	DESCRIPTION	QTY.
1	61329400	Pit Retarder Cover Assy.	2
2	61319507	Support Leg Assy, Pit Retarder Cover	1
3	21217513	CALIBRATION COVER,4WD	2
4	21919101	Retarder Cover Mounting Foot	6
5	36561045	SCREW,1/4-20x5/8",PH,TORX	12
6	DM150-011-002	3/8 FLAT WASHER	16
7	37513200	ANCHOR,REDHEAD,3/8"	8
8	36932100	WASHER, 3/8, SPLITLOCK, STL	16
9	36582477	BOLT,3/8-16x1-1/2",HEX	8
10	DM150-019-012	BOLT, 3/8 X 1, HEX	8
11	36487100	3/8-16 Rivet Nut	8

DETAIL C
SCALE 1 : 4

DETAIL B
SCALE 1 : 4

Dynojet
DYNOJET RESEARCH, INC. 200 ARDEN DRIVE, BELGRADE MT 59714

KIT, RETARDER COVER, 424xLC/2 IN GND

PART NO. 78119004   REV 01

Enlarged details show the fasteners in this assembly drawing. *Courtesy of Dynojet Research, Inc.*

452

KEY WORDS

Thread Form
Screw Thread
External Thread
Internal Thread
Major Diameter
Minor Diameter
Pitch
Pitch Diameter
Lead
Angle of Thread
Crest
Root
Side
Axis of Screw
Depth of Thread
Form of Thread
Series of Thread
Sharp-V thread
American National Thread
Unified Thread
Unified Extra Fine Thread Series
Metric Thread
Square Thread
Acme Thread
Standard Worm Thread
Whitworth Thread
Knuckle Thread
Buttress Thread
Thread Pitch Gage
Coarse Thread
Fine Thread
Single Thread
Multiple Threads
Clearance Holes
Bolt Types
Finish
Thread Lengths
Bolt Lengths
Square Key
Flat Key
Feather Key
Gib Head Key
Pratt & Whitney Key
Woodruff Keys
Compression Springs
Extension Springs
Torsion Springs

CHAPTER SUMMARY

- There are many types of thread forms; however, metric and unified are the most common.
- The method of showing threads on a drawing is called the thread representation. The three types of thread representation are detailed, schematic, and simplified.
- The major diameter, pitch, and form are the most important parts of a thread specification.
- Thread specifications are dimensioned using a leader, usually pointing to the rectangular view of the threaded shaft or to the circular view of a threaded hole. The thread specification tells the manufacturing technician what kind of thread needs to be created.
- The nut and bolt is still the most common type of fastener. Many new types of fasteners are being created to streamline the production process.
- Keys and pins are special fasteners for attachment, for example, a pulley to a shaft.
- The screw head determines what kind of tool will be necessary to install the fastener.

REVIEW QUESTIONS

1. Draw a typical screw thread using detailed representation, and label the parts of the thread.
2. Why are phantom lines used to represent the middle part of a long spring?
3. Draw several types of screw heads.
4. List five types of screws.
5. Why is the simplified thread representation the most commonly used drawing style?
6. List five fasteners that do not have any threads.
7. Write out a metric thread specification and a unified thread specification and label each part of the specification.
8. Which type of thread form is used on a lightbulb?
9. How are multiple threads designated in a thread note?
10. Using known abbreviations, give a specification for a slotted headless flat point set screw.

EXERCISES

Thread and Fastener Projects

Use the information in this chapter and in various manufacturers' catalogs in connection with the working drawings, where many different kinds of threads and fasteners are required. Several projects are included here (Exercises 1 to 5).

Design Project

Design a system that uses thread to transmit power, for use in helping transfer a handicapped person from a bed to a wheelchair. Use either schematic or detailed representation to show the thread in your design sketches.

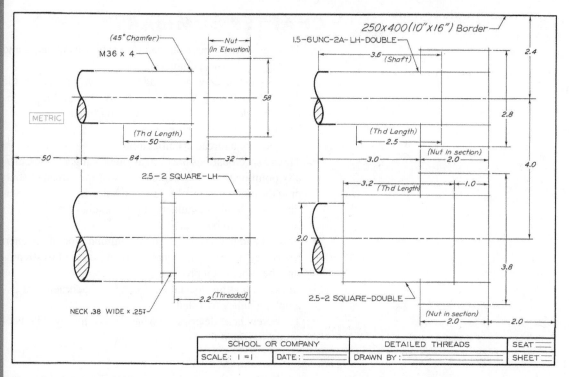

Exercise 1 Draw specified detailed threads arranged as shown. Omit all dimensions and notes given in inclined letters. Letter only the thread notes and the title strip. (Some dimensions are given to help you match the sheet layout.)

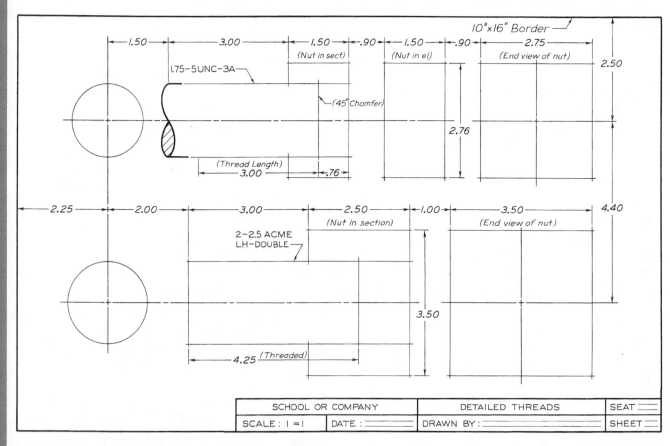

Exercise 2 Draw specified detailed notes given in inclined letters. Letter only the thread notes and the title strip. (Some dimensions are given to help you match the sheet layout.)

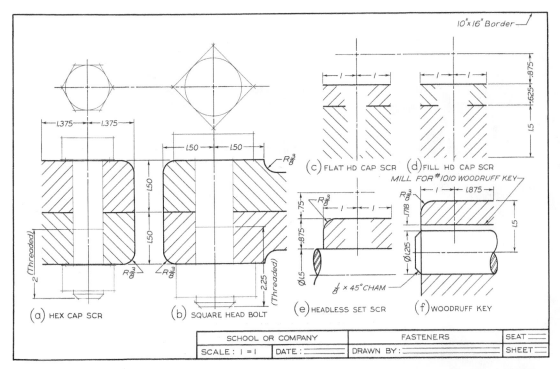

Exercise 3 Draw fasteners, arranged as shown. At (a) draw 7/8-9 UNC-2A × 4 Hex Cap Screw. At (b) draw 7 UNC-2A × 41/4 Sq Hd Bolt. At (c) draw 3/8-16 UNC-2A × 11/2 Flat Hd Cap Screw. At (d) draw 7/16-14 UNC-2A × 1 Fill Hd Cap Screw. At (e) draw 1/2 × 1 Headless Slotted Set Screw. At (f) draw front view of No. 1010 Woodruff Key. Draw simplified or schematic thread symbols as assigned. Letter titles under each figure as shown. (Some dimensions are given to help you match the sheet layout.)

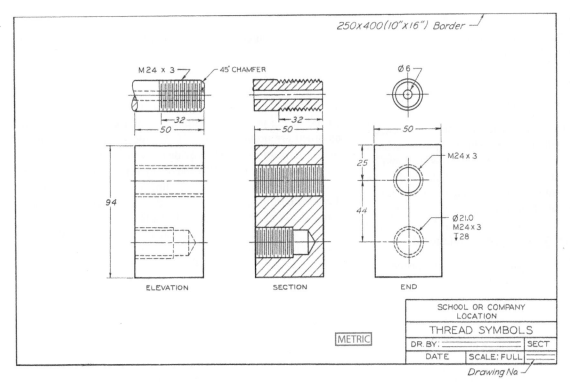

Exercise 4 Draw specified thread symbols, arranged as shown. Draw simplified or schematic symbols, as assigned by instructor, using Layout B-5 or A3-5. Omit all dimensions and notes given in inclined letters. Letter only the drill and thread notes, the titles of the views, and the title strip. (Some dimensions are given to help you match the sheet layout.)

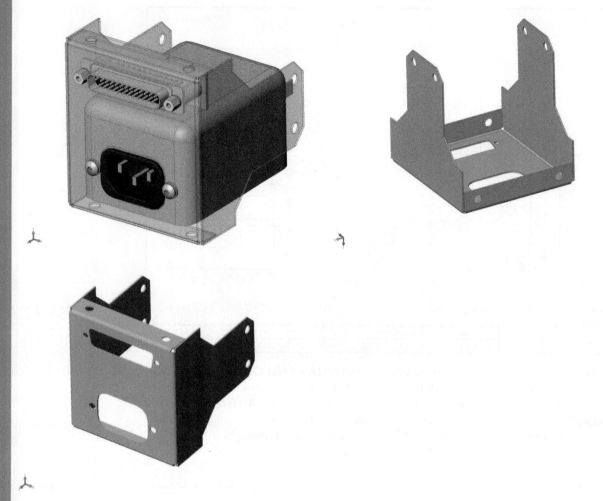

Exercise 5 Specify fasteners for attaching the sheet metal and standard electrical components shown. Use the Web to research power and electrical connectors.

Exercise 6 Captive hardware.

Captive hardware is a term for fasteners that once installed, cannot be easily or accidentally removed. This is typically achieved by removing a portion of the threading on a screw shaft and then threading the captive hardware into a special sleeve that once installed, prevents the hardware from backing out. Captive hardware is useful in situations where many fasteners are necessary—for example in sheet metal covers and large panels and when the fastener must be repeatedly unfastened and refastened.

For this exercise, modify a standard 6-32 × .75" socket head cap screw (SHCS) so it can be installed into a sleeve that you will

design. The dimensions for the lock and flat washer are provided on the facing page, and the dimensions from the screw to be modified are provided from a CAD file downloaded from the McMaster-Carr Web site. Provide dimensions for turning down the thread on the 6-32 SHCS and the missing callouts on the captive screw sleeve. Ensure the dimensions provided for the threaded portion of the screw and the clearance for the captive screw sleeve allow the screw to be fully inserted, and allow it to be completely removed from the threaded blank material without causing interference.

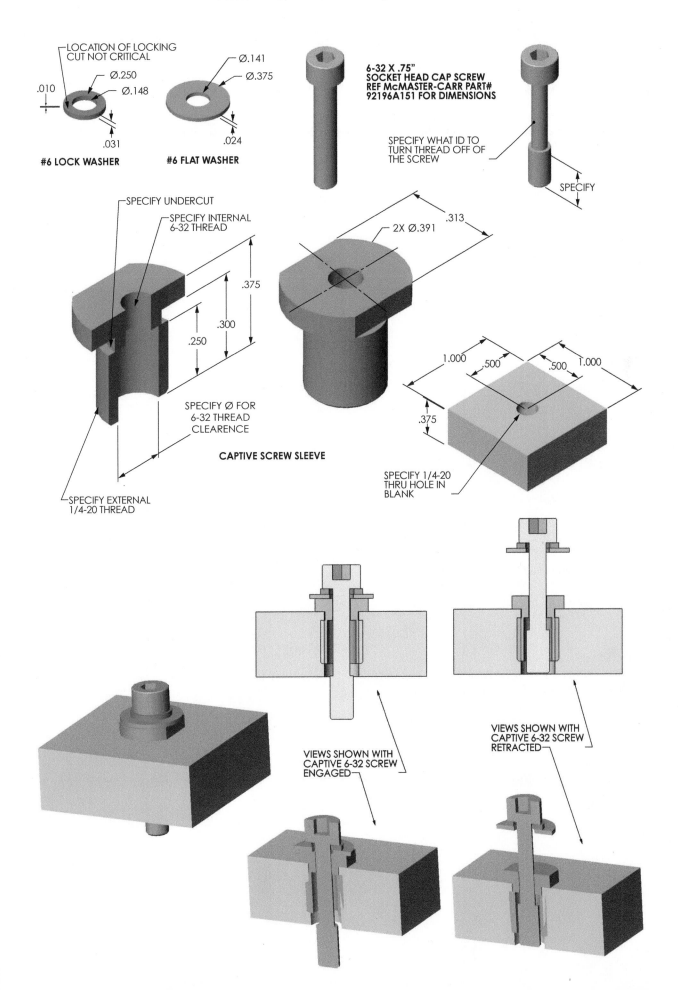

LOCATION OF LOCKING CUT NOT CRITICAL

Ø.250
Ø.148
.010
.031

#6 LOCK WASHER

Ø.141
Ø.375
.024

#6 FLAT WASHER

6-32 X .75"
SOCKET HEAD CAP SCREW
REF McMASTER-CARR PART#
92196A151 FOR DIMENSIONS

SPECIFY WHAT ID TO TURN THREAD OFF OF THE SCREW

SPECIFY

SPECIFY UNDERCUT
SPECIFY INTERNAL 6-32 THREAD

.375
.300
.250

SPECIFY Ø FOR 6-32 THREAD CLEARENCE

2X Ø.391
.313

CAPTIVE SCREW SLEEVE

1.000
.500
.500
1.000
.375

SPECIFY 1/4-20 THRU HOLE IN BLANK

SPECIFY EXTERNAL 1/4-20 THREAD

VIEWS SHOWN WITH CAPTIVE 6-32 SCREW ENGAGED

VIEWS SHOWN WITH CAPTIVE 6-32 SCREW RETRACTED

457

SKETCHING THREAD SYMBOLS

1. Sketch the proper threads on the sketches below using detailed representation.
2. Complete the sketches below using either schematic or simplified thread symbols, as specified.
3. Sketch single threads in section and elevation below.

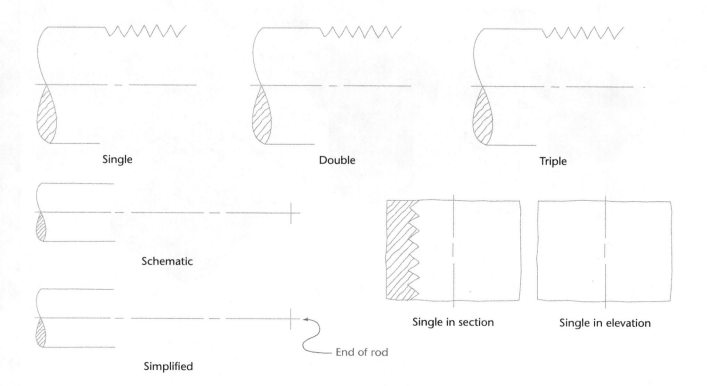

Single

Double

Triple

Schematic

Simplified

End of rod

Single in section

Single in elevation

SKETCHING HEXAGONAL BOLTS, CAP SCREWS, AND NUTS

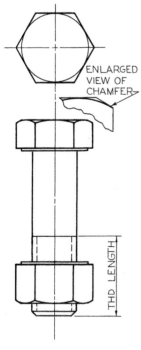

ENLARGED VIEW OF CHAMFER

1. Determine the diameter of the bolt, the length (from the underside of the bearing surface to the tip), the style of head (square or hexagon), the type (regular or heavy), and the finish before starting to draw.

2. Lightly sketch the top view as shown, where *D* is the diameter of the bolt. Project the corners of the hexagon or square to the front view. Sketch the head and nut heights. Add the 1/64″ (0.4 mm) washer face if needed. Its diameter is equal to the distance across flats of the bolt head or nut. Only the metric and finished hexagon screws or nuts have a washer face. The washer face is 1/64″ thick but is shown at about 1/32″ (1 mm) for clearness. The head or nut height includes the washer face.

3. Represent the curves produced by the chamfer on the bolt heads and nuts as circular arcs, although they are actually hyperbolas. On drawings of small bolts or nuts under approximately 1/2″ (12 mm) in diameter, where the chamfer is hardly noticeable, omit the chamfer in the rectangular view.

4. Chamfer the threaded end of the screw at 45° from the schematic thread depth.

5. Show threads in simplified or schematic form for diameters of 1″ (25 mm) or less on the drawing. Detailed representation is rarely used because it clutters the drawing and takes too much time.

6. Finish each of the hex bolts started below. Darken your final lines.

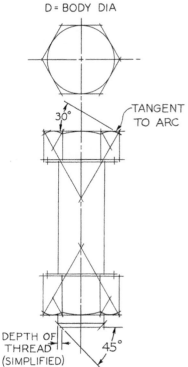

D = BODY DIA

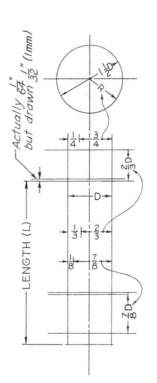

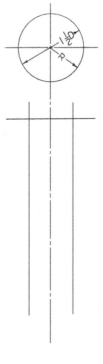

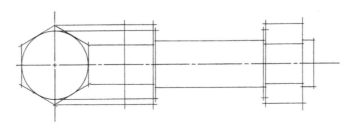

TOLERANCING

From Chapter 10 of *Modern Graphics Communication*, Fourth Edition, Frederick E. Giesecke, Alva Mitchell, Henry Cecil Spencer, Ivan Leroy Hill, John Thomas Dygdon, James E. Novak, Shawna Lockhart. Copyright © 2010 by Pearson Education, Inc. Published by Pearson Prentice Hall.

TOLERANCING

OBJECTIVES

After studying the material in this chapter, you should be able to:

1. Describe the nominal size, tolerance, limits, and allowance of two mating parts.

2. Identify a clearance fit, interference fit, and transition fit.

3. Describe the basic hole and basic shaft systems.

4. Dimension mating parts using limit dimensions, unilateral tolerances, and bilateral tolerances.

5. Describe the classes of fit and give examples of each.

6. Draw geometric tolerancing symbols.

7. Specify geometric tolerances.

Refer to the following standards:
- ANSI/ASME Y14.5-1994 Dimensioning and Tolerancing
- ANSI B4.1-1967 (R. 1994) Preferred Limits and Fits for Cylindrical Parts
- ANSI B4.2-1978 (R. 1994) Preferred Metric Limits and Fits
- ISO 5459
- ISO 286-1:1988, ISO 286-2:1988
- ISO 1101:1983 (E)

The companion website for this text is www.prenhall.com/chet_giesecke_modgraphic_4.

Specifying Tolerance Is Essential to Ensure that Interchangeable Parts Fit Together in Assemblies. A worker makes notes on a new John Deere engine at a factory in Pune, Maharashtra, India. *Courtesy of JOERG BOETHLING/Peter Arnold, Inc.*

OVERVIEW

Interchangeable manufacturing requires effective size control by the engineer or detailer because, in mass production, all parts must fit together properly, regardless of where they are made.

For example, an automobile manufacturer might subcontract parts manufacturing to other companies—both parts for new automobiles and replacement parts for repairs. All parts must be enough alike that each can fit properly in any assembly.

The maximum acceptable amount that an actual part feature can vary from a specified dimension is called tolerance. On technical drawings, tolerances specify the degree of accuracy required for the provided dimensions.

Parts can be made to very precise dimensions, even to a few millionths of an inch or thousandths of a millimeter—as in gage blocks—but highly accurate parts are extremely expensive to produce and there is still some variation between the exact dimension and the actual size of the part. Fortunately, perfectly exact sizes are not needed. The accuracy needed in a part depends on its function.

One aspect of quality is determined by manufacturing tolerances. Products with small variations in shape may fit together more precisely and command higher prices. However, it wouldn't be practical for all products to be manufactured to high precision. For example, a manufacturer of children's tricycles might go out of business if the parts were made with jet engine accuracy—no one would be willing to pay the price.

Waste results when the manufacturing process cannot maintain shape and size within prescribed limits. By monitoring the manufacturing processes and reducing waste, a company can improve profits. This direct relationship to profit is one of the main reasons that tolerancing is critical to manufacturing success.

The inner workings of a watch are an example of parts that must fit precisely in order to work. *Courtesy of SuperStock, Inc.*

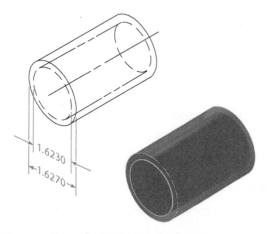

1   Upper and Lower Limits of Dimension

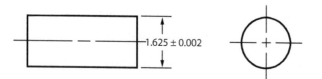

2   Direct Limits Used to Specify a Bilateral Tolerance

UNDERSTANDING TOLERANCE

Tolerancing is an extension of dimensioning. It allows you to specify a range of accuracy for the shape, size, and position of every feature of a product, so that the manufactured parts will fit together and function properly when assembled. CAD software often provide features for dimensioning, tolerancing, and checking fits and interferences that aid in the tolerancing process. In order to effectively provide tolerances in your drawings and CAD models, you must:

- Understand the fit required between mating parts.
- Have a clear picture of how inspection measurements are performed.
- Be able to apply tolerance symbols to a drawing or model.

Tolerance

Tolerance is the total amount a specific dimension is permitted to vary (ANSI/ASME Y14.5M-1994). Tolerances are specified so that any two mating parts will fit together. Specify as generous a tolerance as possible that still permits satisfactory function of the part since increased precision makes the part more expensive to manufacture. In this chapter, you will learn several ways of stating the tolerance.

One method of providing a tolerance is to specify the dimension and give a plus or minus range after it. This direct limit applies solely to that feature being controlled by that dimension. Figure 1 shows an example of a direct limit. A dimension given as 1.625 ± 0.002 means that the manufactured part may be 1.627 or 1.623 or anywhere between these maximum and minimum limit dimensions. The tolerance (the total amount the actual part feature is allowed to vary from what is specified) is 0.0040.

Quality Control

When you purchase parts or have them manufactured by another company, you must have a way to ensure that the parts are manufactured precisely enough to fit together with their mating parts and perform the intended function.

Before paying for parts, most companies have a process to **quality certify** (QC) the parts against the drawing or model. Larger batches of parts may use statistical methods to control quality where a relevant sample of the parts are inspected instead of all the parts. Some companies require certification from the part vendor rather than inspecting parts themselves.

A tolerance must be specified for each dimension so that it can be determined how accurately the part must be manufactured to be acceptable. The tolerances that you specify are based on the part's function and fit. Figure 2 shows the tolerance specified on a drawing.

3 Part is waisted.

4 Part is bowed.

5 Part is tapered.

6 Part is barreled.

Variations in Form

Look at the cylinder dimensioned in Figure 2. The dimensions specify a **bilateral tolerance** that allow the part to be +.002 or −.002 from the 1.625 dimension specified. The drawing or model of the cylinder specifies the shape and the dimensions and tolerance specify its size and the allowable variation that the size may have.

But what about imperfections of the form? Figures 3–6 show imperfections of form that may occur in manufacturing cylinders. Of course they are greatly exaggerated in the illustration for clarity. Visually, a difference of a few thousandths of an inch would not be discernable. Since nothing can be made to exact perfection, some of these types of variations will occur in manufacturing. The objective of providing a tolerance is to limit it to an acceptable amount of variation so that the parts will still fit and function.

You can think of tolerance as defining a **perfect form envelope** that the real produced part must fit inside in order to be acceptable. Figure 7a illustrates the idea of a part fitting inside the perfect form boundary. The part (in this case a shaft) is represented in green and the upper and lower boundaries are shown as blue areas. The part can be any size that is no larger than the upper boundary and is no smaller than the lower boundary.

Figure 7c illustrates the idea of a **bowed** part that extends outside the perfect form boundary. An acceptable part also must not extend beyond the boundary formed by the lower limit. Figure 7d illustrates a **waisted** part that extends below the lower limit.

> **TIP**
>
> You can sometimes notice variations in form by placing a machinists' scale along the edge of the part and checking to see if you can slip a feeler gage between the scale and the edge of the part.

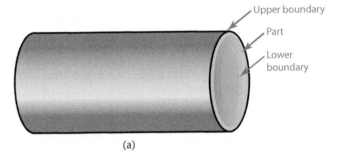

Upper boundary
Part
Lower boundary

(a)

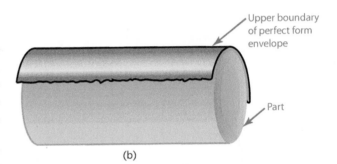

Upper boundary of perfect form envelope

Part

(b)

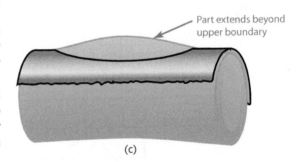

Part extends beyond upper boundary

(c)

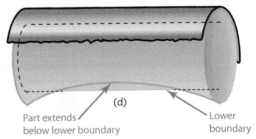

Part extends below lower boundary

(d)

Lower boundary

7 (a) Fitting; (b) section showing fit; (c) part extends beyond perfect form boundary; (d) part extends beyond lower limit (Variations are exaggerated for the purpose of illustration.)

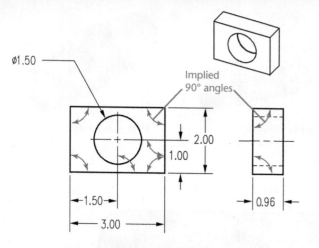

ALL TOLERANCES ±0.002 UNLESS OTHERWISE NOTED.
ANGULAR TOLERANCES ±1°.

8 Noted tolerances apply to implied 90° angles the same as they do to dimensioned angles that are not noted otherwise.

Implied Right Angles

When lines or centerlines intersect on a drawing at angles of 90°, it is customary not to dimension the angle. This is called an implied 90° angle. If the angle is something other than 90°, it must be dimensioned to be understood clearly.

Implied 90° angles have the same general tolerances applied to them as do any other angles covered by a general note. Figure 8 shows a simple dimensioned drawing with a general tolerance note. The tolerance of plus or minus 1 degree applies to the implied 90° angles as well as to the dimensioned angles in the drawing. Figure 9 shows a drawing where implied 90° angles are controlled by the tolerance noted in the title block. Later in this chapter you will learn to use geometric dimensioning and tolerancing to control angles with greater precision.

Centerlines and part surfaces drawn at right angles on a drawing, or using specific geometric controls or basic dimensions (as you will learn to do starting in Section 11), are all ways to define the accuracy requirements for right angles on the part.

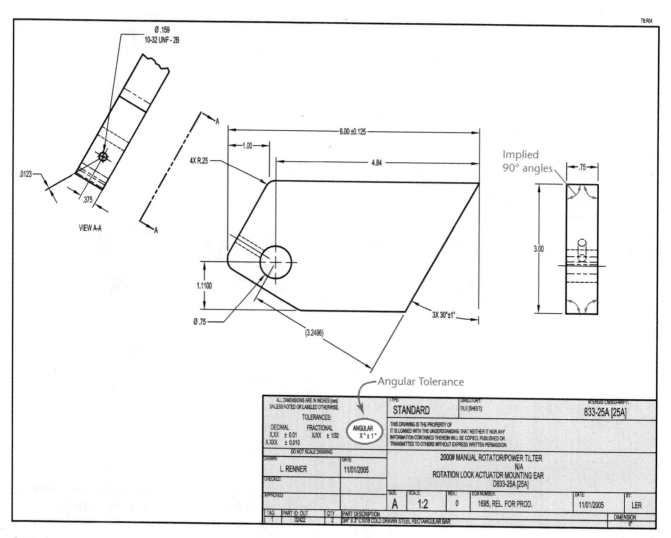

9 Tolerance block note is applied to implied 90° angles in the drawing. *Courtesy of Wood's Power-Grip Co., Inc.*

Fits between Mating Parts

Fit is the range of tightness or looseness resulting from the allowances and tolerances in mating parts. The loosest fit, or maximum clearance, occurs when the smallest internal part (shaft) is in the largest external part (hole), as shown in Figure 10a. The tightest fit, or minimum clearance, occurs when the largest shaft is in the smallest hole, as shown in Figure 10b. The difference between the largest allowable shaft size and the smallest allowable hole size (0.002" in this case) is called the **allowance**. There are three general types of fits between parts:

Clearance Fit **Clearance fit** occurs when an internal part fits into an external part with space (or clearance) between the parts. In Figure 11 the largest shaft is 1.248" and the smallest hole is 1.250", giving a minimum space (allowance) of .002" between the

parts. In a clearance fit the allowance is always positive.

Interference Fit An **interference fit** occurs when the internal part is larger than the external part, so the parts must be forced together. In Figure 12 the smallest shaft is 1.2513" and the largest hole is 1.2506", so the interference of metal between parts is at least .00070". For the largest shaft and smallest hole, the interference is 0.0019". In an interference fit the allowance is always negative.

Transition Fit A **transition fit** refers to either a tight clearance or interference. In Figure 13 the smallest shaft, 1.2503" will fit into the largest hole, 1.2506". But the largest shaft, 1.2509", will have to be forced into the smallest hole, 1.2500".

Line fit is sometimes used to indicate limits that are specified so that a clearance or surface contact results when mating parts are assembled.

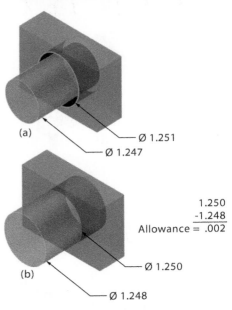

10   (a) Loosest and (b) Tightest Fit

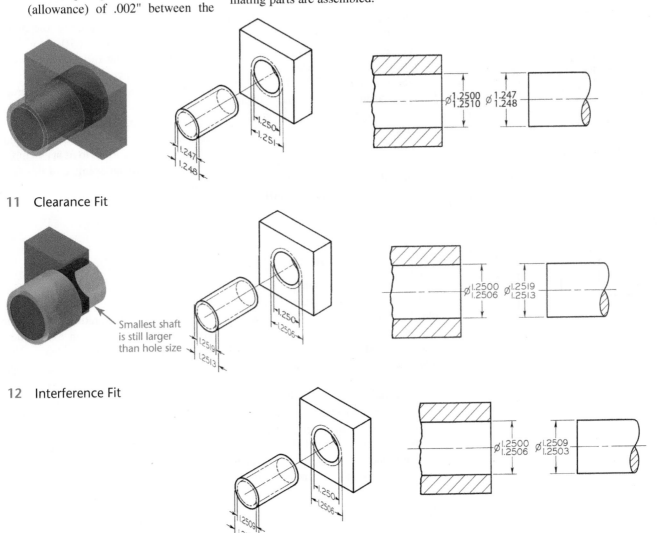

11   Clearance Fit

12   Interference Fit

13   Transition Fit

467

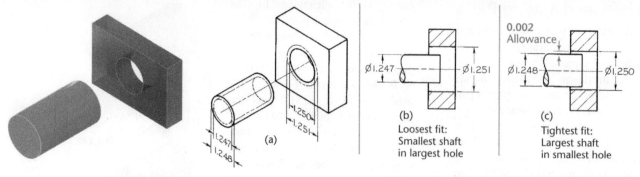

Shaft tolerance = 1.248 – 1.247 = 0.001   Allowance = 1.250 – 1.248 = 0.002

Hole tolerance = 1.251 – 1.250 = 0.001   Max clearance = 1.251 – 1.247 = 0.004

(b) Loosest fit: Smallest shaft in largest hole

(c) Tightest fit: Largest shaft in smallest hole

14 Specifying Fit through Limit Dimensions

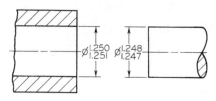

(a) Limit dimensions

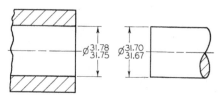

(b) Limit dimensions, metric

15   Fits between Mating Parts

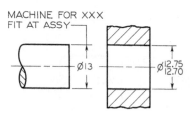

16   Noninterchangeable Fit

Specifying Fit Using Limit Dimensions

Limit dimensions are a method of directly specifying tolerance by providing dimensions for the upper and lower limits of the feature's size.

In the example shown in Figure 14, the actual hole may not be less than 1.250" and not more than 1.251". These are the limits for the dimension, and the difference between them (.001") is the tolerance as is indicated in Figure 15a.

Likewise, the shaft must be between limits 1.248" and 1.247". The difference between these limits is .001" so the tolerance for the shaft is .001". The minimum clearance is .002", so any shaft will fit inside any hole interchangeably.

In metric dimensions, the limits for the hole are 31.75 mm and 31.78 mm. Their difference, 0.03 mm, is the tolerance (Figure 15b). Similarly, the limits for the shaft are 31.70 mm and 31.67 mm, and the difference between them, the tolerance, is 0.03 mm.

When parts are required to fit properly in assembly but are not required to be interchangeable, they are not always toleranced, but it is indicated on the drawing that they are to be made to fit at assembly. Figure 16 shows an example of this type of note.

Selective Assembly

If allowances and tolerances are specified properly, mating parts are completely interchangeable, but for close fits, it is necessary to specify very small allowances and tolerances. The cost of manufacturing parts to such precision may be very high.

To avoid this expense, either manual or computer-controlled selective assembly is often used. In **selective assembly,** all parts are inspected and classified into several grades according to actual sizes, so that "small" shafts can be matched with "small" holes, "medium" shafts with "medium" holes, and so on. Figure 17 shows varation among the sizes of mating parts at an exaggerated size to illustrate the general idea.

Using selective assembly, acceptable fits may be obtained at less expense than by machining all mating parts to highly accurate dimensions. This method is often effective when using transition fits, since either clearance or interference is allowed.

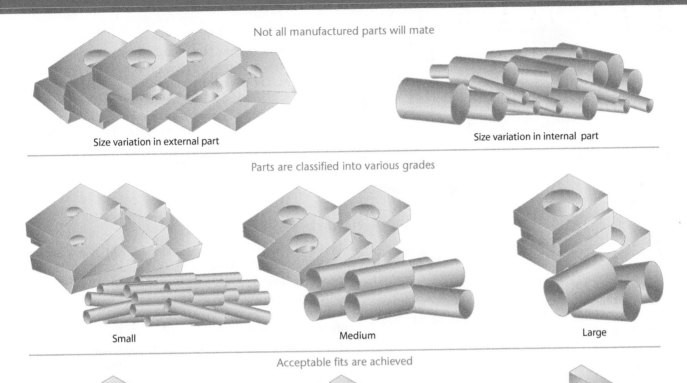

Not all manufactured parts will mate

Size variation in external part

Size variation in internal part

Parts are classified into various grades

Small   Medium   Large

Acceptable fits are achieved

17   Selective Assembly. Difference between the sizes of mating parts is exaggerated for visibility.

Definitions for Size Designation

You should become familiar with the definitions of size designation terms that apply in tolerancing (ANSI/ASME Y14.5M-1994).

Nominal size   **Nominal size** is used for general identification and is usually expressed in decimals or less often common fractions. In Figure 11 the nominal size of both hole and shaft, which is 1-1/4", would be 1.25 inches or 31.75 mm.

Basic size   **Basic size** is the size from which limits of size are determined by applying allowances and tolerances. It is the size from which limits are determined for the size of a feature.

Actual size   **Actual size** is the measured size of the finished part.

Allowance   **Allowance** is the minimum clearance space (or maximum interference) that is specified to achieve a fit between two mating parts. In Figure 18, the allowance is the difference between the size of the smallest hole, 1.250", and the size of the largest shaft, 1.248"—or .002". Allowance represents the tightest permissible fit. For clearance fits this difference will be positive, but for interference fits it will be negative.

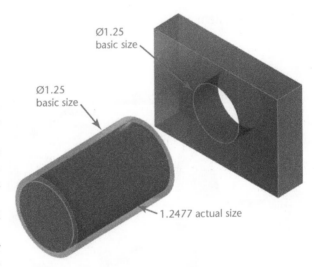

Ø1.25 basic size

Ø1.25 basic size

1.2477 actual size

18   Nominal Size, Basic Dimension, Actual Size, Allowance

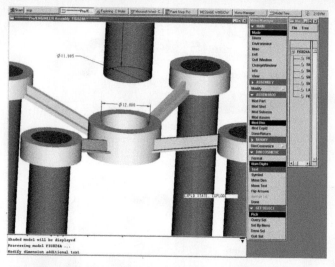

19 Tolerances are usually based on the hole size since holes are usually formed using standard tool sizes. *Reprinted by permission of Pearson Education, Inc., Upper Saddle River, NJ.*

Basic Hole System

Reamers, broaches, and other standard tools are often used to produce holes, and standard plug gages are used to check the actual sizes. On the other hand, shafts are easily machined down to any size desired. Therefore, toleranced dimensions are commonly determined using the **basic hole system,** in which the minimum hole is taken as the basic size. Then the allowance is determined, and tolerances are applied. Figure 19 shows a CAD model where several shafts assemble into different holes. Figure 20 shows the fit between two parts sized based on the hole diameter.

Basic Shaft System

In some industries, such as textile machinery manufacturing, which use a great deal of cold-finished shafting, the **basic shaft system** is used. It is advantageous when several parts having different fits are required on a single shaft like in Figure 21, or when the shaft for some reason can't be machined to size easily. This system should be used only when there is a reason for it. In this system, the maximum shaft is taken as the basic size, an allowance for each mating part is assigned, and tolerances are applied.

In Figure 22, the maximum size of the shaft, .500", is the basic size. For a clearance fit, an allowance of .002" is decided upon, giving the minimum hole size of .502". Tolerances of .003" and .001", respectively, are applied to the hole and the shaft to obtain the maximum hole, .505", and the minimum shaft, .499". The minimum clearance is the difference between the smallest hole and the largest shaft, and the maximum clearance is the difference between the largest hole and the smallest shaft.

In the case of an interference fit, the minimum hole size would be found by subtracting the desired allowance from the basic shaft size.

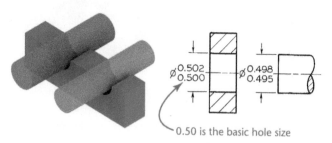

20 Basic Hole System

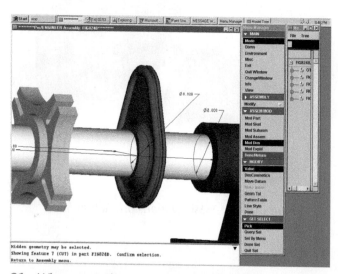

21 When several parts fit to a single shaft, tolerances may be based on the shaft size. *Reprinted by permission of Pearson Education, Inc., Upper Saddle River, NJ.*

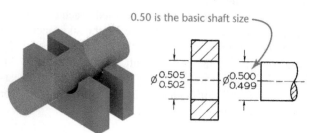

22 Basic Shaft System

USING THE BASIC HOLE SYSTEM

1 Determine where mating parts fit. Since the hole will be machined with a standard-size tool, its size will be used to determine the fit. In the figure shown, the minimum size of the hole, .500", is used as the basic size.

2 Determine the type of fit and apply the allowance to the basic size. For a clearance fit, an allowance of .002" is subtracted from the basic hole size, making the maximum shaft size .498" since it is easier to machine the shaft down to a smaller size than to apply the allowance to the hole.

3 Apply the tolerance. Tolerances of .002" and .003", respectively, are applied to the hole and the shaft to obtain the maximum hole of .502" and the minimum shaft of .495". Thus, the minimum clearance is the difference between the smallest hole and the largest shaft, and the maximum clearance is the difference between the largest hole and the smallest shaft.

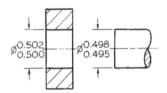

Basic hole fit

STEP by STEP

Interference Fit

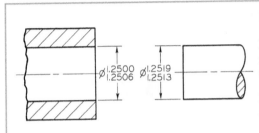

In the case of an interference fit, the maximum shaft size would be found by adding the desired allowance (the maximum interference) to the basic hole size.

In the figure at left, the basic size is 1.2500". The maximum interference decided upon was .0019", which when added to the basic size gives 1.2519", the largest shaft size.

MANUFACTURING TO ONE MILLIONTH OF AN INCH

Gage blocks, used for inspection and calibration, must be manufactured to extremely precise tolerances.

Gage blocks, also known as "Jo blocks" are made from steel, chrome, or ceramic and lapped and honed to accuracies of even just a few millionths of an inch (0.0000254 mm). These precise blocks are used in calibration and inspection. They are often used with a sine bar to precisely measure angles. Using the equation sine Angle = Height/ Distance and knowing the fixed distance of the sine bar and the precise height by raising one end of the sine bar on a gage block or stack of gage blocks, you can find precise angles. The angle is typically known and the height of the gage blocks is calculated from the equation. Often tables are used to quickly look up the needed height to produce the required angle for setting up a machine.

Gage blocks are finished so precisely (flatness of around 1 microinch) that they "ring" when slowly slid together and aligned. These blocks are not magnetic. There is some debate as to the exact combination of air pressure, surface tension from the light film of oil or water vapor on the gage blocks, and the interchange of electrons between the atoms of the surfaces of the two blocks being so close together creating an attractive molecular force that hold the blocks together.

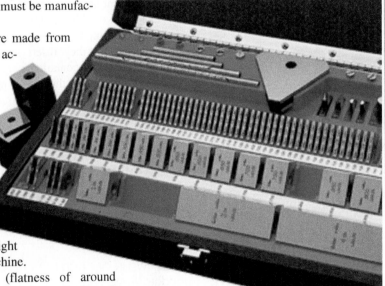

Set of Starrett-Weber gage blocks.
Courtesy of L.S. Starrett Company.

1 SPECIFYING TOLERANCES

Every dimension on a drawing should have a tolerance, either direct or by a tolerance note. The primary ways to indicate tolerances in a drawing are

- a general tolerance note;
- a note providing a tolerance for a specific dimension;
- a reference on the drawing to another document that specifies the required tolerances;
- adding limit tolerances to dimensions;
- adding direct plus/minus tolerances to dimensions;
- geometric tolerances.

Many of these tolerancing methods can be used in combination with one another in the same drawing.

23 General Tolerance Notes

2 GENERAL TOLERANCE NOTES

General notes are usually located in the lower right corner of the drawing sheet near the title block. Often **general tolerance notes** are included in the title block itself. For example, a general tolerance note might state,

"ALL TOLERANCES ±1 MM
UNLESS OTHERWISE NOTED.
ANGLES ±1 DEGREE."

This indicates that for a dimension value written as 25, for example, any measurement between 24 and 26 on the actual part would be acceptable.

Many companies have standard title blocks that they insert into CAD drawing files that contain general tolerancing standards for the type of production that is common to their industry. Figure 23 shows an example of a general tolerance note.

Another way general tolerances are stated is with a table on or near the title block indicating the tolerance by the number of digits used in the dimension as shown in Figure 24. For example:

DIGITS	TOLERANCE
.X	±.2 INCH
.XX	±.02 INCH
.XXX	±.001 INCH
X°	±.1°

This type of table indicates that single-place decimal dimensions have a tolerance of ±.2. For example, a dimension value written as 3.5 could range anywhere from 3.3 to 3.7 on the actual part and still be acceptable. A dimension written as 3.55 could range from 3.53 to 3.57 on the actual part. And a value written as 3.558 could range from 3.557 to 3.559 and be acceptable. It is uncommon to see more than three decimal places listed for inch drawings because precisions of ±.0001 are very high precision manufacturing and would be unlikely to be indicated merely by a general tolerance note.

24 General Tolerance in Title Block. *Courtesy of Dynojet Research, Inc.*

3 LIMIT TOLERANCES

Limit tolerances state the upper and lower limits for the dimension range in place of the dimension values as shown in Figure 25. Figure 26 shows examples of limit tolerances in a drawing. The upper value is always placed above the lower value or, if the two values are written horizontally, to the left of the lower value separated by a dash, as in 32–29.

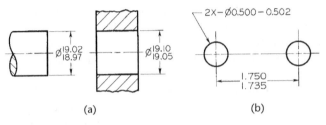

(a)   (b)

25   Method of Giving Limits

Single-Limit Dimensioning

It is not always necessary to specify both limits using a single-limit tolerance. The note MIN or MAX is placed after a number to indicate minimum or maximum dimensions desired where other elements of design determine the other unspecified limit. For example, a thread length may be dimensioned as MIN-FULLTHD or a radius dimensioned as R .05 MAX. Other applications include depths of holes and chamfers.

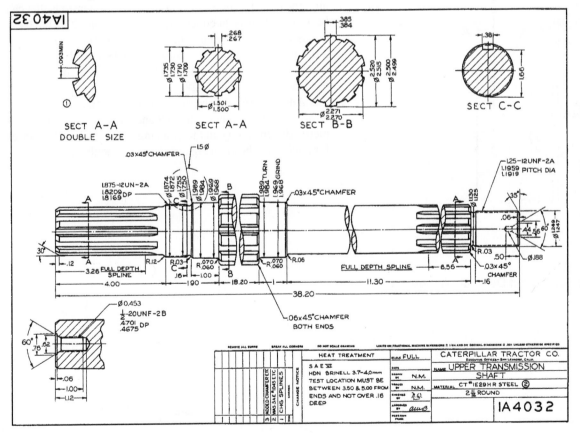

26   Limit Dimensions

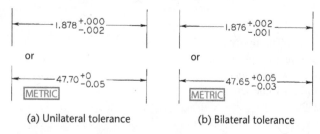

(a) Unilateral tolerance   (b) Bilateral tolerance

27 Tolerance Expression

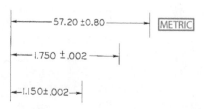

28 Bilateral Tolerances

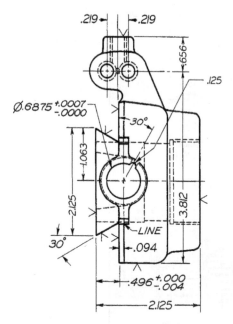

29 Plus/Minus Toleranced Decimal Dimensions

4 PLUS-OR-MINUS TOLERANCES

In this method the basic size is followed by a plus-or-minus expression for the tolerance (Figure 27). The result can be:

- Unilateral where the tolerance applies in only one direction so that one value is zero; or,
- Bilateral where either the same or different values are added and subtracted.

If two unequal tolerance numbers are given—one plus and one minus—the plus is placed above the minus. One of the numbers may be zero. If the plus value and minus value are the same, a single value is given, preceded by the plus-or-minus symbol (±) as shown in Figure 28.

The **unilateral system** of tolerances allows variations in only one direction from the basic size. This method is advantageous when a critical size is approached as material is removed during manufacture, as in the case of close-fitting holes and shafts. In Figure 27a the basic size is 1.878" (47.70 mm). The tolerance of .002" (0.05 mm) is all in one direction—toward the smaller size. If the dimension is for a shaft diameter, the basic size of 1.878" (47.70 mm) is nearer the critical size, so the tolerance is taken away from the critical size. A unilateral tolerance is always all plus or all minus, but the zeros for the other tolerance value should be shown as in Figure 27a.

The **bilateral system** of tolerances allows variations in both directions from the basic size. Bilateral tolerances are usually given for location dimensions or any dimensions that can be allowed to vary in either direction. In Figure 27b, the basic size is 1.876" (47.65 mm), and the actual size may be larger by .002" (0.05 mm) or smaller by .001" (0.03 mm). If equal variation in both directions is allowed, the plus-or-minus symbol is used, as shown in Figure 28.

Angular tolerances are usually bilateral and given in terms of degrees, minutes, and seconds (Figure 29), unless geometric dimensioning and tolerancing is used. Limit tolerances for angles, as shown in 30b, are less commonly used.

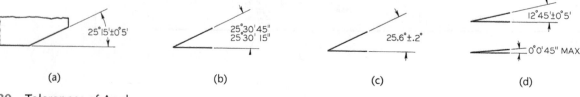

(a)   (b)   (c)   (d)

30 Tolerances of Angles

5 TOLERANCE STACKING

It is very important to consider the effect of one tolerance on another. When the location of a surface is affected by more than one tolerance value, the tolerances are cumulative. In some cases, for functional reasons, it may be desirable to define dimensions such as X, Y, and Z shown in Figure 31a chain fashion, without regard to the overall width of the part. This allows the tolerance to accumulate or "stack up." If the overall width dimension is shown in Figure 31a, the part is controlled in too many different ways—it is over-dimensioned. In such cases, if it is shown, the overall dimension should be a **reference dimension** placed inside parentheses to indicate that it is for reference only.

In other cases it may be desired to hold two dimensions (such as X and Y in Figure 31a), and the overall width of the part closely by giving the overall width dimension. In that case, a dimension such as Z shown in Figure 31a should be omitted or given as a reference dimension only. As a rule, it is best to dimension each surface so that it is affected by only one dimension. This can be done by referring all dimensions to a single datum surface, such as B, as shown in Figure 31b.

Chained or Continuous Dimensioning

When dimensions are specified as a chain, the tolerances for the part may add up. A **chained dimension** uses the end of one dimension as the beginning of the next. **Tolerance stacking** refers to the way the tolerance for one dimension is added to the next dimension in the chain and so on from one feature to the next, resulting in a large variation in the location of the last feature in the chain. Figure 31a illustrates this effect on a part where the surface labeled A is dimensioned chain fashion. Consider the location of the right end surface relative to the left-hand surface of the part. When features X, Y, and Z are at their maximum size the surface at the right end of the part can vary within a .015 wide zone. Tolerance stacking is not necessarily bad, if that is the intent for the relative locations of the features. You should be aware of the effect that tolerance has on chained dimensions and specify the tolerances this way when you want the tolerance to accumulate.

Baseline Dimensioning

Baseline dimensioning locates a series of features from a common base feature. Tolerances do not stack up because dimensions are not based on other, toleranced dimensions. Figure 31b illustrates how the same part in Figure 31a could be dimensioned using baseline dimensioning. Baseline dimensioning can make it easy to inspect the part because features are measured from a common base feature. Dimensioning from a zero point as the base feature can also be a useful technique for dimensioning parts for NC machining.

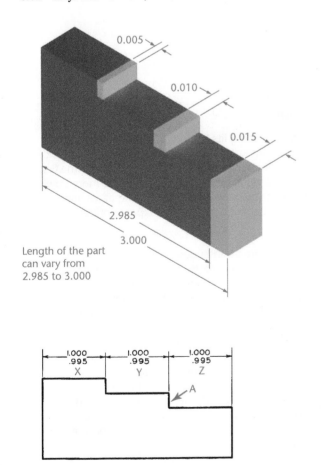

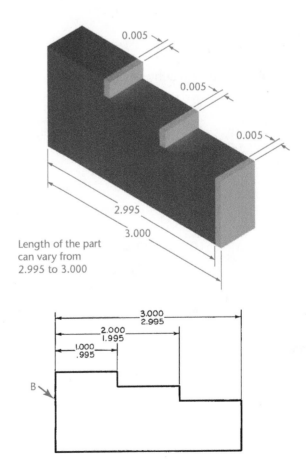

31 Cumulative versus Baseline Tolerances

6 USING AMERICAN NATIONAL STANDARD LIMITS AND FIT TABLES

The American National Standards Institute has issued ANSI B4.1-1967 (R1994), "Preferred Limits and Fits for Cylindrical Parts," defining terms and recommending preferred standard sizes, allowances, tolerances, and fits in terms of the decimal inch. This standard gives a series of standard classes of fits on a unilateral-hole basis so that the fit produced by mating parts of a class of fit will produce approximately similar performance throughout the range of sizes. These tables give standard allowances for any given size or type of fit; they also prescribe the standard limits for the mating parts that will produce the fit.

The tables are designed for the basic hole system.

Table 1 gives the three general types of fits, the five subtypes, their letter symbols, and descriptions.

In the fit tables for each class of fit, the range of nominal sizes of shafts or holes is given in inches. To simplify the tables and reduce the space required to present them, the other values are given in thousandths of an inch as in the example shown in Figure 32. Minimum and maximum limits of clearance are given; the top number is the least clearance, or the allowance, and the lower number the maximum clearance, or loosest fit. Then, under the heading "Standard Limits," are the limits for the hole and for the shaft that are to be applied to the basic size to obtain the limits of size for the parts, using the basic hole system.

| Nominal Size Range, inches | | Class RC 8 | | |
| Over | To | Limits of Clearance | Standard Limits | |
			Hole H10	Shaft c9
0–0.12		2.5 5.1	11.6 20	22.5 23.5
0.12–0.24		2.8 5.8	11.8 20	22.8 24.0
0.24–0.40		3.0 6.6	12.2 20	23.0 24.4
0.40–0.71		3.5 7.9	12.8 20	23.5 25.1
0.71–1.19		4.5 10.0	13.5 20	24.5 26.5
1.19–1.97		5.0 11.5	14.0 20	25.0 27.5
1.97–3.15		6.0 13.5	14.5 20	26.0 29.0

Values in inches

Values in thousandths

32 Portion of RC8 Fit Table. The International Standards Organization (ISO) publishes a similar series of fit tables for metric values.

Table 1 General Fit Types and Subtypes.

Fit Type	Symbol	Subtype	Description
Clearance	RC	Running or sliding fits	Running and sliding fits are intended to provide a similar running performance, with suitable lubrication allowance, throughout the range of sizes. The clearances for the first two classes, used chiefly as slide fits, increase more slowly with diameter than the other classes, so that accurate location is maintained even at the expense of free relative motion.
Locational	LC	Clearance fits	Locational fits are fits intended to determine only the location of the mating parts; they may provide rigid or accurate location, as with interference fits, or provide some freedom of location, as with clearance fits. Accordingly, they are divided into three groups: clearance fits, transition fits, and interference fits.
	LT	Transition clearance or interference fits	
	LN	Locational interference fits	
Interference	FN	Force or shrink fits	Force or shrink fits constitute a special type of interference fit, normally characterized by the maintenance of constant bore pressures throughout the range of sizes. The interference therefore varies almost directly with diameter and the difference between its minimum and maximum value is small in order to maintain the resulting pressures within reasonable limits.

Milling machines can produce parts within tolerances of .5 mm, or a few thousandths of an inch. *Courtesy of Ron Sherman/Creative Eye/MIRA.com*

7 TOLERANCES AND MACHINING PROCESSES

Tolerances should be as generous as possible and still permit satisfactory use of the part. The tighter the tolerance, the more expensive it is to manufacture the part. Great savings can be gained from the use of less expensive tools, from lower labor and inspection costs, and from reduced scrapping of material.

Table 2 is a chart to be used as a general guide, with the tolerances achievable by the indicated machining processes. You can convert these to metric values by multiplying by 25.4 and rounding to one less decimal place.

Table 2 Tolerances Related to Machining Processes.

Range of Sizes From	To and Including	Tolerances								
.000	.599	.00015	.0002	.0003	.0005	.0008	.0012	.002	.003	.005
.600	.999	.00015	.00025	.0004	.0006	.001	.0015	.0025	.004	.006
1.000	1.499	.0002	.0003	.0005	.0008	.0012	.002	.003	.005	.008
1.500	2.799	.00025	.0004	.0006	.001	.0015	.0025	.004	.006	.010
2.800	4.499	.0003	.0005	.0008	.0012	.002	.003	.005	.008	.012
4.500	7.799	.0004	.0006	.001	.0015	.0025	.004	.006	.010	.015
7.800	13.599	.0005	.0008	.0012	.002	.003	.005	.008	.012	.020
13.600	20.999	.0006	.001	.0015	.0025	.004	.006	.010	.015	.025

Process									
Lapping and Honing	▓	▓	▓						
Grinding, Diamond Turning, and Boring	▓	▓	▓						
Broaching		▓	▓						
Reaming			▓	▓					
Turning, Boring, Slotting, Planing, and Shaping					▓	▓			
Milling						▓	▓		
Drilling							▓	▓	

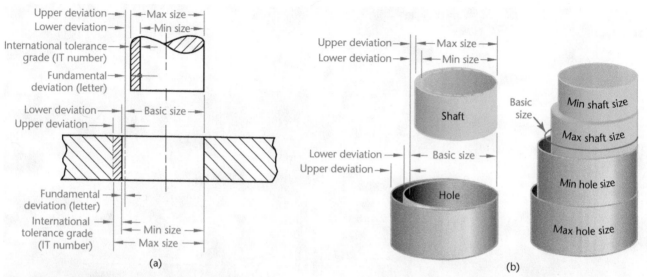

(a)

(b)

33 Terms Related to Metric Limits and Fits. *Reprinted from B4.2-1978, by permission of The American Society of Mechanical Engineers. All rights reserved.*

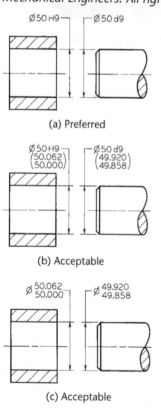

(a) Preferred

(b) Acceptable

(c) Acceptable

34 Specifying Tolerances with Symbols for Mating Parts

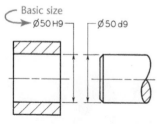

35 Specifying Tolerances with Symbols for Mating Parts

8 METRIC SYSTEM OF TOLERANCES AND FITS

The preceding material on limits and fits between mating parts applies for both systems of measurement. A system of preferred metric limits and fits by the International Organization for Standardization (ISO) is in the ANSI B4.2 standard. The system is specified for holes, cylinders, and shafts, but it is also adaptable to fits between parallel surfaces of such features as keys and slots. The following terms for metric fits, shown in Figure 33a, are somewhat similar to those for decimal inch fits:

Basic size **Basic size** is the size from which limits or deviations are assigned. Basic sizes, usually diameters, should be selected from a table of preferred sizes, as shown in Table 3. Figure 34 shows examples of preferred and accceptable methods of specifying tolerances on a drawing.

Deviation The **deviation** is the difference between the basic size and the hole or shaft size. This is equivalent to the tolerance in the decimal inch system.

Upper deviation The **upper deviation** is the difference between the basic size and the permitted maximum size of the part. This is comparable to the maximum tolerance in the decimal inch system.

Lower deviation The **lower deviation** is the difference between the basic size and the minimum permitted size of the part. This is comparable to the minimum tolerance in the decimal inch system.

Fundamental deviation The **fundamental deviation** is the deviation closest to the basic size. This is comparable to the minimum allowance in the decimal inch system.

Tolerance The **tolerance** is the difference between the permitted minimum and maximum sizes of a part.

International tolerance grade The **international tolerance grade (IT)** is a set of tolerances that varies according to the basic size and provides a uniform level of accuracy within the grade. For example, in the dimension 50H9 for a close-running fit in Figure 35, the IT grade is indicated by the numeral 9. (The letter H indicates that the tolerance is on the hole for the 50 mm dimension.) In all, there are 18 IT grades—IT01, IT0, and IT1 through IT16 (see Figures 36 and 37)—for IT grades related to machining processes and for the practical use of the IT grades.

Tolerance zone The **tolerance zone** refers to the relationship of the tolerance to basic size. It is established by a combination of the fundamental deviation indicated by a letter and the IT grade number. In the dimension 50H8, for the close-running fit, the H8 specifies the tolerance zone, as shown in Figure 38.

Basic hole system The **basic hole system** of preferred fits uses the basic diameter as the minimum size. For the generally preferred hole-basis system, shown in Figure 38a, the

	IT Grades							
	4	5	6	7	8	9	10	11
Lapping & Honing	▓	▓						
Cylindrical grinding		▓	▓	▓				
Surface grinding		▓	▓	▓	▓			
Diamond turning		▓	▓	▓				
Diamond boring		▓	▓	▓				
Broaching		▓	▓	▓	▓			
Powder metal-sizes			▓	▓				
Reaming				▓	▓	▓	▓	
Turning				▓	▓	▓	▓	▓
Powder metal-sintered				▓	▓			
Boring					▓	▓	▓	▓
Milling						▓	▓	▓
Planing & Shaping							▓	▓
Punching						▓	▓	▓
Die casting							▓	▓

36 International Tolerance Grades Related to Machining Processes. *Reprinted from B4.2-1978, by permission of The American Society of Mechanical Engineers. All rights reserved.*

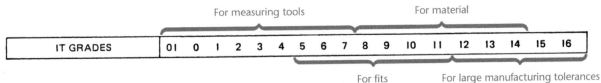

		For measuring tools									For material					
IT GRADES	01	0	1	2	3	4	5	6	7	8	9	10	11	12	13	14	15	16

For fits   For large manufacturing tolerances

37 Practical Use of the International Tolerance Grades

fundamental deviation is specified by the uppercase letter H.

Basic shaft system The basic shaft system of preferred fits is a system in which the basic diameter is the maximum size of the shaft. The fundamental deviation is given by the lowercase letter f, as shown in Figure 38b.

Interference fit An interference fit results in an interference between two mating parts under all tolerance conditions.

Transition fit A transition fit results in either a clearance or an interference condition between two assembled parts.

Tolerance symbols **Tolerance symbols** are used to specify the tolerances and fits for mating parts, as shown in Figure 38c. For the hole-basis system, the 50 indicates the diameter in millimeters, the capital letter H indicates the fundamental deviation for the hole, and the lowercase letter f indicates the deviation for the shaft. The numbers following the letters indicate the IT grade. Note that the symbols for the hole and shaft are separated by a slash. Tolerance symbols for a 50-mm-diameter hole may be given in several acceptable forms, as shown in Figure 39. The values in parentheses are for reference only and may be omitted.

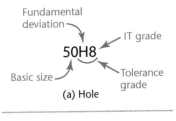

(a) Hole

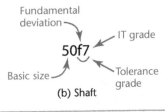

(b) Shaft

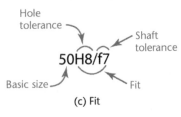

(c) Fit

38 Applications of Definitions and Symbols to Holes and Shafts. *Reprinted from B4.2-1978, by permission of The American Society of Mechanical Engineers. All rights reserved.*

39 Acceptable Methods of Giving Tolerance Symbols. *Reprinted from Y14.5M-1994, by permission of The American Society of Mechanical Engineers. All rights reserved.*

9 PREFERRED SIZES

The preferred basic sizes for computing tolerances are given in Table 3. Basic diameters should be selected from the first choice column since these are readily available stock sizes for round, square, and hexagonal products.

10 PREFERRED FITS

The symbols for either the hole-basis or shaft-basis preferred fits (clearance, transition, and interference) are given in Table 4. Fits should be selected from this table for mating parts where possible.

Although second- and third-choice basic size diameters are possible, they must be calculated from tables not included in this text. For the generally preferred hole-basis system, note that the ISO symbols range from H11/c11 (loose running) to H7/u6 (force fit). For the shaft-basis system, the preferred symbols range from C11/h11 (loose fit) to U7/h6 (force fit).

Suppose that you want to use the symbols to specify the dimensions for a free running (hole-basis) fit for a proposed diameter of 48 mm. Since 48 mm is not listed as a preferred size in Table 3, the design is altered to use the acceptable 50-mm diameter. From the preferred fit descriptions in Table 4, the free-running (hole-basis) fit is H9/d9. To determine the upper and lower deviation limits of the hole as given in the preferred hole-basis table follow across from the basic size of 50 to H9 under "Free Running." The limits for the hole are 50.000 and 50.062 mm. Then the upper and lower limits of deviation for the shaft are found in the d9 column under "Free Running." They are 49.920 and 49.858 mm, respectively. Limits for other fits are established in a similar way.

Limits for the shaft-basis dimensioning are determined similarly from the preferred shaft-basis table. Refer back to Figures 34 and 39 for acceptable methods of specifying tolerances by symbols on drawings. A single note for the mating parts (free running fit, hole basis) would be H9/d9, as was shown in Figure 34.

Table 3 Preferred Sizes. *Reprinted from B4.2-1978, by permission of The American Society of Mechanical Engineers. All rights reserved.*

Basic Size, mm		Basic Size, mm		Basic Size, mm	
First Choice	Second Choice	First Choice	Second Choice	First Choice	Second Choice
1		10		100	
	1.1		11		110
1.2		12		120	
	1.4		14		140
1.6		16		160	
	1.8		18		180
2		20		200	
	2.2		22		220
2.5		25		250	
	2.8		28		280
3		30		300	
	3.5		35		350
4		40		400	
	4.5		45		450
5		50		500	
	5.5		55		550
6		60		600	
	7		70		700
8		80		800	
	9		90		900
				1000	

11 GEOMETRIC DIMENSIONING AND TOLERANCING

Geometric tolerances state the maximum allowable variations of a form or its position from the perfect geometry implied on the drawing. The term "geometric" refers to various forms, such as a plane, a cylinder, a cone, a square, or a hexagon. Theoretically, these are perfect forms, but because it is impossible to produce perfect forms, it may be necessary to specify the amount of variation permitted. Geometric tolerances specify either the diameter or the width of a tolerance zone within which a surface or the axis of a cylinder or a hole must be if the part is to meet the required accuracy for proper function and fit. When tolerances of form are not given on a drawing, it is customary to assume that, regardless of form variations, the part will fit and function satisfactorily.

Tolerances of form and position (or location) control such characteristics as straightness, flatness, parallelism, perpendicularity (squareness), concentricity, roundness, angular displacement, and so on.

Methods of indicating geometric tolerances by means of geometric characteristic symbols, rather than by traditional notes, are recommended. See the latest Dimensioning and Tolerancing Standard, ANSI/ASME Y14.5M-1994, for more complete coverage.

Table 4 Preferred Fits. *Reprinted from B4.2-1978, by permission of The American Society of Mechanical Engineers. All rights reserved.*

ISO Symbol				
	Hole Basis	**Shaft Basis***	**Description**	
Clearance Fits	H11/c11	C11/h11	**Loose-running** fit for wide commercial tolerances or allowances on external members.	More Clearance →
	H9/d9	D9/h9	**Free-running** fit not for use where accuracy is essential, but good for large temperature variations, high running speeds, or heavy journal pressures.	
	H8/f7	F8/h7	**Close-running** fit for running on accurate machines and for accurate location at moderate speeds and journal pressures.	
Transition Fits	H7/g6	G7/h6	**Sliding** fit not intended to run freely, but to move and turn freely and locate accurately.	
	H7/h6	H7/h6	**Locational clearance** fit provides snug fit for locating stationary parts; but can be freely assembled and disassembled.	
	H7/k6	K7/h6	**Locational transition** fit for accurate location, a compromise between clearance and interference.	
	H7/n6	N7/h6	**Locational transition** fit for more accurate location where greater interference is permissible.	
Interference Fits	H7/p6	P7/h6	**Locational interference** fit for parts requiring rigidity and alignment with prime accuracy of location but without special bore pressure requirements.	← More interference
	H7/s6	S7/h6	**Medium drive** fit for ordinary steel parts or shrink fits on light sections, the tightest fit usable with cast iron.	
	H7/u6	U7/h6	**Force** fit suitable for parts that can be highly stressed or for shrink fits where the heavy pressing forces required are impractical.	

The transition and interference shaft-basis fits shown do not convert to exactly the same hole-basis fit conditions for basic sizes in the range from Q through 3 mm. Interference fit P7/h6 converts to a transition fit H7/p6 in the above size range.

12 SYMBOLS FOR TOLERANCES OF POSITION AND FORM

Since traditional notes for specifying tolerances of position (location) and form (shape) may be confusing or unclear, may require too much space, and may not be understood internationally, most multinational companies have adopted symbols for such specifications (ANSI/ASME Y14.5M-1994). These ANSI symbols, shown in Table 5, provide an accurate and concise means of specifying **geometric characteristics** and tolerances in a minimum of space. A **feature control frame** specifies the tolerance for the geometric characteristic to be controlled and any modifying conditions that are required. The symbols may be supplemented by notes if the precise geometric requirements cannot be conveyed by the symbols.

Table 5 Geometric Characteristic and Modifying Symbols. *Reprinted from Y14.5M-1994, by permission of The American Society of Mechanical Engineers. All rights reserved.*

Geometric Characteristic Symbols				Modifying Symbols	
Type of Tolerance		**Characteristic**	**Symbol**	**Term**	**Symbol**
For individual features	Form	Straightness	—	At maximum material condition	Ⓜ
		Flatness	▱	At least material condition	Ⓛ
		Circularity (roundness)	○	Projected tolerance zone	Ⓟ
		Cylindricity	⌭	Free state	Ⓕ
For individual or related features	Profile	Profile of a line	⌒	Tangent plane	Ⓣ
		Profile of a surface	⌓	Diameter	⌀
For related features	Orientation	Angularity	∠	Spherical diameter	S⌀
		Perpendicularity	⊥	Radius	R
		Parallelism	//	Spherical radius	SR
	Location	Position	⊕	Controlled radius	CR
		Concentricity	◎	Reference	( )
	Runout	Symmetry	≡	Arc length	⌒
		Circular runout *	↗	Statistical tolerance	⟨ST⟩
		Total runout *	↗↗	Between *	↔

Arrowheads may be filled or not filled.

482

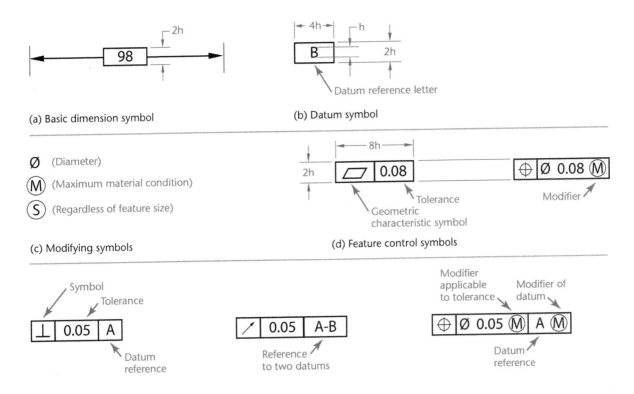

(a) Basic dimension symbol

(b) Datum symbol

(c) Modifying symbols

(d) Feature control symbols

(e) Feature control symbols with datum references

40 Use of Symbols for Tolerance of Position and Form. *Reprinted from Y14.5M-1994, by permission of The American Society of Mechanical Engineers. All rights reserved.*

Figure 40 shows combinations of the various symbols and their meanings. The geometric characteristic symbols and the supplementary symbols are explained below with material adapted from ANSI/ASME Y14.5M-1994:

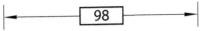

Basic dimension symbol The **basic dimension symbol** is identified by the enclosing frame symbol, as shown in Figure 40a. The basic dimension, or size, is the value used to describe the theoretically exact size, shape, or location of a feature. It is the basis from which permissible variations are established either by specifying tolerances on other dimensions, by tolerances given in notes, or by using feature control frames.

Datum identifying symbol The **datum identifying symbol** consists of a capital letter in a square frame and a leader line extending from the frame to the concerned feature and terminating with a triangle. The triangle may be filled or not filled. Letters of the alphabet (except I, O, and Q) are used as datum identifying letters.

Supplementary symbols **Supplementary symbols** include the symbols for MMC (**maximum material condition**—or minimum hole diameter, maximum shaft diameter) and LMC (least material condition—or maximum hole diameter, minimum shaft diameter), as shown in Figure 40c. The abbreviations MMC and LMC are also used in notes (see also Table 5).

When needed, the symbol for diameter precedes the specified tolerance in a feature control symbol, as shown in Figure 40d. This symbol for diameter should precede the dimension. For narrative notes, you can use the abbreviation DIA for diameter.

Combined symbols **Combined symbols** are found when individual symbols, datum reference letters, and needed tolerances are combined in a single frame, as shown in Figure 40e.

Form tolerance The **form tolerance** is given by a feature control symbol made up of a frame around the appropriate geometric characteristic symbol plus the allowable tolerance. A vertical line separates the symbol and the tolerance, as shown in Figure 40d. Where needed, the tolerance should be preceded by the symbol for the diameter and followed by the symbol for MMC or LMC.

Reference to a datum The **reference to a datum** is indicated in the feature control symbol by placing the datum reference letter after either the geometric characteristic symbol or the tolerance. Vertical lines separate the entries, and where applicable, the datum reference letter entry includes the symbol for MMC or LMC, as shown in Figure 40.

Figure 41 shows how geometric dimensioning and tolerance symbols are applied to a drawing. Understanding da-tum surfaces and features is important to the application of geometric dimensioning and tolerancing.

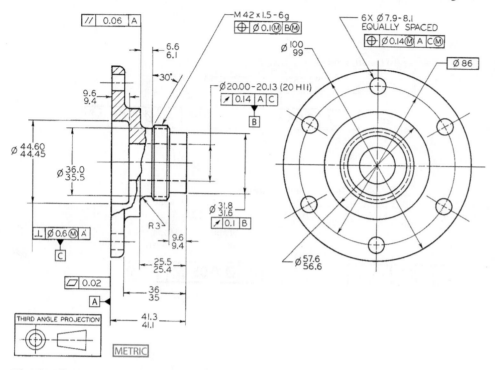

41 Application of Symbols to Position and Form Tolerance Dimensions. *Reprinted from Y14.5M-1994, by permission of The American Society of Mechanical Engineers. All rights reserved.*

13 DATUM SURFACES AND FEATURES

Datum surfaces and **datum features** are used as references to control other features on the part. For example, when defining the location of a hole, you can specify its distance from a datum surface on the part. Datums should be geometric features on the actual part, such as a point or a plane (or in special cases, an axis) as shown in Figure 42. Centerlines on drawings are not used as datums.

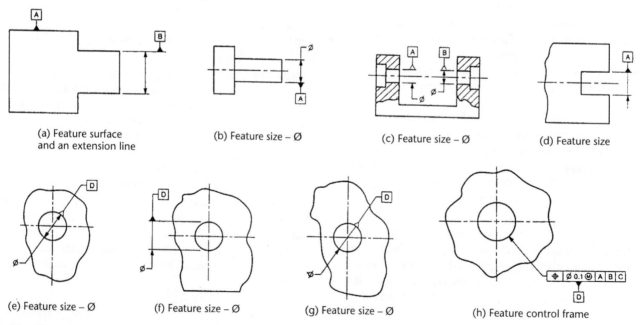

(a) Feature surface and an extension line

(b) Feature size – Ø

(c) Feature size – Ø

(d) Feature size

(e) Feature size – Ø

(f) Feature size – Ø

(g) Feature size – Ø

(h) Feature control frame

42 Placement of Datum Feature Symbol. *Reprinted from Y14.5M-1994, by permission of The American Society of Mechanical Engineers. All rights reserved.*

484

Three mutually perpendicular planes, referred to as the **datum reference frame,** are used to immobilize the part to be inspected and provide a way to make accurate measurements. Datum feature symbols on the drawing identify **primary datum surfaces, secondary datum surfaces,** and **tertiary datum surfaces** (meaning first, second, and third datum surfaces) to create a datum reference frame (Figure 43). Figure 44 shows the datum reference frame pictorially. Figure 45 shows the part oriented on the datum reference frame.

Datums are assumed to be exact, but of course this is not possible in the real world. To simulate the datum reference plane in real life, the person inspecting the part uses a fixture where the primary datum surface on the part makes contact with three points on the fixture. Once the primary datum plane is established, only two additional contact points are needed to establish the secondary datum plane. Once the primary and secondary planes are established, a single additional point will establish the tertiary datum plane. **Datum targets,** as shown in Figure 46a, can be added to drawings to specify where these points of contact should occur on the part.

You can find detailed information on datum targets and inspection methods in standard geometric dimensioning and tolerancing texts.

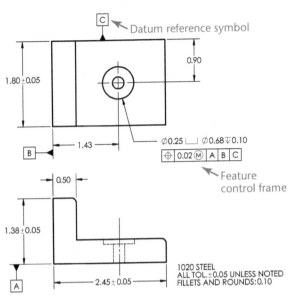

43 Datum reference symbols identify datum surfaces on a drawing.

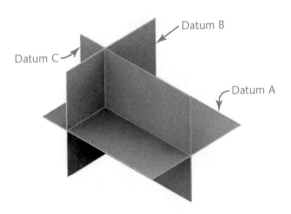

44 Datum Reference Frame

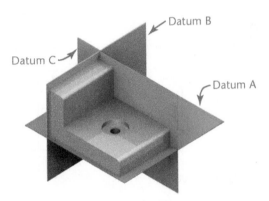

45 A Part Oriented on a Datum Reference Frame

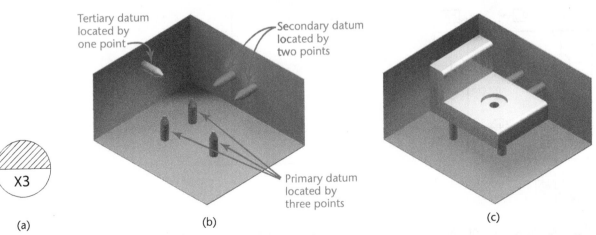

46 (a) Datum Target Symbol, (b) Establishing the Datum Reference Frame, (c) Part Immobilized on Datum Reference Frame

14 POSITIONAL TOLERANCES

Figure 47a shows a hole located from two surfaces at right angles to each other. The center may lie anywhere within a square tolerance zone, with sides equal to the tolerances. Using coordinate dimensioning, the total variation allowed along the diagonals of the square is 1.4 times the indicated tolerance. In contrast, when a circular area is used to specify the allowable variation for the center's location, 57% more parts measure acceptable.

If four holes are dimensioned with rectangular coordinates, as in Figure 48a, the tolerance describes a square zone in which the center of the hole must be located (Figure 48b and c). This square-shaped zone allows the center of the hole to vary more in the diagonal direction than the stated tolerance value.

In Figure 48a, hole A is located from the corner of the part, and the other three are located from A. The tolerances applied to the locations for hole A results in a square tolerance zone. The other three holes are located from the previous hole. Their tolerances produce square zones whose locations vary according to the actual location of hole A. Two of the many possible zone patterns are shown in Figure 48b and c.

With the dimensions shown in Figure 48a, the resulting parts may not fit with mating parts, even though they meet the drawing tolerances.

Tolerancing features based on their geometry can prevent these problems. Geometric tolerancing controls the shape of the tolerance zone using geometric characteristics in the feature control frame. This is also called **true-position dimensioning**. Using it, the tolerance zone for holes can be a circle, with the size of the circle depending on the variation permitted from true position as specified using a feature control frame.

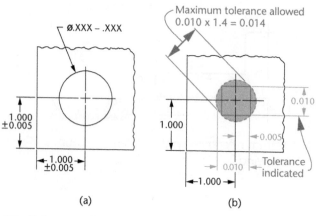

47 Tolerance Zones

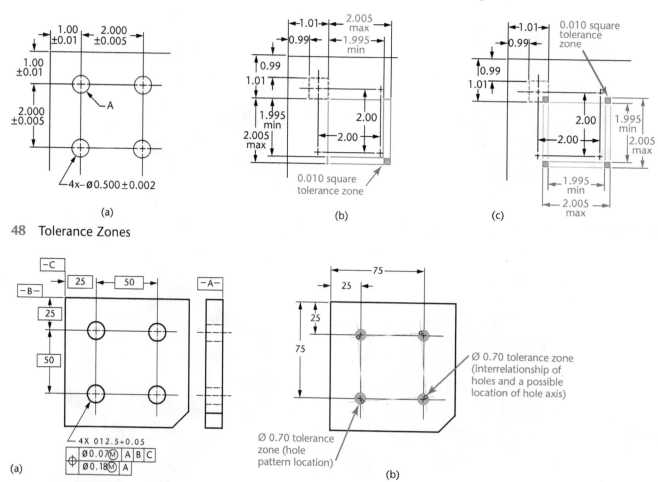

48 Tolerance Zones

49 True-Position Dimensioning. *Reprinted from Y14.5M-1994, by permission of The American Society of Mechanical Engineers. All rights reserved.*

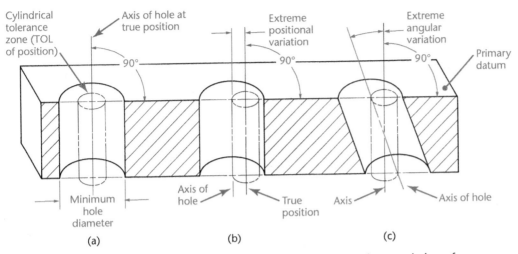

50 Cylindrical Tolerance Zone. *Reprinted from Y14.5M-1994, by permission of The American Society of Mechanical Engineers. All rights reserved.*

Methods for relating feature control symbols to the feature were shown in Figure 41. The following are preferred:

1. Add the symbol to a feature's note or dimension.
2. Run a leader from the symbol to the feature.
3. Attach the side, end, or corner of the symbol frame to an extension line from the feature.
4. Attach a side or end of the symbol frame to the dimension line pertaining to the feature.

A true-position dimension specifies the theoretically exact position of a feature. The location of each feature, such as a hole, slot, or stud, is given by untoleranced basic dimensions identified by an enclosing box. True position is usually established with respect to a datum.

A feature control frame for a positional tolerance describes a cylindrical tolerance zone with a diameter equal to the positional tolerance and a length equal to the length of the feature unless otherwise specified (Figure 49). The axis of the hole center must be within the cylindrical zone as shown in Figure 50.

The centerline of the hole may coincide with the centerline of the cylindrical tolerance zone (Figure 50a). It may be parallel to it but displaced so that it remains within the tolerance cylinder (Figure 50b). Or it may be inclined and remain within the tolerance cylinder (Figure 50c).

A positional tolerance specifies that all elements on the hole surface must be on or outside a cylinder whose diameter is equal to the minimum diameter or the maximum diameter of the hole minus the positional tolerance diameter, when the centerline of the cylinder is located at true position.

Special untoleranced basic dimensions locate features at true position, avoiding tolerance accumulation as shown in Figure 51.

Features such as slots may vary on either side of a true-position plane, as shown in Figure 52.

The exact locations of the true positions are given by untoleranced basic dimensions, ensuring that general tolerances are not applied to them. Add a note to the drawing, such as

GENERAL TOLERANCES DO NOT
APPLY TO BASIC DIMENSIONS.

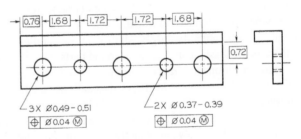

51 No Tolerance Accumulation

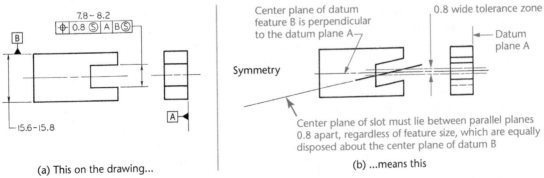

(a) This on the drawing...   (b) ...means this

52 Positional Tolerancing for Symmetry. *Reprinted from Y14.5M-1994, by permission of The American Society of Mechanical Engineers. All rights reserved.*

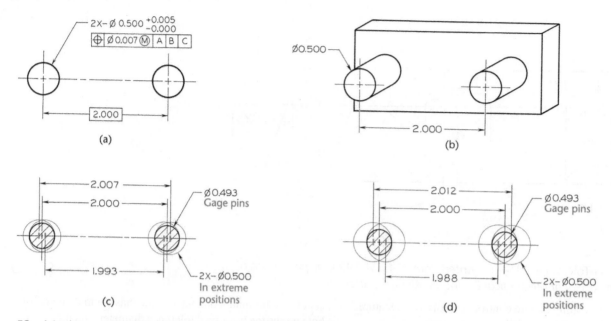

53 Maximum and Minimum Material Conditions—Two-Hole Pattern. *Reprinted from Y14.5M-1994, by permission of The American Society of Mechanical Engineers. All rights reserved.*

15 MAXIMUM MATERIAL CONDITION

Maximum material condition, or MMC, means that a feature of a finished product contains the maximum amount of material permitted by the toleranced dimensions shown for that feature. Holes, slots, or other internal features are at MMC when at minimum size. Shafts, pads, bosses, and other external features are at MMC when at their maximum size. A feature is at MMC for both mating parts when the largest shaft is in the smallest hole and there is the least clearance between the parts.

In assigning positional tolerance to a hole, consider the size limits of the hole. If the hole is at MMC, or its smallest size, the positional tolerance is not affected, but if the hole is larger, the available positional tolerance is greater. In Figure 53a, two half-inch holes are shown. If they are exactly .500" in diameter (MMC, or smallest size) and are exactly 2.000" apart, a gage made of two round pins .500" in diameter fixed in a plate 2.000" apart, as shown in Figure 53b, should fit into them. However, the center-to-center distance between the holes may vary from 1.993" to 2.007" as specified by the Ø.007 positional tolerance in the feature control frame in Figure 53a.

If the .500" diameter holes are at their extreme positions, as in Figure 53c, the pins in the gage would have to be .007" smaller, or .493" in diameter, to fit into the holes. If the .500" diameter holes are located at the maximum distance apart, the .493" diameter gage pins would contact the inner sides of the holes; and if the holes are located at the minimum distance apart,

the .493" diameter pins would contact the outer surfaces of the holes, as shown. If gage-maker's tolerances are not disregarded, the gage pins would have to be .493" in diameter and exactly 2.000" apart if the holes are .500" in diameter, or MMC.

If the holes are .505" in diameter—that is, at maximum size—the same .493" diameter gage pins at 2.000" apart will fit with the inner sides of the holes contacting the inner sides of the gage pins and the outer sides of the holes contacting the outer sides of the gage pins, as shown in Figure 53d. When the holes are larger, they may be further apart and still fit the pins. In this case they may be 2.012" apart, which is beyond the tolerance permitted for the center-to-center distance between the holes. Similarly, the holes may be as close together as 1.988" from center to center, which again is outside the specified positional tolerance.

So when holes are at maximum size, a greater positional tolerance becomes available. Since all features may vary in size, it is necessary to make clear on the drawing at what basic dimension the true position applies. In all but a few exceptional cases, when the holes are larger, the additional positional tolerance is available without affecting the function. They can still be freely assembled whether or not the holes or other features are within the specified positional tolerance. This practice has been recognized and used in manufacturing for years in designing fixed-pin gages, which are commonly used to inspect parts and control the least favorable condition of assembly. It has become common practice for both manufacturing and inspection to assume that positional tolerance applies to MMC and that greater positional tolerance becomes permissible when the part is not at MMC.

To avoid misinterpretation as to whether the maximum material condition (MMC) applies, it should be clearly stated on the drawing by adding MMC symbols to each applicable tolerance or by a document referenced on the drawing. When MMC is not specified on the drawing with respect to an individual tolerance, datum reference, or both, the following rules apply:

1. True-position tolerances and related datum references apply at maximum material condition (MMC). For a tolerance of position, regardless of feature size (RFS) may be specified on the drawing with respect to the individual tolerance, datum reference, or both, as applicable.

2. All applicable geometric tolerances—such as angularity, parallelism, perpendicularity, concentricity, and symmetry tolerances, including related datum references, apply regardless of feature size when no modifying symbol is specified. Circular runout, total runout, concentricity, and symmetry are applicable regardless of feature size and cannot be modified to maximum material condition or least material condition (LMC).

3. No element of the actual feature will extend beyond the envelope of the perfect form at maximum material condition. Maximum material condition or least material condition must be specified on the drawing where it is required.

16 TOLERANCES OF ANGLES

Bilateral tolerances have traditionally been given on angles, as shown in Figure 54. Using bilateral tolerances, the wedge-shaped tolerance zone increases as the distance from the vertex of the angle increases. The use of angular tolerances may be avoided by using gages. Taper turning is often handled by machining to fit a gage or by fitting to the mating part.

If an angular surface is located by a linear and an angular dimension, as shown in Figure 55a, the surface must lie within a tolerance zone, as shown in Figure 55b. The angular zone will be wider as the distance from the vertex increases. To avoid the accumulation of tolerance further out from the angle's vertex, the **basic angle tolerancing method,** shown in Figure 55c, is recommended (ASME Y14.5M-1994). The angle is indicated as a basic dimension, and no angular tolerance is specified. The tolerance zone is now defined by two parallel planes, resulting in improved angular control, as shown in Figure 55d.

Use specific controls such as angular geometric controls or a basic dimension to prevent general tolerances from applying to implied right angles.

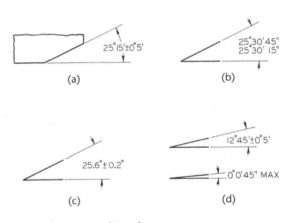

54 Tolerances of Angles

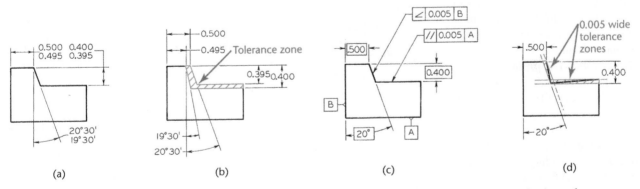

55 Angular Tolerance Zones. *Reprinted from Y14.5M-1994, by permission of The American Society of Mechanical Engineers. All rights reserved.*

17 FORM TOLERANCES FOR SINGLE FEATURES

Straightness, flatness, roundness, cylindricity, and in some instances, profile, are form tolerances that apply to single features regardless of feature size.

Straightness tolerance The **straightness tolerance** specifies a tolerance zone within which an axis or all points of the considered element must lie (Figure 56). Straightness is a condition in which an element of a surface or an axis is a straight line.

Flatness tolerance The **flatness tolerance** specifies a tolerance zone defined by two parallel planes within which the surface must lie (Figure 57). Flatness is the condition of a surface having all elements in one plane.

Roundness (circularity) tolerance The **roundness (circularity) tolerance** specifies a tolerance zone bounded by two concentric circles within which each circular element of the surface must lie (Figure 58). Roundness is a condition of a surface of revolution in which, for a cone or cylinder, all points of the surface intersected by any plane perpendicular to a common axis are equidistant from that axis. For a sphere, all points of the surface intersected by any plane passing through a common center are equidistant from that center.

Cylindricity tolerance The **cylindricity tolerance** specifies a tolerance zone bounded by two concentric cylinders within which the surface must lie (Figure 59). This tolerance applies to both circular and longitudinal elements of the entire surface. Cylindricity is a condition of a surface of revolution in which all points of the surface are equidistant from a common axis. When no tolerance of form is given, many possible shapes may exist within a tolerance zone (Figure 60).

Profile tolerance The **profile tolerance** specifies a uniform boundary or zone along the true profile within which all elements of the surface must lie (Figures 61 and 62). A profile is the outline of an object in a given plane, or 2D, figure. Profiles are formed by projecting a 3D figure onto a plane or by taking cross sections through the figure, with the resulting profile composed of elements such as straight lines, arcs, or other curves.

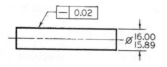

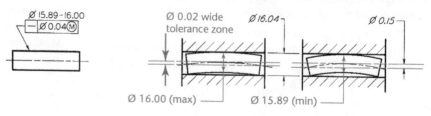

Each longitudinal element of the surface must be within the specified tolerance size of the perfect form at MMC and lie between two parallel lines (0.02 apart) where the two lines and the nominal axis share a common plane.

This on the drawing...   Means this

Each circular element of the figure must be within the specified tolerance size. The centerline of the feature must lie within a cylindrical tolerance zone of 0.04 at MMC. The allowed straightness tolerance increases equal to the amount the feature departs from MMC.

56 Specifying Straightnes. *Reprinted from Y14.5M-1994, by permission of The American Society of Mechanical Engineers. All rights reserved.*

This on the drawing...   Means this   The surface must be within the specified tolerance of size and must lie between two parallel planes 0.25 apart

57 Specifying Flatness. *Reprinted from Y14.5M-1994, by permission of The American Society of Mechanical Engineers. All rights reserved.*

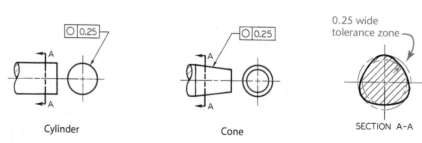

Cylinder   Cone   SECTION A-A

This on the drawing...   Means this

Each circular element of the surface in any plane perpendicular to a common axis must be within the specified tolerance of size and must lie between two concentric circles — one having a radius 0.25 larger than the other

58 Specifying Roundness for a Cylinder or Cone. *Reprinted from Y14.5M-1994, by permission of The American Society of Mechanical Engineers. All rights reserved.*

490

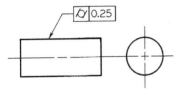
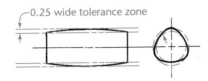
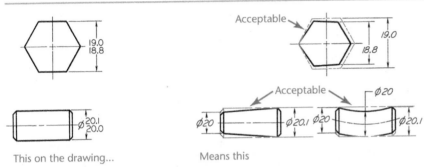

This on the drawing...

Means this   The cylindrical surface must be within the specified tolerance of size and must lie between two concentric cylinders — one having a radius 0.25 larger than the other.

59 Specifying Cylindricity. *Reprinted from Y14.5M-1994, by permission of The American Society of Mechanical Engineers. All rights reserved.*

Acceptable

This on the drawing...   Means this

60 Acceptable Variations of Form—No Specified Tolerance of Form

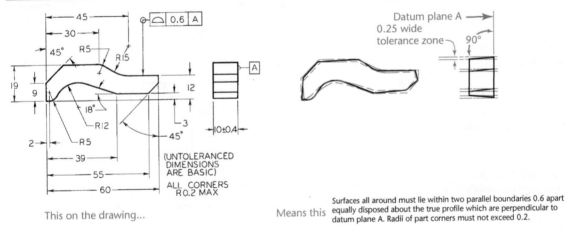

Surfaces all around must lie within two parallel boundaries 0.6 apart equally disposed about the true profile which are perpendicular to datum plane A. Radii of part corners must not exceed 0.2.

This on the drawing...   Means this

61 Specifying Profile of a Surface All Around. *Reprinted from Y14.5M-1994, by permission of The American Society of Mechanical Engineers. All rights reserved.*

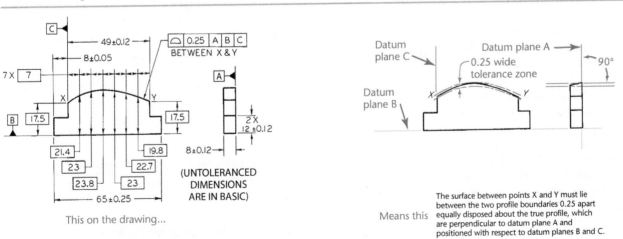

The surface between points X and Y must lie between the two profile boundaries 0.25 apart equally disposed about the true profile, which are perpendicular to datum plane A and positioned with respect to datum planes B and C.

This on the drawing...   Means this

62 Specifying Profile of a Surface between Points. *Reprinted from Y14.5M-1994, by permission of The American Society of Mechanical Engineers. All rights reserved.*

18 FORM TOLERANCES FOR RELATED FEATURES

Angularity, parallelism, perpendicularity, and in some instances, profile, are form tolerances that apply to related features. These tolerances control the attitude of features to one another (ASME Y14.5M-1994).

Angularity tolerance The **angularity tolerance** specifies a tolerance zone defined by two parallel planes at the specified basic angle (other than 90°, in which case use perpendicularity) from a datum plane or axis within which the surface or the axis of the feature must lie (Figure 63).

Parallelism tolerance The **parallelism tolerance** specifies a tolerance zone defined by two parallel planes or lines parallel to a datum plane or axis, respectively, within which the surface or axis of the feature must lie (Figures 64–66). Also, parallelism tolerance may specify a cylindrical tolerance zone parallel to a datum axis within which the axis of the feature must lie.

Perpendicularity tolerance The **perpendicularity tolerance** specifies one of the following:

1. A tolerance zone is defined by two parallel planes perpendicular to a datum plane, datum axis, or axis within which the surface of the feature must lie (Figure 67).
2. A cylindrical tolerance zone perpendicular to a datum plane within which the axis of the feature must lie (Figure 68).

(Perpendicularity is the condition of a surface, median plane, or axis which is at 90° to a datum plane or axis.)

Concentricity tolerance The **concentricity tolerance** specifies a cylindrical tolerance zone whose axis coincides with a datum axis and within which all cross-sectional axes of the feature being controlled must lie (Figure 69). Concentricity is the condition in which the axes of all cross-sectional elements of a feature's surface of revolution are common to the axis of a datum feature.

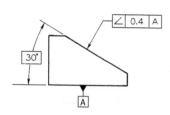
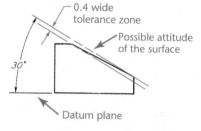

This on the drawing...　　Means this　The surface must be within the specified tolerance of size and must lie between two parallel planes 0.4 apart which are inclined at 30° to the datum plane A.

63 Specifying Angularity for a Plane Surface. *Reprinted from Y14.5M-1994, by permission of The American Society of Mechanical Engineers. All rights reserved.*

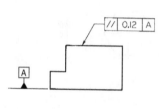
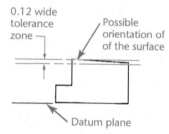

This on the drawing...　　Means this　The surface must be within the specified tolerance of size and must lie between two planes 0.12 apart which are parallel to the datum plane A.

64 Specifying Parallelism for a Plane Surface. *Reprinted from Y14.5M-1994, by permission of The American Society of Mechanical Engineers. All rights reserved.*

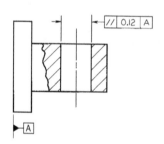
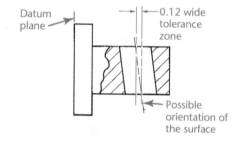

This on the drawing...　　Means this　The feature axis must be within the specified tolerance of location and must lie between two planes 0.12 apart which are parallel to the datum plane, regardless of feature size.

65 Specifying Parallelism for an Axis Feature RFS. *Reprinted from Y14.5M-1994, by permission of The American Society of Mechanical Engineers. All rights reserved.*

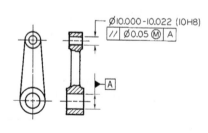
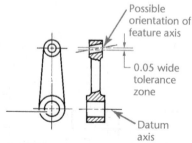

This on the drawing...　　Means this　The feature axis must be within the specified tolerance of location. Where the feature is at maximum material condition (10.00), the maximum parallelism tolerance is 0.05 diameter. Where the feature departs from its MMC size, an increase in the parallelism tolerance is allowed which is equal to the amount of such departure.

66 Specifying Parallelism for an Axis Feature at MMC. *Reprinted from Y14.5M-1994, by permission of The American Society of Mechanical Engineers. All rights reserved.*

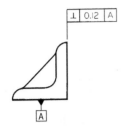

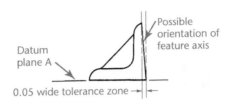

Datum plane A

Possible orientation of feature axis

0.05 wide tolerance zone

The surface must be within the specified tolerance of size and must lie between two parallel planes 0.12 apart which are perpendicular to the datum plane A

Perpendicularity for a plane surface

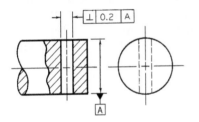

0.12 wide tolerance zone

Possible orientation of the feature center plane

Datum plane A

The feature center plane must be within the specified tolerance of location and must lie between two parallel planes 0.12 apart, regardless of feature size, which are perpendicular to the datum plane A

Perpendicularity for a median plane

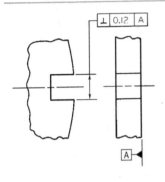

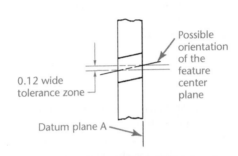

0.2 wide tolerance zone

Datum axis A

Possible orientation of the feature axis

The feature axis must be within the specified tolerance of location and must lie between two planes 0.2 apart, regardless of feature size, which are perpendicular to the datum axis A

Perpendicularity for an axis

67 Specifying Perpendicularity. *Reprinted from Y14.5M-1994, by permission of The American Society of Mechanical Engineers. All rights reserved.*

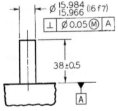

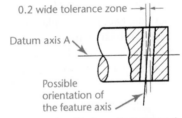

Gage

Datum plane A

The feature axis must be within the specified tolerance of location. Where the feature is at MMC (15.984) the maximum perpendicularity tolerance is 0.05 diameter. Where the feature departs from its MMC size, an increase in the perpendicularity tolerance is allowed that is equal to the amount of such departure.

This on the drawing...   Means this

68 Specifying Perpendicularity for an Axis. Pin, or Boss. *Reprinted from Y14.5M-1994, by permission of The American Society of Mechanical Engineers. All rights reserved.*

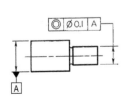

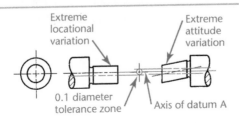

Extreme locational variation

Extreme attitude variation

0.1 diameter tolerance zone

Axis of datum A

The feature axis must be within a cylindrical zone of 0.1 diameter, regardless of feature size, and whose axis coincides with the datum axis.

This on the drawing...   Means this

69 Specifying Concentricity. *Reprinted from Y14.5M-1994, by permission of The American Society of Mechanical Engineers. All rights reserved.*

19 USING GEOMETRIC DIMENSIONING AND TOLERANCING

Geometric dimensioning and tolerancing (GDT) has evolved over the last forty years to become an indispensable tool for defining parts and features more accurately. GDT not only considers an individual part and its dimensions and tolerances, but views that part in relation to its related parts. This allows the designer more latitude in defining the part's features more accurately by not only considering the part's dimensions, but its tolerances at the initial design stage. GDT also simplifies the inspection process. This is accomplished through the use of ASME standards (ASME-Y14.5M), as we have discussed previously.

Individually manufactured parts and components must eventually be assembled into products. We take for granted that each part of a lawnmower, for example, will mate properly with its other components when assembled. The wheels will slip into their axles, the pistons will fit properly into their cylinders, and so on. Nothing should be too tight or too loose.

Geometric dimensioning and tolerancing, therefore, is important to both the design and manufacturing processes.

Applying GDT principles to the design process requires five steps.

Step 1 Define the part's functions. It is best to break the part down to its simplest functions. Be as specific as possible. For example, a lawnmower wheel's functions are to (a) Give the product mobility; (b) Lift the mowing deck off the ground; (c) Add rigidity to the body, etc.

Step 2 List the functions by priority. Only one function should have top priority. This step can be difficult since many parts are designed to incorporate multiple functions. In our lawnmower wheels example, the function with top priority would be to give the product mobility.

Step 3 Define the datum reference frame. This step should be based on your list of priorities. This may mean creating several reference frames, each based on a priority on your list. The frame should be set up in either one, two, or three planes.

Step 4 Control selection. In most cases, several controls will be needed (e.g., runout, position, concentricity, roughness, etc.). Begin with the simplest control. By "simplest" we mean least restrictive. Work from the least restrictive to the most restrictive set of controls.

Step 5 Calculate tolerances. Most tolerances are mathematically based. This step should be the easiest. Apply MMC, RFS, or LMC where indicated. Avoid completing this step first; it should always be your final step.

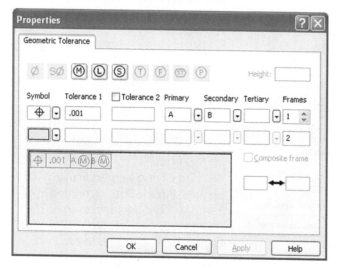

70 SolidWorks dialog box aids in creating geometric dimensioning and tolerancing symbols. *Courtesy of Solidworks Corporation.*

20 COMPUTER GRAPHICS

CAD programs generally allow the user to add tolerances to dimension values in the drawings. See Figure 70. Geometric dimensioning and tolerancing symbols, finish marks, and other standard symbols are typically available as a part of the CAD program or as a symbol library.

Geometric dimensioning and tolerancing has become an essential part of today's manufacturing industry. To compete in today's marketplace, companies are required to develop and produce products of the highest quality, at lowest cost, and guarantee on-time delivery. Although considered by most to be a design specification language, GDT is a manufacturing and inspection language as well, providing a means for uniform interpretation and understanding by these various groups. It provides both a national and international contract base for customers and suppliers.

21 TOLERANCES AND DIGITAL PRODUCT DEFINITION

Dimensioning and tolerancing can take place directly in the 3D digital database. The electronic file can be transmitted as the digital product definition specifying the shape, size, and finish to the company that will manufacture and/or assemble the parts.

When you create a 3D model, it represents the ideal geometric shape of the part. The part can be manufactured very precisely, but as precision is increased, so is the price of the part. Adding tolerances to the model informs the manufacturer of the accuracy that is required on the finished part for it to function in your design as you intend. Essentially, you need to tell the manufacturer when to stop trying to achieve the level of perfection that is represented in your model.

When you include annotations in the solid model, the annotation should:

- Be in a plane that is clearly associated with the corresponding surface or view.
- Be clearly associated with the corresponding model geometry.
- Be capable of being printed and meet applicable drawing standards.
- Be possible to display on the screen or turn off.

In general, tolerances and annotations provided directly in the model need to be interpreted to achieve the result that you intend. A combination of drawings and the model, only drawings, or a fully annotated model are all available methods for documenting a design. Each method has its advantages and disadvantages. You should investigate which method is suitable for your use and understand the applicable standards. See Figures 71 and 72 for examples of tolerancing in CAD.

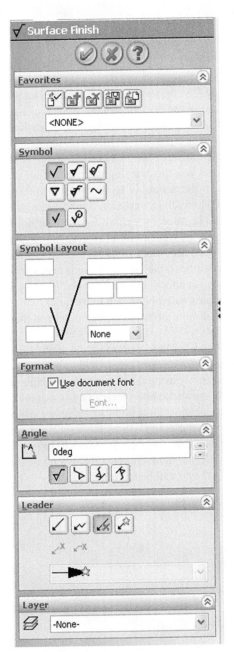

71 SolidWorks software makes it easy to select surface finish symbols. *Courtesy of Solidworks Corporation.*

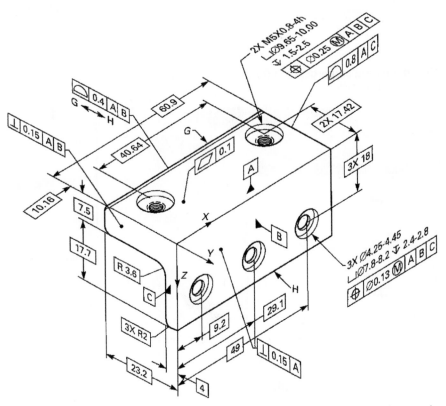

72 Tolerances can be added directly to a 3D model so that it can be used as the digital product definition. *Reprinted from Y14.41-2003, by permission of The American Society of Mechanical Engineers. All rights reserved.*

USING PRO/ENGINEER WILDFIRE 3.0 TO PERFORM A FIT STUDY

Tolerances are important to consider, not just for each individual part, but also for the entire assembly of parts. A tolerance accumulation may happen from feature to feature of a part and tolerances may also stack up from part to part in an assembly. One way to analyze the tolerances in the design of your assembly is to do a fit study. Pro/Engineer software has some useful tools for performing a fit study.

Figure A shows the dimensions properties for the size of the 0.25" diameter hole. The upper and lower tolerance for the hole size are set to 0.01". The bottom part has four pins that must fit through the four 0.25" diameter holes. If the locations for the holes are off, the pins may not fit through.

The Wildfire 3 software has a feature called the Dimension Bound Table that allows you to set a single, group, or all the dimensions for parts in the assembly to its upper, lower, or nominal size. Figure B shows the Dimension Bound Table with the value for the R1.00 location dimension for the four holes set to its upper limit. The model automatically regenerates so that the features are sized according to the tolerance applied and the limit set in the bounds table. Saving bounds tables with groups of dimensions set to upper or lower limits helps you analyze the fit for a complex assembly much more quickly than having to change each dimension value in the model and then regenerating the assembly.

Once the bounds table has been used to set the model sizes to the desired dimension limits, you can quickly analyze the interferences in the assembly using the commands available in the software. Figure C shows the interference in this assembly caused by setting the location dimension to its upper limit, when the tolerances for the entire assembly have not been worked out in a way that allows the parts to always fit together. As you can well imagine, the more complex the assembly, the more valuable this CAD tool will be to you.

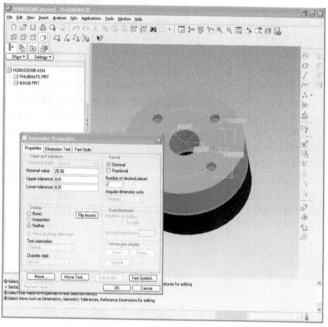

(A)

Dimensions and properties for a 0.25" diameter hole, as seen in Pro/Engineer Wildfire.

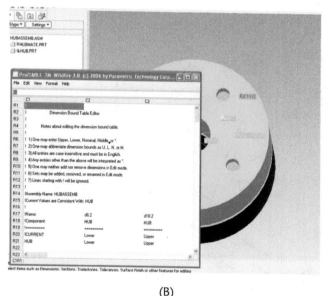

(B)

The Dimension Bound Table with the value for the R1.00 location dimension for the four holes set to its upper limit.

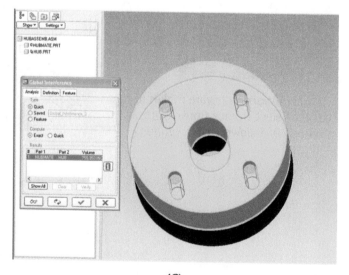

(C)

Interference in the assembly is shown, based on the location dimension limits that you have selected.

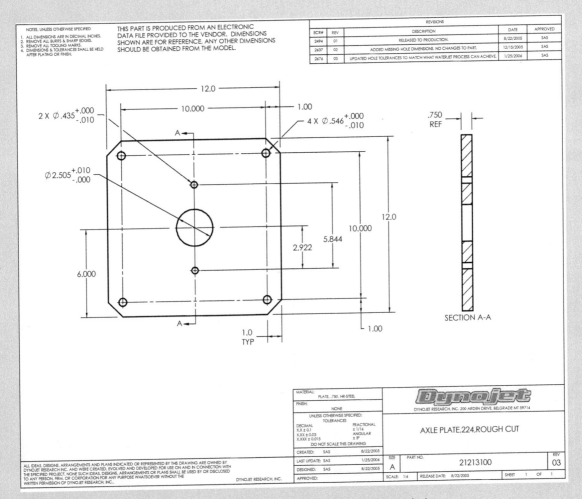

Uniliateral tolerances are specified for hole sizes. *Courtesy of Dynojet Research, Inc.*

PORTFOLIO

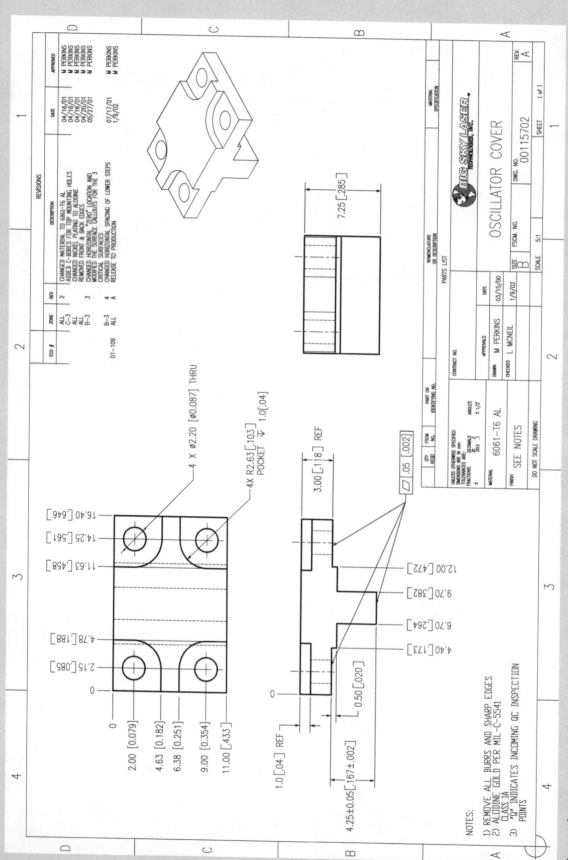

Form tolerances are specified on this dual-dimensioned drawing—Big Sky Laser adds a Q to indicate inspection. *Courtesy of Big Sky Laser.*

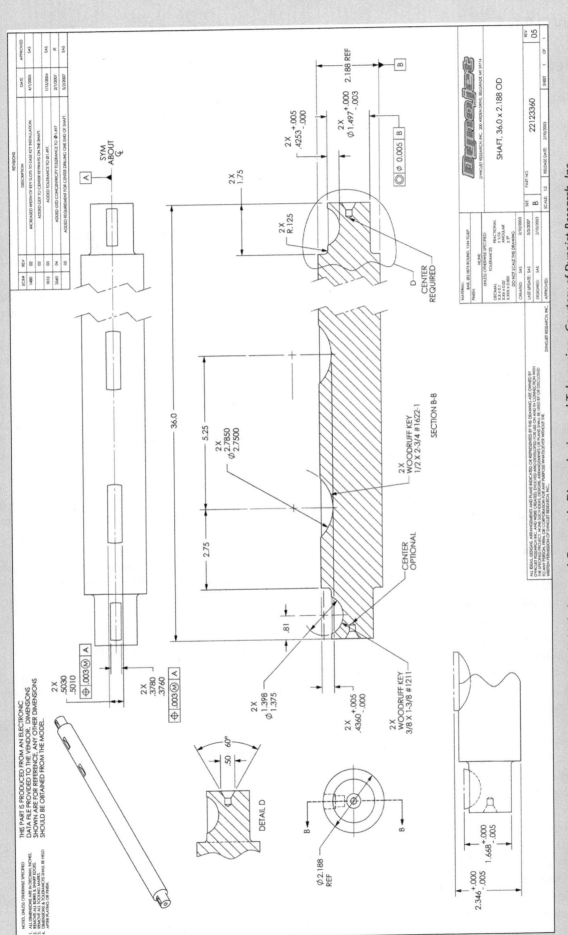

PORTFOLIO

Dimensioned and Toleranced Part Drawing Using Limit, Variation, and Geometric Dimensioning and Tolerancing. *Courtesy of Dynojet Research, Inc.*

KEY WORDS

Tolerance
Quality Certify
Bilateral Tolerance
Perfect Form Envelope
Bowed
Waisted
Fit
Allowance
Clearance Fit
Interference Fit
Transition Fit
Line Fit
Limit Dimensions
Selective Assembly
Nominal Size
Basic Size
Actual Size
Basic Hole System
Basic Shaft System
General Tolerance Notes
Limit Tolerances
Unilateral System
Bilateral System
Angular Tolerances
Reference Dimension
Chained Dimension
Tolerance Stacking
Baseline Dimensioning
Deviation
Upper Deviation
Lower Deviation
Fundamental Deviation
International Tolerance Grade (IT)
Tolerance Zone
Tolerance Symbols
Geometric Tolerances
Geometric Characteristics
Feature Control Frame
Basic Dimension Symbol
Datum Identifying Symbol
Supplementary Symbols
Maximum Material Condition
Combined Symbols
Datum Surfaces
Datum Features
Datum Reference Frame
Primary Datum Surfaces
Secondary Datum Sufaces
Tertiary Datum Surfaces
Datum Targets
True-Position Dimensioning
Basic Angle Tolerancing Method

Straightness Tolerance
Flatness Tolerance
Roundness (Circularity) Tolerance
Cylindricity Tolerance
Profile Tolerance
Angularity Tolerance
Parallelism Tolerance
Perpendicularity Tolerance
Concentricity Tolerance
Geometric Dimensioning and Tolerancing (GDT)

CHAPTER SUMMARY

- Tolerance dimensioning describes the minimum and maximum limits for a size or location of a feature.
- There are several ways of dimensioning tolerances, including limit dimensions, unilateral tolerances, bilateral tolerances, and geometric tolerancing.
- Basic hole tolerance systems are the most commonly used tolerance systems because they assume the hole is nominal size and adjust the shaft to accommodate the tolerance.
- The amount of space between two mating parts at maximum material condition is called the allowance.
- Mating parts with large allowances are classified as having a clearance fit or a running and sliding fit.
- Mating parts with negative allowances are classified as having an interference fit or force fit.
- Mating parts are designed around a nominal size and class of fit. Other tolerances are calculated from these two values.
- High quality parts are often dimensioned with geometric tolerancing to ensure that the size, shape, and relative geometric characteristics are properly defined.
- GDT has become an essential part of today's manufacturing industry. GDT is not only a design language, but an inspection language as well.

REVIEW QUESTIONS

1. What do the two numbers of a limit dimension mean?
2. Draw three different geometric tolerances that reference a datum. Label the information in each box.
3. Why is the basic hole system more common than the basic shaft system?
4. Give five examples of nominal sizes in everyday life. What is the purpose of a nominal size?
5. Give an example of two parts that would require a running and sliding fit. A force fit.
6. List five classes of fit.
7. Can one part have an allowance? Why?
8. Can two parts have a tolerance? Why?
9. Give an example of how GDT could be used as both a design and inspection tool.
10. List the five steps required to apply GDT to the design process.

Design Project

Exercise 1 Design a bike rack using standard tubing products and standard fittings. Provide a means for mounting the rack to concrete. What accuracy is required for your design to function? Research the manufacturing accuracy for the parts you specify. What is the maximum allowance your mounting can be off and still allow the parts to fit?

Tolerancing Projects

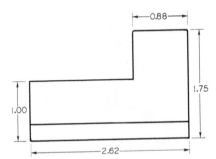
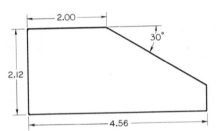

Exercise 2 Sketch the figure shown above. Use either limit dimensions, bilateral tolerances, or geometric tolerancing to add a hole to the left end of the part, located .50" from the bottom surface and 2" from the right end of the part. The location should be accurate to ±.005 and its size accurate to within ±.002.

Exercise 3 Add geometric dimensioning and tolerancing symbols to the drawing to do the following: (a) Control the flatness of the bottom surface to a total tolerance of .001. (b) Control perpendicularity of the left surface and bottom surface to .003. (c) Control the tolerance for the 30° angle to .01.

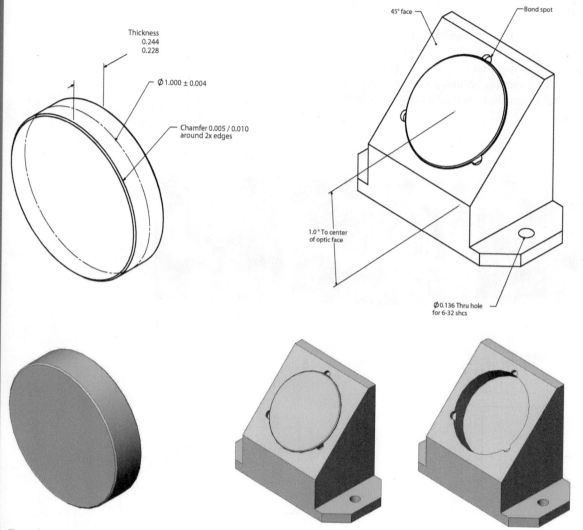

Exercise 4 An optic mount is needed for a dielectric mirror as shown above. The specifications for the design are listed below.

You have been tasked with mounting a dielectric mirror at a 45° angle. This will be done by creating a mount out of 6061-T6 aluminum machined with a 45° face. The face will have a machined c-bore to mount the optic in and three bond spots to attach the optic.

- Reference the provided drawing for stock 1" dielectric mirror.
- The diameter for the c-bore must be .005" to .010" larger than the maximum diameter of the optic.
- The optic must sit at a minimum of .010" and maximum of .020" above the mounting surface.
- The optic will be bonded to the mount using ultraviolet curing adhesive. The adhesive bond spots will be .100" diameter by .050" deep, equally spaced around the perimeter of the optic c-bore.
- The center point of the outer surface of the optic will be located 1 ± .05" from the bottom of the mount.
- The mount will be attached to a laser structure using two 6-32 socket heat cap screws.

Answer these questions:

1. What diameter of c-bore is used to ensure the c-bore is .005" to .010" larger than the maximum diameter of the optic?
2. What depth of c-bore is used to ensure a .010"/.020" protrusion height of the optic?
3. Create a full mechanical drawing with appropriate tolerances for the designed mount.

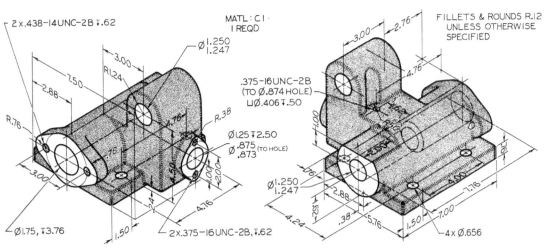

Exercise 5 Create a detail drawing for the automatic stop box shown in the two isometric views. Use standardized dimensioning and tolerancing symbols to replace notes as much as possible.

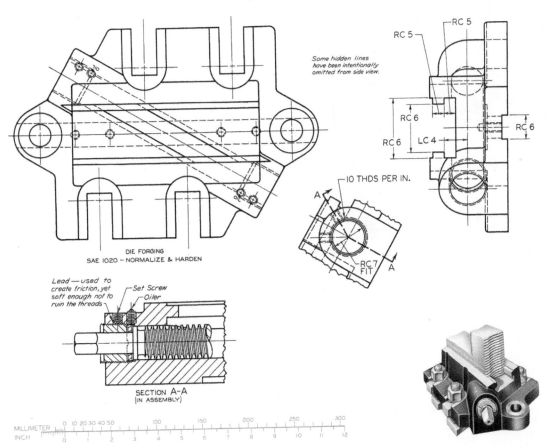

Exercise 6 Complete the following for this jaw base for chuck jaw, with top, right-side, and partial auxiliary views shown. (a) Create top, left-side (beside top), front, and partial auxiliary views complete with dimensions, if assigned. Use metric or decimal inch dimensions. Use American National Standard tables for indicated fits or convert for metric values. (b) Create solid models for parts and assembly. Make detail drawings for parts and provide tolerances for critical fits. Use a general tolerance note for all other sizes.

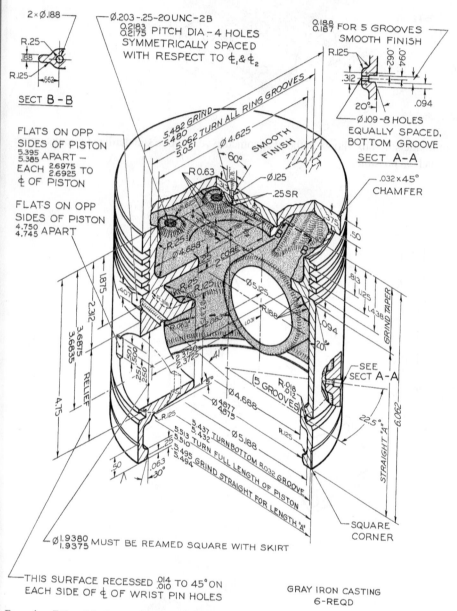

SECT B-B

2 × Ø.188

R.25
.188
R.125 .562

Ø.203 -.25 -20UNC-2B
0.2183
0.2175 PITCH DIA - 4 HOLES
SYMMETRICALLY SPACED
WITH RESPECT TO ₵₁ & ₵₂

0.188
0.187 FOR 5 GROOVES
SMOOTH FINISH

R.125
.312
.060
.090
.094
20°
.094

Ø.109 -8 HOLES
EQUALLY SPACED,
BOTTOM GROOVE

SECT A-A

FLATS ON OPP
SIDES OF PISTON
5.395
5.385 APART -
EACH 2.6975
2.6925 TO
₵ OF PISTON

FLATS ON OPP
SIDES OF PISTON
4.750
4.745 APART

5.482 GRIND
5.480
5.062 TURN ALL RING GROOVES
5.051
Ø 4.625
60°
SMOOTH FINISH

R0.63
Ø.125
.25SR

.032 × 45°
CHAMFER

Ø4.688
2 CORE
R.25
R.125
Ø5.125
R.188

.375
.50
.813
1.125
1.438 TAPER
GRIND TAPER

.094
20°

SEE
SECT A-A

R.018
.012

Ø4877
4875
(5 GROOVES)
Ø4.688

Ø5.188
R.125

R.125

6.062

STRAIGHT "A"
22.5°

5.437 TURNBOTTOM R.032 GROOVE
5.432
5.513 TURN FULL LENGTH OF PISTON
5.510
5.495 GRIND STRAIGHT FOR LENGTH "A"
5.494

SQUARE
CORNER

Ø1.9380
1.9375 MUST BE REAMED SQUARE WITH SKIRT

THIS SURFACE RECESSED .014 TO 45° ON
.010
EACH SIDE OF ₵ OF WRIST PIN HOLES

GRAY IRON CASTING
6-REQD

Exercise 7 For this Caterpillar tractor piston, make a detail drawing full size. If assigned, use the unidirectional decimal inch system, converting all fractions to two-place decimal dimensions, or convert all dimensions to metric. Use standard symbols for dimensioning and tolerancing to replace notes.

DETERMINING MINIMUM AND MAXIMUM CLEARANCES

Determine the hole tolerance, shaft tolerance, allowance (minimum clearance), and maximum clearance for the parts shown. Write your answers in the spaces provided.

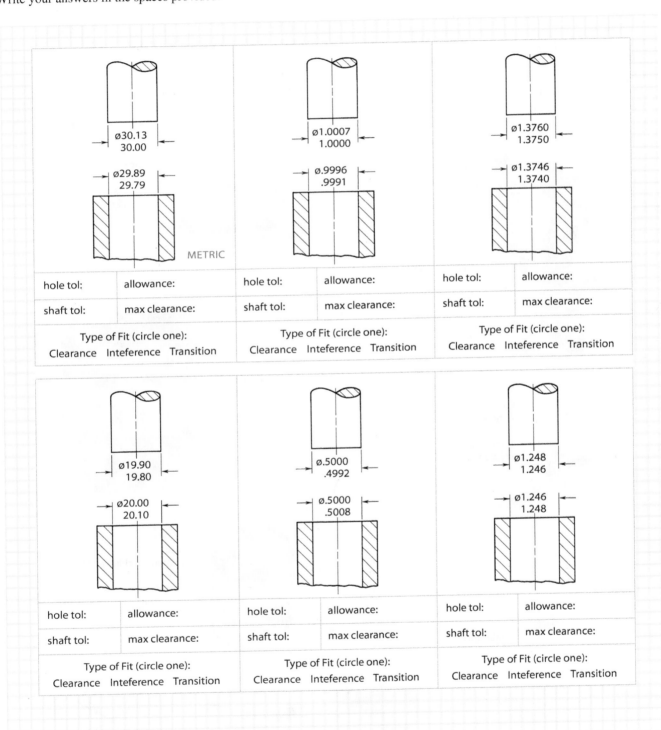

ø30.13		ø1.0007		ø1.3760	
30.00		1.0000		1.3750	
ø29.89		ø.9996		ø1.3746	
29.79		.9991		1.3740	

METRIC

hole tol:	allowance:	hole tol:	allowance:	hole tol:	allowance:
shaft tol:	max clearance:	shaft tol:	max clearance:	shaft tol:	max clearance:

Type of Fit (circle one):
Clearance Inteference Transition

Type of Fit (circle one):
Clearance Inteference Transition

Type of Fit (circle one):
Clearance Inteference Transition

ø19.90		ø.5000		ø1.248	
19.80		.4992		1.246	
ø20.00		ø.5000		ø1.246	
20.10		.5008		1.248	

hole tol:	allowance:	hole tol:	allowance:	hole tol:	allowance:
shaft tol:	max clearance:	shaft tol:	max clearance:	shaft tol:	max clearance:

Type of Fit (circle one):
Clearance Inteference Transition

Type of Fit (circle one):
Clearance Inteference Transition

Type of Fit (circle one):
Clearance Inteference Transition

TOLERANCES

You can get a feeling for the concept of tolerance by considering examples. What would be the most reasonable tolerance in the following cases?

Case:	A window opening in a building
Tolerance:	±1 ft. ±1 in. ±.125 in.
Case:	A model fashioned out of soap
Tolerance:	±.03 mm ±.3 mm ±3 mm
Case:	Socket for a lightbulb
Tolerance:	±6 in. ±.6 in. ±.06 in.
Case:	Gears for a bicycle

Tolerance:	±.5 in. ±.05 in. ±.005 in.
Case:	A fitting for chimney pipe
Tolerance:	±.1 mm ±1 mm ±10 mm
Case:	The hinge for a car door
Tolerance:	±2 in. ±.2 in. ±.02 in.
Case:	A shovel handle
Tolerance:	±30 mm ±3 mm ±.3 mm

Case:
A window opening in a building

Tolerance:
+/- 1ft.

+/- 1 in.

+/- .125 in.

Case:
Gears for a bicycle

Tolerance:
+/- .5 in.

+/- .05 in.

+/- .005 in.

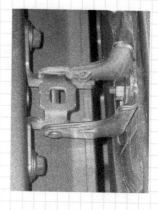

Case:
The hinge for a car door

Tolerance:
+/- 2 in.

+/- .2 in.

+/- .02 in.

Case:
A model made out of soap

Tolerance:
+/- .03 mm   +/- .3 mm   +/- 3 mm

Case:
A fitting for chimney pipe

Tolerance:
+/- .1 mm   +/- 1 mm   +/- 10 mm

Case:
Socket for a lightbulb

Tolerance:
+/- 6 in.

+/- .6 in.

+/- .06 in.

Case:
A shovel handle

Tolerance:
+/- 30 mm   +/- 3 mm   +/- .3 mm

SKETCHING DIMENSIONS WITH TOLERANCES

The dimensions given for the single view at right do not have tolerances shown. Follow the directions below to add tolerances to the dimensions using limit tolerance and bilateral tolerance methods.

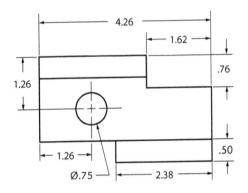

Add the given dimensions using limit tolerances of ±.01.

Add the given dimensions using bilateral tolerances.

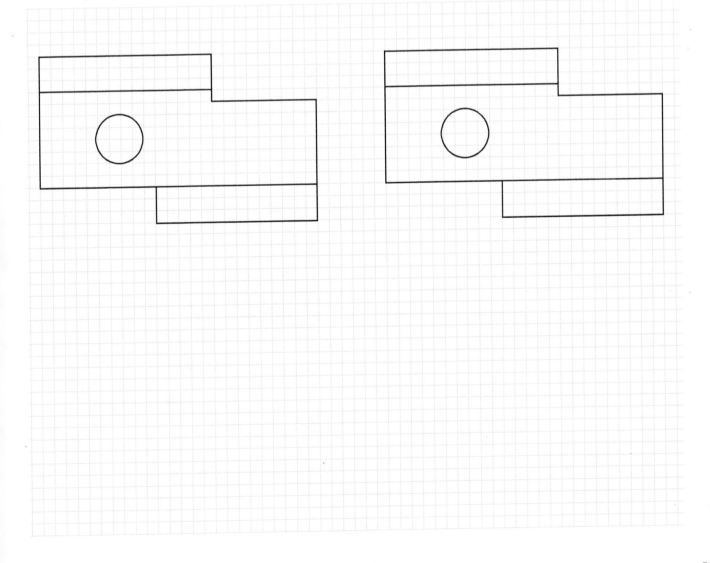

MATCHING

Instructions: Match the description with the symbol by writing the letter of the correct description in the blank next to the symbol.

Ⓜ _____   a. Straightness

Ⓛ _____   b. Radius

Ⓟ _____   c. Parallelism

Ⓕ _____   d. Profile of a line

Ⓣ _____   e. At maximum material condition

∅ _____   f. Symmetry

S∅ _____   g. Arc length

R _____   h. Cylindricity

SR _____   i. Total runout

CR _____   j. Statistical tolerance

( ) _____   k. At least material condition

⌒ _____   l. Diameter

⟨ST⟩ _____   m. Flatness

↔ _____   n. Angularity

▱ _____   o. Projected tolerance zone

◯ _____   p. Spherical diameter

— │ _____   q. Perpendicularity

⌀ _____   r. Profile of a surface

⌒ _____   s. Position

⌓ _____   t. Spherical radius

∠ _____   u. Free state

⊥ _____   v. Angularity

// _____   w. Circularity (roundness)

⊕ _____   x. Between

◎ _____   y. Tangent plane

= _____   z. Concentricity

↗* _____   aa. Controlled radius

↗↗* _____   bb. Circular runout

APPENDIX: TECHNICAL TERMS

"The beginning of wisdom is to call things by their right names."

—CHINESE PROVERB

n *means* a noun; v *means* a verb

acme (n)   Screw thread form.

addendum (n)   Radial distance from pitch circle to top of gear tooth.

allen screw (n)   Special set screw or cap screw with hexagon socket in head.

allowance (n)   Minimum clearance between mating parts.

alloy (n)   Two or more metals in combination, usually a fine metal with a baser metal.

aluminum (n)   A lightweight but relatively strong metal. Often alloyed with copper to increase hardness and strength.

anneal (v)   To heat and cool gradually, to reduce brittleness and increase ductility.

arc weld (v)   To weld by electric arc. The work is usually the positive terminal.

babbitt (n)   A soft alloy for bearings, mostly of tin with small amounts of copper and antimony.

bearing (n)   A supporting member for a rotating shaft.

bevel (n)   An inclined edge, not at a right angle to the joining surface.

bolt circle (n)   A circular centerline on a drawing, containing the centers of holes about a common center.

bore (v)   To enlarge a hole with a boring mill.

boss (n)   A cylindrical projection on a casting or a forging.

BOSS

brass (n)   An alloy of copper and zinc.

braze (v)   To join with a hard solder of brass or zinc.

Brinell (n)   A method of testing hardness of metal.

broach (n)   A long cutting tool with a series of teeth that gradually increase in size which is forced through a hole or over a surface to produce a desired shape.

bronze (n)   An alloy of eight or nine parts copper and one part tin.

buff (v)   To finish or polish on a buffing wheel composed of fabric with abrasive powders.

burnish (v)   To finish or polish by pressure upon a smooth rolling or sliding tool.

burr (n)   A jagged edge on metal resulting from punching or cutting.

bushing (n)   A replaceable lining or sleeve for a bearing.

calipers (n)   Instrument (of several types) for measuring diameters.

cam (n)   A rotating member for changing circular motion to reciprocating motion.

carburize (v)   To heat a low-carbon steel to approximately 2000°F in contact with material that adds carbon to the surface of the steel, and to cool slowly in preparation for heat treatment.

case harden (v)   To harden the outer surface of a carburized steel by heating and then quenching.

castellate (v)   To form like a castle, as a castellated shaft or nut.

casting (n)   A metal object produced by pouring molten metal into a mold.

cast iron (n)   Iron melted and poured into molds.

center drill (n)   A special drill to produce bearing holes in the ends of a workpiece to be mounted between centers.

COMBINED DRILL
& C SINK

chamfer (n)   A narrow inclined surface along the intersection of two surfaces.

CHAMFER

chase (v)   To cut threads with an external cutting tool.

chill (v)   To harden the outer surface of cast iron by quick cooling, as in a metal mold.

chip (v)   To cut away metal with a cold chisel.

chuck (n)   A mechanism for holding a rotating tool or workpiece.

coin (v)   To form a part in one stamping operation.

cold rolled steel (CRS) (n)   Open hearth or Bessemer steel containing 0.12–0.20% carbon that has been rolled while cold to produce a smooth, quite accurate stock.

collar (n)   A round flange or ring fitted on a shaft to prevent sliding.

COLLAR

color harden (v)   Same as *case harden*, except that it is done to a shallower depth, usually for appearance only.

cotter pin (n)   A split pin used as a fastener, usually to prevent a nut from unscrewing.

counterbore (v)   To enlarge an end of a hole cylindrically with a *counterbore*.

COUNTERBORE

From Appendix 2 of *Modern Graphics Communication*, Fourth Edition, Frederick E. Giesecke, Alva Mitchell, Henry Cecil Spencer, Ivan Leroy Hill, John Thomas Dygdon, James E. Novak, Shawna Lockhart. Copyright © 2010 by Pearson Education, Inc. Published by Pearson Prentice Hall. All rights reserved.

countersink (*v*)   To enlarge an end of a hole conically, usually with a *countersink*.

COUNTERSINK

crown (*n*)   A raised contour, as on the surface of a pulley.

cyanide (*v*)   To surface-harden steel by heating in contact with a cyanide salt, followed by quenching.

dedendum (*n*)   Distance from the pitch circle to the bottom of the tooth space.

development (*n*)   Drawing of the surface of an object unfolded or rolled out on a plane.

diametral pitch (*n*)   Number of gear teeth per inch of pitch diameter.

die (*n*)   (1) Hardened metal piece shaped to cut or form a required shape in a sheet of metal by pressing it against a mating die, (2) Also used for cutting small male threads. In a sense, a die is the opposite of a tap.

die casting (*n*)   Process of forcing molten metal under pressure into metal dies or molds, producing a very accurate and smooth casting.

die stamping (*n*)   Process of cutting or forming a piece of sheet metal with a die.

dog (*n*)   A small auxiliary clamp for preventing work from rotating in relation to the face plate of a lathe.

dowel (*n*)   A cylindrical pin, commonly used to prevent sliding between two contacting flat surfaces.

DOWEL

draft (*n*)   The tapered shape of the parts of a pattern to permit it to be easily withdrawn from the sand or, on a forging, to permit it to be easily withdrawn from the dies.

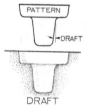
PATTERN
DRAFT
DRAFT

draw (*v*)   To stretch or otherwise to deform metal. Also to temper steel.

drill (*v*)   To cut a cylindrical hole with a drill. A *blind hole* does not go through the piece.

drill press (*n*)   A machine for drilling and other hole forming operations.

drop forge (*v*)   To form a piece while hot between dies in a drop hammer or with great pressure.

face (*v*)   To finish a surface at right angles, or nearly so, to the centerline of rotation on a lathe.

(FAO) (*v*)   An instruction on a drawing to employ the desired surface finish on all surfaces.

feather (key) (*n*)   A flat key, which is partly sunk in a shaft and partly in a hub, permitting the hub to slide lengthwise of the shaft.

file (*v*)   To finish or smooth with a file.

fillet (*n*)   An interior rounded intersection between two surfaces.

fin (*n*)   A thin extrusion of metal at the intersection of dies or sand molds.

fit (*n*)   Degree of tightness or looseness between two mating parts, as a *loose fit,* a *snug fit,* or a *tight fit.*

fixture (*n*)   A special device for holding the work in a machine tool, but not for guiding the cutting tool. Compare with *jig.*

flange (*n*)   A relatively thin rim around a piece.

FLANGE

flash (*n*)   Same as *fin.*

flask (*n*)   A box made of two or more parts for holding the sand in sand molding.

flute (*n*)   Groove, as on twist drills, reamers, and taps.

forge (*v*)   To force metal while it is hot to take on a desired shape by hammering or pressing.

galvanize (*v*)   To cover a surface with a thin layer of molten alloy, composed mainly of zinc, to prevent rusting.

gasket (*n*)   A thin piece of rubber, metal, or some other material, placed between surfaces to make a tight joint.

gate (*n*)   The opening in a sand mold at the bottom of the *sprue* through which the molten metal passes to enter the cavity or mold.

graduate (*v*)   To set off accurate divisions on a scale or dial.

grind (*v*)   To remove metal by means of an abrasive wheel, often made of carborundum. Use chiefly where accuracy is required.

harden (*v*)   To heat steel above a critical temperature and then quench in water or oil.

heat-treat (*v*)   To change the properties of metals by heating and then cooling.

interchangeable (*adj.*)   Refers to a part made to limit dimensions so that it will fit any mating part similarly manufactured.

jig (*n*)   A device for guiding a tool in cutting a piece. Usually it holds the work in position. Compare with *fixture.*

journal (*n*)   Portion of a rotating shaft supported by a bearing.

kerf (*n*)   Groove or cut made by a saw.

KERF

key (*n*)   A small piece of metal sunk partly into both shaft and hub to prevent rotation.

keyseat (n)   A slot or recess in a shaft to hold a key.

KEYSEAT

keyway (n)   A slot in a hub or portion surrounding a shaft to receive a key.

KEYWAY

knurl (v)   To impress a pattern of dents in a turned surface with a knurling tool to produce a better hand grip.

lap (v)   To produce a very accurate finish by sliding contact with a *lap*, or piece of wood, leather, or soft metal impregnated with abrasive powder.

lathe (n)   A machine used to shape metal or other materials by rotating against a tool.

lug (n)   An irregular projection of metal, but not round as in the case of a *boss*, usually with a hole in it for a bolt or screw.

malleable casting (n)   A casting that has been made less brittle and tougher by annealing.

mill (v)   To remove material by means of a rotating cutter on a milling machine.

mold (n)   The mass of sand or other material that forms the cavity into which molten metal is poured.

MS (n)   Machinery steel, sometimes called *mild steel,* with a small percentage of carbon. Cannot be hardened.

neck (v)   To cut a groove called a *neck* around a cylindrical piece.

NECK

normalize (v)   To heat steel above its critical temperature and then to cool it in air.

pack harden (v)   To *carburize,* then to *case harden.*

pad (n)   A slight projection, usually to provide a bearing surface around one or more holes.

PAD

pattern (n)   A model, usually of wood, used in forming a mold for a casting. In sheet metal work a pattern is called a *development.*

peen (v)   To hammer into shape with a ballpeen hammer.

pickle (v)   To clean forgings or castings in dilute sulfuric acid.

pinion (n)   The smaller of two mating gears.

pitch circle (n)   An imaginary circle corresponding to the circumference of the friction gear from which the spur gear was derived.

plane (v)   To remove material by means of the *planer.*

planish (v)   To impart a planished surface to sheet metal by hammering with a smooth-surfaced hammer.

plate (v)   To coat a metal piece with another metal, such as chrome or nickel, by electrochemical methods.

polish (v)   To produce a highly finished or polished surface by friction, using a very fine abrasive.

profile (v)   To cut any desired outline by moving a small rotating cutter, usually with a master template as a guide.

punch (v)   To cut an opening of a desired shape with a rigid tool having the same shape, by pressing the tool through the work.

quench (v)   To immerse a heated piece of metal in water or oil to harden it.

rack (n)   A flat bar with gear teeth in a straight line to engage with teeth in a gear.

ream (v)   To enlarge a finished hole slightly to give it greater accuracy, with a *reamer.*

relief (n)   An offset of surfaces to provide clearance for machining.

RELIEF

rib (n)   A relatively thin flat member acting as a brace or support.

RIB

rivet (v)   To connect with rivets or to clench over the end of a pin by hammering.

round (n)   An exterior rounded intersection of two surfaces.

SAE   Society of Automotive Engineers.

sandblast (v)   To blow sand at high velocity with compressed air against castings or forgings to clean them.

scleroscope (n)   An instrument for measuring hardness of metals.

scrape (v)   To remove metal by scraping with a hand scraper, usually to fit a bearing.

shape (v)   To remove metal from a piece with a *shaper.*

shear (v)   To cut metal by means of shearing with two blades in sliding contact.

sherardize (v)   To galvanize a piece with a coating of zinc by heating it in a drum with zinc powder, to a temperature of 575°F–850°F.

shim (n)   A thin piece of metal or other material used as a spacer in adjusting two parts.

solder (v)   To join with solder, usually composed of lead and tin.

spin (v)   To form a rotating piece of sheet metal into a desired shape by pressing it with a smooth tool against a rotating form.

spline (n)   A keyway, usually one of a series cut around a shaft or hole.

SPLINED HOLE

spotface (v)   To produce a round spot or bearing surface around a hole, usually with a *spotfacer*. The spotface may be on top of a boss or it may be sunk into the surface.

SPOTFACE

sprue (n)   A hole in the sand leading to the *gate* which leads to the mold, through which the metal enters.

steel casting (n)   Like cast iron casting except that in the furnace scrap steel has been added to the casting.

swage (v)   To hammer metal into shape while it is held over a *swage*, or die, which fits in a hole in the *swage block*, or anvil.

sweat (v)   To fasten metal together by the use of solder between the pieces and by the application of heat and pressure.

tap (v)   To cut relatively small internal threads with a *tap*.

taper (n)   Conical form given to a shaft or a hole. Also refers to the slope of a plane surface.

taper pin (n)   A small tapered pin for fastening, usually to prevent a collar or hub from rotating on a shaft.

TAPER PIN

taper reamer (n)   A tapered reamer for producing accurate tapered holes, as for a taper pin.

temper (v)   To reheat hardened steel to bring it to a desired degree of hardness.

template or templet (n)   A guide or pattern used to mark out the work, guide the tool in cutting it, or check the finished product.

tin (n)   A silvery metal used in alloys and for coating other metals, such as tin plate.

tolerance (n)   Total amount of variation permitted in limit dimension of a part.

trepan (v)   To cut a circular groove in the flat surface at one end of a hole.

tumble (v)   To clean rough castings or forgings in a revolving drum filled with scrap metal.

turn (v)   To produce, on a lathe, a cylindrical surface parallel to the centerline.

twist drill (n)   A drill for use in a drill press.

undercut (n)   A recessed cut or a cut with inwardly sloping sides.

UNDERCUT

upset (v)   To form a head or enlarged end on a bar or rod by pressure or by hammering between dies.

web (n)   A thin flat part joining larger parts. Also known as a *rib*.

weld (v)   Uniting metal pieces by pressure or fusion welding processes.

Woodruff (key) (n)   A semicircular flat key.

wrought iron (n)   Iron of low carbon content useful because of its toughness, ductility, and malleability.

APPENDIX: Running and Sliding Fits[a]—American National Standard

RC 1   *Close sliding fits* are intended for the accurate location of parts which must assemble without perceptible play.

RC 2   *Sliding fits* are intended for accurate location, but with greater maximum clearance than class RC 1. Parts made to this fit move and turn easily but are not intended to run freely, and in the larger sizes may seize with small temperature changes.

RC 3   *Precision running fits* are about the closest fits which can be expected to run freely and are intended for precision work at slow speeds and light journal pressures, but they are not suitable where appreciable temperature differences are likely to be encountered.

RC 4   *Close running fits* are intended chiefly for running fits on accurate machinery with moderate surface speeds and journal pressures, where accurate location and minimum play are desired.

Basic hole system. **Limits are in thousandths of an inch.** Limits for hole and shaft are applied algebraically to the basic size to obtain the limits of size for the parts. Data in **boldface** are in accordance with ABC agreements. Symbols H5, g5, etc., are hole and shaft designations used in ABC System.

Nominal Size Range, inches Over To	Class RC 1			Class RC 2			Class RC 3			Class RC 4		
	Limits of Clearance	Standard Limits		Limits of Clearance	Standard Limits		Limits of Clearance	Standard Limits		Limits of Clearance	Standard Limits	
		Hole H5	Shaft g4		Hole H6	Shaft g5		Hole H7	Shaft f6		Hole H8	Shaft f7
0–0.12	0.1 0.45	+0.2 −0	−0.1 −0.25	0.1 0.55	+0.25 −0	−0.1 −0.3	0.3 0.95	+0.4 −0	−0.3 −0.55	0.3 1.3	+0.6 −0	−0.3 −0.7
0.12–0.24	0.15 0.5	+0.2 −0	−0.15 −0.3	0.15 0.65	+0.3 −0	−0.15 −0.35	0.4 1.12	+0.5 −0	−0.4 −0.7	0.4 1.6	+0.7 −0	−0.4 −0.9
0.24–0.40	0.2 0.6	+0.25 −0	−0.2 −0.35	0.2 0.85	+0.4 −0	−0.2 −0.45	0.5 1.5	+0.6 −0	−0.5 −0.9	0.5 2.0	+0.9 −0	−0.5 −1.1
0.40–0.71	0.25 0.75	+0.3 −0	−0.25 −0.45	0.25 0.95	+0.4 −0	−0.25 −0.55	0.6 1.7	+0.7 −0	−0.6 −1.0	0.6 2.3	+1.0 −0	−0.6 −1.3
0.71–1.19	0.3 0.95	+0.4 −0	−0.3 −0.55	0.3 1.2	+0.5 −0	−0.3 −0.7	0.8 2.1	+0.8 −0	−0.8 −1.3	0.8 2.8	+1.2 −0	−0.8 −1.6
1.19–1.97	0.4 1.1	+0.4 −0	−0.4 −0.7	0.4 1.4	+0.6 −0	−0.4 −0.8	1.0 2.6	+1.0 −0	−1.0 −1.6	1.0 3.6	+1.6 −0	−1.0 −2.0
1.97–3.15	0.4 1.2	+0.5 −0	−0.4 −0.7	0.4 1.6	+0.7 −0	−0.4 −0.9	1.2 3.1	+1.2 −0	−1.2 −1.9	1.2 4.2	+1.8 −0	−1.2 −2.4
3.15–4.73	0.5 1.5	+0.6 −0	−0.5 −0.9	0.5 2.0	+0.9 −0	−0.5 −1.1	1.4 3.7	+1.4 −0	−1.4 −2.3	1.4 5.0	+2.2 −0	−1.4 −2.8
4.73–7.09	0.6 1.8	+0.7 −0	−0.6 −1.1	0.6 2.3	+1.0 −0	−0.6 −1.3	1.6 4.2	+1.6 −0	−1.6 −2.6	1.6 5.7	+2.5 −0	−1.6 −3.2
7.09–9.85	0.6 2.0	+0.8 −0	−0.6 −1.2	0.6 2.6	+1.2 −0	−0.6 −1.4	2.0 5.0	+1.8 −0	−2.0 −3.2	2.0 6.6	+2.8 −0	−2.0 −3.8
9.85–12.41	0.8 2.3	+0.9 −0	−0.8 −1.4	0.8 2.9	+1.2 −0	−0.8 −1.7	2.5 5.7	+2.0 −0	−2.5 −3.7	2.5 7.5	+3.0 −0	−2.5 −4.5
12.41–15.75	1.0 2.7	+1.0 −0	−1.0 −1.7	1.0 3.4	+1.4 −0	−1.0 −2.0	3.0 6.6	+2.2 −0	−3.0 −4.4	3.0 8.7	+3.5 −0	−3.0 −5.2

[a]From ANSI B4.1-1967 (R1994). For larger diameters, see the standard.

From Appendix 7 of *Modern Graphics Communication*, Fourth Edition, Frederick E. Giesecke, Alva Mitchell, Henry Cecil Spencer, Ivan Leroy Hill, John Thomas Dygdon, James E. Novak, Shawna Lockhart. Copyright © 2010 by Pearson Education, Inc. Published by Pearson Prentice Hall. All rights reserved.

Running and Sliding Fits[a]—American National Standard (continued)

RC 5 }
RC 6 } *Medium running fits* are intended for higher running speeds, or heavy journal pressures, or both.

RC 7 *Free running fits* are intended for use where accuracy is not essential, or where large temperature variations are likely to be encountered, or under both these conditions.

RC 8 }
RC 9 } *Loose running fits* are intended for use where wide commercial tolerances may be necessary, together with an allowance, on the external member.

Nominal Size Range, inches Over To	Class RC 5			Class RC 6			Class RC 7			Class RC 8			Class RC 9		
	Limits of Clearance	Standard Limits		Limits of Clearance	Standard Limits		Limits of Clearance	Standard Limits		Limits of Clearance	Standard Limits		Limits of Clearance	Standard Limits	
		Hole H8	Shaft e7		Hole H9	Shaft e8		Hole H9	Shaft d8		Hole H10	Shaft c9		Hole H11	Shaft
0–0.12	0.6	+0.6	−0.6	0.6	+1.0	−0.6	1.0	+1.0	−1.0	2.5	+1.6	−2.5	4.0	+2.5	−4.0
	1.6	−0	−1.0	2.2	−0	−1.2	2.6	−0	−1.6	5.1	−0	−3.5	8.1	−0	−5.6
0.12–0.24	0.8	+0.7	−0.8	0.8	+1.2	−0.8	1.2	+1.2	−1.2	2.8	+1.8	−2.8	4.5	+3.0	−4.5
	2.0	−0	−1.3	2.7	−0	−1.5	3.1	−0	−1.9	5.8	−0	−4.0	9.0	−0	−6.0
0.24–0.40	1.0	+0.9	−1.0	1.0	+1.4	−1.0	1.6	+1.4	−1.6	3.0	+2.2	−3.0	5.0	+3.5	−5.0
	2.5	−0	−1.6	3.3	−0	−1.9	3.9	−0	−2.5	6.6	−0	−4.4	10.7	−0	−7.2
0.40–0.71	1.2	+1.0	−1.2	1.2	+1.6	−1.2	2.0	+1.6	−2.0	3.5	+2.8	−3.5	6.0	+4.0	−6.0
	2.9	−0	−1.9	3.8	−0	−2.2	4.6	−0	−3.0	7.9	−0	−5.1	12.8	−0	−8.8
0.71–1.19	1.6	+1.2	−1.6	1.6	+2.0	−1.6	2.5	+2.0	−2.5	4.5	+3.5	−4.5	7.0	+5.0	−7.0
	3.6	−0	−2.4	4.8	−0	−2.8	5.7	−0	−3.7	10.0	−0	−6.5	15.5	−0	−10.5
1.19–1.97	2.0	+1.6	−2.0	2.0	+2.5	−2.0	3.0	+2.5	−3.0	5.0	+4.0	−5.0	8.0	+6.0	−8.0
	4.6	−0	−3.0	6.1	−0	−3.6	7.1	−0	−4.6	11.5	−0	−7.5	18.0	−0	−12.0
1.97–3.15	2.5	+1.8	−2.5	2.5	+3.0	−2.5	4.0	+3.0	−4.0	6.0	+4.5	−6.0	9.0	+7.0	−9.0
	5.5	−0	−3.7	7.3	−0	−4.3	8.8	−0	−5.8	13.5	−0	−9.0	20.5	−0	−13.5
3.15–4.73	3.0	+2.2	−3.0	3.0	+3.5	−3.0	5.0	+3.5	−5.0	7.0	+5.0	−7.0	10.0	+9.0	−10.0
	6.6	−0	−4.4	8.7	−0	−5.2	10.7	−0	−7.2	15.5	−0	−10.5	24.0	−0	−15.0
4.73–7.09	3.5	+2.5	−3.5	3.5	+4.0	−3.5	6.0	+4.0	−6.0	8.0	+6.0	−8.0	12.0	+10.0	−12.0
	7.6	−0	−5.1	10.0	−0	−6.0	12.5	−0	−8.5	18.0	−0	−12.0	28.0	−0	−18.0
7.09–9.85	4.0	+2.8	−4.0	4.0	+4.5	−4.0	7.0	+4.5	−7.0	10.0	+7.0	−10.0	15.0	+12.0	−15.0
	8.6	−0	−5.8	11.3	−0	−6.8	14.3	−0	−9.8	21.5	−0	−14.5	34.0	−0	−22.0
9.85–12.41	5.0	+3.0	−5.0	5.0	+5.0	−5.0	8.0	+5.0	−8.0	12.0	+8.0	−12.0	18.0	+12.0	−18.0
	10.0	−0	−7.0	13.0	−0	−8.0	16.0	−0	−11.0	25.0	−0	−17.0	38.0	−0	−26.0
12.41–15.75	6.0	+3.5	−6.0	6.0	+6.0	−6.0	10.0	+6.0	−10.0	14.0	+9.0	−14.0	22.0	+14.0	−22.0
	11.7	−0	−8.2	15.5	−0	−9.5	19.5	−0	13.5	29.0	−0	−20.0	45.0	−0	−31.0

[a]From ANSI B4.1-1967 (R1994). For larger diameters, see the standard.

APPENDIX: Clearance Locational Fits[a]—American National Standard

LC   *Locational clearance fits* are intended for parts which are normally stationary but which can be freely assembled or disassembled. They run from snug fits for parts requiring accuracy of location, through the medium clearance fits for parts such as spigots, to the looser fastener fits, where freedom of assembly is of prime importance.

Basic hole system. **Limits are in thousandths of an inch.** Limits for hole and shaft are applied algebraically to the basic size to obtain the limits of size for the parts. Data in **boldface** are in accordance with ABC agreements. Symbols H6, H5, etc., are hole and shaft designations used in ABC System.

Nominal Size Range, inches Over To	Class LC 1 Limits of Clearance	Class LC 1 Hole H6	Class LC 1 Shaft h5	Class LC 2 Limits of Clearance	Class LC 2 Hole H7	Class LC 2 Shaft h6	Class LC 3 Limits of Clearance	Class LC 3 Hole H8	Class LC 3 Shaft h7	Class LC 4 Limits of Clearance	Class LC 4 Hole H10	Class LC 4 Shaft h9	Class LC 5 Limits of Clearance	Class LC 5 Hole H7	Class LC 5 Shaft g6
0–0.12	0 / 0.45	+0.25 / −0	+0 / −0.2	0 / 0.65	+0.4 / −0	+0 / −0.25	0 / 1	+0.6 / −0	+0 / −0.4	0 / 2.6	+1.6 / −0	+0 / −1.0	0.1 / 0.75	+0.4 / −0	−0.1 / −0.35
0.12–0.24	0 / 0.5	+0.3 / −0	+0 / −0.2	0 / 0.8	+0.5 / −0	+0 / −0.3	0 / 1.2	+0.7 / −0	+0 / −0.5	0 / 3.0	+1.8 / −0	+0 / −1.2	0.15 / 0.95	+0.5 / −0	−0.15 / −0.45
0.24–0.40	0 / 0.65	+0.4 / −0	+0 / −0.25	0 / 1.0	+0.6 / −0	+0 / −0.4	0 / 1.5	+0.9 / −0	+0 / −0.6	0 / 3.6	+2.2 / −0	+0 / −1.4	0.2 / 1.2	+0.6 / −0	−0.2 / −0.6
0.40–0.71	0 / 0.7	+0.4 / −0	+0 / −0.3	0 / 1.1	+0.7 / −0	+0 / −0.4	0 / 1.7	+1.0 / −0	+0 / −0.7	0 / 4.4	+2.8 / −0	+0 / −1.6	0.25 / 1.35	+0.7 / −0	−0.25 / −0.65
0.71–1.19	0 / 0.9	+0.5 / −0	+0 / −0.4	0 / 1.3	+0.8 / −0	+0 / −0.5	0 / 2	+1.2 / −0	+0 / −0.8	0 / 5.5	+3.5 / −0	+0 / −2.0	0.3 / 1.6	+0.8 / −0	−0.3 / −0.8
1.19–1.97	0 / 1.0	+0.6 / −0	+0 / −0.4	0 / 1.6	+1.0 / −0	+0 / −0.6	0 / 2.6	+1.6 / −0	+0 / −1	0 / 6.5	+4.0 / −0	+0 / −2.5	0.4 / 2.0	+1.0 / −0	−0.4 / −1.0
1.97–3.15	0 / 1.2	+0.7 / −0	+0 / −0.5	0 / 1.9	+1.2 / −0	+0 / −0.7	0 / 3	+1.8 / −0	+0 / −1.2	0 / 7.5	+4.5 / −0	+0 / −3	0.4 / 2.3	+1.2 / −0	−0.4 / −1.1
3.15–4.73	0 / 1.5	+0.9 / −0	+0 / −0.6	0 / 2.3	+1.4 / −0	+0 / −0.9	0 / 3.6	+2.2 / −0	+0 / −1.4	0 / 8.5	+5.0 / −0	+0 / −3.5	0.5 / 2.8	+1.4 / −0	−0.5 / −1.4
4.73–7.09	0 / 1.7	+1.0 / −0	+0 / −0.7	0 / 2.6	+1.6 / −0	+0 / −1.0	0 / 4.1	+2.5 / −0	+0 / −1.6	0 / 10	+6.0 / −0	+0 / −4	0.6 / 3.2	+1.6 / −0	−0.6 / −1.6
7.09–9.85	0 / 2.0	+1.2 / −0	+0 / −0.8	0 / 3.0	+1.8 / −0	+0 / −1.2	0 / 4.6	+2.8 / −0	+0 / −1.8	0 / 11.5	+7.0 / −0	+0 / −4.5	0.6 / 3.6	+1.8 / −0	−0.6 / −1.8
9.85–12.41	0 / 2.1	+1.2 / −0	+0 / −0.9	0 / 3.2	+2.0 / −0	+0 / −1.2	0 / 5	+3.0 / −0	+0 / −2.0	0 / 13.0	+8.0 / −0	+0 / −5	0.7 / 3.9	+2.0 / −0	−0.7 / −1.9
12.41–15.75	0 / 2.4	+1.4 / −0	+0 / −1.0	0 / 3.6	+2.2 / −0	+0 / −1.4	0 / 5.7	+3.5 / −0	+0 / −2.2	0 / 15.0	+9.0 / −0	+0 / −6	0.7 / 4.3	+2.2 / −0	−0.7 / −2.1

[a]From ANSI B4.1-1967 (R1994). For larger diameters, see the standard.

From Appendix 8 of *Modern Graphics Communication*, Fourth Edition, Frederick E. Giesecke, Alva Mitchell, Henry Cecil Spencer, Ivan Leroy Hill, John Thomas Dygdon, James E. Novak, Shawna Lockhart. Copyright © 2010 by Pearson Education, Inc. Published by Pearson Prentice Hall. All rights reserved.

Clearance Locational Fits[a]—American National Standard (continued)

Nominal Size Range, inches Over To	Class LC 6 Limits of Clearance	Class LC 6 Standard Limits Hole H9	Class LC 6 Standard Limits Shaft f8	Class LC 7 Limits of Clearance	Class LC 7 Standard Limits Hole H10	Class LC 7 Standard Limits Shaft e9	Class LC 8 Limits of Clearance	Class LC 8 Standard Limits Hole H10	Class LC 8 Standard Limits Shaft d9	Class LC 9 Limits of Clearance	Class LC 9 Standard Limits Hole H11	Class LC 9 Standard Limits Shaft c10	Class LC 10 Limits of Clearance	Class LC 10 Standard Limits Hole H12	Class LC 10 Standard Limits Shaft	Class LC 11 Limits of Clearance	Class LC 11 Standards Limits Hole H13	Class LC 11 Standards Limits Shaft
0–0.12	0.3 / 1.9	+1.0 / -0	-0.3 / -0.9	0.6 / 3.2	+1.6 / -0	-0.6 / -1.6	1.0 / 3.6	+1.6 / -0	-1.0 / -2.0	2.5 / 6.6	+2.5 / -0	-2.5 / -4.1	4 / 12	+4 / -0	-4 / -8	5 / 17	+6 / -0	-5 / -11
0.12–0.24	0.4 / 2.3	+1.2 / -0	-0.4 / -1.1	0.8 / 3.8	+1.8 / -0	-0.8 / -2.0	1.2 / 4.2	+1.8 / -0	-1.2 / -2.4	2.8 / 7.6	+3.0 / -0	-2.8 / -4.6	4.5 / 14.5	+5 / -0	-4.5 / -9.5	6 / 20	+7 / -0	-6 / -13
0.24–0.40	0.5 / 2.8	+1.4 / -0	-0.5 / -1.4	1.0 / 4.6	+2.2 / -0	-1.0 / -2.4	1.6 / 5.2	+2.2 / -0	-1.6 / -3.0	3.0 / 8.7	+3.5 / -0	-3.0 / -5.2	5 / 17	+6 / -0	-5 / -11	7 / 25	+9 / -0	-7 / -16
0.40–0.71	0.6 / 3.2	+1.6 / -0	-0.6 / -1.6	1.2 / 5.6	+2.8 / -0	-1.2 / -2.8	2.0 / 6.4	+2.8 / -0	-2.0 / -3.6	3.5 / 10.3	+4.0 / -0	-3.5 / -6.3	6 / 20	+7 / -0	-6 / -13	8 / 28	+10 / -0	-8 / -18
0.71–1.19	0.8 / 4.0	+2.0 / -0	-0.8 / -2.0	1.6 / 7.1	+3.5 / -0	-1.6 / -3.6	2.5 / 8.0	+3.5 / -0	-2.5 / -4.5	4.5 / 13.0	+5.0 / -0	-4.5 / -8.0	7 / 23	+8 / -0	-7 / -15	10 / 34	+12 / -0	-10 / -22
1.19–1.97	1.0 / 5.1	+2.5 / -0	-1.0 / -2.6	2.0 / 8.5	+4.0 / -0	-2.0 / -4.5	3.0 / 9.5	+4.0 / -0	-3.0 / -5.5	5 / 15	+6 / -0	-5 / -9	8 / 28	+10 / -0	-8 / -18	12 / 44	+16 / -0	-12 / -28
1.97–3.15	1.2 / 6.0	+3.0 / -0	-1.2 / -3.0	2.5 / 10.0	+4.5 / -0	-2.5 / -5.5	4.0 / 11.5	+4.5 / -0	-4.0 / -7.0	6 / 17.5	+7 / -0	-6 / -10.5	10 / 34	+12 / -0	-10 / -22	14 / 50	+18 / -0	-14 / -32
3.15–4.73	1.4 / 7.1	+3.5 / -0	-1.4 / -3.6	3.0 / 11.5	+5.0 / -0	-3.0 / -6.5	5.0 / 13.5	+5.0 / -0	-5.0 / -8.5	7 / 21	+9 / -0	-7 / -12	11 / 39	+14 / -0	-11 / -25	16 / 60	+22 / -0	-16 / -38
4.73–7.09	1.6 / 8.1	+4.0 / -0	-1.6 / -4.1	3.5 / 13.5	+6.0 / -0	-3.5 / -7.5	6.0 / 16.0	+6 / -0	-6 / -10	8 / 24	+10 / -0	-8 / -14	12 / 44	+16 / -0	-12 / -28	18 / 68	+25 / -0	-18 / -43
7.09–9.85	2.0 / 9.3	+4.5 / -0	-2.0 / -4.8	4.0 / 15.5	+7.0 / -0	-4.0 / -8.5	7.0 / 18.5	+7 / -0	-7 / -11.5	10 / 29	+12 / -0	-10 / -17	16 / 52	+18 / -0	-16 / -34	22 / 78	+28 / -0	-22 / -50
9.85–12.41	2.2 / 10.2	+5.0 / -0	-2.2 / -5.2	4.5 / 17.5	+8.0 / -0	-4.5 / -9.5	7.0 / 20.0	+8 / -0	-7 / -12	12 / 32	+12 / -0	-12 / -20	20 / 60	+20 / -0	-20 / -40	28 / 88	+30 / -0	-28 / -58
12.41–15.75	2.5 / 12.0	+6.0 / -0	-2.5 / -6.0	5.0 / 20.0	+9.0 / -0	-5 / -11	8.0 / 23.0	+9 / -0	-8 / -14	14 / 37	+14 / -0	-14 / -23	22 / 66	+22 / -0	-22 / -44	30 / 100	+35 / -0	-30 / -65

[a]From ANSI B4.1-1967 (R1994). For larger diameters, see the standard.

Appendix: Transition Locational Fits[a]—American National Standard

LT Transition fits are a compromise between clearance and interference fits, for application where accuracy of location is important, but either a small amount of clearance or interference is permissible.

Basic hole system. **Limits are in thousandths of an inch.** Limits for hole and shaft are applied algebraically to the basic size to obtain the limits of size for the mating parts. Data in **boldface** are in accordance with ABC agreements. "Fit" represents the maximum interference (minus values) and the maximum clearance (plus values). Symbols H7, js6, etc., are hole and shaft designations used in ABC System.

Nominal Size Range, inches Over To	Class LT 1 Fit	Class LT 1 Std Limits Hole H7	Class LT 1 Std Limits Shaft js6	Class LT 2 Fit	Class LT 2 Std Limits Hole H8	Class LT 2 Std Limits Shaft js7	Class LT 3 Fit	Class LT 3 Std Limits Hole H7	Class LT 3 Std Limits Shaft k6	Class LT 4 Fit	Class LT 4 Std Limits Hole H8	Class LT 4 Std Limits Shaft k7	Class LT 5 Fit	Class LT 5 Std Limits Hole H7	Class LT 5 Std Limits Shaft n6	Class LT 6 Fit	Class LT 6 Std Limits Hole H7	Class LT 6 Std Limits Shaft n7
0–0.12	−0.10 / +0.50	+0.4 / −0	+0.10 / −0.10	−0.2 / +0.8	+0.6 / −0	+0.2 / −0.2							−0.5 / +0.15	+0.4 / −0	+0.5 / +0.25	−0.65 / +0.15	+0.4 / −0	+0.65 / +0.25
0.12–0.24	−0.15 / +0.65	+0.5 / −0	+0.15 / −0.15	−0.25 / +0.95	+0.7 / −0	+0.25 / −0.25							−0.6 / +0.2	+0.5 / −0	+0.6 / +0.3	−0.8 / +0.2	+0.5 / −0	+0.8 / +0.3
0.24–0.40	−0.2 / +0.8	+0.6 / −0	+0.2 / −0.2	−0.3 / +1.2	+0.9 / −0	+0.3 / −0.3	−0.5 / +0.5	+0.6 / −0	+0.5 / +0.1	−0.7 / +0.8	+0.9 / −0	+0.7 / +0.1	−0.8 / +0.2	+0.6 / −0	+0.8 / +0.4	−1.0 / +0.2	+0.6 / −0	+1.0 / +0.4
0.40–0.71	−0.2 / +0.9	+0.7 / −0	+0.2 / −0.2	−0.35 / +1.35	+1.0 / −0	+0.35 / −0.35	−0.5 / +0.6	+0.7 / −0	+0.5 / +0.1	−0.8 / +0.9	+1.0 / −0	+0.8 / +0.1	−0.9 / +0.2	+0.7 / −0	+0.9 / +0.5	−1.2 / +0.2	+0.7 / −0	+1.2 / +0.5
0.71–1.19	−0.25 / +1.05	+0.8 / −0	+0.25 / −0.25	−0.4 / +1.6	+1.2 / −0	+0.4 / −0.4	−0.6 / +0.7	+0.8 / −0	+0.6 / +0.1	−0.9 / +1.1	+1.2 / −0	+0.9 / +0.1	−1.1 / +0.2	+0.8 / −0	+1.1 / +0.6	−1.4 / +0.2	+0.8 / −0	+1.4 / +0.6
1.19–1.97	−0.3 / +1.3	+1.0 / −0	+0.3 / −0.3	−0.5 / +2.1	+1.6 / −0	+0.5 / −0.5	−0.7 / +0.9	+1.0 / −0	+0.7 / +0.1	−1.1 / +1.5	+1.6 / −0	+1.1 / +0.1	−1.3 / +0.3	+1.0 / −0	+1.3 / +0.7	−1.7 / +0.3	+1.0 / −0	+1.7 / +0.7
1.97–3.15	−0.3 / +1.5	+1.2 / −0	+0.3 / −0.3	−0.6 / +2.4	+1.8 / −0	+0.6 / −0.6	−0.8 / +1.1	+1.2 / −0	+0.8 / +0.1	−1.3 / +1.7	+1.8 / −0	+1.3 / +0.1	−1.5 / +0.4	+1.2 / −0	+1.5 / +0.8	−2.0 / +0.4	+1.2 / −0	+2.0 / +0.8
3.15–4.73	−0.4 / +1.8	+1.4 / −0	+0.4 / −0.4	−0.7 / +2.9	+2.2 / −0	+0.7 / −0.7	−1.0 / +1.3	+1.4 / −0	+1.0 / +0.1	−1.5 / +2.1	+2.2 / −0	+1.5 / +0.1	−1.9 / +0.4	+1.4 / −0	+1.9 / +1.0	−2.4 / +0.4	+1.4 / −0	+2.4 / +1.0
4.73–7.09	−0.5 / +2.1	+1.6 / −0	+0.5 / −0.5	−0.8 / +3.3	+2.5 / −0	+0.8 / −0.8	−1.1 / +1.5	+1.6 / −0	+1.1 / +0.1	−1.7 / +2.4	+2.5 / −0	+1.7 / +0.1	−2.2 / +0.4	+1.6 / −0	+2.2 / +1.2	−2.8 / +0.4	+1.6 / −0	+2.8 / +1.2
7.09–9.85	−0.6 / +2.4	+1.8 / −0	+0.6 / −0.6	−0.9 / +3.7	+2.8 / −0	+0.9 / −0.9	−1.4 / +1.6	+1.8 / −0	+1.4 / +0.2	−2.0 / +2.6	+2.8 / −0	+2.0 / +0.2	−2.6 / +0.4	+1.8 / −0	+2.6 / +1.4	−3.2 / +0.4	+1.8 / −0	+3.2 / +1.4
9.85–12.41	−0.6 / +2.6	+2.0 / −0	+0.6 / −0.6	−1.0 / +4.0	+3.0 / −0	+1.0 / −1.0	−1.4 / +1.8	+2.0 / −0	+1.4 / +0.2	−2.2 / +2.8	+3.0 / −0	+2.2 / +0.2	−2.6 / +0.6	+2.0 / −0	+2.6 / +1.4	−3.4 / +0.6	+2.0 / −0	+3.4 / +1.4
12.41–15.75	−0.7 / +2.9	+2.2 / −0	+0.7 / −0.7	−1.0 / +4.5	+3.5 / −0	+1.0 / −1.0	−1.6 / +2.0	+2.2 / −0	+1.6 / +0.2	−2.4 / +3.3	+3.5 / −0	+2.4 / +0.2	−3.0 / +0.6	+2.2 / −0	+3.0 / +1.6	−3.8 / +0.6	+2.2 / −0	+3.8 / +1.6

[a]From ANSI B4.1-1967 (R1994). For larger diameters, see the standard.

Appendix: Interference Locational Fits[a]—American National Standard

LN   *Locational interference fits* are used where accuracy of location is of prime importance and for parts requiring rigidity and alignment with no special requirements for bore pressure. Such fits are not intended for parts designed to transmit frictional loads from one part to another by virtue of the tightness of fit, as these conditions are covered by force fits.

Basic hole system. **Limits are in thousandths an inch.** Limits for hole and shaft are applied algebraically to the basic size to obtain the limits of size for the parts. Data in **boldface** are in accordance with ABC agreements. Symbols H7, p6, etc., are hole and shaft designations used in ABC System.

Nominal Size Range, inches Over To	Class LN 1			Class LN 2			Class LN 3		
	Limits of Interference	Standard Limits		Limits of Interference	Standard Limits		Limits of Interference	Standard Limits	
		Hole H6	Shaft n5		Hole H7	Shaft p6		Hole H7	Shaft r6
0–0.12	**0** **0.45**	+0.25 −0	+0.45 +0.25	**0** **0.65**	+0.4 −0	+0.65 +0.4	**0.1** **0.75**	+0.4 −0	+0.75 +0.5
0.12–0.24	**0** **0.5**	+0.3 −0	+0.5 +0.3	**0** **0.8**	+0.5 −0	+0.8 +0.5	**0.1** **0.9**	+0.5 −0	+0.9 +0.6
0.24–0.40	**0** **0.65**	+0.4 −0	+0.65 +0.4	**0** **1.0**	+0.6 −0	+1.0 +0.6	**0.2** **1.2**	+0.6 −0	+1.2 +0.8
0.40–0.71	**0** **0.8**	+0.4 −0	+0.8 +0.4	**0** **1.1**	+0.7 −0	+1.1 +0.7	**0.3** **1.4**	+0.7 −0	+1.4 +1.0
0.71–1.19	**0** **1.0**	+0.5 −0	+1.0 +0.5	**0** **1.3**	+0.8 −0	+1.3 +0.8	**0.4** **1.7**	+0.8 −0	+1.7 +1.2
1.19–1.97	**0** **1.1**	+0.6 −0	+1.1 +0.6	**0** **1.6**	+1.0 −0	+1.6 +1.0	**0.4** **2.0**	+1.0 −0	+2.0 +1.4
1.97–3.15	**0.1** **1.3**	+0.7 −0	+1.3 +0.7	**0.2** **2.1**	+1.2 −0	+2.1 +1.4	**0.4** **2.3**	+1.2 −0	+2.3 +1.6
3.15–4.73	**0.1** **1.6**	+0.9 −0	+1.6 +1.0	**0.2** **2.5**	+1.4 −0	+2.5 +1.6	**0.6** **2.9**	+1.4 −0	+2.9 +2.0
4.73–7.09	**0.2** **1.9**	+1.0 −0	+1.9 +1.2	**0.2** **2.8**	+1.6 −0	+2.8 +1.8	**0.9** **3.5**	+1.6 −0	+3.5 +2.5
7.09–9.85	**0.2** **2.2**	+1.2 −0	+2.2 +1.4	**0.2** **3.2**	+1.8 −0	+3.2 +2.0	**1.2** **4.2**	+1.8 −0	+4.2 +3.0
9.85–12.41	**0.2** **2.3**	+1.2 −0	+2.3 +1.4	**0.2** **3.4**	+2.0 −0	+3.4 +2.2	**1.5** **4.7**	+2.0 −0	+4.7 +3.5

[a]From ANSI B4.1-1967 (R1994). For larger diameters, see the standard.

From Appendix 10 of *Modern Graphics Communication*, Fourth Edition, Frederick E. Giesecke, Alva Mitchell, Henry Cecil Spencer, Ivan Leroy Hill, John Thomas Dygdon, James E. Novak, Shawna Lockhart. Copyright © 2010 by Pearson Education, Inc. Published by Pearson Prentice Hall. All rights reserved.

Appendix: Force and Shrink Fits[a]—American National Standard

FN 1 — Light drive fits are those requiring light assembly pressures, and produce more or less permanent assemblies. They are suitable for thin sections or long fits, or in cast-iron external members.

FN 2 — Medium drive fits are suitable for ordinary steel parts, or for shrink fits on light sections. They are about the tightest fits that can be used with high-grade cast-iron external members.

FN 3 — Heavy drive fits are suitable for heavier steel parts or for shrink fits in medium sections.

FN 4 } FN 5 } — Force fits are suitable for parts which can be highly stressed, or for shrink fits where the heavy pressing forces required are impractical.

Basic hole system. **Limits are in thousandths of an inch.** Limits for hole and shaft are applied algebraically to the basic size to obtain the limits of size for the parts. Data in **boldface** are in accordance with ABC agreements. Symbols H7, s6, etc., are hole and shaft designations used in ABC System.

Nominal Size Range, inches Over–To	Class FN 1 Limits of Interference	FN 1 Standard Limits Hole H6	FN 1 Standard Limits Shaft	Class FN 2 Limits of Interference	FN 2 Standard Limits Hole H7	FN 2 Standard Limits Shaft s6	Class FN 3 Limits of Interference	FN 3 Standard Limits Hole H7	FN 3 Standard Limits Shaft t6	Class FN 4 Limits of Interference	FN 4 Standard Limits Hole H7	FN 4 Standard Limits Shaft u6	Class FN 5 Limits of Interference	FN 5 Standard Limits Hole H8	FN 5 Standard Limits Shaft x7
0–0.12	0.05 / 0.5	+0.25 / –0	+0.5 / +0.3	0.2 / 0.85	+0.4 / –0	+0.85 / +0.6				0.3 / 0.95	+0.4 / –0	+0.95 / +0.7	0.3 / 1.3	+0.6 / –0	+1.3 / +0.9
0.12–0.24	0.1 / 0.6	+0.3 / –0	+0.6 / +0.4	0.2 / 1.0	+0.5 / –0	+1.0 / +0.7				0.4 / 1.2	+0.5 / –0	+1.2 / +0.9	0.5 / 1.7	+0.7 / –0	+1.7 / +1.2
0.24–0.40	0.1 / 0.75	+0.4 / –0	+0.75 / +0.5	0.4 / 1.4	+0.6 / –0	+1.4 / +1.0				0.6 / 1.6	+0.6 / –0	+1.6 / +1.2	0.5 / 2.0	+0.9 / –0	+2.0 / +1.4
0.40–0.56	0.1 / 0.8	+0.4 / –0	+0.8 / +0.5	0.5 / 1.6	+0.7 / –0	+1.6 / +1.2				0.7 / 1.8	+0.7 / –0	+1.8 / +1.4	0.6 / 2.3	+1.0 / –0	+2.3 / +1.6
0.56–0.71	0.2 / 0.9	+0.4 / –0	+0.9 / +0.6	0.5 / 1.6	+0.7 / –0	+1.6 / +1.2				0.7 / 1.8	+0.7 / –0	+1.8 / +1.4	0.8 / 2.5	+1.0 / –0	+2.5 / +1.8
0.71–0.95	0.2 / 1.1	+0.5 / –0	+1.1 / +0.7	0.6 / 1.9	+0.8 / –0	+1.9 / +1.4				0.8 / 2.1	+0.8 / –0	+2.1 / +1.6	1.0 / 3.0	+1.2 / –0	+3.0 / +2.2
0.95–1.19	0.3 / 1.2	+0.5 / –0	+1.2 / +0.8	0.6 / 1.9	+0.8 / –0	+1.9 / +1.4	0.8 / 2.1	+0.8 / –0	+2.1 / +1.6	1.0 / 2.3	+0.8 / –0	+2.3 / +1.8	1.3 / 3.3	+1.2 / –0	+3.3 / +2.5
1.19–1.58	0.3 / 1.3	+0.6 / –0	+1.3 / +0.9	0.8 / 2.4	+1.0 / –0	+2.4 / +1.8	1.0 / 2.6	+1.0 / –0	+2.6 / +2.0	1.5 / 3.1	+1.0 / –0	+3.1 / +2.5	1.4 / 4.0	+1.6 / –0	+4.0 / +3.0

[a]ANSI B4.1-1967 (R1994).

From Appendix 11 of *Modern Graphics Communication*, Fourth Edition, Frederick E. Giesecke, Alva Mitchell, Henry Cecil Spencer, Ivan Leroy Hill, John Thomas Dygdon, James E. Novak, Shawna Lockhart. Copyright © 2010 by Pearson Education, Inc. Published by Pearson Prentice Hall. All rights reserved.

Force and Shrink Fits[a]—American National Standard (continued)

Nominal Size Range, inches Over–To	Class FN 1 Limits of Interference	Class FN 1 Standard Limits Hole H6	Class FN 1 Standard Limits Shaft	Class FN 2 Limits of Interference	Class FN 2 Standard Limits Hole H7	Class FN 2 Standard Limits Shaft s6	Class FN 3 Limits of Interference	Class FN 3 Standard Limits Hole H7	Class FN 3 Standard Limits Shaft t6	Class FN 4 Limits of Interference	Class FN 4 Standard Limits Hole H7	Class FN 4 Standard Limits Shaft u6	Class FN 5 Limits of Interference	Class FN 5 Standard Limits Hole H8	Class FN 5 Standard Limits Shaft x7
1.58–1.97	0.4 / 1.4	+0.6 / −0	+1.4 / −1.0	0.8 / 2.4	+1.0 / −0	+2.4 / +1.8	1.2 / 2.8	+1.0 / −0	+2.8 / +2.2	1.8 / 3.4	+1.0 / −0	+3.4 / +2.8	2.4 / 5.0	+1.6 / −0	+5.0 / +4.0
1.97–2.56	0.6 / 1.8	+0.7 / −0	+1.8 / +1.3	0.8 / 2.7	+1.2 / −0	+2.7 / +2.0	1.3 / 3.2	+1.2 / −0	+3.2 / +2.5	2.3 / 4.2	+1.2 / −0	+4.2 / +3.5	3.2 / 6.2	+1.8 / −0	+6.2 / +5.0
2.56–3.15	0.7 / 1.9	+0.7 / −0	+1.9 / +1.4	1.0 / 2.9	+1.2 / −0	+2.9 / +2.2	1.8 / 3.7	+1.2 / −0	+3.7 / +3.0	2.8 / 4.7	+1.2 / −0	+4.7 / +4.0	4.2 / 7.2	+1.8 / −0	+7.2 / +6.0
3.15–3.94	0.9 / 2.4	+0.9 / −0	+2.4 / +1.8	1.4 / 3.7	+1.4 / −0	+3.7 / +2.8	2.1 / 4.4	+1.4 / −0	+4.4 / +3.5	3.6 / 5.9	+1.4 / −0	+5.9 / +5.0	4.8 / 8.4	+2.2 / −0	+8.4 / +7.0
3.94–4.73	1.1 / 2.6	+0.9 / −0	+2.6 / +2.0	1.6 / 3.9	+1.4 / −0	+3.9 / +3.0	2.6 / 4.9	+1.4 / −0	+4.9 / +4.0	4.6 / 6.9	+1.4 / −0	+6.9 / +6.0	5.8 / 9.4	+2.2 / −0	+9.4 / +8.0
4.73–5.52	1.2 / 2.9	+1.0 / −0	+2.9 / +2.2	1.9 / 4.5	+1.6 / −0	+4.5 / +3.5	3.4 / 6.0	+1.6 / −0	+6.0 / +5.0	5.4 / 8.0	+1.6 / −0	+8.0 / +7.0	7.5 / 11.6	+2.5 / −0	+11.6 / +10.0
5.52–6.30	1.5 / 3.2	+1.0 / −0	+3.2 / +2.5	2.4 / 5.0	+1.6 / −0	+5.0 / +4.0	3.4 / 6.0	+1.6 / −0	+6.0 / +5.0	5.4 / 8.0	+1.6 / −0	+8.0 / +7.0	9.5 / 13.6	+2.5 / −0	+13.6 / +12.0
6.30–7.09	1.8 / 3.5	+1.0 / −0	+3.5 / +2.8	2.9 / 5.5	+1.6 / −0	+5.5 / +4.5	4.4 / 7.0	+1.6 / −0	+7.0 / +6.0	6.4 / 9.0	+1.6 / −0	+9.0 / +8.0	9.5 / 13.6	+2.5 / −0	+13.6 / +12.0
7.09–7.88	1.8 / 3.8	+1.2 / −0	+3.8 / +3.0	3.2 / 6.2	+1.8 / −0	+6.2 / +5.0	5.2 / 8.2	+1.8 / −0	+8.2 / +7.0	7.2 / 10.2	+1.8 / −0	+10.2 / +9.0	11.2 / 15.8	+2.8 / −0	+15.8 / +14.0
7.88–8.86	2.3 / 4.3	+1.2 / −0	+4.3 / +3.5	3.2 / 6.2	+1.8 / −0	+6.2 / +5.0	5.2 / 8.2	+1.8 / −0	+8.2 / +7.0	8.2 / 11.2	+1.8 / −0	+11.2 / +10.0	13.2 / 17.8	+2.8 / −0	+17.8 / +16.0
8.86–9.85	2.3 / 4.3	+1.2 / −0	+4.3 / +3.5	4.2 / 7.2	+1.8 / −0	+7.2 / +6.0	6.2 / 9.2	+1.8 / −0	+9.2 / +8.0	10.2 / 13.2	+1.8 / −0	+13.2 / +12.0	13.2 / 17.8	+2.8 / −0	+17.8 / +16.0
9.85–11.03	2.8 / 4.9	+1.2 / −0	+4.9 / +4.0	4.0 / 7.2	+2.0 / −0	+7.2 / +6.0	7.0 / 10.2	+2.0 / −0	+10.2 / +9.0	10.0 / 13.2	+2.0 / −0	+13.2 / +12.0	15.0 / 20.0	+3.0 / −0	+20.0 / +18.0
11.03–12.41	2.8 / 4.9	+1.2 / −0	+4.9 / +4.0	5.0 / 8.2	+2.0 / −0	+8.2 / +7.0	7.0 / 10.2	+2.0 / −0	+10.2 / +9.0	12.0 / 15.2	+2.0 / −0	+15.2 / +14.0	17.0 / 22.0	+3.0 / −0	+22.0 / +20.0
12.41–13.98	3.1 / 5.5	+1.4 / −0	+5.5 / +4.5	5.8 / 9.4	+2.2 / −0	+9.4 / +8.0	7.8 / 11.4	+2.2 / −0	+11.4 / +10.0	13.8 / 17.4	+2.2 / −0	+17.4 / +16.0	18.5 / 24.2	+3.5 / +0	+24.2 / +22.0

[a]From ANSI B4.1-1967 (R1994). For larger diameters, see the standard.

Appendix: International Tolerance Grades[a]

Dimensions are in millimeters.

Basic Sizes Over	Basic Sizes Up to and Including	IT01	IT0	IT1	IT2	IT3	IT4	IT5	IT6	IT7	IT8	IT9	IT10	IT11	IT12	IT13	IT14	IT15	IT16
0	3	0.0003	0.0005	0.0008	0.0012	0.002	0.003	0.004	0.006	0.010	0.014	0.025	0.040	0.060	0.100	0.140	0.250	0.400	0.600
3	6	0.0004	0.0006	0.001	0.0015	0.0025	0.004	0.005	0.008	0.012	0.018	0.030	0.048	0.075	0.120	0.180	0.300	0.480	0.750
6	10	0.0004	0.0006	0.001	0.0015	0.0025	0.004	0.006	0.009	0.015	0.022	0.036	0.058	0.090	0.150	0.220	0.360	0.580	0.900
10	18	0.0005	0.0008	0.0012	0.002	0.003	0.005	0.008	0.011	0.018	0.027	0.043	0.070	0.110	0.180	0.270	0.430	0.700	1.100
18	30	0.0006	0.001	0.0015	0.0025	0.004	0.006	0.009	0.013	0.021	0.033	0.052	0.084	0.130	0.210	0.330	0.520	0.840	1.300
30	50	0.0006	0.001	0.0015	0.0025	0.004	0.007	0.011	0.016	0.025	0.039	0.062	0.100	0.160	0.250	0.390	0.620	1.000	1.600
50	80	0.0008	0.0012	0.002	0.003	0.005	0.008	0.013	0.019	0.030	0.046	0.074	0.120	0.190	0.300	0.460	0.740	1.200	1.900
80	120	0.001	0.0015	0.0025	0.004	0.006	0.010	0.015	0.022	0.035	0.054	0.087	0.140	0.220	0.350	0.540	0.870	1.400	2.200
120	180	0.0012	0.002	0.0035	0.005	0.008	0.012	0.018	0.025	0.040	0.063	0.100	0.160	0.250	0.400	0.630	1.000	1.600	2.500
180	250	0.002	0.003	0.0045	0.007	0.010	0.014	0.020	0.029	0.046	0.072	0.115	0.185	0.290	0.460	0.720	1.150	1.850	2.900
250	315	0.0025	0.004	0.006	0.008	0.012	0.016	0.023	0.032	0.052	0.081	0.130	0.210	0.320	0.520	0.810	1.300	2.100	3.200
315	400	0.003	0.005	0.007	0.009	0.013	0.018	0.025	0.036	0.057	0.089	0.140	0.230	0.360	0.570	0.890	1.400	2.300	3.600
400	500	0.004	0.006	0.008	0.010	0.015	0.020	0.027	0.040	0.063	0.097	0.155	0.250	0.400	0.630	0.970	1.550	2.500	4.000
500	630	0.0045	0.006	0.009	0.011	0.016	0.022	0.030	0.044	0.070	0.110	0.175	0.280	0.440	0.700	1.100	1.750	2.800	4.400
630	800	0.005	0.007	0.010	0.013	0.018	0.025	0.035	0.050	0.080	0.125	0.200	0.320	0.500	0.800	1.250	2.000	3.200	5.000
800	1000	0.0055	0.008	0.011	0.015	0.021	0.029	0.040	0.056	0.090	0.140	0.230	0.360	0.560	0.900	1.400	2.300	3.600	5.600
1000	1250	0.0065	0.009	0.013	0.018	0.024	0.034	0.046	0.066	0.105	0.165	0.260	0.420	0.660	1.050	1.650	2.600	4.200	6.600
1250	1600	0.008	0.011	0.015	0.021	0.029	0.040	0.054	0.078	0.125	0.195	0.310	0.500	0.780	1.250	1.950	3.100	5.000	7.800
1600	2000	0.009	0.013	0.018	0.025	0.035	0.048	0.065	0.092	0.150	0.230	0.370	0.600	0.920	1.500	2.300	3.700	6.000	9.200
2000	2500	0.011	0.015	0.022	0.030	0.041	0.057	0.077	0.110	0.175	0.280	0.440	0.700	1.100	1.750	2.800	4.400	7.000	11.000
2500	3150	0.013	0.018	0.026	0.036	0.050	0.069	0.093	0.135	0.210	0.330	0.540	0.860	1.350	2.100	3.300	5.400	8.600	13.500

Tolerance Grades[b]

[a]From ANSI B4.2-1978 (R1994).

[b]IT Values for tolerance grades larger than IT16 can be calculated by using the formulas: $IT17 = IT \times 10$, $IT18 = IT13 \times 10$, etc.

Dimensions are in millimeters.

Basic Size		Loose Running			Free Running			Close Running			Sliding			Locational Clearance		
		Hole H11	Shaft c11	Fit	Hole H9	Shaft d9	Fit	Hole H8	Shaft f7	Fit	Hole H7	Shaft g6	Fit	Hole H7	Shaft h6	Fit
1	Max	1.060	0.940	0.180	1.025	0.980	0.070	1.014	0.994	0.030	1.010	0.998	0.018	1.010	1.000	0.016
	Min	1.060	0.880	0.060	1.000	0.955	0.020	1.000	0.984	0.006	1.000	0.992	0.002	1.000	0.994	0.000
1.2	Max	1.260	1.140	0.180	1.225	1.180	0.070	1.214	1.194	0.030	1.210	1.198	0.018	1.210	1.200	0.016
	Min	1.200	1.080	0.060	1.200	1.155	0.020	1.200	1.184	0.006	1.200	1.192	0.002	1.200	1.194	0.000
1.6	Max	1.660	1.540	0.180	1.625	1.580	0.070	1.614	1.594	0.030	1.610	1.598	0.018	1.610	1.600	0.016
	Min	1.600	1.480	0.060	1.600	1.555	0.020	1.600	1.584	0.006	1.600	1.592	0.002	1.600	1.594	0.000
2	Max	2.060	1.940	0.180	2.025	1.980	0.070	2.014	1.994	0.030	2.010	1.998	0.018	2.010	2.000	0.016
	Min	2.000	1.880	0.060	2.000	1.955	0.020	2.000	1.984	0.006	2.000	1.992	0.002	2.000	1.994	0.000
2.5	Max	2.560	2.440	0.180	2.525	2.480	0.070	2.514	2.494	0.030	2.510	2.498	0.018	2.510	2.500	0.016
	Min	2.500	2.380	0.060	2.500	2.455	0.020	2.500	2.484	0.006	2.500	2.492	0.002	2.500	2.494	0.000
3	Max	3.060	2.940	0.180	3.025	2.980	0.070	3.014	2.994	0.030	3.010	2.998	0.018	3.010	3.000	0.016
	Min	3.000	2.880	0.060	3.000	2.955	0.020	3.000	2.984	0.006	3.000	2.992	0.002	3.000	2.994	0.000
4	Max	4.075	3.930	0.220	4.030	3.970	0.090	4.018	3.990	0.040	4.012	3.996	0.024	4.012	4.000	0.020
	Min	4.000	3.855	0.070	4.000	3.940	0.030	4.000	3.978	0.010	4.000	3.988	0.004	4.000	3.992	0.000
5	Max	5.075	4.930	0.220	5.030	4.970	0.090	5.018	4.990	0.040	5.012	4.996	0.024	5.012	5.000	0.020
	Min	5.000	4.855	0.070	5.000	4.940	0.030	5.000	4.978	0.010	5.000	4.988	0.004	5.000	4.992	0.000
6	Max	6.075	5.930	0.220	6.030	5.970	0.090	6.018	5.990	0.040	6.012	5.996	0.024	6.012	6.000	0.020
	Min	6.000	5.855	0.070	6.000	5.940	0.030	6.000	5.978	0.010	6.000	5.988	0.004	6.000	5.992	0.000
8	Max	8.090	7.920	0.260	8.036	7.960	0.112	8.022	7.987	0.050	8.015	7.995	0.029	8.015	8.000	0.024
	Min	8.000	7.830	0.080	8.000	7.924	0.040	8.000	7.972	0.013	8.000	7.986	0.005	8.000	7.991	0.000
10	Max	10.090	9.920	0.260	10.036	9.960	0.112	10.022	9.987	0.050	10.015	9.995	0.029	10.015	10.000	0.024
	Min	10.000	9.830	0.080	10.000	9.924	0.040	10.000	9.972	0.013	10.000	9.986	0.005	10.000	9.991	0.000
12	Max	12.110	11.905	0.315	12.043	11.950	0.136	12.027	11.984	0.061	12.018	11.994	0.035	12.018	12.000	0.029
	Min	12.000	11.795	0.095	12.000	11.907	0.050	12.000	11.966	0.016	12.000	11.983	0.006	12.000	11.989	0.000
16	Max	16.110	15.905	0.315	16.043	15.950	0.136	16.027	15.984	0.061	16.018	15.994	0.035	16.018	16.000	0.029
	Min	16.000	15.795	0.095	16.000	15.907	0.050	16.000	15.966	0.016	16.000	15.983	0.006	16.000	15.989	0.000
20	Max	20.130	19.890	0.370	20.052	19.935	0.169	20.033	19.980	0.074	20.021	19.993	0.041	20.021	20.000	0.034
	Min	20.000	19.760	0.110	20.000	19.883	0.065	20.000	19.959	0.020	20.000	19.980	0.007	20.000	19.987	0.000
25	Max	25.130	24.890	0.370	25.052	24.935	0.169	25.033	24.980	0.074	25.021	24.993	0.041	25.021	25.000	0.034
	Min	25.000	24.760	0.110	25.000	24.883	0.065	25.000	24.959	0.020	25.000	24.980	0.007	25.000	24.987	0.000
30	Max	30.130	29.890	0.370	30.052	29.935	0.169	30.033	29.980	0.074	30.021	29.993	0.041	30.021	30.000	0.034
	Min	30.000	29.760	0.110	30.000	29.883	0.065	30.000	29.959	0.020	30.000	29.980	0.007	30.000	29.987	0.000

[a]From ANSI B4.2-1978 (R1994).

Preferred Metric Hole Basis Clearance Fits[a]— American National Standard (continued)

Dimensions are in millimeters.

Basic Size		Loose Running			Free Running			Close Running			Sliding			Locational Clearance		
		Hole H11	Shaft c11	Fit	Hole H9	Shaft d9	Fit	Hole H8	Shaft f7	Fit	Hole H7	Shaft g6	Fit	Hole H7	Shaft h6	Fit
40	Max	40.160	39.880	0.440	40.062	39.920	0.204	40.039	39.975	0.089	40.025	39.991	0.050	40.025	40.000	0.041
	Min	40.000	39.720	0.120	40.000	39.858	0.080	40.000	39.950	0.025	40.000	39.975	0.009	40.000	39.984	0.000
50	Max	50.160	49.870	0.450	50.062	49.920	0.204	50.039	49.975	0.089	50.025	49.991	0.050	50.025	50.000	0.041
	Min	50.000	49.710	0.130	50.000	49.858	0.080	50.000	49.950	0.025	50.000	49.975	0.009	50.000	49.984	0.000
60	Max	60.190	59.860	0.520	60.074	59.900	0.248	60.046	59.970	0.106	60.030	59.990	0.059	60.030	60.000	0.049
	Min	60.000	59.670	0.140	60.000	59.826	0.100	60.000	59.940	0.030	60.000	59.971	0.010	60.000	59.981	0.000
80	Max	80.190	79.950	0.530	80.074	79.900	0.248	80.046	79.970	0.106	80.030	79.990	0.059	80.030	80.000	0.049
	Min	80.000	79.660	0.150	80.000	79.826	0.100	80.000	79.940	0.030	80.000	79.971	0.010	80.000	79.981	0.000
100	Max	100.220	99.830	0.610	100.087	99.880	0.294	100.054	99.964	0.125	100.035	99.988	0.069	100.035	100.000	0.057
	Min	100.000	99.610	0.170	100.000	99.793	0.120	100.000	99.929	0.036	100.000	99.966	0.012	100.000	99.978	0.000
120	Max	120.220	119.820	0.620	120.087	119.880	0.294	120.054	119.964	0.125	120.035	119.988	0.069	120.035	120.000	0.057
	Min	120.000	119.600	0.180	120.000	119.793	0.120	120.000	119.929	0.036	120.000	119.966	0.012	120.000	119.978	0.000
160	Max	160.250	159.790	0.710	160.100	159.855	0.345	160.063	159.957	0.146	160.040	159.986	0.079	160.040	160.000	0.065
	Min	160.000	159.540	0.210	160.000	159.755	0.145	160.000	159.917	0.043	160.000	159.961	0.014	160.000	159.975	0.000
200	Max	200.290	199.760	0.820	200.115	199.830	0.400	200.072	199.950	0.168	200.046	199.985	0.090	200.046	200.000	0.075
	Min	200.000	199.470	0.240	200.000	199.715	0.170	200.000	199.904	0.050	200.000	199.956	0.015	200.000	199.971	0.000
250	Max	250.290	249.720	0.860	250.115	249.830	0.400	250.072	249.950	0.168	250.046	249.985	0.090	250.046	250.000	0.075
	Min	250.000	249.430	0.280	250.000	249.715	0.170	250.000	249.904	0.050	250.000	249.956	0.015	250.000	249.971	0.000
300	Max	300.320	299.670	0.970	300.130	299.810	0.450	300.081	299.944	0.189	300.052	299.983	0.101	300.052	300.000	0.084
	Min	300.000	299.350	0.330	300.000	299.680	0.190	300.000	299.892	0.056	300.000	299.951	0.017	300.000	299.968	0.000
400	Max	400.360	399.600	1.120	400.140	399.790	0.490	400.089	399.938	0.208	400.057	399.982	0.111	400.057	400.000	0.093
	Min	400.000	399.240	0.400	400.000	399.650	0.210	400.000	399.881	0.062	400.000	399.946	0.018	400.000	399.964	0.000
500	Max	500.400	499.520	1.280	500.155	499.770	0.540	500.097	499.932	0.228	500.063	499.980	0.123	500.063	500.000	0.103
	Min	500.000	499.120	0.480	500.000	499.615	0.230	500.000	499.869	0.068	500.000	499.940	0.020	500.000	499.960	0.000

[a]From ANSI B4.2-1978 (R1994).

Appendix: Preferred Metric Hole Basis Transition and Interference Fits[a]— American National Standard

Dimensions are in millimeters.

Basic Size		Locational Transn. Hole H7	Locational Transn. Shaft k6	Locational Transn. Fit	Locational Transn. Hole H7	Locational Transn. Shaft n6	Locational Transn. Fit	Locational Interf. Hole H7	Locational Interf. Shaft p6	Locational Interf. Fit	Medium Drive Hole H7	Medium Drive Shaft s6	Medium Drive Fit	Force Hole H7	Force Shaft u6	Force Fit
1	Max	1.010	1.006	0.010	1.010	1.010	0.006	1.010	1.012	0.004	1.010	1.020	-0.004	1.010	1.024	-0.008
	Min	1.000	1.000	-0.006	1.000	1.004	-0.010	1.000	1.006	-0.012	1.000	1.014	-0.020	1.000	1.018	-0.024
1.2	Max	1.210	1.206	0.010	1.210	1.210	0.006	1.210	1.212	0.004	1.210	1.220	-0.004	1.210	1.224	-0.008
	Min	1.200	1.200	-0.006	1.200	1.204	-0.010	1.200	1.206	-0.012	1.200	1.214	-0.020	1.200	1.218	-0.024
1.6	Max	1.610	1.606	0.010	1.610	1.610	0.006	1.610	1.612	0.004	1.610	1.620	-0.004	1.610	1.624	-0.008
	Min	1.600	1.600	-0.006	1.600	1.604	-0.010	1.600	1.606	-0.012	1.600	1.614	-0.020	1.600	1.618	-0.024
2	Max	2.010	2.006	0.010	2.010	2.010	0.006	2.010	2.012	0.004	2.010	2.020	-0.004	2.010	2.024	-0.008
	Min	2.000	2.000	-0.006	2.000	2.004	-0.010	2.000	2.006	-0.012	2.000	2.014	-0.020	2.000	2.018	-0.024
2.5	Max	2.510	2.506	0.010	2.510	2.510	0.006	2.510	2.512	0.004	2.510	2.520	-0.004	2.510	2.524	-0.008
	Min	2.500	2.500	-0.006	2.500	2.504	-0.010	2.500	2.506	-0.012	2.500	2.514	-0.020	2.500	2.518	-0.024
3	Max	3.010	3.006	0.010	3.010	3.010	0.006	3.010	3.012	0.004	3.010	3.020	-0.004	3.010	3.024	-0.008
	Min	3.000	3.000	-0.006	3.000	3.004	-0.010	3.000	3.006	-0.012	3.000	3.014	-0.020	3.000	3.018	-0.024
4	Max	4.012	4.009	0.011	4.012	4.016	0.004	4.012	4.020	0.000	4.012	4.027	-0.007	4.012	4.031	-0.011
	Min	4.000	4.001	-0.009	4.000	4.008	-0.016	4.000	4.012	-0.020	4.000	4.019	-0.027	4.000	4.023	-0.031
5	Max	5.012	5.009	0.011	5.012	5.016	0.004	5.012	5.020	0.000	5.012	5.027	-0.007	5.012	5.031	-0.011
	Min	5.000	5.001	-0.009	5.000	5.008	-0.016	5.000	5.012	-0.020	5.000	5.019	-0.027	5.000	5.023	-0.031
6	Max	6.012	6.009	0.011	6.012	6.016	0.004	6.012	6.020	0.000	6.012	6.027	-0.007	6.012	6.031	-0.011
	Min	6.000	6.001	-0.009	6.000	6.008	-0.016	6.000	6.012	-0.020	6.000	6.019	-0.027	6.000	6.023	-0.031
8	Max	8.015	8.010	0.014	8.015	8.019	0.005	8.015	8.024	0.000	8.015	8.032	-0.008	8.015	8.037	-0.013
	Min	8.000	8.001	-0.010	8.000	8.010	-0.019	8.000	8.015	-0.024	8.000	8.023	-0.032	8.000	8.028	-0.037
10	Max	10.015	10.010	0.014	10.015	10.019	0.005	10.015	10.024	0.000	10.015	10.032	-0.008	10.015	10.037	-0.013
	Min	10.000	10.001	-0.010	10.000	10.010	-0.019	10.000	10.015	-0.024	10.000	10.023	-0.032	10.000	10.028	-0.037
12	Max	12.018	12.012	0.017	12.018	12.023	0.006	12.018	12.029	0.000	12.018	12.039	-0.010	12.018	12.044	-0.015
	Min	12.000	12.001	-0.012	12.000	12.012	-0.023	12.000	12.018	-0.029	12.000	12.028	-0.039	12.000	12.033	-0.044
16	Max	16.018	16.012	0.017	16.018	16.023	0.006	16.018	16.029	0.000	16.018	16.039	-0.010	16.018	16.044	-0.015
	Min	16.000	16.001	-0.012	16.000	16.012	-0.023	16.000	16.018	-0.029	16.000	16.028	-0.039	16.000	16.033	-0.044
20	Max	20.081	20.015	0.019	20.021	20.028	0.006	20.021	20.035	-0.001	20.021	20.048	-0.014	20.021	20.054	-0.020
	Min	20.000	20.002	-0.015	20.000	20.015	-0.028	20.000	20.022	-0.035	20.000	20.035	-0.048	20.000	20.041	-0.054
25	Max	25.021	25.015	0.019	25.021	25.028	0.006	25.021	25.035	-0.001	25.021	25.048	-0.014	25.021	25.061	-0.027
	Min	25.000	25.002	-0.015	25.000	25.015	-0.028	25.000	25.022	-0.035	25.000	25.035	-0.048	25.000	25.048	-0.061
30	Max	30.021	30.015	0.019	30.021	30.028	0.006	30.021	30.035	-0.001	30.021	30.048	-0.014	30.021	30.061	-0.027
	Min	30.000	30.002	-0.015	30.000	30.015	-0.028	30.000	30.022	-0.035	30.000	30.035	-0.048	30.000	30.048	-0.061

[a]From ANSI B4.2-1978 (R1994).

Preferred Metric Hole Basis Transition and Interference Fits[a]— American National Standard (continued)

Dimensions are in millimeters.

Basic Size		Locational Transn. Hole H7	Shaft k6	Fit	Locational Transn. Hole H7	Shaft n6	Fit	Locational Interf. Hole H7	Shaft p6	Fit	Medium Drive Hole H7	Shaft s6	Fit	Force Hole H7	Shaft u6	Fit
40	Max	40.025	40.018	0.023	40.025	40.033	0.008	40.025	40.042	-0.001	40.025	40.059	-0.018	40.025	40.076	-0.035
	Min	40.000	40.002	-0.018	40.000	40.017	-0.033	40.000	40.026	-0.042	40.000	40.043	-0.059	40.000	40.060	-0.076
50	Max	50.025	50.018	0.023	50.025	50.033	0.008	50.025	50.042	-0.001	50.025	50.059	-0.018	50.025	50.086	-0.045
	Min	50.000	50.002	-0.018	50.000	50.017	-0.033	50.000	50.026	-0.042	50.000	50.043	-0.059	50.000	50.070	-0.086
60	Max	60.030	60.021	0.028	60.030	60.039	0.010	60.030	60.051	-0.002	60.030	60.072	-0.023	60.030	60.106	-0.057
	Min	60.000	60.002	-0.021	60.000	60.020	-0.039	60.000	60.032	-0.051	60.000	60.053	-0.072	60.000	60.087	-0.106
80	Max	80.030	80.021	0.028	80.030	80.039	0.010	80.030	80.051	-0.002	80.030	80.078	-0.029	80.030	80.121	-0.072
	Min	80.000	80.002	-0.021	80.000	80.020	-0.039	80.000	80.032	-0.051	80.000	80.059	-0.078	80.000	80.102	-0.121
100	Max	100.035	100.025	0.032	100.035	100.045	0.012	100.035	100.059	-0.002	100.035	100.093	-0.036	100.035	100.146	-0.089
	Min	100.000	100.003	-0.025	100.000	100.023	-0.045	100.000	100.037	-0.059	100.000	100.071	-0.093	100.000	100.124	-0.146
120	Max	120.035	120.025	0.032	120.035	120.045	0.012	120.035	120.059	-0.002	120.035	120.101	-0.044	120.035	120.166	-0.109
	Min	120.000	120.003	-0.025	120.000	120.023	-0.045	120.000	120.037	-0.059	120.000	120.079	-0.101	120.000	120.144	-0.166
160	Max	160.040	160.028	0.037	160.040	160.052	0.013	160.040	160.068	-0.003	160.040	160.125	-0.060	160.040	160.215	-0.150
	Min	160.000	160.003	-0.028	160.000	160.027	-0.052	160.000	160.043	-0.068	160.000	160.100	-0.125	160.000	160.190	-0.215
200	Max	200.046	200.033	0.042	200.046	200.060	0.015	200.046	200.079	-0.004	200.046	200.151	-0.076	200.046	200.265	-0.190
	Min	200.000	200.004	-0.033	200.000	200.031	-0.060	200.000	200.050	-0.079	200.000	200.122	-0.151	200.000	200.236	-0.265
250	Max	250.046	250.033	0.042	250.046	250.060	0.015	250.046	250.079	-0.004	250.046	250.169	-0.094	250.046	250.313	-0.238
	Min	250.000	250.004	-0.033	250.000	250.031	-0.060	250.000	250.050	-0.079	250.000	250.140	-0.169	250.000	250.284	-0.313
300	Max	300.052	300.036	0.048	300.052	300.066	0.018	300.052	300.088	-0.004	300.052	300.202	-0.118	300.052	300.382	-0.298
	Min	300.000	300.004	-0.036	300.000	300.034	-0.066	300.000	300.056	-0.088	300.000	300.170	-0.202	300.000	300.350	-0.382
400	Max	400.057	400.040	0.053	400.057	400.073	0.020	400.057	400.098	-0.005	400.057	400.244	-0.151	400.057	400.471	-0.378
	Min	400.000	400.004	-0.040	400.000	400.037	-0.073	400.000	400.062	-0.098	400.000	400.208	-0.244	400.000	400.435	-0.471
500	Max	500.063	500.045	0.058	500.063	500.080	0.023	500.063	500.108	-0.005	500.063	500.292	-0.189	500.063	500.580	-0.477
	Min	500.000	500.005	-0.045	500.000	500.040	-0.080	500.000	500.068	-0.108	500.000	500.252	-0.292	500.000	500.540	-0.580

[a] From ANSI B4.2-1978 (R1994).

Appendix: Preferred Metric Shaft Basis Clearance Fitsᵃ—American National Standard

Dimensions are in millimeters.

Basic Size		Loose Running Hole C11	Loose Running Shaft h11	Loose Running Fit	Free Running Hole D9	Free Running Shaft h9	Free Running Fit	Close Running Hole F8	Close Running Shaft h7	Close Running Fit	Sliding Hole G7	Sliding Shaft h6	Sliding Fit	Locational Clearance Hole H7	Locational Clearance Shaft h6	Locational Clearance Fit
1	Max	1.120	1.000	0.180	1.045	1.000	0.070	1.020	1.000	0.030	1.012	1.000	0.018	1.010	1.000	0.016
	Min	1.060	0.940	0.060	1.020	0.975	0.020	1.006	0.990	0.006	1.002	0.994	0.002	1.000	0.994	0.000
1.2	Max	1.320	1.200	0.180	1.245	1.200	0.070	1.220	1.200	0.030	1.212	1.200	0.018	1.210	1.200	0.016
	Min	1.260	0.140	0.060	1.220	0.175	0.020	1.206	1.190	0.006	1.202	1.194	0.002	1.200	1.194	0.000
1.6	Max	1.720	1.600	0.180	1.645	1.600	0.070	1.620	1.600	0.030	1.612	1.600	0.018	1.610	1.600	0.016
	Min	1.660	0.540	0.060	1.620	0.575	0.020	1.606	1.590	0.006	1.602	1.594	0.002	1.600	1.594	0.000
2	Max	2.120	2.000	0.180	2.045	2.000	0.070	2.020	2.000	0.030	2.012	2.000	0.018	2.010	2.000	0.016
	Min	2.060	1.940	0.060	2.020	1.975	0.020	2.006	1.990	0.006	2.002	1.994	0.002	2.000	1.994	0.000
2.5	Max	2.620	2.500	0.180	2.545	2.500	0.070	2.520	2.500	0.030	2.512	2.500	0.018	2.510	2.500	0.016
	Min	2.560	2.440	0.060	2.520	2.475	0.020	2.506	2.490	0.006	2.502	2.494	0.002	2.500	2.494	0.000
3	Max	3.120	3.000	0.180	3.045	3.000	0.070	3.020	3.000	0.030	3.012	3.000	0.018	3.010	3.000	0.016
	Min	3.060	2.940	0.060	3.020	2.975	0.020	3.006	2.990	0.006	3.002	2.994	0.002	3.000	2.994	0.000
4	Max	4.145	4.000	0.220	4.060	4.000	0.090	4.028	4.000	0.040	4.016	4.000	0.024	4.012	4.000	0.020
	Min	4.070	3.925	0.070	4.030	3.970	0.030	4.010	3.988	0.010	4.004	3.992	0.004	4.000	3.992	0.000
5	Max	5.145	5.000	0.220	5.060	5.000	0.090	5.028	5.000	0.040	5.016	5.000	0.024	5.012	5.000	0.020
	Min	5.070	4.925	0.070	5.030	4.970	0.030	5.010	4.988	0.010	5.004	4.992	0.004	5.000	4.992	0.000
6	Max	6.145	6.000	0.220	6.060	6.000	0.090	6.028	6.000	0.040	6.016	6.000	0.024	6.012	6.000	0.020
	Min	6.070	5.925	0.070	6.030	5.970	0.030	6.010	5.988	0.010	6.004	5.992	0.004	6.000	5.992	0.000
8	Max	8.170	8.000	0.260	8.076	8.000	0.112	8.035	8.000	0.050	8.020	8.000	0.029	8.015	8.000	0.024
	Min	8.080	7.910	0.080	8.040	7.964	0.040	8.013	7.985	0.013	8.005	7.991	0.005	8.000	7.991	0.000
10	Max	10.170	10.000	0.260	10.076	10.000	0.112	10.035	10.000	0.050	10.020	10.000	0.029	10.015	10.000	0.024
	Min	10.080	9.910	0.080	10.040	9.964	0.040	10.013	9.985	0.013	10.005	9.991	0.005	10.000	9.991	0.000
12	Max	12.205	12.000	0.315	12.093	12.000	0.136	12.043	12.000	0.061	12.024	12.000	0.035	12.018	12.000	0.029
	Min	12.095	11.890	0.095	12.050	11.957	0.050	12.016	11.982	0.016	12.006	11.989	0.006	12.000	11.989	0.000
16	Max	16.205	16.000	0.315	16.093	16.000	0.136	16.043	16.000	0.061	16.024	16.000	0.035	16.018	16.000	0.029
	Min	16.095	15.890	0.095	16.050	15.957	0.050	16.016	15.982	0.016	16.006	15.989	0.006	16.000	15.989	0.000
20	Max	20.240	20.000	0.370	20.117	20.000	0.169	20.053	20.000	0.074	20.028	20.000	0.041	20.021	20.000	0.034
	Min	20.110	19.870	0.110	20.065	19.948	0.065	20.020	19.979	0.020	20.007	19.987	0.007	20.000	19.987	0.000
25	Max	25.240	25.000	0.370	25.117	25.000	0.169	25.053	25.000	0.074	25.028	25.000	0.041	25.021	25.000	0.034
	Min	25.110	24.870	0.110	25.065	24.948	0.065	25.020	24.979	0.020	25.007	24.987	0.007	25.000	24.987	0.000
30	Max	30.240	30.000	0.370	30.117	30.000	0.169	30.053	30.000	0.074	30.028	30.000	0.041	30.021	30.000	0.034
	Min	30.110	29.870	0.110	30.065	29.948	0.065	30.020	29.979	0.020	30.007	29.987	0.007	30.000	29.987	0.000

ᵃFrom ANSI B4.2-1978 (R1994).

From Appendix 15 of *Modern Graphics Communication*, Fourth Edition, Frederick E. Giesecke, Alva Mitchell, Henry Cecil Spencer, Ivan Leroy Hill, John Thomas Dygdon, James E. Novak, Shawna Lockhart. Copyright © 2010 by Pearson Education, Inc. Published by Pearson Prentice Hall. All rights reserved.

Preferred Metric Shaft Basis Clearance Fits[a]—American National Standard (continued)

Dimensions are in millimeters.

Basic Size		Loose Running Hole C11	Shaft h11	Fit	Free Running Hole D9	Shaft h9	Fit	Close Running Hole F8	Shaft h7	Fit	Sliding Hole G7	Shaft h6	Fit	Locational Clearance Hole H7	Shaft h6	Fit
40	Max	40.280	40.000	0.440	40.142	40.000	0.204	40.064	40.000	0.089	40.034	40.000	0.050	40.025	40.000	0.041
	Min	40.120	39.840	0.120	40.080	39.938	0.080	40.025	39.975	0.025	40.009	39.984	0.009	40.000	39.984	0.000
50	Max	50.290	50.000	0.450	50.142	50.000	0.204	50.064	50.000	0.089	50.034	50.000	0.050	50.025	50.000	0.041
	Min	50.130	49.840	0.130	50.080	49.938	0.080	50.025	49.975	0.025	50.009	49.984	0.009	50.000	49.984	0.000
60	Max	60.330	60.000	0.520	60.174	60.000	0.248	60.076	60.000	0.106	60.040	60.000	0.059	60.030	60.000	0.049
	Min	60.140	59.810	0.140	60.100	59.926	0.100	60.030	59.970	0.030	60.010	59.981	0.010	60.000	59.981	0.000
80	Max	80.340	80.000	0.530	80.174	80.000	0.248	80.076	80.000	0.106	80.040	80.000	0.059	80.030	80.000	0.049
	Min	80.150	79.810	0.150	80.100	79.926	0.100	80.030	79.970	0.030	80.010	79.981	0.010	80.000	79.981	0.000
100	Max	100.390	100.000	0.610	100.207	100.000	0.294	100.090	100.000	0.125	100.047	100.000	0.069	100.035	100.000	0.057
	Min	100.170	99.780	0.170	100.120	99.913	0.120	100.036	99.965	0.036	100.012	99.978	0.012	100.000	99.978	0.000
120	Max	120.400	120.000	0.620	120.207	120.000	0.294	120.090	120.000	0.125	120.047	120.000	0.069	120.035	120.000	0.057
	Min	120.180	119.780	0.180	120.120	119.913	0.120	120.036	119.965	0.036	120.012	119.978	0.012	120.000	119.978	0.000
160	Max	160.460	160.000	0.710	160.245	160.000	0.345	160.106	160.000	0.146	160.054	160.000	0.079	160.040	160.000	0.065
	Min	160.210	159.750	0.210	160.145	159.900	0.145	160.043	159.960	0.043	160.014	159.975	0.014	160.000	159.975	0.000
200	Max	200.530	200.000	0.820	200.285	200.000	0.400	200.122	200.000	0.168	200.061	200.000	0.090	200.046	200.000	0.075
	Min	200.240	199.710	0.240	200.170	199.885	0.170	200.050	199.954	0.050	200.015	199.971	0.015	200.000	199.971	0.000
250	Max	250.570	250.000	0.860	250.285	250.000	0.400	250.122	250.000	0.168	250.061	250.000	0.090	250.046	250.000	0.075
	Min	250.280	249.710	0.280	250.170	249.885	0.170	250.050	249.954	0.050	250.015	249.971	0.015	250.000	249.971	0.000
300	Max	300.650	300.000	0.970	300.320	300.000	0.450	300.137	300.000	0.189	300.069	300.000	0.101	300.052	300.000	0.084
	Min	300.330	299.680	0.330	300.190	299.870	0.190	300.056	299.948	0.056	300.017	299.968	0.017	300.000	299.968	0.000
400	Max	400.760	400.000	1.120	400.350	400.000	0.490	400.151	400.000	0.208	400.075	400.000	0.111	400.057	400.000	0.093
	Min	400.400	399.640	0.400	400.210	399.860	0.210	400.062	399.943	0.062	400.018	399.964	0.018	400.000	399.964	0.000
500	Max	500.880	500.000	1.280	500.385	500.000	0.540	500.165	500.000	0.228	500.083	500.000	0.123	500.063	500.000	0.103
	Min	500.480	499.600	0.480	500.230	499.845	0.230	500.068	499.937	0.068	500.020	499.960	5.020	500.000	499.960	0.000

[a]From ANSI B4.2-1978 (R1994).

Appendix: Preferred Metric Shaft Basis Transition and Interference Fits[a]— American National Standard

Dimensions are in millimeters.

Basic Size		Locational Transn. Hole K7	Locational Transn. Shaft h6	Locational Transn. Fit	Locational Transn. Hole N7	Locational Transn. Shaft h6	Locational Transn. Fit	Locational Interf. Hole P7	Locational Interf. Shaft h6	Locational Interf. Fit	Medium Drive Hole S7	Medium Drive Shaft h6	Medium Drive Fit	Force Hole U7	Force Shaft h6	Force Fit
1	Max	1.000	1.000	0.006	0.996	1.000	0.002	0.994	1.000	0.000	0.986	1.000	−0.008	0.982	1.000	−0.012
	Min	0.990	0.994	−0.010	0.986	0.994	−0.014	0.984	0.994	−0.016	0.976	0.994	−0.024	0.972	0.994	−0.028
1.2	Max	1.200	1.200	0.006	1.196	1.200	0.002	1.194	1.200	0.000	1.186	1.200	−0.008	1.182	1.200	−0.012
	Min	1.190	1.194	−0.010	1.186	1.194	−0.014	1.184	1.194	−0.016	1.176	1.194	−0.024	1.172	1.194	−0.028
1.6	Max	1.600	1.600	0.006	1.596	1.600	0.002	1.594	1.600	0.000	1.586	1.600	−0.008	1.582	1.600	−0.012
	Min	1.590	1.594	−0.010	1.586	1.594	−0.014	1.584	1.594	−0.016	1.576	1.594	−0.024	1.572	1.594	−0.028
2	Max	2.000	2.000	0.006	1.996	2.000	0.002	1.994	2.000	0.000	1.986	2.000	−0.008	1.982	2.000	−0.012
	Min	1.990	1.994	−0.010	1.986	1.994	−0.014	1.984	1.994	−0.016	1.976	1.994	−0.024	1.972	1.994	−0.028
2.5	Max	2.500	2.500	0.006	2.496	2.500	0.002	2.494	2.500	0.000	2.486	2.500	−0.008	2.482	2.500	−0.012
	Min	2.490	2.494	−0.010	2.486	2.494	−0.014	2.484	2.494	−0.016	2.476	2.494	−0.024	2.472	2.494	−0.028
3	Max	3.000	3.000	0.006	2.996	3.000	0.002	2.994	3.000	0.000	2.986	3.000	−0.008	2.982	3.000	−0.012
	Min	2.990	2.994	−0.010	2.986	2.994	−0.014	2.984	2.994	−0.016	2.976	2.994	−0.024	2.972	2.994	−0.028
4	Max	4.003	4.000	0.011	3.996	4.000	0.004	3.992	4.000	0.000	3.985	4.000	−0.007	3.981	4.000	−0.011
	Min	3.991	3.992	−0.009	3.984	3.992	−0.016	3.980	3.992	−0.020	3.973	3.992	−0.027	3.969	3.992	−0.031
5	Max	5.003	5.000	0.011	4.996	5.000	0.004	4.992	5.000	0.000	4.985	5.000	−0.007	4.981	5.000	−0.011
	Min	4.991	4.992	−0.009	4.984	4.992	−0.016	4.980	4.992	−0.020	4.973	4.992	−0.027	4.969	4.992	−0.031
6	Max	6.003	6.000	0.011	5.996	6.000	0.004	5.992	6.000	0.000	5.985	6.000	−0.007	5.981	6.000	−0.011
	Min	5.991	5.992	−0.009	5.984	5.992	−0.016	5.980	5.992	−0.020	5.973	5.992	−0.027	5.969	5.992	−0.031
8	Max	8.005	8.000	0.014	7.996	8.000	0.005	7.991	8.000	0.000	7.983	8.000	−0.008	7.978	8.000	−0.013
	Min	7.990	7.991	−0.010	7.981	7.991	−0.019	7.976	7.991	−0.024	7.968	7.991	−0.032	7.963	7.991	−0.037
10	Max	10.005	10.000	0.014	9.996	10.000	0.005	9.991	10.000	0.000	9.983	10.000	−0.008	9.978	10.000	−0.013
	Min	9.990	9.991	−0.010	9.981	9.991	−0.019	9.976	9.991	−0.024	9.968	9.991	−0.032	9.963	9.991	−0.037
12	Max	12.006	12.000	0.017	11.995	12.000	0.006	11.989	12.000	0.000	11.979	12.000	−0.010	11.974	12.000	−0.015
	Min	11.988	11.989	−0.012	11.977	11.989	−0.023	11.971	11.989	−0.029	11.961	11.989	−0.039	11.956	11.989	−0.044
16	Max	16.006	16.000	0.017	15.995	16.000	0.006	15.989	16.000	0.000	15.979	16.000	−0.010	15.974	16.000	−0.015
	Min	15.988	15.989	−0.012	15.977	15.989	−0.023	15.971	15.989	−0.029	15.961	15.989	−0.039	15.956	15.989	−0.044
20	Max	20.006	20.000	0.019	19.993	20.000	0.006	19.986	20.000	−0.001	19.973	20.000	−0.014	19.967	20.000	−0.020
	Min	19.985	19.987	−0.015	19.972	19.987	−0.028	19.965	19.987	−0.035	19.952	19.987	−0.048	19.946	19.987	−0.054
25	Max	25.006	25.000	0.019	24.993	25.000	0.006	24.986	25.000	−0.001	24.973	25.000	−0.014	24.960	25.000	−0.027
	Min	24.985	24.987	−0.015	24.972	24.987	−0.028	24.965	24.987	−0.035	24.952	24.987	−0.048	24.939	24.987	−0.061
30	Max	30.006	30.000	0.019	29.993	30.000	0.006	29.986	30.000	−0.001	29.973	30.000	−0.014	29.960	30.000	−0.027
	Min	29.985	29.987	−0.015	29.972	29.987	−0.028	29.965	29.987	−0.035	29.952	29.987	−0.048	29.939	29.987	−0.061

[a]From ANSI B4.2-1978 (R1994).

Preferred Metric Basis Transition and Interference Fits[a]— American National Standard (continued)

Dimensions are in millimeters.

Basic Size		Locational Transn. Hole K7	Shaft h6	Fit	Locational Transn. Hole N7	Shaft h6	Fit	Locational Interf. Hole P7	Shaft h6	Fit	Medium Drive Hole S7	Shaft h6	Fit	Force Hole U7	Shaft h6	Fit
40	Max	40.007	40.000	0.023	39.992	40.000	0.008	39.983	40.000	-0.001	39.966	40.000	-0.018	39.949	40.000	-0.035
	Min	39.982	39.984	-0.018	39.967	39.984	-0.033	39.958	39.984	-0.042	39.941	39.984	-0.059	39.924	39.984	-0.076
50	Max	50.007	50.000	0.023	49.992	50.000	0.008	49.983	50.000	-0.001	49.966	50.000	-0.018	49.939	50.000	-0.045
	Min	49.982	49.984	-0.018	49.967	49.984	-0.033	49.958	49.984	-0.042	49.941	49.984	-0.059	49.914	49.984	-0.086
60	Max	60.009	60.000	0.028	59.991	60.000	0.010	59.979	60.000	-0.002	59.958	60.000	-0.023	59.924	60.000	-0.057
	Min	59.979	59.981	-0.021	59.961	59.981	-0.039	59.949	59.981	-0.051	59.928	59.981	-0.072	59.894	59.981	-0.106
80	Max	80.009	80.000	0.028	79.991	80.000	0.010	79.979	80.000	-0.002	79.952	80.000	-0.029	79.909	80.000	-0.072
	Min	79.979	79.981	-0.021	79.961	79.981	-0.039	79.949	79.981	-0.051	79.922	79.981	-0.078	79.879	79.981	-0.121
100	Max	100.010	100.000	0.032	99.990	100.000	0.012	99.976	100.000	-0.002	99.942	100.000	-0.036	99.889	100.000	-0.089
	Min	99.975	99.978	-0.025	99.955	99.978	-0.045	99.941	99.978	-0.059	99.907	99.978	-0.093	99.854	99.978	-0.146
120	Max	120.010	120.000	0.032	119.990	120.000	0.012	119.976	120.000	-0.002	119.934	120.000	-0.044	119.869	120.000	-0.109
	Min	119.975	119.978	-0.025	119.955	119.978	-0.045	119.941	119.978	-0.059	119.899	119.978	-0.101	119.834	119.978	-0.166
160	Max	160.012	160.000	0.037	159.988	160.000	0.013	159.972	160.000	-0.003	159.915	160.000	-0.060	159.825	160.000	-0.150
	Min	159.972	159.975	-0.028	159.948	159.975	-0.052	159.932	159.975	-0.068	159.875	159.975	-0.125	159.785	159.975	-0.215
200	Max	200.013	200.000	0.042	199.986	200.000	0.015	199.967	200.000	-0.004	199.895	200.000	-0.076	199.781	200.000	-0.190
	Min	199.967	199.971	-0.033	199.940	199.971	-0.060	199.921	199.971	-0.079	199.849	199.971	-0.151	199.735	199.971	-0.265
250	Max	250.013	250.000	0.042	249.986	250.000	0.015	249.967	250.000	-0.004	249.877	250.000	-0.094	249.733	250.000	-0.238
	Min	249.967	249.971	-0.033	249.940	249.971	-0.060	249.921	249.971	-0.079	249.831	249.971	-0.169	249.687	249.971	-0.313
300	Max	300.016	300.000	0.048	299.986	300.000	0.018	299.964	300.000	-0.004	299.850	300.000	-0.118	299.670	300.000	-0.298
	Min	299.964	299.968	-0.036	299.934	299.968	-0.066	299.912	299.968	-0.088	299.798	299.968	-0.202	299.618	299.968	-0.382
400	Max	400.017	400.000	0.053	399.984	400.000	0.020	399.959	400.000	-0.005	399.813	400.000	-0.151	399.586	400.000	-0.378
	Min	399.960	399.964	-0.040	399.927	399.964	-0.073	399.902	399.964	-0.098	399.756	399.964	-0.244	399.529	399.964	-0.471
500	Max	500.018	500.000	0.058	499.983	500.000	0.023	499.955	500.000	-0.005	499.771	500.000	-0.189	499.483	500.000	-0.477
	Min	499.955	499.960	-0.045	499.920	499.960	-0.080	499.892	499.960	-0.108	499.708	499.960	-0.292	499.420	499.960	-0.580

[a]From ANSI B4.2-1978 (R1994).

Appendix: Screw Threads, American National, Unified, and Metric

American National Standard Unified and American National Screw Threads.[a]

Nominal Diameter	Coarse[b] NC UNC		Fine[b] NF UNF		Extra Fine[c] NEF UNEF		Nominal Diameter	Coarse[b] NC UNC		Fine[b] NF UNF		Extra Fine[c] NEF UNEF	
	Thds. per Inch	Tap Drill[d]	Thds. per Inch	Tap Drill[d]	Thds. per Inch	Tap Drill[d]		Thds. per Inch	Tap Drill[d]	Thds. per Inch	Tap Drill[d]	Thds. per Inch	Tap Drill[d]
0 (.060)			80	$\frac{3}{64}$			1	8	$\frac{7}{8}$	12	$\frac{59}{64}$	20	$\frac{61}{64}$
1 (.073)	64	No. 53	72	No. 53	...	...	$1\frac{1}{16}$	...	...	...	...	18	1
2 (.086)	56	No. 50	64	No. 50	...	...	$1\frac{1}{8}$	7	$\frac{63}{64}$	12	$1\frac{3}{64}$	18	$1\frac{5}{64}$
3 (.099)	48	No. 47	56	No. 45	...	...	$1\frac{3}{16}$	...	...	...	...	18	$1\frac{9}{64}$
4 (.112)	40	No. 43	48	No. 42	...	...	$1\frac{1}{4}$	7	$1\frac{7}{64}$	12	$1\frac{11}{64}$	18	$1\frac{3}{16}$
5 (.125)	40	No. 38	44	No. 37	...	...	$1\frac{5}{16}$	...	...	...	...	18	$1\frac{17}{64}$
6 (.138)	32	No. 36	40	No. 33	...	...	$1\frac{3}{8}$	6	$1\frac{7}{32}$	12	$1\frac{19}{64}$	18	$1\frac{5}{16}$
8 (.164)	32	No. 29	36	No. 29	...	...	$1\frac{7}{16}$	...	...	...	...	18	$1\frac{3}{8}$
10 (.190)	24	No. 25	32	No. 21	...	...	$1\frac{1}{2}$	6	$1\frac{11}{32}$	12	$1\frac{27}{64}$	18	$1\frac{7}{16}$
12 (.216)	24	No. 16	28	No. 14	32	No. 13	$1\frac{9}{16}$	...	...	...	...	18	$1\frac{1}{2}$
$\frac{1}{4}$	20	No. 7	28	No. 3	32	$\frac{7}{32}$	$1\frac{5}{8}$	...	...	...	...	18	$1\frac{9}{16}$
$\frac{5}{16}$	18	F	24	I	32	$\frac{9}{32}$	$1\frac{11}{16}$	...	...	...	...	18	$1\frac{5}{8}$
$\frac{3}{8}$	16	$\frac{5}{16}$	24	Q	32	$\frac{11}{32}$	$1\frac{3}{4}$	5	$1\frac{9}{16}$	...	...	...	...
$\frac{7}{16}$	14	U	20	$\frac{25}{64}$	28	$\frac{13}{32}$	2	$4\frac{1}{2}$	$1\frac{25}{32}$	...	...	...	...
$\frac{1}{2}$	13	$\frac{27}{64}$	20	$\frac{29}{64}$	28	$\frac{15}{32}$	$2\frac{1}{4}$	$4\frac{1}{2}$	$2\frac{1}{32}$	...	...	...	...
$\frac{9}{16}$	12	$\frac{31}{64}$	18	$\frac{33}{64}$	24	$\frac{33}{64}$	$2\frac{1}{2}$	4	$2\frac{1}{4}$	...	...	...	...
$\frac{5}{8}$	11	$\frac{17}{32}$	18	$\frac{37}{64}$	24	$\frac{37}{64}$	$2\frac{3}{4}$	4	$2\frac{1}{2}$	...	...	...	...
$\frac{11}{16}$	...	...	...	...	24	$\frac{41}{64}$	3	4	$2\frac{3}{4}$	...	...	...	...
$\frac{3}{4}$	10	$\frac{21}{32}$	16	$\frac{11}{16}$	20	$\frac{45}{64}$	$3\frac{1}{4}$	4	...	...	...	...	...
$\frac{13}{16}$	...	...	...	...	20	$\frac{49}{64}$	$3\frac{1}{2}$	4	...	...	...	...	...
$\frac{7}{8}$	9	$\frac{49}{64}$	14	$\frac{13}{16}$	20	$\frac{53}{64}$	$3\frac{3}{4}$	4	...	...	...	...	...
$\frac{15}{16}$	...	...	...	...	20	$\frac{57}{64}$	4	4	...	...	...	...	...

[a]ANSI/ASME B1.1-1989. For 8-, 12-, and 16-pitch thread series, see next page.
[b]Classes 1A, 2A, 3A, 1B, 2B, 3B, 2, and 3.
[c]Classes 2A, 2B, 2, and 3.
[d]For approximate 75% full depth of thread.

From Appendix 17 of *Modern Graphics Communication*, Fourth Edition, Frederick E. Giesecke, Alva Mitchell, Henry Cecil Spencer, Ivan Leroy Hill, John Thomas Dygdon, James E. Novak, Shawna Lockhart. Copyright © 2010 by Pearson Education, Inc. Published by Pearson Prentice Hall.

Screw Threads, American National, Unified, and Metric (continued)

American National Standard Unified and American National Screw Threads[a] (continued)

Nominal Diameter	8-Pitch[b] Series 8N and 8UN		12-Pitch[b] Series 12N and 12UN		16-Pitch[b] Series 16N and 16UN	
	Thds. per Inch	Tap Drill[c]	Thds. per Inch	Tap Drill[c]	Thds. per Inch	Tap Drill[c]
$\frac{1}{2}$	...	...	12	$\frac{27}{64}$	...	...
$\frac{9}{16}$	...	...	12[e]	$\frac{31}{64}$	...	...
$\frac{5}{8}$	...	...	12	$\frac{35}{64}$	...	...
$\frac{11}{16}$	...	...	12	$\frac{39}{64}$	...	...
$\frac{3}{4}$	...	...	12	$\frac{43}{64}$	16[e]	$\frac{11}{16}$
$\frac{13}{16}$	...	...	12	$\frac{47}{64}$	16	$\frac{3}{4}$
$\frac{7}{8}$	...	...	12	$\frac{51}{64}$	16	$\frac{13}{16}$
$\frac{15}{16}$	...	...	12	$\frac{55}{64}$	16	$\frac{7}{8}$
1	8[e]	$\frac{7}{8}$	12	$\frac{59}{64}$	16	$\frac{15}{16}$
$1\frac{1}{16}$	...	...	12	$\frac{63}{64}$	16	1
$1\frac{1}{8}$	8	1	12[e]	$1\frac{3}{64}$	16	$1\frac{1}{16}$
$1\frac{3}{16}$	...	...	12	$1\frac{7}{64}$	16	$1\frac{1}{8}$
$1\frac{1}{4}$	8	$1\frac{1}{8}$	12	$1\frac{11}{64}$	16	$1\frac{3}{16}$
$1\frac{5}{16}$	...	...	12	$1\frac{15}{64}$	16	$1\frac{1}{4}$
$1\frac{3}{8}$	8	$1\frac{1}{4}$	12[e]	$1\frac{19}{64}$	16	$1\frac{5}{16}$
$1\frac{7}{16}$	...	...	12	$1\frac{23}{64}$	16	$1\frac{3}{8}$
$1\frac{1}{2}$	8	$1\frac{3}{8}$	12[e]	$1\frac{27}{64}$	16	$1\frac{7}{16}$
$1\frac{9}{16}$	...	...	...	...	16	$1\frac{1}{2}$
$1\frac{5}{8}$	8	$1\frac{1}{2}$	12	$1\frac{35}{64}$	16	$1\frac{9}{16}$
$1\frac{11}{16}$	...	...	...	...	16	$1\frac{5}{8}$
$1\frac{3}{4}$	8	$1\frac{5}{8}$	12	$1\frac{43}{64}$	16[e]	$1\frac{11}{16}$
$1\frac{13}{16}$	...	...	...	...	16	$1\frac{3}{4}$
$1\frac{7}{8}$	8	$1\frac{3}{4}$	12	$1\frac{51}{64}$	16	$1\frac{13}{16}$
$1\frac{15}{16}$	...	...	...	...	16	$1\frac{7}{8}$
2	8	$1\frac{7}{8}$	12	$1\frac{59}{64}$	16[e]	$1\frac{15}{16}$

Nominal Diameter	8-Pitch[b] Series 8N and 8UN		12-Pitch[b] Series 12N and 12UN		16-Pitch[c] Series 16N and 16UN	
	Thds. per Inch	Tap Drill[c]	Thds. per Inch	Tap Drill[c]	Thds. per Inch[d]	Tap Drill[c]
$2\frac{1}{16}$	...	...	...	...	**16**	2
$2\frac{1}{8}$	...	...	12	$2\frac{3}{64}$	16	$2\frac{1}{16}$
$2\frac{3}{16}$	...	...	...	...	**16**	$2\frac{1}{8}$
$2\frac{1}{4}$	8	$2\frac{1}{8}$	12	$2\frac{17}{64}$	16	$2\frac{3}{16}$
$2\frac{5}{16}$	...	...	...	...	**16**	$2\frac{1}{4}$
$2\frac{3}{8}$	...	...	12	$2\frac{19}{64}$	16	$2\frac{5}{16}$
$2\frac{7}{16}$	...	...	...	...	**16**	$2\frac{3}{8}$
$2\frac{1}{2}$	8	$2\frac{3}{8}$	12	$2\frac{27}{64}$	16	$2\frac{7}{16}$
$2\frac{5}{8}$	...	...	12	$2\frac{35}{64}$	16	$2\frac{9}{16}$
$2\frac{3}{4}$	8	$2\frac{5}{8}$	12	$2\frac{43}{64}$	16	$2\frac{11}{16}$
$2\frac{7}{8}$	...	...	12	...	16	...
3	8	$2\frac{7}{8}$	12	...	16	...
$3\frac{1}{8}$	8	...	12	...	16	...
$3\frac{1}{4}$	8	...	12	...	16	...
$3\frac{3}{8}$	...	...	12	...	16	...
$3\frac{1}{2}$	8	...	12	...	16	...
$3\frac{3}{4}$	8	...	12	...	16	...
$3\frac{7}{8}$	...	...	12	...	16	...
4	8	...	12	...	16	...
$4\frac{1}{4}$	8	...	12	...	16	...
$4\frac{1}{2}$	8	...	12	...	16	...
$4\frac{3}{4}$	8	...	12	...	16	...
5	8	...	12	...	16	...
$5\frac{1}{4}$	8	...	12	...	16	...

[a]ANSI/ASME B1.1-1989.
[b]Classes 2A, 3A, 2B, 3B, 2, and 3.
[c]For approximate 75% full depth of thread.
[d]Boldface type indicates Amrican National Threads only.
[e]This is a standard size of the Unified or American National threads of the coarse, fine, or extra fine series. See preceding page.

Screw Threads, American National, Unified, and Metric (continued)

Metric Screw Threads.[a]

Preferred sizes for commercial threads and fasteners are shown in **boldface** type.

Coarse (general purpose)		Fine	
Nominal Size & Thd Pitch	Tap Drill Diameter, mm	Nominal Size & Thd Pitch	Tap Drill Diameter, mm
M1.6 × 0.35	1.25	—	—
M1.8 × 0.35	1.45	—	—
M2 × 0.4	1.6	—	—
M2.2 × 0.45	1.75	—	—
M2.5 × 0.45	2.05	—	—
M3 × 0.5	2.5	—	—
M3.5 × 0.6	2.9	—	—
M4 × 0.7	3.3	—	—
M4.5 × 0.75	3.75	—	—
M5 × 0.8	4.2	—	—
M6 × 1	5.0	—	—
M7 × 1	6.0	—	—
M8 × 1.25	6.8	**M8 × 1**	7.0
M9 × 1.25	7.75	—	—
M10 × 1.5	8.5	**M10 × 1.25**	8.75
M11 × 1.5	9.50	—	—
M12 × 1.75	10.30	**M12 × 1.25**	10.5
M14 × 2	12.00	**M14 × 1.5**	12.5
M16 × 2	14.00	**M16 × 1.5**	14.5
M18 × 2.5	15.50	**M18 × 1.5**	16.5
M20 × 2.5	17.5	**M20 × 1.5**	18.5
M22 × 25[b]	19.5	**M22 × 1.5**	20.5
M24 × 3	21.0	**M24 × 2**	22.0
M27 × 3[b]	24.0	**M27 × 2**	25.0
M30 × 3.5	26.5	**M30 × 2**	28.0
M33 × 3.5	29.5	**M30 × 2**	31.0
M36 × 4	32.0	**M36 × 2**	33.0
M39 × 4	35.0	M39 × 2	36.0
M42 × 4.5	37.5	**M42 × 2**	39.0
M45 × 4.5	40.5	M45 × 1.5	42.0
M48 × 5	43.0	**M48 × 2**	45.0
M52 × 5	47.0	M52 × 2	49.0
M56 × 5.5	50.5	**M56 × 2**	52.0
M60 × 5.5	54.5	M60 × 1.5	56.0
M64 × 6	58.0	**M64 × 2**	60.0
M68 × 6	62.0	M68 × 2	64.0
M72 × 6	66.0	**M72 × 2**	68.0
M80 × 6	74.0	**M80 × 2**	76.0
M90 × 6	84.0	**M90 × 2**	86.0
M100 × 6	94.0	**M100 × 2**	96.0

[a]ANSI/ASME B1.13M-1995.
[b]Only for high strength structural steel fasteners.

Index